Austin-Healey Sprite Mk. 3
MG Midget Mk. 2 and Mk. 3
Parts Catalogue

Part no.
AKM 0036
February 1977
1st Edition

British Leyland UK Limited
Service & Parts Division
Cowley
Oxford OX4 2PG
England

Telephone: Oxford (0865) 778941
Telex: 83331
Cables: BLAMSERV Oxford England

The Austin-Healey Sprite (Mark IV)

M.G. Midget (Mark III)

CONTENTS

The Austin-Healey Sprite (Mark III)

The M.G. Midget (Mark II)

INDEX PAGE

IMPORTANT

Replacement parts that are not of genuine British Leyland manufacture cannot be relied upon to be of British Leyland specification, material, and workmanship, and therefore British Leyland cannot be expected to extend their Warranty to vehicles which have been fitted with parts not of their manufacture.

British Leyland reserve the right to make changes or improvements in the construction or equipment of their products at any time.

In order to ensure prompt and correct execution of your orders it is essential to quote:

1. The relative **Unit Number**, together with prefixes, suffixes, and specification reference where applicable:

   e.g.: Axle, Body, Cab, Car, Chassis, Commission, Engine, and Gearbox Numbers, etc.
2. The **Part Number** and **description** (prefix letters to Part Numbers must always be quoted).
3. Always state the **colour** of carpets, painted items, trim items, etc.
4. The **quantity** required, bearing in mind that the quantities shown are those used in the application actually illustrated. Sometimes only minimum packaged quantities are available. These packs may well contain more parts than are required for a single job; for details of packaged quantities, see the Service Parts Price List.
5. The listing or illustrating of an item does not guarantee its availability.

ABBREVIATIONS: Standard abbreviations are employed. The complete range of abbreviations covering all lists is given below.

A	Ambulance
A/M	Austin Morris
A/R	As required
B	Basic
(B)	Body number
BG	Bathgate production
(BP)	Belt pulley number
B.R.S.	British Road Services
C	Chassis number
(C)	Car number
(CB)	Cab number
cm	Centimetres
(CN)	Commission number
CP	Chrome-plated
D	Coupe or GT
(D)	De-luxe
DC	Double-coil
D/E	Double-ended
dia	Diameter
E	G.P.O. Engineering
(E)	Engine number
E.C.E.	Economic Commission of Europe
EP	G.P.O. Planning
EXP	Export
(FA)	Front axle number
G	G.P.O. Postal
(G)	Gearbox number
GP	General Purpose Carrier
G.V.W.	Gross Vehicle Weight
H	Hearse
HC	High compression
(HU)	Hydraulic unit number
ID	Inside diameter
I.P.T.O.	Independent Power Take-Off
J	Convertible
K	Truck
KPH	Kilometres per hour
L	Hire Car
LC	Low compression
LH	Left-hand
LHD	Left-hand drive
LHT	Left-hand thread
(LP)	Low pressure
LWB	Long wheelbase
m	Metres
M	Limousine
MB	Minibus/Omnicoach
mm	Millimetres
MPH	Miles per hour
N	2-seater Tourer
N.A.D.A.	North American Dollar Area
N L A	No longer available
No.	Number
NSP	Non-serviceable part
OD	Outside diameter
(OD)	Overdrive number
O/S	Oversize
P	Hard Top
PK	Perkins production
pr	Pair
psi	Pounds/square inch
PSV	Public Service Vehicle
P.T.O.	Power Take-Off
Q	Chassis and Cab
R	Chassis and Scuttle
(RA)	Rear axle number
RH	Right-hand
RHD	Right-hand drive
RHT	Right-hand thread
(RP)	Rear pulley number
S	4-door Saloon
(S)	Super de-luxe
ST	Soft Top
STD	Standard
SWB	Short wheelbase
2S	2-door Saloon
T	4-seater Tourer
T.I.B.	Technical Information Bulletin
U	Pick-up
UK	Great Britain and Northern Ireland
U/S	Undersize
U.S.A.	United States of America
V	Van
W	Dual-purpose (wood framing)
WB	Wheelbase
Wol.	Wolseley
Ws	Dual-purpose (all metal)
W.S.E.	When Stock Exhausted
X	Taxi
(+)	Change point not available
$	This item is subject to safety regulations

PART NUMBER SUFFIX LETTERS

E	Exchange scheme item
M	Part supplied in multiples of metres (39.37")
N	New condition (i.e. not exchange)
R	Reconditioned unit

KEY BLANK CROSS REFERENCE CHART

KEY SERIES	CODES:	LOCK MANUFACTURER	KEY BLANK PART No.
CONVENTIONAL KEYS:			
BC	301 – 360	LOWE & FLETCHER	CZK 3438
FK	876 – 955	WILMOT BREEDEN	17H 2475
FP	626 – 750	WILMOT BREEDEN	AKA 463
FR	751 – 875	WILMOT BREEDEN	37H 7189
FS	001 – 099, 876 – 955	WILMOT BREEDEN	17H 2475
FT	101 – 225, 301 – 360	WILMOT BREEDEN	CZK 3438
SS	201 – 229	STREBOR	37H 8688
TS	300 – 369	STREBOR	37H 4557
STEERING LOCK TYPE KEYS:			
B	001 – 1000	BRITAX	37H 7194
B	001 – 1000	BRITAX	37H 7195*
BL	1001 – 2000	LOWE & FLETCHER	37H 7191
BL	1001N – 2000N	LOWE & FLETCHER	AAU 1887
BP	001 – 1000	BRITAX	37H 7194
BP	001 – 1000	BRITAX	37H 7195*
D	1 – 64	BRITAX	37H 7196
FH (LONG TIP)	1 – 3948	WASO	37H 7192
FH	1 – 3948	WASO	37H 7193
FR	1 – 1080	WASO	37H 7193
L & F	17001 – 18000	BRITAX	37H 7197
L & F	86001 – 88000	BRITAX	37H 7197
LR	001 – 1000	BRITAX	37H 7194
LR	001 – 1000	BRITAX	37H 7195*
NH	2001 – 3000	WILMOT BREEDEN	37H 6108
NJ	001 – 1500	WILMOT BREEDEN	37H 1494
RO	1001 – 2000	LOWE & FLETCHER	37H 7191
TM	3001 – 4000	C. E. MARSHALL	37H 8689
VV	1001 – 2000	LOWE & FLETCHER	37H 7191
A	11225 – 53332	NIEMAN–TEX	27H 9391
NO SERIES LETTER	2001 – 3000	NIEMAN–TEX	37H 7190
NO SERIES LETTER	7001 – 9000	NIEMAN–TEX	AAU 1888
VL (Cut to VV Code)	1001 – 2000	LOWE & FLETCHER	AAU 1887

*PRE CUT No. 3 DEPTH FIRST CUT BLANK.

The Austin-Healey Sprite (Mark IV)

M.G. Midget (Mark III)

The Austin-Healey Sprite (Mark III)

The M.G. Midget (Mark II)

IDENTIFICATION DATA

AUSTIN-HEALEY SPRITE

Model		Commencing	Finishing
Sprite Mark III	Engine No. Car No. Body No.	10CC/Da/H101 H–AN8–38829 ABL 030580	10CC/Da/H16300 H–AN8–64734
Sprite Mark IV	Engine No. Car No. Car No. H–AN9 Body No. H–AN10 Body No.	12CC/Da/H101 12CE/Da/H101 12CG/Da/H101 H–AN9–64735 H–AN10–85287 ABL 055500 ABL 064518	12CC/Da/H16300 H–AN9–85286 H–AN10–86403 Not available

AUSTIN SPRITE

Model		Commencing	Finishing
Sprite Mark IV	Engine No. Car No. Body No.	12CE/Da/H101 12CG/Da/H101 A–AN10–86804 Not available	Not available A–AN10–87824 Not available

M.G. MIDGET

Model		Commencing	Finishing
Midget Mark II	Engine No. Car No. Body No.	10CC/Da/H101 G–AN3–25788 GBE 025654	10CC/Da/H16300 G–AN3–52389 GBE 052153
Midget Mark III	Engine No. USA (USA) (USA) (USA) (USA) (USA) (USA) Car No. Car No. G–AN4 Body No. G–AN5 Body No.	12CC/Da/H101 12CD/Da/H101 12CE/Da/H101 12CF/Da/H101 12CG/Da/H101 12CH/Da/H101 12CJ/Da/H21201 12CK/Da/H101 12V/586F/101 12V/587Z/101 12V/671Z/101 12V/588F/101 12V/778F/101 G–AN4–52390 G–AN5–74886 G–AN6–154101 GBE–052400 GBE–064374 GBE-100101 (Except USA and Sweden) GUN–150101 (USA) GSN–05000 (Sweden)	12CC/Da/H16300 Not available Not available G–AN4–74885 G–AN5–154100 GBE–064373 GBE–100100

VEHICLE IDENTIFICATION

SERIAL NUMBER PREFIX CODE

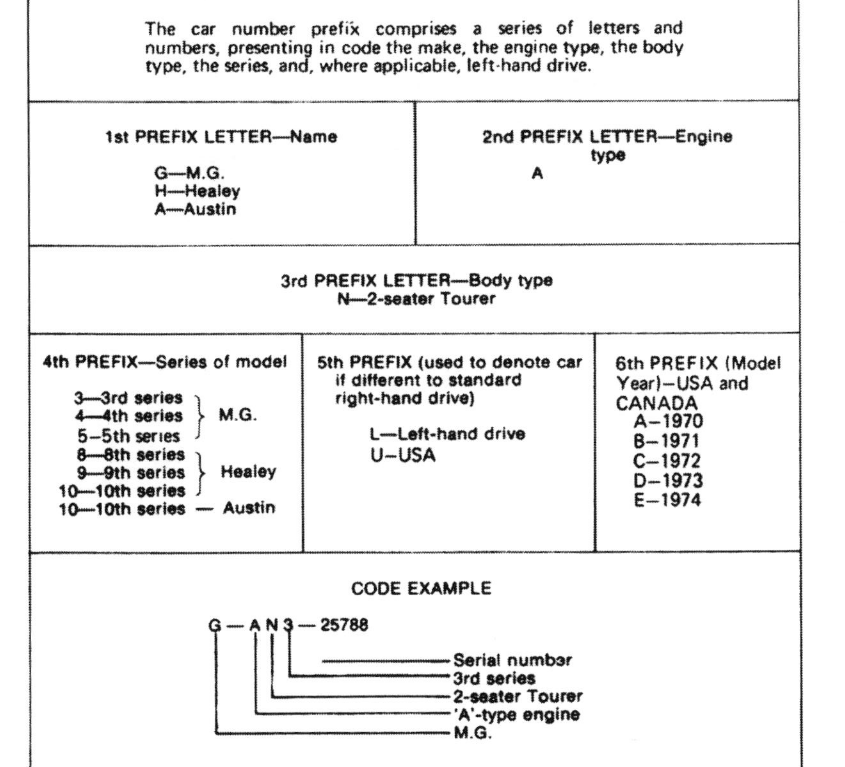

The car number prefix comprises a series of letters and numbers, presenting in code the make, the engine type, the body type, the series, and, where applicable, left-hand drive.

1st PREFIX LETTER—Name	2nd PREFIX LETTER—Engine type
G—M.G. H—Healey A—Austin	A

3rd PREFIX LETTER—Body type
N—2-seater Tourer

4th PREFIX—Series of model	5th PREFIX (used to denote car if different to standard right-hand drive)	6th PREFIX (Model Year)—USA and CANADA
3—3rd series } M.G. 4—4th series } M.G. 5—5th series } M.G. 8—8th series } Healey 9—9th series } Healey 10—10th series } Healey 10—10th series — Austin	L—Left-hand drive U—USA	A–1970 B–1971 C–1972 D–1973 E–1974

CODE EXAMPLE

G — A N 3 — 25788

- 25788 — Serial number
- 3 — 3rd series
- N — 2-seater Tourer
- A — 'A'-type engine
- G — M.G.

Always quote these prefixes with Car Serial Numbers

POWER UNIT IDENTIFICATION

SERIAL NUMBER PREFIX LETTER CODE

The engine number prefix comprises a series of letters and numbers, presenting in code the cubic capacity and make, the ancillaries fitted, and the type of compression.

1st PREFIX GROUP—Cubic capacity, make, and type

1st Prefix number:	10—1000 to 1100 cc 12—1200 to 1300 cc
Prefix letter:	CC—Austin Healey Sprite—Austin Sprite and M.G. Midget

2nd PREFIX GROUP—Gearbox and ancillaries

Da—Close-ratio centre change gearbox

3rd GROUP—Compression and serial number

H—High compression } and serial number of unit
L—Low compression } and serial number of unit

CODE EXAMPLE

10CC / Da / H 101

- 101 — Serial number
- H — High compression
- Da — Close-ratio centre change gearbox
- 10 — 1098 cc

Always quote these prefixes with Engine Serial Numbers

Location of Unit Numbers

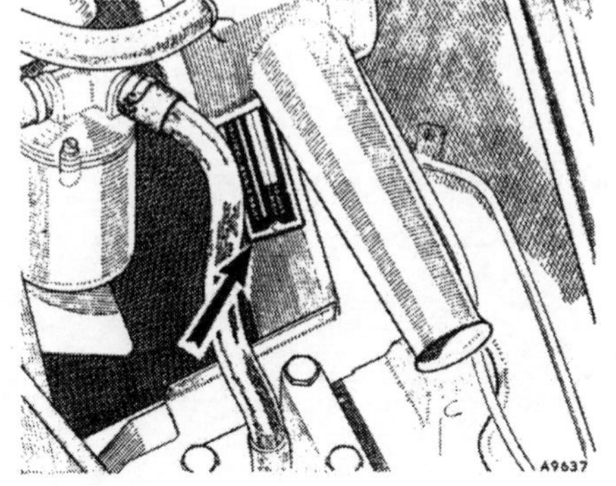

The **Car Number** is stamped on a plate secured to the left-hand inner wheel arch valance under the bonnet

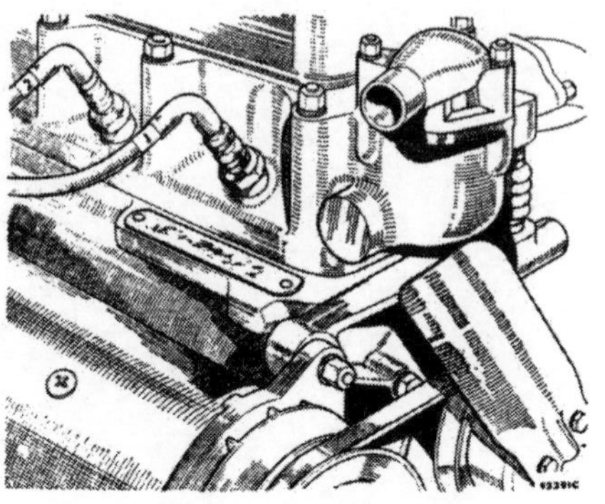

The **Engine Number** is stamped on a plate secured to the right-hand side of the cylinder block above the dynamo

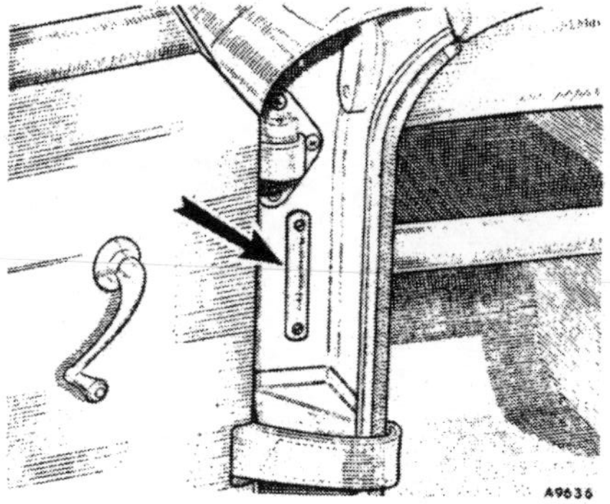

The **Body Number** is stamped on a plate secured to the left-hand front door pillar

Location of Unit Numbers—*continued*

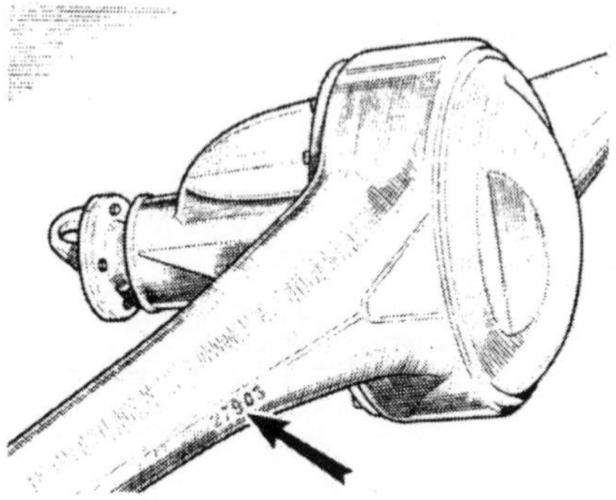

The **Rear Axle Number** is stamped on the rear of the left-hand rear axle tube adjacent to the spring anchorage

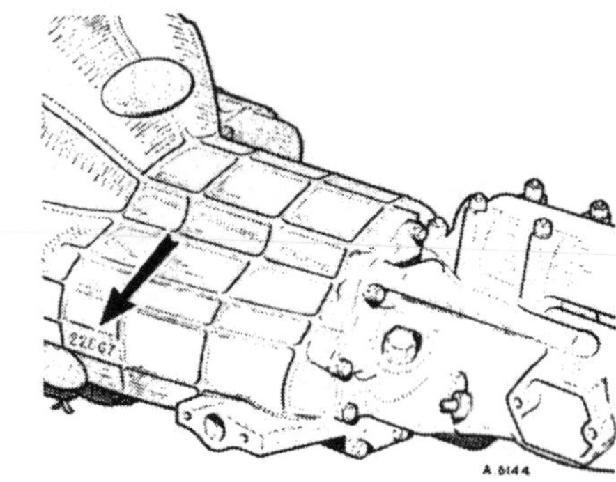

The **Gearbox Number** is stamped on the left-hand side of the gearbox casing

KEY TO BODY EXTERIOR AND MAIN TRIM COLOUR COMBINATIONS, FROM START OF VEHICLE PRODUCTION

The colour code numbers quoted in the following text relate to the paint colour samples in the Approved Manufacturer's Brochures.

Body Exterior and Paint Code	Model	Seats, Liners and Door Seals	Hood, Tonneau Cover and Hard Top	Carpets/Mats
BLACK (BK. 1)	Sprite Midget	Red	Black	Red
		Black	Black	Black
		Autumn Leaf	Black	Autumn Leaf
BRONZE YELLOW (BLVC 15)	Sprite Midget	Black	Black	Black
		Navy	Black	Navy
MUSTARD (BLVC 19)	Midget	Navy	Black	Navy
GREEN MALLARD (BLVC 22)	Midget	Ochre	Black	Ochre
		Autumn Leaf	Black	Autumn Leaf
GLACIER WHITE (BLVC 59)	Sprite Midget	Autumn Leaf	Black	Autumn Leaf
		Black	Black	Black
		Navy	Black	Navy
AQUA (BLVC 60)	Midget	Navy	Black	Navy
FLAME RED (BLVC 61)	Sprite Midget	Black	Black	Black
		Navy	Black	Navy
MINERAL BLUE (BU. 9)	Sprite Midget	Black	Black	Black
BASILICA BLUE (BU. 11)	Sprite Midget	Black	Black	Black
BLUE ROYALE (BU. 38)	Sprite Midget	Black	Black	Black
RIVIERA BLUE (BU. 44)	Sprite Midget	Blue	Blue	Blue
CHARTREUSE (BLVC 167)	Midget	Black	Black	Black

KEY TO BODY EXTERIOR AND MAIN TRIM COLOUR COMBINATIONS, FROM START OF VEHICLE PRODUCTION—continued

Body Exterior and Paint Code	Model	Seats, Liners and Door Seals	A–Hood B–Tonneau Cover C–Hard Top	Carpets/Mats
BRITISH RACING GREEN (GN. 29)	Sprite Midget	Black	Black	Black
DOVE GREY (GR. 26)	Sprite Midget	Red	A. Grey B. Red C. Black	Red
TARTAN RED (RD. 9)	Sprite Midget	Red	Red	Red
		Red	Black	Red
		Black	Black	Black
OLD ENGLISH WHITE (WT. 3)	Sprite Midget	Black	A.] Black B.] C. Old English White	Black
		Black	Black	Black
		Red	A. Grey B. Red C. Old English White	Red
		Red	Black	Red
SNOWBERRY WHITE (WT. 4)	Sprite Midget	Black	Black	Black
FIESTA (YL. 11)	Sprite	Black	Black	Black
PALE PRIMROSE (YL. 12)	Sprite Midget	Black	Black	Black
TEAL BLUE (BLVC 18)	Sprite Midget	Autumn Leaf	Black	Autumn Leaf
		Black	Black	Black
		Ochre	Black	Ochre
BLAZE (BLVC 16)	Sprite Midget	Black	Black	Black
		Navy	Black	Navy
BROOKLANDS GREEN (BLVC 169)	Midget	Autumn Leaf	Black	Autumn Leaf

KEY TO BODY EXTERIOR AND MAIN TRIM COLOUR COMBINATIONS, FROM START OF VEHICLE PRODUCTION—continued

Body Exterior and Paint Code	Model	Seats, Liners and Door Seals	Hood, Tonneau Cover and Hard Top	Carpets/Mats
MIDNIGHT BLUE (BLVC 12)	Sprite Midget	Black	Black	Black
BEDOUIN (BLVC 4)	Sprite Midget	Autumn Leaf	Black	Autumn Leaf
		Black	Black	Black
RACING GREEN (BLVC 25)	Sprite Midget	Black	Black	Black
		Autumn Leaf	Black	Autumn Leaf
LIMEFLOWER (BLVC 20)	Midget	Navy	Black	Navy
BLACK TULIP (BLVC 23)	Midget	Ochre	Black	Ochre
DAMASK RED (BLVC 99)	Midget	Navy	Black	Navy
		Black	Black	Black
HARVEST GOLD (BLVC 19)	Midget	Navy	Black	Navy
		Black	Black	Black
CITRON (BLVC 73)	Midget	Black	Black	Black
TUNDRA (BLVC 94)	Midget	Autumn Leaf	Black	Autumn Leaf
ACONITE (BLVC 95)	Midget	Autumn Leaf	Black	Autumn Leaf
BRACKEN (BLVC 93)	Midget	Autumn Leaf	Black	Autumn Leaf
		Black	Black	Black
MIRAGE (BLVC 11)	Midget	Black	Black	Black
FLAMENCO (BLVC 133)	Midget	Black	Black	Black
TAHITI BLUE (BLVC 65)	Midget	Autumn Leaf	Black	Autumn Leaf
		Black	Black	Black
SAND GLOW (BLVC 63)	Midget	Autumn Leaf	Black	Autumn Leaf

This page intentionally left blank

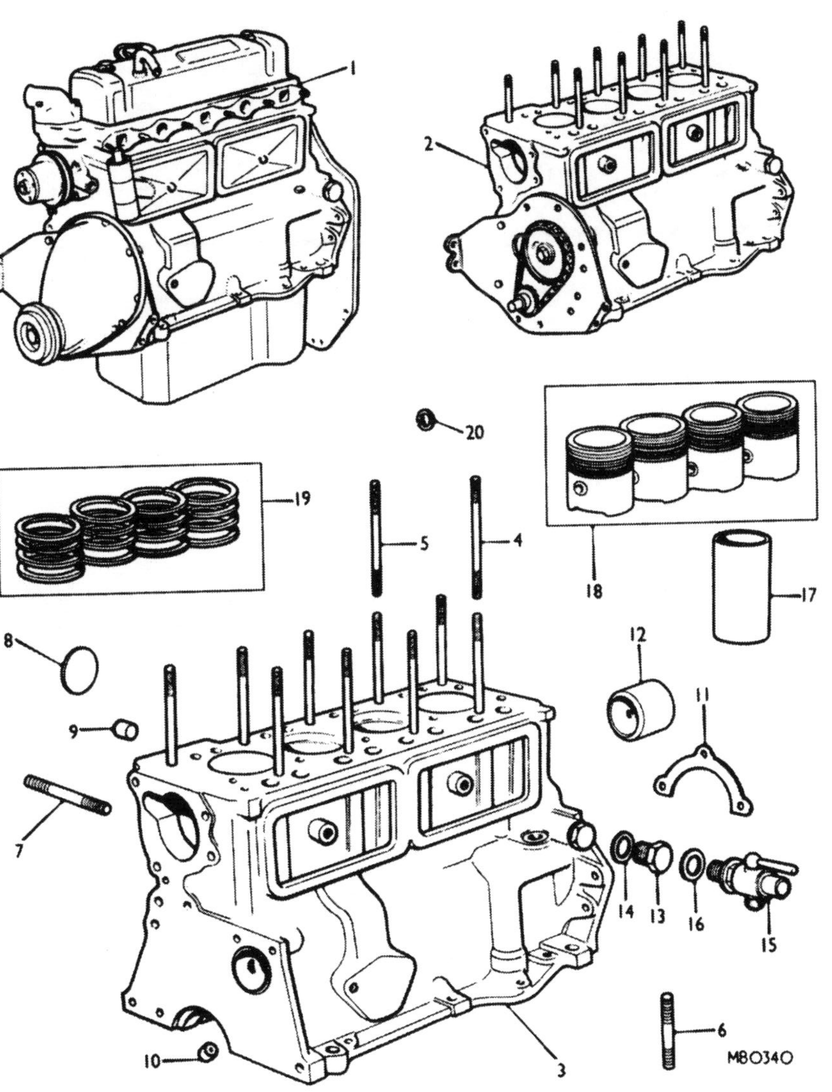

AUSTIN-HEALEY SPRITE MK. 3 AND MK. 4 & MG MIDGET MK. 2 AND MK. 3

ENGINE UNIT-1098cc,10CC

NO.	PART NO.	DESCRIPTION	QTY	CHANGE POINT	REMARKS
	8G 150	ENGINE UNIT-STRIPPED-HC	NLA		
	8G 149	ENGINE UNIT-STRIPPED-LC	NLA		
2	38G 372 N	ENGINE UNIT-HALF-HC	NLA		
2	38G 371	ENGINE UNIT-HALF-LC	1		
3	38G 370	BLOCK ASSEMBLY-CYLINDER-HC	1		
	38G 369	BLOCK ASSEMBLY-CYLINDER-LC	NLA		
4	51K 277	Stud-cylinder head-long	NLA		Use 51K 279.
4	51K 279	Stud-cylinder head-long	4		
5	51K 276	Stud-cylinder head-short	NLA		Use 51K 280
5	51K 280	Stud-cylinder head-short	NLA		Use CAM 151
5	CAM 151	Stud-cylinder head-short	5		
6	12G 478	Stud-main bearing cap	6		
7	53K 615	Stud-oil filter	2		
8	2K 8169	Plug-welch	4	(E)10CC/Da/H101 TO H3495	
8	AEH 592	Plug-core	4	(E)10CC/Da/H3496 ON	
9	2K 1345	Plug-oil release valve passage	2		
9	12H 1734	Plug-oil gallery	2		
10	1A 1964	Restrictor-oil feed-camshaft bearing	1		
	LNZ 607	Locknut-main bearing cap-stud	6		
11	AEG 240	Washer-joint-cover	1		
	SH 604061	Screw-cover	3		
	LWZ 206	Washer-spring	3		
12	28G 133	Liner-camshaft bearing	1SET		
13	53K 2853	Plug-drain tap boss	1		
14	6K 638	Washer-plug	1		
15	3H 576	Tap-cylinder drain	1	Service purposes ONLY.	
16	2K 4954	Washer-tap	1	Service purposes ONLY.	Alternatives.
16	2K 4975	Washer-tap	1	Service purposes ONLY.	Alternatives.
17	12G 164	Liner-cylinder	4	Service purposes ONLY.	

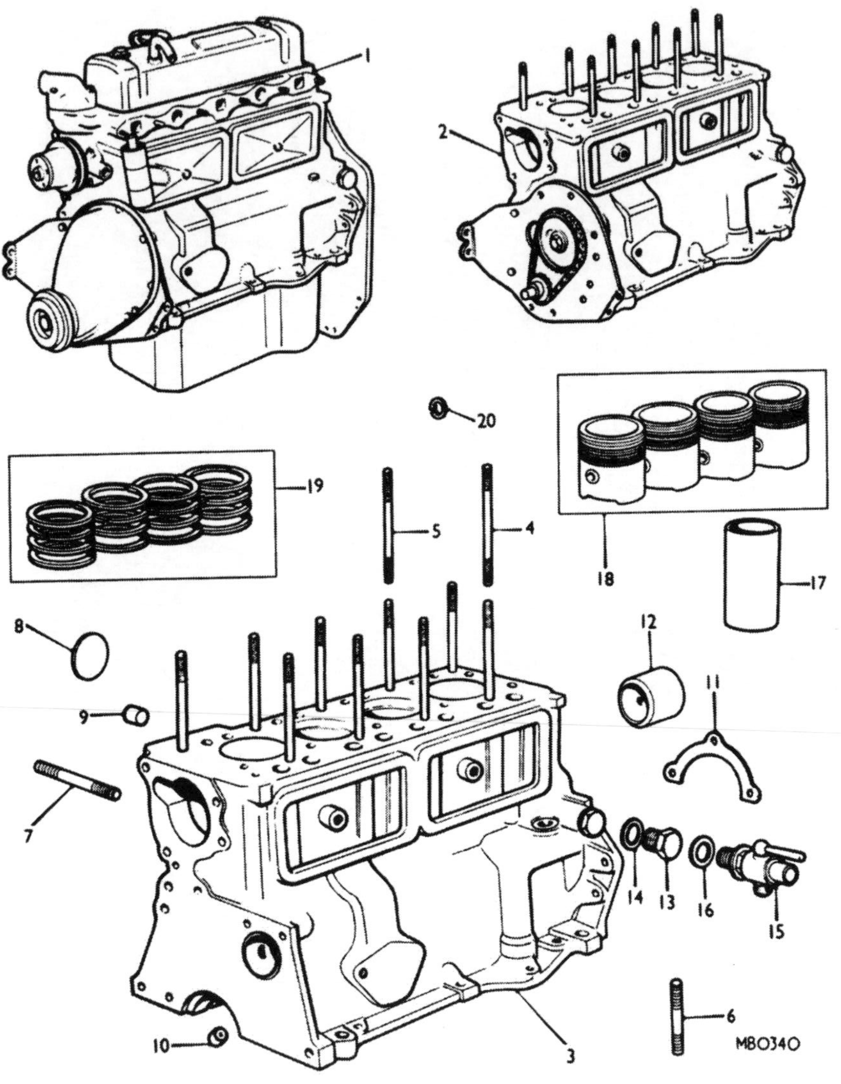

AUSTIN-HEALEY SPRITE MK. 3 AND MK. 4 & MG MIDGET MK. 2 AND MK. 3

ENGINE UNIT-1098cc,10CC-continued.

NO.	PART NO.	DESCRIPTION	QTY	CHANGE POINT	REMARKS
		PISTON ASSEMBLY-ENGINE SET-GRADE 3-HC			
18	8G 2441 3	Standard	1SET		
18	8G 2441 23	.020"(.508mm)O/S	1SET		
		PISTON ASSEMBLY-ENGINE SET-GRADE 3-LC			
18	8G 2443 3	Standard	1SET		
18	8G 2443 13	.010"(.254mm)O/S	1SET		
18	8G 2443 23	.020"(.508mm)O/S	1SET		
		PISTON ASSEMBLY-ENGINE SET-GRADE 6-HC			
18	8G 2441 6	Standard	1SET		
		PISTON ASSEMBLY-ENGINE SET-GRADE 6-LC			
18	8G 2443 6	Standard	1SET		
18	8G 2443 26	.020"(.508mm)O/S	1SET		
		RING-PISTON-ENGINE SET			
19	8G 745	Standard	1SET		
19	8G 745 20	.020"(.508mm)	1SET		
20	CCN 210	Circlip-gudgeon pin	8		

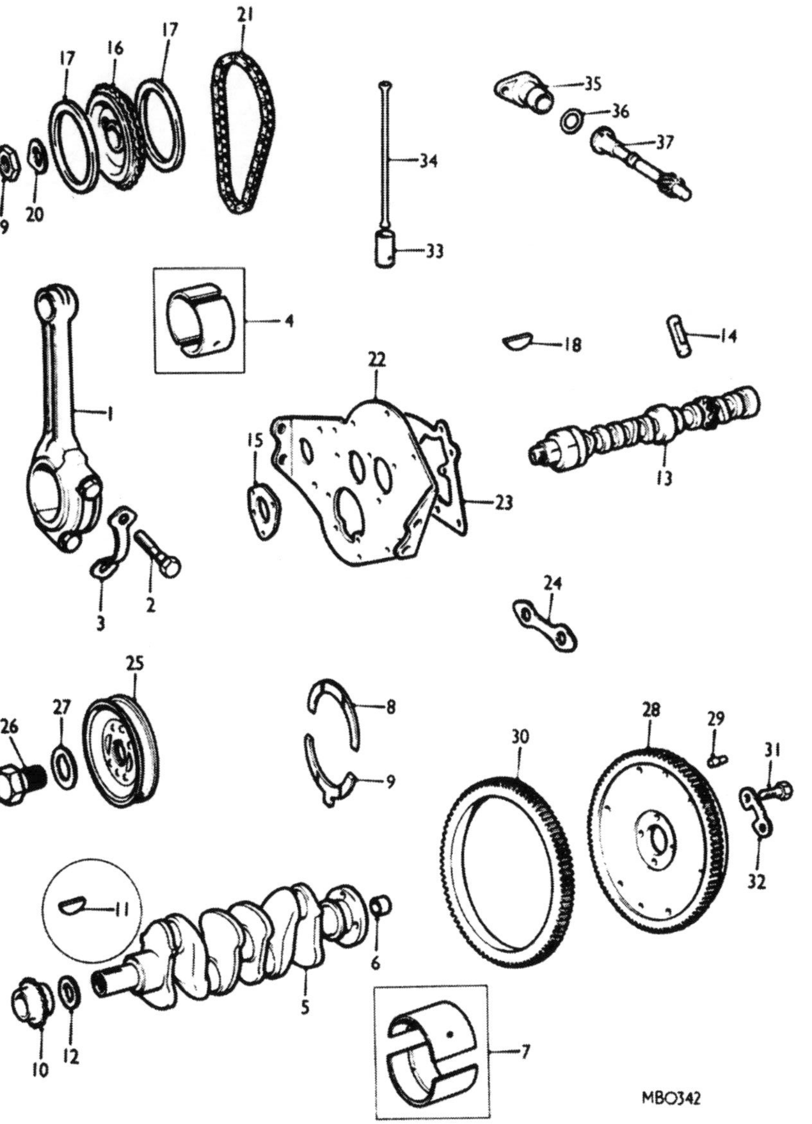

AUSTIN-HEALEY SPRITE MK. 3 AND MK. 4 & MG MIDGET MK. 2 AND MK. 3

ENGINE UNIT-1098cc,10CC-continued.

NO.	PART NO.	DESCRIPTION	QTY	CHANGE POINT	REMARKS
1	12G 126	CONNECTING ROD ASSEMBLY-NOS.1 AND 3 CYLINDERS	2		
1	12G 123	CONNECTING ROD ASSEMBLY-NOS.2 AND 4 CYLINDERS	3		
2	12G 2217	Screw-cap	8		
3	2A 660	Washer-lock	4		
		BEARING-CONNECTING ROD			
4	8G 2198	Standard	1SET		
4	8G 2198 10	.010"(.254mm)U/S	1SET		
4	8G 2198 20	.020"(.508mm)U/S	1SET		
4	8G 2198 30	.030"(.762mm)U/S	1SET		
4	8G 2198 40	.040"(1.016mm)U/S	1SET		
5	12G 429	CRANKSHAFT ASSEMBLY(WITH BUSH)	NLA		
6	1A 1559	Bush-1st motion shaft	1		
		BEARING-MAIN			
7	8G 2391	Standard	1SET		
7	8G 2391 10	.101"(.254mm)U/S	1SET		
7	8G 2391 20	.020"(.508mm)U/S	1SET		
7	8G 2391 30	.030"(.762mm)U/S	1SET		
7	8G 2391 40	.040"(1.016mm)U/S	1SET		
		WASHER-THRUST-UPPER			
8	AEG 159	Standard	2		
8	AEG 159 3	.003"(.076mm)O/S	2		
8	AEG 159 30	.030"(.762mm)O/S	2		
		WASHER-THRUST-LOWER			
9	AEG 160	Standard	2		
9	AEG 160 3	.003"(.076mm)O/S	2		
9	AEG 160 30	.030"(.762mm)O/S	2		
10	8G 725	Gear-crankshaft	1		
11	6K 836	Key	1		
12	6K 628	Washer-packing	A/R		
13	AEG 148	CAMSHAFT ASSEMBLY(WITH DRIVING PIN FOR OIL PUMP)	1		
14	2A 299	Pin	1		
15	2A 84	Plate-locating-camshaft	1		
	SH 604061	Screw-plate to crankcase	3		
	LWZ 404	Washer-shakeproof	3		
16	2A 85	GEAR ASSEMBLY-CAMSHAFT (WITH TENSIONER RINGS)	NLA		Use 12G 2622.
16	12G 2622	GEAR ASSEMBLY-CAMSHAFT (WITH TENSIONER RINGS)	NLA		Use 12G 4337.
17	8G 549	Ring	2		
	12G 4337	Gear-camshaft	1		
18	WKN 505	Key-gear	1		
19	6K 629	Nut-gear to camshaft	1		
20	2A 759	Washer-lock	1		
21	3H 2127	Chain-gear	1		

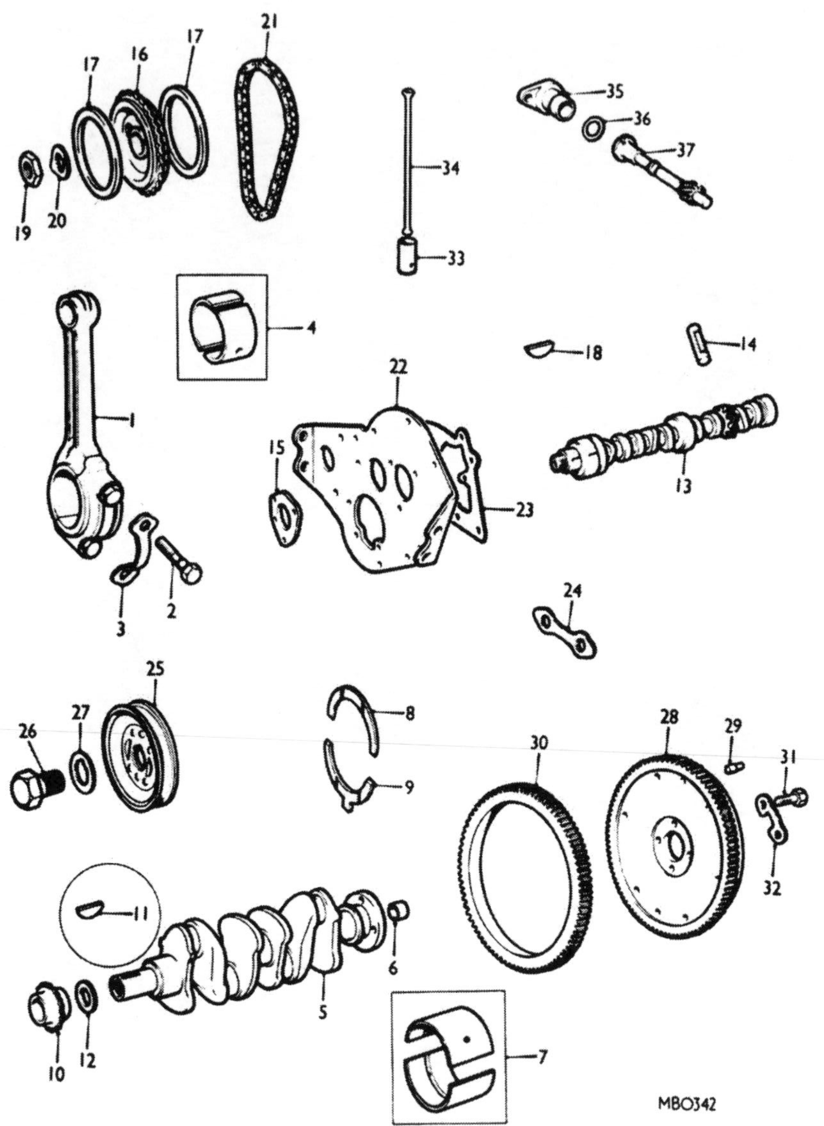

AUSTIN-HEALEY SPRITE MK. 3 AND MK. 4 & MG MIDGET MK. 2 AND MK. 3

ENGINE UNIT-1098cc,10CC-continued.

NO.	PART NO.	DESCRIPTION	QTY	CHANGE POINT	REMARKS
22	12G 1309	Plate-engine mounting-front	1		
23	12G 619	Gasket-plate to crankcase	1		
	AEA 687	Screw-plate to main bearing cap	1		
	HZS 505	Screw-plate to crankcase	2		
	LWZ 305	Washer-spring	2		
24	6K 831	Plate-locking-screw	1		
25	2A 940	Pulley-crankshaft	1		
26	AEA 312	Bolt	1		
27	1G 1319	Washer-lock	1		
28	12G 483	FLYWHEEL ASSEMBLY	1		
29	1G 2984	Dowel-flywheel to clutch	2		
30	12G 290	Ring gear-starter	1		
31	6K 630	Screw-flywheel to crankshaft	4		
32	12G 612	Washer-lock	2		
		TAPPET			
33	2A 13	Standard	8		
33	2A 13 10	.010"(.254mm)O/S	8		
33	2A 13 20	.020"(.508mm)O/S	8		
34	2A 14	Push-rod	8		Alternative (IN SETS)
34	12A 250	Push-rod	8		
34	12A 747	Push-rod	NLA		
35	12A 1136	Housing-distributor	1		
36	13H 2792	'O'ring	1		
	SH 604061	Screw-housing to crankcase	1		
	LWZ 404	Washer-shakeproof	1		
37	1G 2062	Spindle-distributor drive	NLA		Use 12G 4499.
37	12G 4499	Spindle-distributor drive	1		

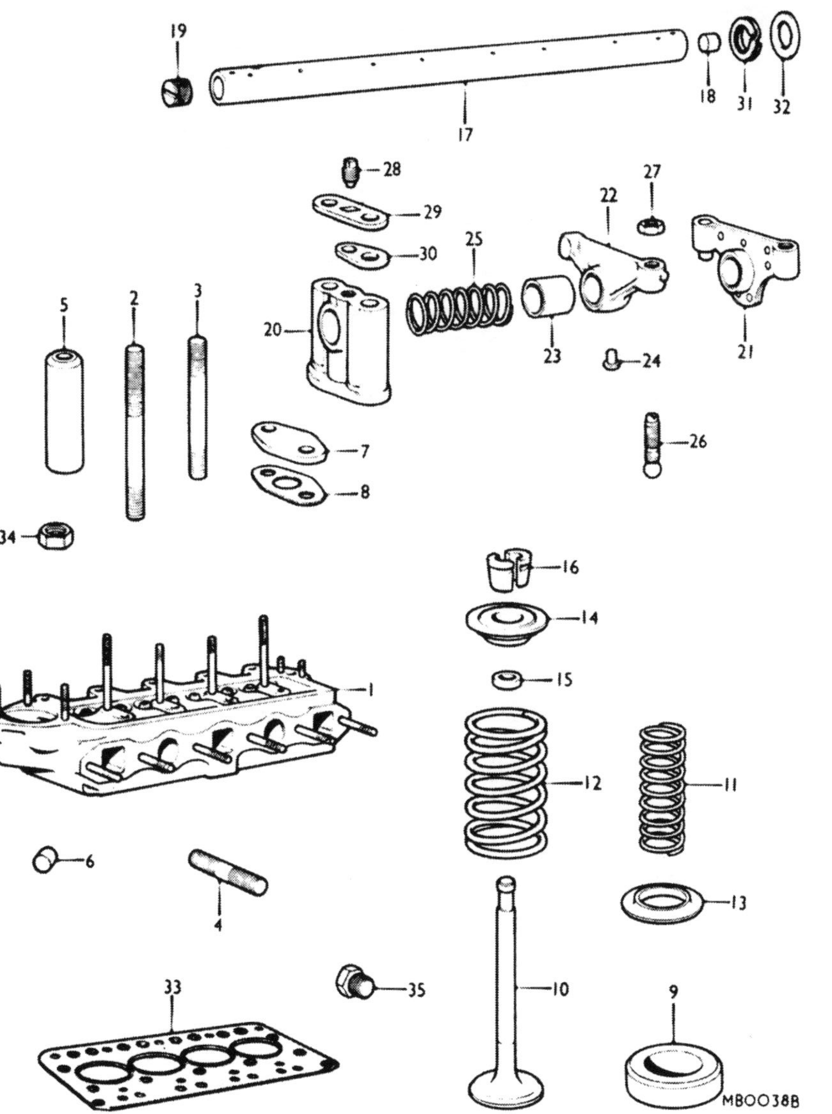

AUSTIN-HEALEY SPRITE MK. 3 AND MK. 4 & MG MIDGET MK. 2 AND MK. 3

NO.	PART NO.	DESCRIPTION	QTY	CHANGE POINT	REMARKS
		ENGINE UNIT-1098cc,10CC-continued.			
	NSP	HEAD ASSEMBLY-CYLINDER (WITH VALVES)	1		
1	28G 222	HEAD ASSEMBLY-CYLINDER	1		
	CHS 2515	Stud-water outlet elbow	3		
2	51K 885	Stud-rocker bracket-long	2		
3	51K 1473	Stud-rocker bracket-short	2		
4	53K 487	Stud-inlet exhaust manifold	6		
4	53K 402	Stud-cover-plate or heater control tap	2		
		GUIDE-VALVE			
5	12A 186	Standard	8		
5	12A 186 10	.010"(.254mm)O/S	NLA		
6	2K 1345	Plug-oil hole	1		
	6K 808	Plug-oil hole	1		
7	2A 180	Plate-cover-heater control tap facing	1		Use when heater is not fitted
8	88G 221	Washer-joint-cover-plate	1		
	FNN 104	Nut-cover-plate or heater control tap stud	2		
	LWN 304	Washer-spring	2		
9	12G 721	Insert-valve seat-inlet	4		For service PURPOSES
9	2A 640	Insert-valve seat-exhaust	4		
9	AEA 763	Insert-valve seat-exhaust-.0625"(1.58mm)O/S	4		
10	12G 296	Valve-inlet	4		
10	AEA 400	Valve-exhaust	4		
11	AEA 401	Spring-valve-inner	8		
12	AEA 311	Spring-valve-outer	8		
13	AEA 402	Collar-valve spring	8		
14	AEA 403	Cup-valve spring	8		
15	2A 879	Ring-valve packing(rubber)	8		
16	2A 11	Cotter-valve(complete)	8		

AUSTIN-HEALEY SPRITE MK. 3 AND MK. 4 & MG MIDGET MK. 2 AND MK. 3

ENGINE UNIT-1098cc,10CC-continued.

NO.	PART NO.	DESCRIPTION	QTY	CHANGE POINT	REMARKS
	NLA	SHAFT ASSEMBLY-VALVE ROCKER	1		
17	12A 1950	SHAFT ASSEMBLY	1		
18	6K 878	Plug-plain-shaft	NLA		
19	2K 4608	Plug-screwed-shaft	1		
20	12G 1927	Bracket-rocker shaft-tapped	1		
20	12G 1926	Bracket-rocker shaft-plain	3		
21	2A 964	Rocker(pressed steel)	8		Alternative to 2A 533;in sets
22	2A 533	ROCKER ASSEMBLY	8		Alternative to 2A 964;in sets
23	2A 21	Bush	8		
24	5C 2436	Rivet-valve rocker	8		
25	6K 556	Spring-rocker spacing	3		
26	12A 1215	Screw-tappet adjusting	8		
27	6K 654	Locknut	8		
28	2A 258	Screw-rocker shaft locating	1		
29	2A 515	Plate-rocker shaft bracket	4	(E)10CC/Da/H101 TO 1373,L101 TO 454	
30	2A 259	Plate-locking-locating screw	1	(E)10CC/Da/H1374 TO 6015,L455 TO 2390	
29	2A 515	Plate-rocker shaft bracket	1	(E)10CC/Da/H6016 ON,L2391 ON	
31	2A 18	Washer-DC spring-rocker shaft	NLA		
32	6K 555	Washer-plain-rocker shaft	2		
	LWN 205	Washer-spring-rocker bracket stud	4		
	FNN 105	Nut-rocker bracket stud	4		
33	GEG 302	Gasket-cylinder head	1		
	PWN 106	Washer-plain-cylinder head stud	5/9		Quantity increased from 5 to 9 at (E)10CC/Da/H1374, L455
	PWN 106	Washer-plain-cylinder head stud	9/8		Quantity reduced from 9 to 8 at (E)10CC/Da/H6016, L2391
34	51K 371	Nut-cylinder head stud	9		
35	ADP 210	Plug-screwed-thermal transmitter boss	1		

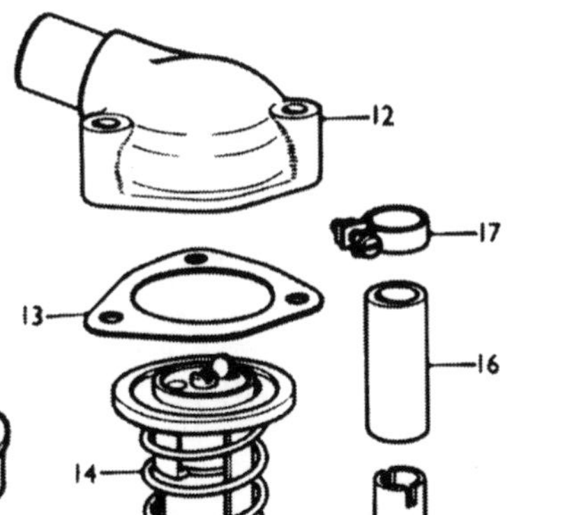
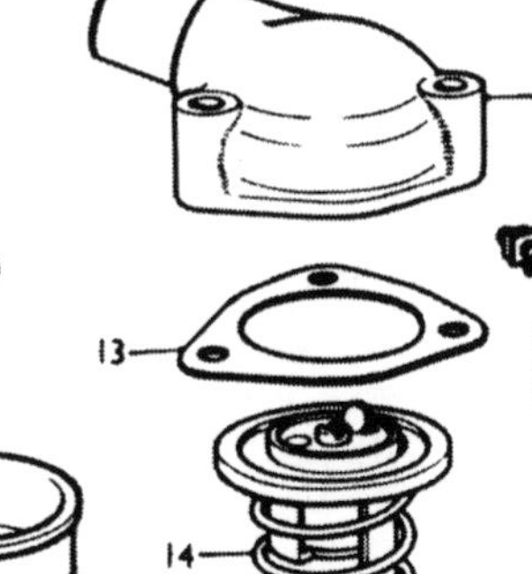
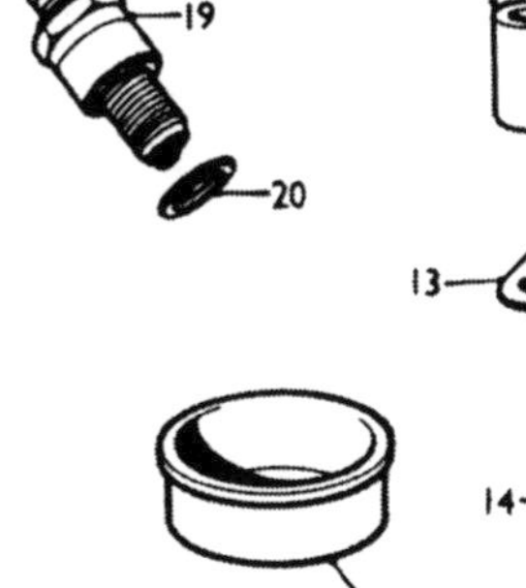

AUSTIN-HEALEY SPRITE MK. 3 AND MK. 4 & MG MIDGET MK. 2 AND MK. 3

NO.	PART NO.	DESCRIPTION	QTY	CHANGE POINT	REMARKS
		ENGINE UNIT-1098cc,10CC-continued.			
1	12A 1530	COVER ASSEMBLY-VALVE ROCKER	1		
2	13H 2296	CAP ASSEMBLY-OIL FILTER	1		
3	12A 403	Washer(rubber)	1		
4	12A 1205	Plate-engine name('Austin')	1	](E)10CC/Da/H25233	
5	12G 826	Plate-engine name('MG')	1	]ON	
6	GEG 401	Gasket-rocker cover to cylinder head	1		
7	12A 1358	Bush-rocker cover(rubber)	2		
8	2A 150	Nut-cap-rocker cover to cylinder head	2		
9	1B 2925	Piece-distance	2		
10	1A 2156	Washer-cup	2		
11	12A 1968	Bracket-engine sling	2		Service purposes only
12	12G 243	Elbow-water outlet	1		
13	GTG 101	Gasket-elbow to cylinder head	1		
	PWZ 105	Washer-plain-elbow stud	3		
	NH 605041	Nut	3		
		THERMOSTAT-WAX TYPE			
14	GTS 102	74C(165F)-Hot climates	1		
14	GTS 104	82C(180F)	1		
14	GTS 106	88C(190F)-Cold climates	1		
15	2A 243	Adaptor-by-pass	1		
16	12A 1093	Connection-by-pass(rubber)	1		
17	3H 2963	Clip	2		
18	11G 176	Sleeve-thermostat by-pass-blanking	1		Use when thermostat is not fitted
19	N 5	PLUG-SPARKING	4		
20	88G 219	Gasket	4		

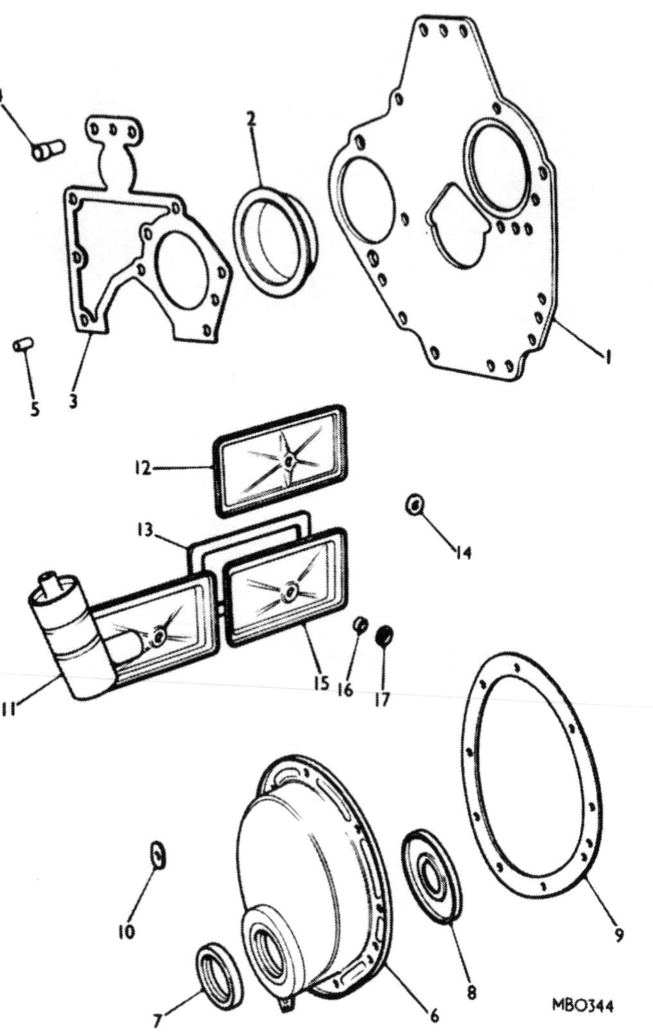

AUSTIN-HEALEY SPRITE MK. 3 AND MK. 4 & MG MIDGET MK. 2 AND MK. 3

ENGINE UNIT-1098cc,10CC-continued.

NO.	PART NO.	DESCRIPTION	QTY	CHANGE POINT	REMARKS
1	12G 453	Plate-engine mounting	1		
2	12G 276	Cover-oil pump	1		
3	AEG 554	Gasket-plate to crankcase	1		
4	12G 422	Dowel-plate to crankcase-top	1		
5	1G 752	Dowel-plate to crankcase-bottom	1		
	HZS 505	Screw-plate to crankcase	7		
	LWZ 305	Washer-spring	7		
6	12G 2506	COVER-CYLINDER-FRONT-(with timing pointer)	1		
7	88G 561	Seal-oil-timing cover	1		
8	12A 1148	Thrower-oil-crankshaft	1		
9	12A 956	Gasket-front cover to crankcase	1		
	HZS 403	Screw-cover to mounting plate	6		
	PWZ 104	Washer-plain	6		
	LWZ 204	Washer-spring	6		
	HZS 505	Screw-cover and mounting plate to crankcase	4		
10	12G 1075	Washer-plain	4		
	LWZ 305	Washer-spring	4		
11	12A 1212	Cover-cylinder-side-front(with oil separator)	1	(E)10CC/Da/101 TO H37547 AND L25599	
12	12H 941	Cover-cylinder-side-rear	1		
13	12A 1139	Gasket-side cover	1		
	HBZ 515	Bolt-cover to crankcase	2		
14	2K 4958	Washer(fibre)	2		
11	12A 1212	Cover-cylinder-side-front(with oil separator)	1	(E)10CC/Da/H37548 AND L25600 ON	
15	12A 1382	Cover-cylinder-side-rear (plain)	1		
13	12A 1175	Gasket-side cover	2		
16	12A 1176	Bush-rubber	2		
17	12A 1177	Washer-cup	2		
	HZS 509	Screw-side cover	2		

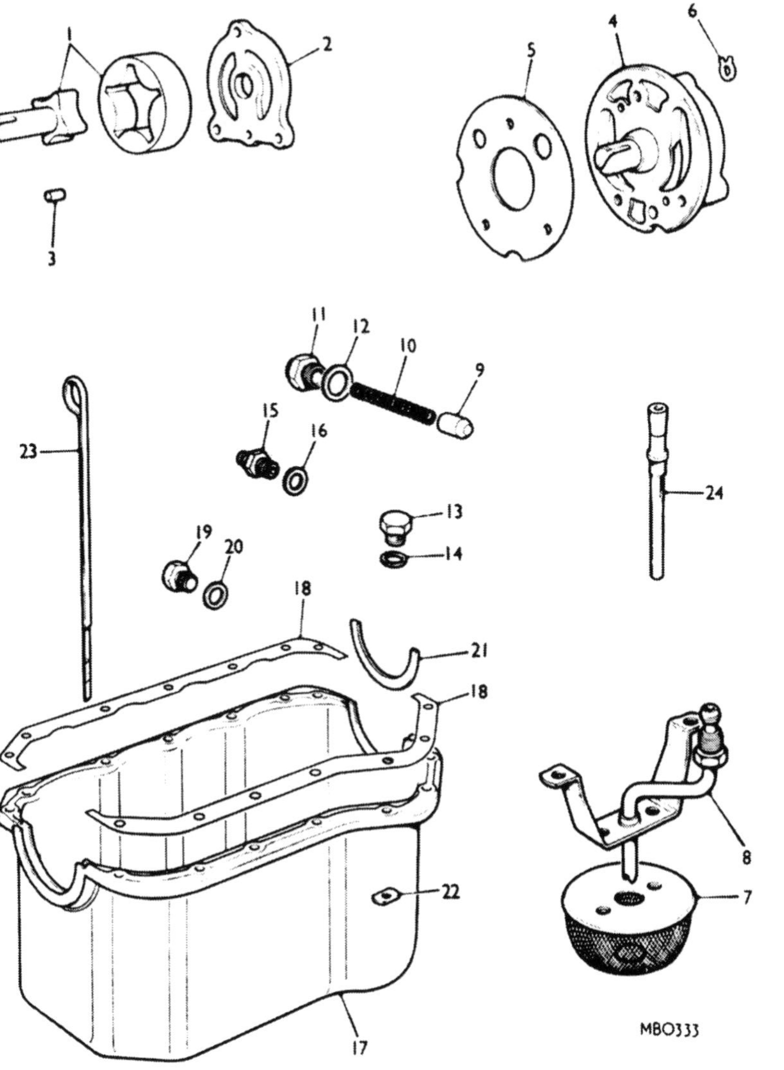

AUSTIN-HEALEY SPRITE MK. 3 AND MK. 4 & MG MIDGET MK. 2 AND MK. 3

ENGINE UNIT-1098cc,10CC-continued.

NO.	PART NO.	DESCRIPTION	QTY	CHANGE POINT	REMARKS
	12A 303	PUMP ASSEMBLY-OIL-(HOBOURN)	NLA		Use 12G 793
1	37H 861	Shaft-and outer rotor	1		
2	37H 863	Cover	1		
3	37H 864	Dowel-spring	NLA		
4	12G 793	Pump(Concentric)	1		
5	12G 730	Gasket-pump	1		
	HBN 414	Screw-pump to crankcase	3		
6	12G 926	Washer-lock for oil pump	1		
7	2A 668	Strainer	1		
8	12A 451	Pipe-oil suction(with strainer bracket)	1		
	HZS 404	Screw-bracket to strainer	2		
	LWN 404	Washer-shakeproof	2		
	HZS 404	Screw-bracket to main bearing cap	2		
	LWN 404	Washer-shakeproof	2		
9	12H 865	Valve-oil release	1		
10	6K 853	Spring	1		
11	12A 1861	Nut-cap	1		
12	6K 431	Washer(copper)	1		
13	2K 4994	Plug-priming	1		
14	6K 464	Washer	1		
15	2A 269	Union-pressure	1		
16	2K 4956	Washer	1		
17	12G 173	Sump	1		
18	GEG 501	Gasket-sump to crankcase	1		
19	88G 257	Plug-drain	1		
20	6K 638	Washer	1		
21	12G 3016	Seal-main bearing cap-front	1		
21	12G 1009	Seal-main bearing cap-rear	1		
	HZS 404	Screw-sump to crankcase	14		
	LWZ 404	Washer-shakeproof	14		
22	2K 5197	Washer-plain	14		
23	12G 175	Rod-dipper	1		
24	12G 107	Tube-rod	1		

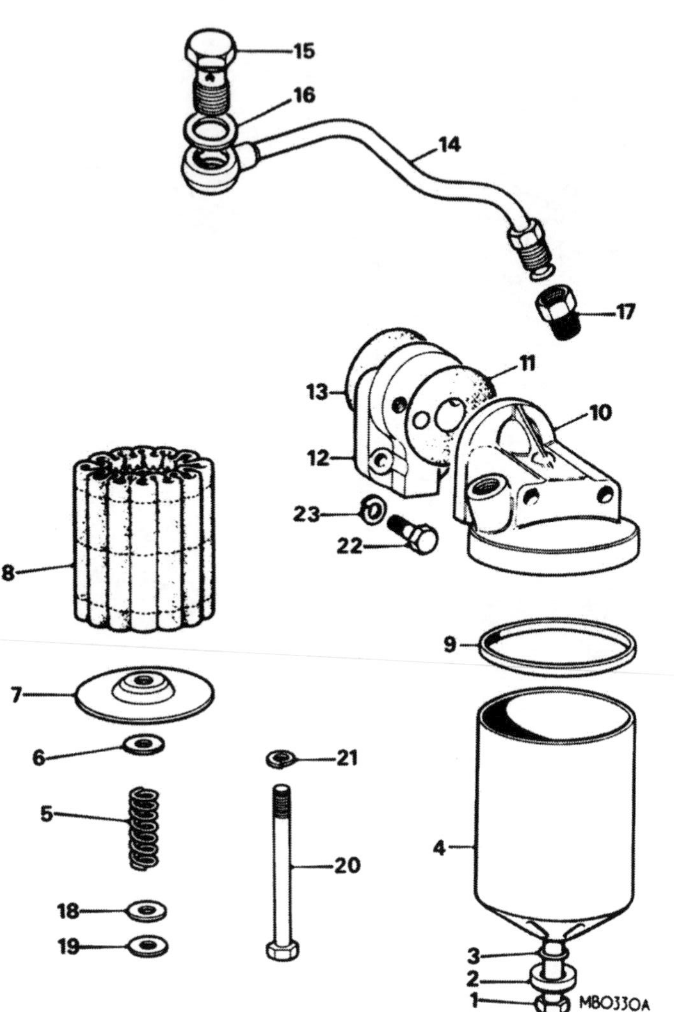

AUSTIN-HEALEY SPRITE MK. 3 AND MK. 4 & MG MIDGET MK. 2 AND MK. 3

ENGINE UNIT-1098cc,10CC-continued.

NO.	PART NO.	DESCRIPTION	QTY	CHANGE POINT	REMARKS
	NSP	FILTER ASSEMBLY-OIL	1		PUROLATOR
1	37H 689	Bolt-centre	1		
2	17H 1172	Collar-bolt	1		
3	17H 1173	Seal-bolt to sump	1		
4	17H 1169	Sump(steel)	1		
5	7H 25	Spring-pressure plate	1	(E)10CC/Da/101 TO H10799 and L2791	
18	WA 110061	Washer-pressure plate spring	1		
6	7H 28	Seal-pressure plate	1		
7	17H 1148	Plate-pressure	1		
8	GFE 103	Element-oil filter	1		
9	12A 1591	Seal-sump to head	1		
10	17H 9463	Head	1		
	NSP	FILTER ASSEMBLY-OIL	1		Purolator
1	37H 689	Bolt-centre	1		
19	PWN 106	Washer	1		
3	17H 2281	Seal-bolt to sump	1		
5	7H 25	Spring-pressure plate	1		
18	WA 110061	Washer-pressure plate spring	1	(E)10CC/Da/H10800 TO H15979 and L2791 TO L13311	
6	7H 28	Seal-pressure plate	1		
7	17H 1148	Plate-pressure	1		
8	GFE 103	Element-oil filter	1		
9	12A 1591	Seal-sump to head	1		
	NSP	FILTER ASSEMBLY-OIL	1		Purolator
1	37H 689	Bolt-centre	1		
2	17H 1172	Collar-bolt	1		
3	17H 1173	Seal-bolt to sump	1		
4	17H 1169	Sump(steel)	1		
5	7H 25	Spring-pressure plate	1		
18	WA 110061	Washer-pressure plate spring	1	(E)10CC/Da/H15980 TO H35286 and L13312 ON	
6	7H 28	Seal-pressure plate	1		
7	17H 1148	Plate-pressure	1		
8	GFE 103	Element-oil filter	1		
9	12A 1591	Seal-sump to head	1		
	NSP	FILTER ASSEMBLY-OIL	1		Purolator
1	37H 689	Bolt-centre	1		
2	17H 1172	Collar-bolt	1		
3	17H 1173	Seal-bolt to sump	1		
4	17H 1169	Sump(steel)	1		
5	7H 25	Spring-pressure plate	1		
18	WA 110061	Washer-pressure plate spring	1	(E)10CC/Da/H32587 ON	
6	7H 28	Seal-pressure plate	1		
7	17H 1148	Plate-pressure	1		
8	GFE 103	Element-oil filter	1		
9	12A 1591	Seal-sump to head	1		
20	HCZ 630	Bolt-filter to adaptor	2		
21	LWZ 206	Washer-spring	2		
11	88G 402	Gasket-filter to adaptor	1		
12	AEA 657	Adaptor-filter to crankcase	1		
13	88G 402	Gasket-adaptor to crankcase	1		
22	HCS 608	Screw-adaptor to crankcase	2		
23	LWZ 306	Washer-spring	2		
14	AEA 658	Pipe-filter to crankcase	NLA		Use when oil COOLER IS NOT fitted
15	12A 715	Screw-banjo union	1		
16	2A 1768	Washer(copper)	2		
17	AEA 678	Connection-pipe to filter	1		

19 20 22 23 30 38 31 32 39 21 18 17 27 24 40 41 28 36 37 42 29 26 25 6 9 7 5 4 3 2 8 12 10 1 13 34 35 33 15 16 11 14 MB0331A

AUSTIN-HEALEY SPRITE MK. 3 AND MK. 4 & MG MIDGET MK. 2 AND MK. 3

ENGINE UNIT-1098cc,10CC-continued.

NO.	PART NO.	DESCRIPTION	QTY	CHANGE POINT	REMARKS
1	GWP 101	PUMP ASSEMBLY-WATER	NLA		Use GWP 132 together with bottom hose GRH 508(with heater) or AHA 8750(less heater)and clip GHC 913 1off
2	2A 664	Vane	1		
3	88G 446	Seal	1		
4	12A 1802	Bearing(with spindle)	1		
5	2A 778	Wire-bearing locating	1		
6	53K 1433	Screw-lubricating point	1		
7	2K 4974	Washer-fibre	1		
8	8G 733	Hub-pulley	1		
9	2A 243	Adaptor-by-pass	1		
10	8G 2570	KIT-WATER PUMP REPAIR	1		
11	GWP 132	PUMP ASSEMBLY-WATER	1		
12	88G 215	Gasket-pump to crankcase	1		
13	12A 1344	Dowel	NLA		
14	HZS 515	Screw-pump to crankcase-1.875"(4.75cm)	2		
15	SH 605101	Screw-pump to crankcase-1.25"(3.17cm)	2		
16	LWZ 305	Washer-spring	4		
17	2A 601	Pulley-water pump	1		
18	2A 803	Stiffener-fan blade	1		
19	SH 604061	Screw-fan to pulley	4		
20	WL 600041	Washer-spring	4		
21	2A 526	Bracket-rear	1		
22	SH 605061	Screw-bracket to crankcase	2		
23	LWZ 305	Washer-spring	2		
24	12G 289	Pillar-dynamo adjusting link	1	(E)10CC/Da/H101 TO 5278,L101 TO 2374	
24	12A 314	Pillar-dynamo adjusting link	1	(E)10CC/Da/H5279 ON,L2375 ON	
25	NT 606041	Nut	1		
26	WL 600061	Washer-spring	1		
27	AEA 679	Link-dynamo adjusting	NLA		
28	LNZ 206	Nut-link to pillar	1		
29	1B 8806	Washer-plain	1		
30	SH 605101	Screw-dynamo to rear bracket	1		
31	LWZ 305	Washer-spring	1		
32	LNZ 205	Nut	1		
33	BH 605141	Bolt-dynamo to water pump	1		
34	LWZ 305	Washer-spring	1		
35	LNZ 205	Nut	1		
36	SH 505051	Screw-dynamo to adjusting link	1		
37	LWZ 305	Washer-spring	1		
38	17D 11	Fan-dynamo	1		
39	12G 2102	Pulley-dynamo	1		
40	AEA 301	Blade-fan	2		
41	GFB 120	Belt-fan	NLA		Use GFB 190
41	GFB 190	Belt-fan	1		
42	11G 176	Sleeve-blanking-by-pass	1		

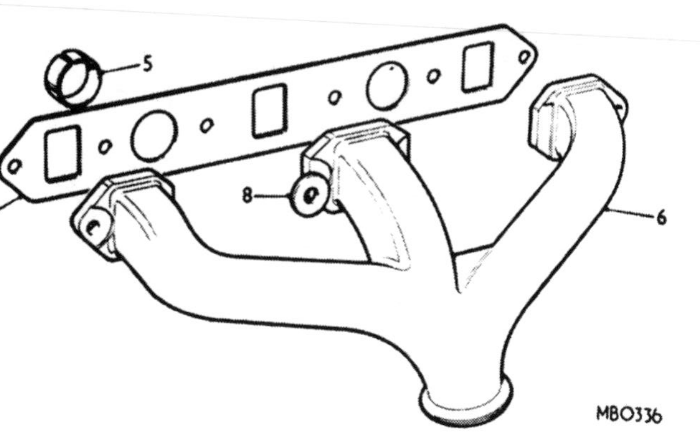

AUSTIN-HEALEY SPRITE MK. 3 AND MK. 4 & MG MIDGET MK. 2 AND MK. 3

ENGINE UNIT-1098cc,10CC-continued.

NO.	PART NO.	DESCRIPTION	QTY	CHANGE POINT	REMARKS
1	12G 583	MANIFOLD ASSEMBLY-INLET	1		
2	AEA 635	Plug-welch	2		
	CHS 2620	Stud-carburetter	NLA		
3	ADP 210	Plug	1		Use when closed-CIRCUIT breathing is not fitted
4	1B 3664	Washer	1		
5	12G 297	Ferrule-inlet manifold	2		
6	12G 420	Manifold-exhaust	1		
7	GEG 601	Gasket-manifold to cylinder head	1		
8	12A 1211	Washer-clamping-manifold stud	4		
	PWZ 105	Washer-plain-manifold	2		
	BNN 105	Nut-manifold stud	6		
	ZCS 406	Screw-heater rail clip to inlet-manifold	1		
	PWZ 104	Washer-plain	1		
	LWZ 204	Washer-spring	1		
		CLOSED-CIRCUIT BREATHING			
9	AEG 351	Bracket-support-control valve	1		
4	1B 3664	Washer-adaptor to manifold	1		
	ZCS 405	Bolt-bracket to manifold	1		
	LWZ 304	Washer-spring	1		
10	12H 1405	Adaptor-breather hose	1		
11	12H 1407	Hose-adaptor to control valve	1		
12	GHC 507	Clip	2		
13	13H 5191	VALVE ASSEMBLY-BREATHER CONTROL	1		
14	27H 7756	Spring-top	1		
15	27H 7757	Sub-assembly of plunger	1		Use with 13H 3609
15	37H 3686	Sub-assembly of plunger	1		Use with 13H 5191
16	27H 7758	Diaphragm	1		
17	27H 7759	Plate-valve cover	1		
18	27H 7760	Clip-spring	1		
	SH 604061	Bolt-bracket to breather valve	1		
	LWZ 304	Washer-spring	1		
	NH 604061	Nut	1		
19	12A 1052	Hose-control valve to cylinder side cover	NLA		Use 37H 7085 M.
19	37H 7085 M	Hose-control valve to cylinder side cover	A/R		Supplied in multiples of metres.
20	GHC 507	Clip	2		

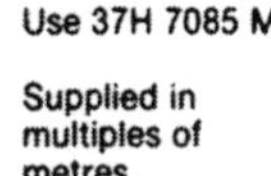

AUSTIN-HEALEY SPRITE MK. 3 AND MK. 4 & MG MIDGET MK. 2 AND MK. 3

ENGINE UNIT-1275cc,12CC,12CD,12CE,12CJ AND 12V.

NO.	PART NO.	DESCRIPTION	QTY	CHANGE POINT	REMARKS
1	8G 180 N	ENGINE UNIT-STRIPPED-HC	1	(E)12CC/Da/101 to (+) (E)12CE/Da/101 TO (+) (E)12V/586F/101 TO(+) (E)12V/588F/101 TO(+) (E)12V/778F/101 ON	For models with cross-flow RADIATOR,use with water outlet elbow 12G 1902.
1	8G 179 N	ENGINE UNIT-STRIPPED-LC	NLA		
2	8G 189 N	ENGINE UNIT-STRIPPED-HC (WITH EXHAUST PORT AIR INJECTION)	1	(E)12CD/Da/101 TO (+) (E)12CJ/Da/H21201 TO(+)	
2	8G 190	ENGINE UNIT-STRIPPED-LC (WITH EXHAUST PORT AIR INJECTION)	1		
2	38G 506 N	ENGINE UNIT-STRIPPED-LC (WITH EXHAUST PORT AIR INJECTION)	1	(E)12V/587Z/101 TO(+) (E)12V/671Z/101 ON	
3	38G 396 N	ENGINE UNIT-PART-HC	1		
3	38G 395 N	ENGINE UNIT-PART-LC	1		
4	38G 398	BLOCK ASSEMBLY-CYLINDER-HC	1		
4	38G 397	BLOCK ASSEMBLY-CYLINDER-LC	1		
5	AEC 876	Plug-core	5		
6	2K 1345	Plug-oil release valve passage	2		
7	12H 1734	Plug-oil gallery	4		
8	51K 279	Stud-cylinder head-long	4		
9	51K 280	Stud-cylinder head-short	NLA		Use CAM 151
9	CAM 151	Stud-cylinder head-short	5		
10	1A 1964	Restrictor-oil feed-camshaft	1		
11	2A 54	Dowel-main bearing cap	6	(E)12CC/Da/H101 TO(+) (E)12CD/Da/101 TO H1556	
12	12A 1002	Screw	6		
13	12A 1381	Washer-lock	6		
11	12G 1268	Dowel-main bearing cap	6	(E)12CC/Da/H(+) TO(+) (E)12CD/Da/H1557 TO(+) (E)12CE/Da/H101 TO(+) (E)12CJ/Da/H21201 TO(+) (E)12V/-/101 ON	
12	12G 1398	Screw-main bearing cap	6		
14	AEG 240	Gasket-cover	1		
	SH 604061	Screw	3		
	LWZ 204	Washer-spring	3		
15	AEG 428	Liner-cylinder block	4		
16	8G 2392	Liner-camshaft bearing	1SET		
17	53K 2853	Plug-drain tap boss	1		
18	6K 638	Washer-plug	1		
19	3H 576	Tap-cylinder drain	1		
20	2K 4954	Washer(fibre)	1		

(+) Change point not available.

MBO338

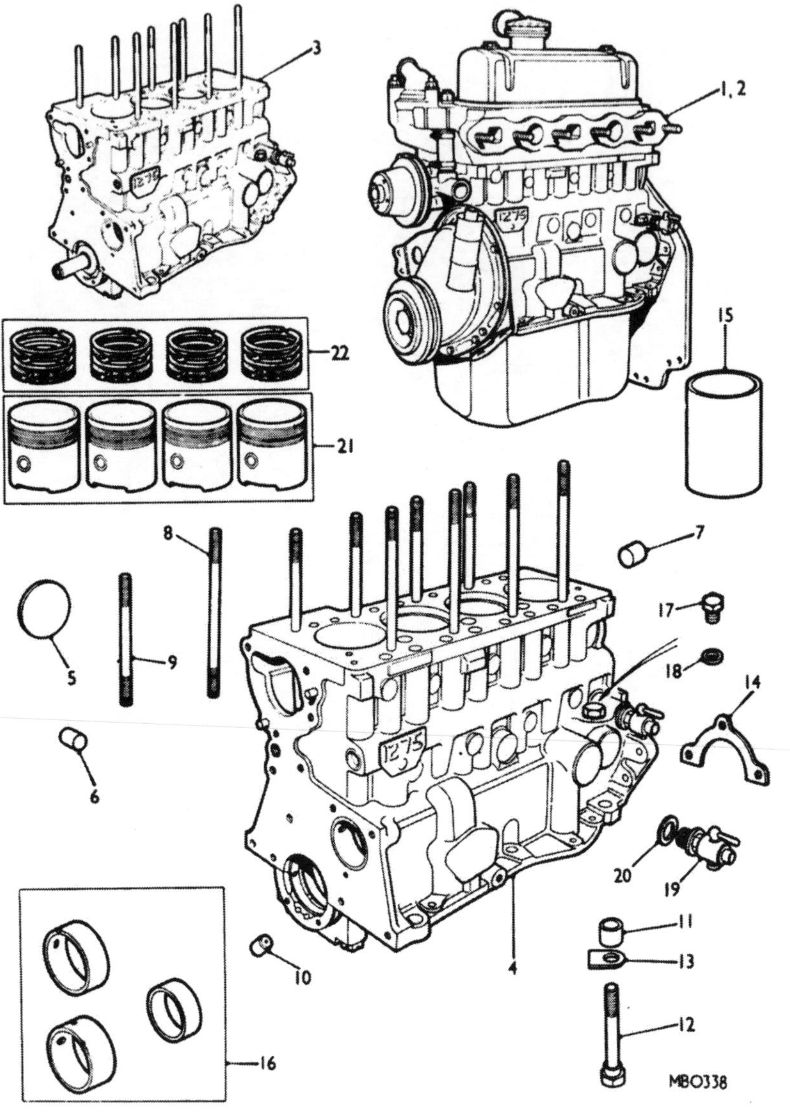

AUSTIN-HEALEY SPRITE MK. 3 AND MK. 4 & MG MIDGET MK. 2 AND MK. 3

NO.	PART NO.	DESCRIPTION	QTY	CHANGE POINT	REMARKS
		ENGINE UNIT-1275cc,12CC,12CD,12CE,12CJ AND 12V-continued.			
		PISTON ASSEMBLY-ENGINE SET-GRADE 3-HC			
21	8G 2670	Standard	1SET		
21	8G 2670 20	.020"(.508mm)O/S	1SET		
		PISTON ASSEMBLY-ENGINE SET-GRADE 3-LC			
21	8G 2669	Standard	1SET		
21	8G 2669 20	.020"(.508mm)O/S	1SET		
		RING-PISTON-ENGINE SET			
22	8G 2671	Standard	1SET		
22	8G 2671 20	.020"(.508mm)O/S	1SET		

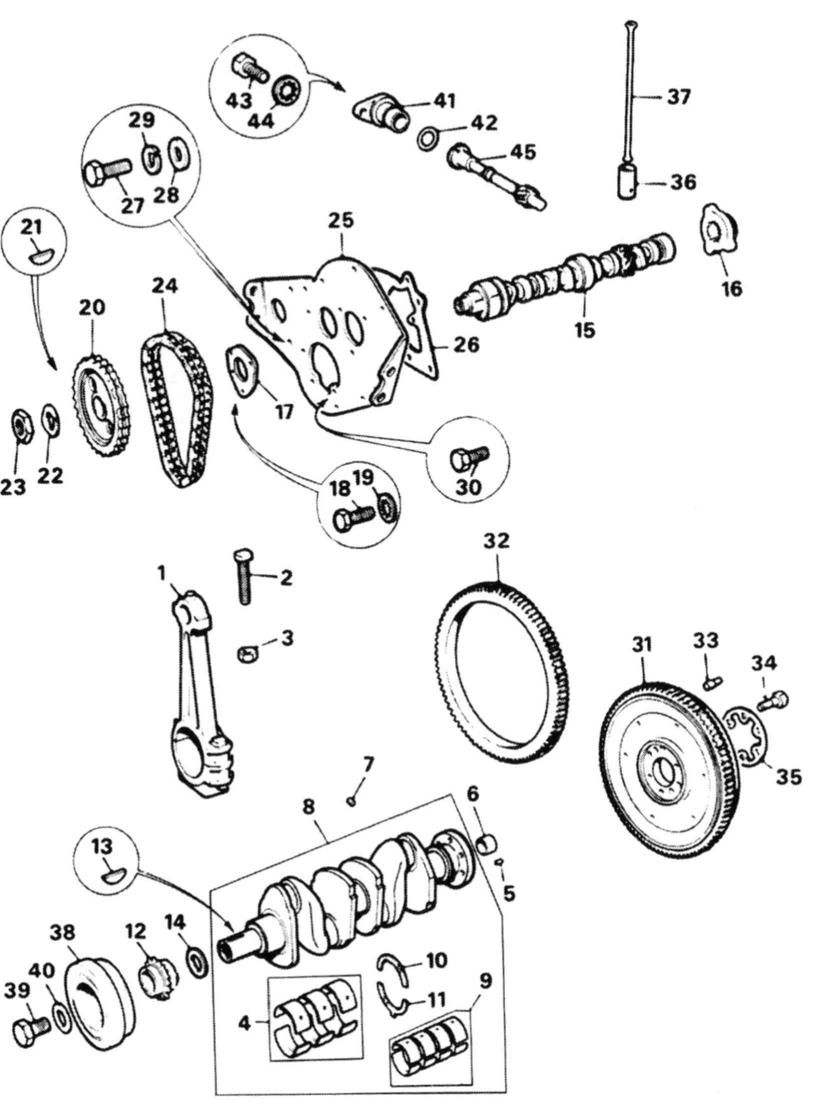

AUSTIN-HEALEY SPRITE MK. 3 AND MK. 4 & MG MIDGET MK. 2 AND MK. 3

ENGINE UNIT-1275cc,12CC,12CD,12CE,12CJ AND 12V-continued

NO.	PART NO.	DESCRIPTION	QTY	CHANGE POINT	REMARKS
1	AEG 520	ROD ASSEMBLY-CONNECTING	4		] Alternatives
1	AEG 624	ROD ASSEMBLY-CONNECTING	4		
2	AEG 519	Screw	8		
3	AEG 147	Nut	8		
	AEG 565	CRANKSHAFT ASSEMBLY	NLA		Use 12G 1320.
5	1A 1559	Bush-1st motion shaft	1		
6	51K 3575	Dowel-flywheel	2		
7	1G 1167	Restrictor-oil	4		
	12G 1320	Crankshaft	NLA		Use 8G 2741.
8	8G 2741	CRANKSHAFT ASSEMBLY-(WITH BEARINGS)	1		
4	8G 2399	Bearing-connecting rod-standard	1SET		
9	8G 2391	Bearing-main-standard	1SET		
10	AEG 159	Washer-thrust-upper-standard	2		
11	AEG 160	Washer-thrust-lower-standard	2		
		BEARING-CONNECTING ROD-UNDERSIZE			
4	8G 2399 10	.254mm(.010")	1SET		
4	8G 2399 20	.508mm(.020")	1SET		
		BEARING-MAIN-UNDERSIZE			
9	8G 2391 10	.254mm(.010")	1SET		
9	8G 2391 20	.508mm(.020")	1SET		
9	8G 2391 30	.762mm(.030")	1SET		
9	8G 2391 40	1.016mm(.040")	1SET		
10	AEG 159 3	Washer-thrust-upper-.016mm(.003")O/S	2		
10	AEG 159 3	Washer-thrust-upper-.162mm(.030")O/S	2		
10	AEG 160 3	Washer-thrust-lower-.016mm(.003")O/S	2		
10	AEG 160 30	Washer-thrust-lower-.162mm(.030")O/S	2		
5	13H 4653	Bush-1st motion shaft	1		
6	51K 3575	Dowel-flywheel	2		
12	AEA 695	Gear-crankshaft	1		
13	6K 836	Key	1		
14	6K 628	Washer-packing	1		

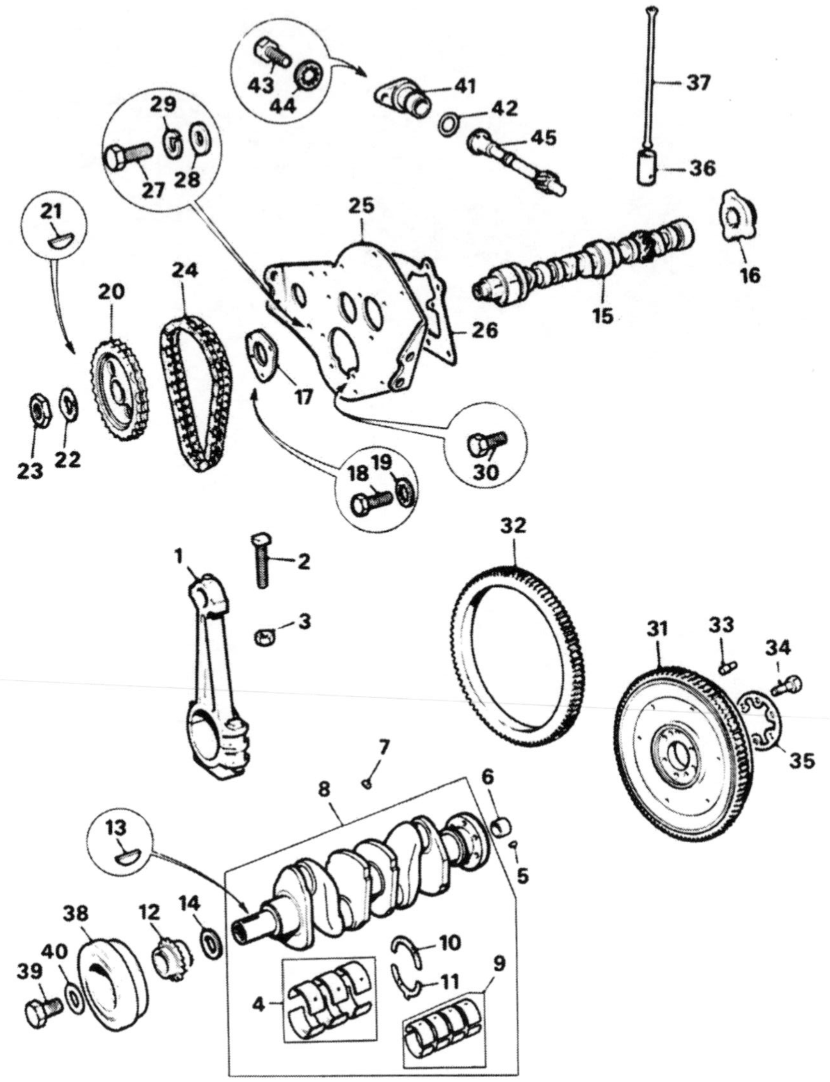

AUSTIN-HEALEY SPRITE MK. 3 AND MK. 4 & MG MIDGET MK. 2 AND MK. 3

NO.	PART NO.	DESCRIPTION	QTY	CHANGE POINT	REMARKS
		ENGINE UNIT-1275cc,12CC,12CD,12CE,12CJ AND 12V-continued			
15	AEG 522	Camshaft	NLA		] Use AEG 523
15	AEG 538	Camshaft	NLA		]
15	AEG 523	Camshaft	1		
16	12G 729	Flange-driving-oil pump	1		
17	2A 84	Plate-camshaft locating	1		
18	SH 604061	Screw	3		
19	WF 600041	Washer-shakeproof	3		
20	AEA 696	Gear-camshaft	1		
21	WKN 505	Key	1		
22	2A 759	Washer-lock	1		
23	6K 629	Nut	1		
24	2H 4905	Chain-timing	1		
25	12G 1309	Plate-engine mounting-front	1		
26	12G 619	Gasket	1		
27	SH 605061	Screw-plate to crankcase	2		
28	WA 108051	Washer-plain	2		
29	LWZ 305	Washer-spring	2		
30	AEA 687	Screw-plate to bearing cap	2		
31	12G 1401	FLYWHEEL ASSEMBLY	1		
32	12G 1444	Gear-ring-starter	1		
33	1G 2984	Dowel	3		
34	51K 1029	Screw-flywheel to crankshaft	6		
35	12G 982	Washer-lock	1		

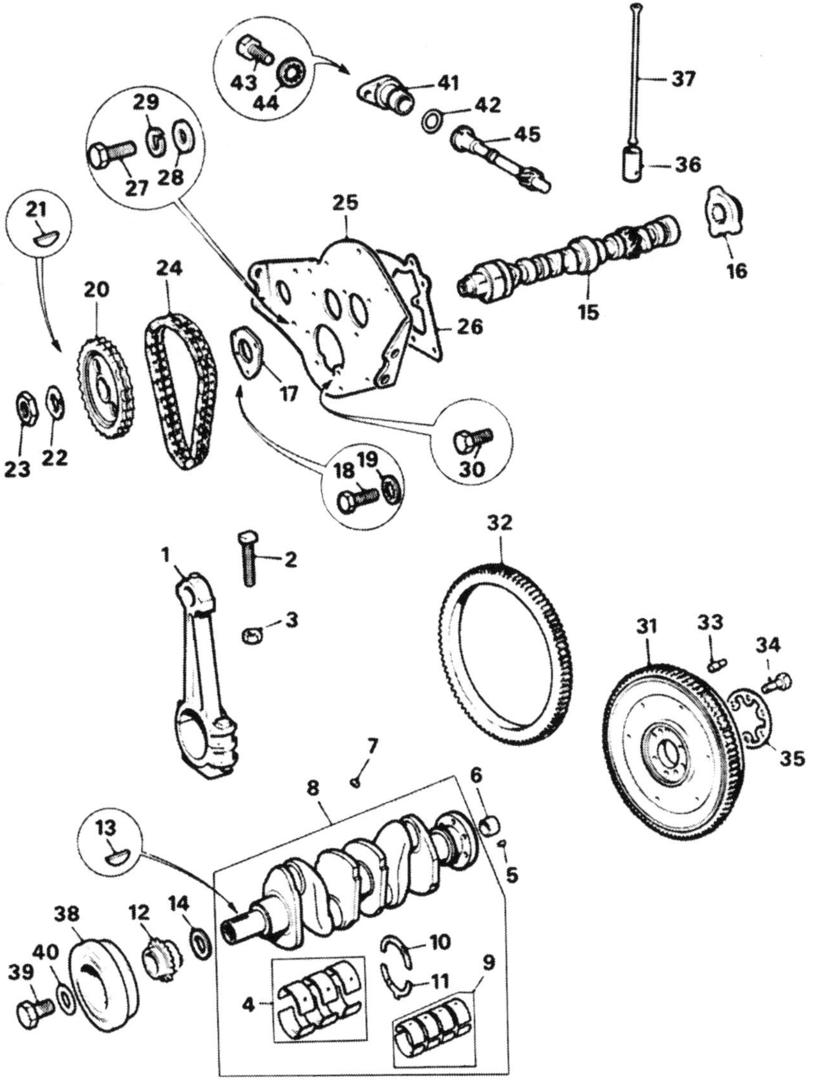

AUSTIN-HEALEY SPRITE MK. 3 AND MK. 4 & MG MIDGET MK. 2 AND MK. 3

ENGINE UNIT-1275cc,12CC,12CD,12CE,12CJ AND 12V-continued

NO.	PART NO.	DESCRIPTION	QTY	CHANGE POINT	REMARKS
		TAPPET			
36	2A 13	Standard	8	(E)12CC/Da/H101 TO H16300 (E)12CD/Da/H101 TO H2452 (E)12CE/Da/H101 TO H958	
36	2A 13 10	.254mm(.010")	8		
36	12A 13 20	.508mm(.020")	8		
36	AEG 584	Standard	NLA	(E)12CD/Da/h2453 TO(+) (E)12CE/Da/h959 TO(+) (E)12CJ/Da/H21201 TO(+) (E)12V/-/101 ON	Use 2A 13.
36	AEG 584 10	.254mm(.010")	8		
36	AEG 584 20	.508mm(.020")	NLA		Use 2A 1320.
37	AEG 314	Push-rod	8		
38	88G 305	Pulley-crankshaft	1		
39	AEA 312	Bolt	1		
40	12A 398	Washer-lock	1		
41	12A 1136	Housing-distributor	1		
42	13H 2792	'O'ring	1		
43	SH 604061	Screw	1		
44	GHF 321	Washer-shakeproof	1		
45	1G 2062	Spindle-distributor drive	NLA		Use 12G 4499.
45	12G 4499	Spindle-distributor drive	1		

(+) Change point not available.

AUSTIN-HEALEY SPRITE MK. 3 AND MK. 4 & MG MIDGET MK. 2 AND MK. 3

ENGINE UNIT-1275cc 12CC,12CD,12CE,12CJ AND 12V-continued

NO.	PART NO.	DESCRIPTION	QTY	CHANGE POINT	REMARKS
1	38G 399	HEAD ASSEMBLY-CYLINDER(WITH GUIDES,PLUGS AND STUDS)	1	(E)12CC/Da/h101 TO(+) (E)12CE/Da/H101 TO(+) (E)12V/586F/101 TO(+) (E)12V/588F/101 TO(+) (E)12V/778F/101 ON	
2	38G 431	HEAD ASSEMBLY-CYLINDER(WITH GUIDES,PLUGS,STUDS AND AIR INJECTOR TUBES)$	1	(E)12CD/Da/H101 TO(+) (E)12CJ/Da/H21201 TO(+) (E)12V/587Z/101 TO(+) (E)12V/671Z/101 ON	
3	12G 1111	Guide-inlet and exhaust	8		Part of cylinder head 38G 399
3	12G 1963	Guide-inlet and exhaust $	8		Part of cylinder head 38G 431
4	12H 1734	Plug-oil hole	2		Part of cylinder head 38G 399
4	2K 1345	Plug-oil hole	1		Part of cylinder HEAD 38G 431
4	12H 1734	Plug-cleaning	2		
	6K 808	Plug-oil hole	1		
5	12G 2092	Plug-water hole	3		
6	AEA 771	Plug-water dowel hole	2		
7	12H 1734	Plug-cylinder head top face	3		
	FHS 2518	Stud-water outlet elbow	3		
8	51K 885	Stud-rocker bracket-long	3		
	CHS 522	Stud-rocker bracket-short	2		
9	53K 487	Stud-inlet and exhaust manifold	6		
10	53K 402	Stud-cover plate or heater tap	2		

(+) Change point not available.

$ This item is subject to safety regulations.

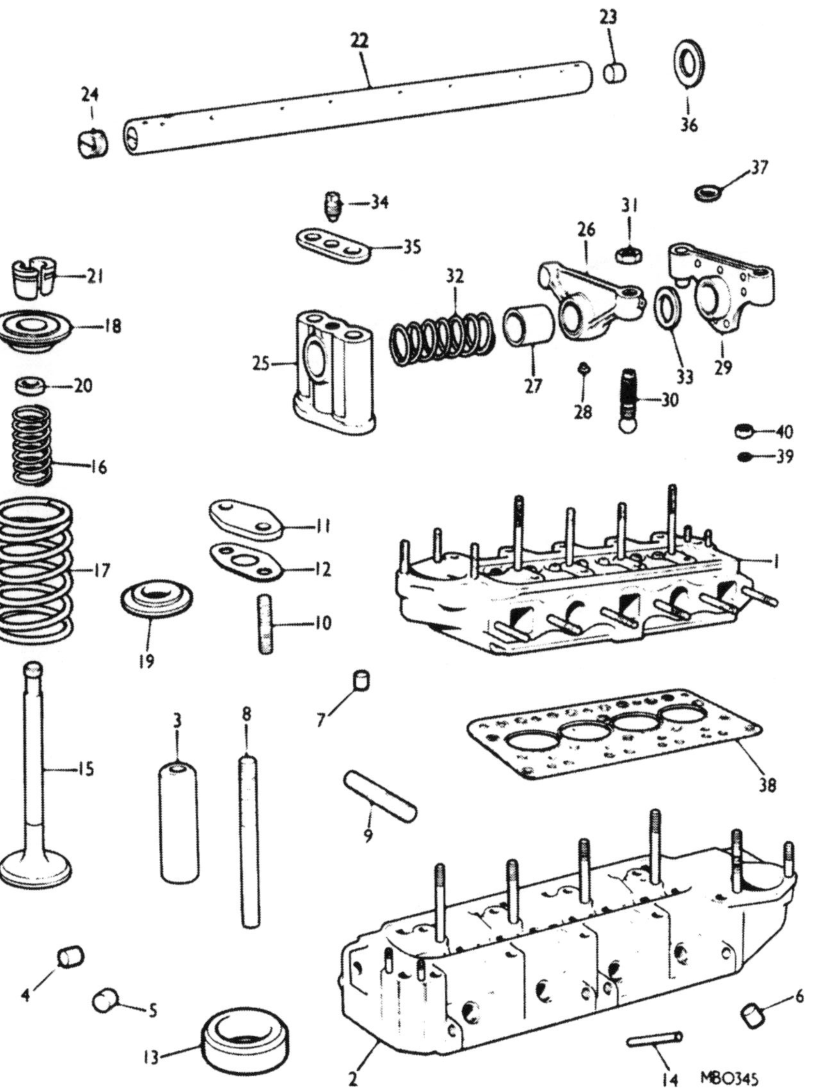

AUSTIN-HEALEY SPRITE MK. 3 AND MK. 4 & MG MIDGET MK. 2 AND MK. 3

ENGINE UNIT-1275cc,12CC,12CD,12CE,12CJ AND 12V-continued

NO.	PART NO.	DESCRIPTION	QTY	CHANGE POINT	REMARKS
11	2A 180	Plate-cover-heater control tap facing	1		
12	88G 221	Gasket	1		
	LWZ 204	Washer-spring	2		
	NH 604041	Nut	2		
13	AEG 477	Insert-valve seat-inlet	4		
13	12G 2675	Insert-valve seat-exhaust	4		
14	12G 1454	Tube-air injector	4	(E)12CD/Da/h101 TO(+) (E)12CJ/Da/H21201 TO(+) (E)12V/587Z/101 TO(+) (E)12V/671Z/101 ON	
15	12G 941	Valve-inlet	4		
15	12G 1322	Valve-exhaust	4		
16	12G 1137	Spring-valve-inner	8		
17	12G 1136	Spring-valve-outer	8		
18	12G 1522	Cup-valve spring-top	8		
19	AEA 403	Cup-valve spring-bottom	8		
20	AEG 327	Seal-oil-valve	8		
21	88G 459	Cotter-valves-complete	8		

(+) Change point not available.

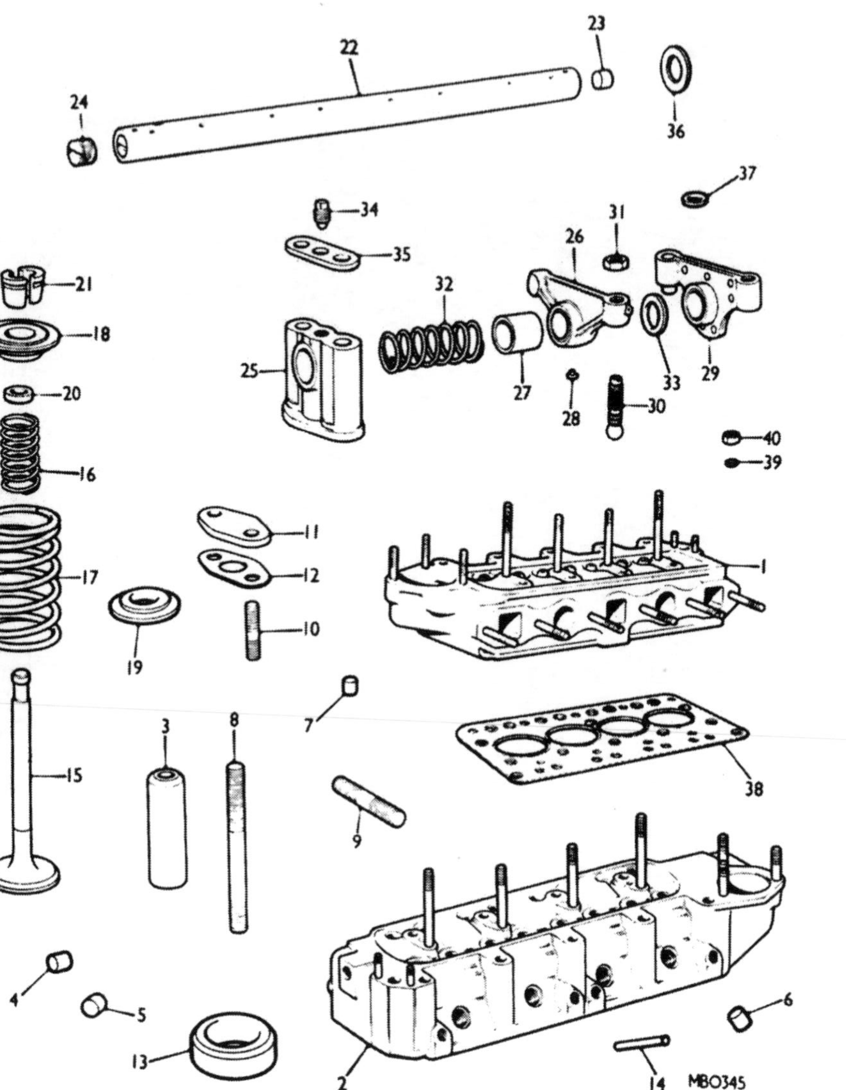

AUSTIN-HEALEY SPRITE MK. 3 AND MK. 4 & MG MIDGET MK. 2 AND MK. 3

ENGINE UNIT-1275cc,12CC,12CD,12CE,12CJ AND 12V-continued.

NO.	PART NO.	DESCRIPTION	QTY	CHANGE POINT	REMARKS
22	12A 1950	SHAFT ASSEMBLY-ROCKER	1	(E)12CC/Da/H101 TO H16596 (E)12CD/Da/H101 TO H404	
23	6K 878	Plug-plain	NLA		
24	2K 4608	Plug-screwed	1		
25	12G 1927	Bracket-rocker shaft-tapped	1		
25	12G 1926	Bracket-rocker shaft-oil hole	3		
22	AEG 399	SHAFT ASSEMBLY	NLA	(E)12CC/Da/h16597 TO(+) (E)12CD/Da/H405 TO(+) (E)12CE/Da/H101 TO(+) (E)12CJ/Da/H21201 TO(+) (E)12V/-/101 ON	Use 12A 1950
23	6K 878	Plug-plain	NLA		
24	2K 4608	Plug-screwed	1		
25	12G 1927	Bracket-rocker shaft-tapped	1		
25	12G 1926	Bracket-rocker shaft-oil hole	3		
26	12G 1221	ROCKER ASSEMBLY-VALVE	8		Alternative to 12G 1313 in sets of 8.
27	2A 21	Bush	8		
28	5C 2436	Rivet	8		
29	12G 1313	Rocker-valve	8		Alternative to 12G 1221 in sets of 8.
30	AEG 167	Screw-tappet adjusting	8		Use with valve ROCKER 12G 1221.
	FNN 605	Nut-lock	8		
30	12A 1215	Screw-tappet adjusting	8		Use with valve ROCKER 12G 1313.
31	6K 654	Locknut	8		
32	6K 556	Spring-spacing	3		
33	AEG 168	Piece-distance	6		
34	2A 258	Screw-locating	1		
35	2A 515	Plate-locating screw	1		
36	6K 555	Washer-rocker shaft	2		
	PWN 105	Washer-rocker shaft bracket	3		
37	12H 2178	Washer-rocker shaft bracket	3		
	LNZ 205	Nut-rocker bracket stud	4		
38	GEG 301	Gasket-cylinder head	1		
	PWN 106	Washer-plain	2		
39	12H 2178	Washer-plain	3		
40	51K 371	Nut	10		

(+) Change point not available.

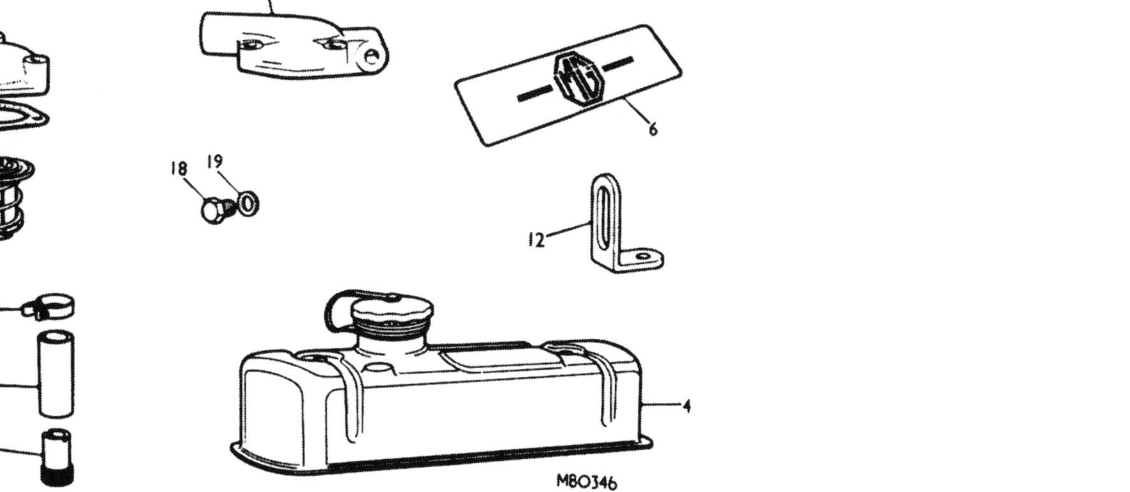

AUSTIN-HEALEY SPRITE MK. 3 AND MK. 4 & MG MIDGET MK. 2 AND MK. 3

ENGINE UNIT-1275cc,12CC,12CD,12CE,12CJ AND 12V-continued.

NO.	PART NO.	DESCRIPTION	QTY	CHANGE POINT	REMARKS
1	12A 1530	COVER ASSEMBLY-VALVE ROCKER	1	(E)12CC/Da/101 TO (+) (E)12CE/Da/101 to (+) (E)12V/586F/101 TO(+) (E)12V/588F/101 TO(+) (E)12V/778F/101 ON	
2	13H 2296	CAP ASSEMBLY-OIL FILLER	1		
3	12A 403	Washer-cap(rubber)	1		
4	12G 2305	COVER ASSEMBLY-VALVE ROCKER	1	(E)12CJ/Da/H21201 TO(+) (E)12V/587Z/101 TO(+) (E)12V/671Z/101 ON	
2	12A 402	Cap-oil filler	1		
3	12A 403	Washer-cap(rubber)	1		
4	12G 2422	COVER ASSEMBLY-VALVE ROCKER	1	(E)12CD/Da/H21201 TO(+)	
2	13H 2296	Cap-oil filler	1		
	1K 2158	Cap-end-purge pipe(rubber)	1		
	GHC 406	Clip-end cap to pipe	1		
5	12A 1205	Plate-name-'Austin'	1		
6	12G 826	Plate-name-'MG'	1		
7	GEG 401	Gasket-rocker cover	1		
8	12A 1358	Bush(rubber)	2		
9	1A 2156	Washer-cup	2		
10	1B 2925	Piece-distance	2		
11	2A 150	Nut-cap	2		
12	12A 1968	Bracket-engine sling	1		For service purposes only.

(+) Change point not available.

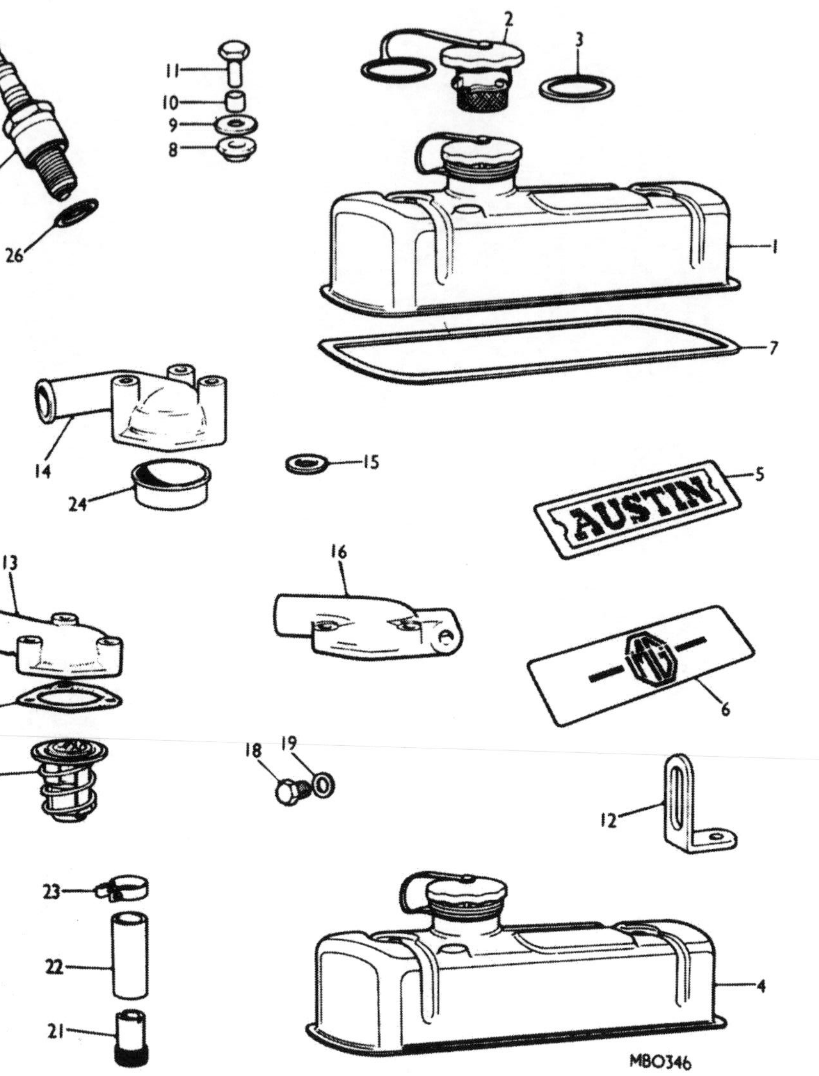

AUSTIN-HEALEY SPRITE MK. 3 AND MK. 4 & MG MIDGET MK. 2 AND MK. 3

ENGINE UNIT-1275cc,12CC,12CD,12CE,12CJ AND 12V-continued.

NO.	PART NO.	DESCRIPTION	QTY	CHANGE POINT	REMARKS
13	12G 243	Elbow-water outlet	1		Use prior to cross-flow radiator.
14	12G 1902	Elbow-water outlet	1		Use when cross-FLOW RADIATOR IS FITTED
	11K 2846	Adaptor-thermal transmitter	1		Use when cross-FLOW RADIATOR IS FITTED
15	12A 1768	Washer-adaptor	1		Use when cross-FLOW RADIATOR IS FITTED
16	12G 1445	Elbow-water outlet	1	(E)12CD,12CJ,12V/587Z	
17	GTG 101	Gasket	1		
	PWZ 105	Washer-plain	3		
	NH 605041	Nut	3		
18	ADP 210	Plug-thermal transmitter boss	1		
19	1B 3664	Washer	1		
		THERMOSTAT(WAX TYPE)			
20	GTS 102	74C(165F)-Hot climates	1		
20	GTS 104	82C(180F)-Temperature climates	1		
20	GTS 106	88C(190F)-Cold climates	1		
22	12A 2178	Connection-by-pass adaptor	1		
	12A 2075	Adaptor-by-pass-cylinder head	1		Use with CONNECTION 12A 2178.
21	88G 618	Adaptor-by-pass-water pump	1		Use with CONNECTION 12A 2178.
23	3H 2963	Clip-connection	2		
24	11G 176	Plate-thermostat blanking	1		
25	N 9 Y	PLUG ASSEMBLY-SPARKING	4		
26	88G 219	Gasket	4		

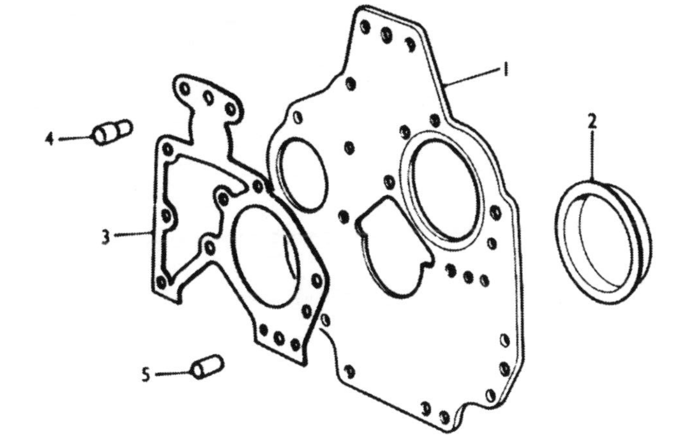

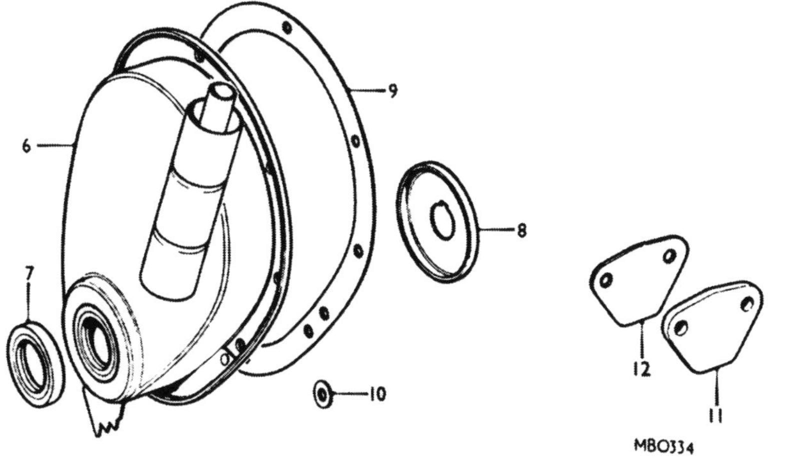

AUSTIN-HEALEY SPRITE MK. 3 AND MK. 4 & MG MIDGET MK. 2 AND MK. 3

ENGINE UNIT-1275cc,12CC,12CD,12CE,12CJ AND 12V-continued

NO.	PART NO.	DESCRIPTION	QTY	CHANGE POINT	REMARKS
1	AEG 552	Plate-gearbox mounting	1		
2	AEG 553	Cover-oil pump	1		
3	AEG 554	Gasket-plate to crankcase	1		
4	12G 422	Dowel-top	1		
5	1G 752	Dowel-bottom	1		
	HZS 507	Screw-plate to crankcase	7		
	LWZ 305	Washer-spring	7		
6	12G 2507	COVER-FRONT-TIMING(WITH OIL SEPARATOR)	1		
7	88G 561	Seal-oil	1		
8	12A 1148	Thrower-oil	1		
9	12A 956	Gasket	1		
	HZS 403	Screw-cover to plate	6		
	PWZ 104	Washer-plain	6		
	LWN 204	Washer-spring	6		
	HZS 506	Screw-cover and plate to crankcase	4		
10	12G 1075	Washer-plain	4		
	LWZ 305	Washer-spring	4		
	HZS 407	Screw-clip to cover and plate	1		
	PWZ 104	Washer-plain	1		
	LWZ 204	Washer-spring	1		
	NH 604041	Nut-screw	1		
11	2A 265	Plate-blanking	1		
12	2A 113	Gasket	1		
	NH 605041	Nut	2		
	WL 600051	Washer-spring	2		

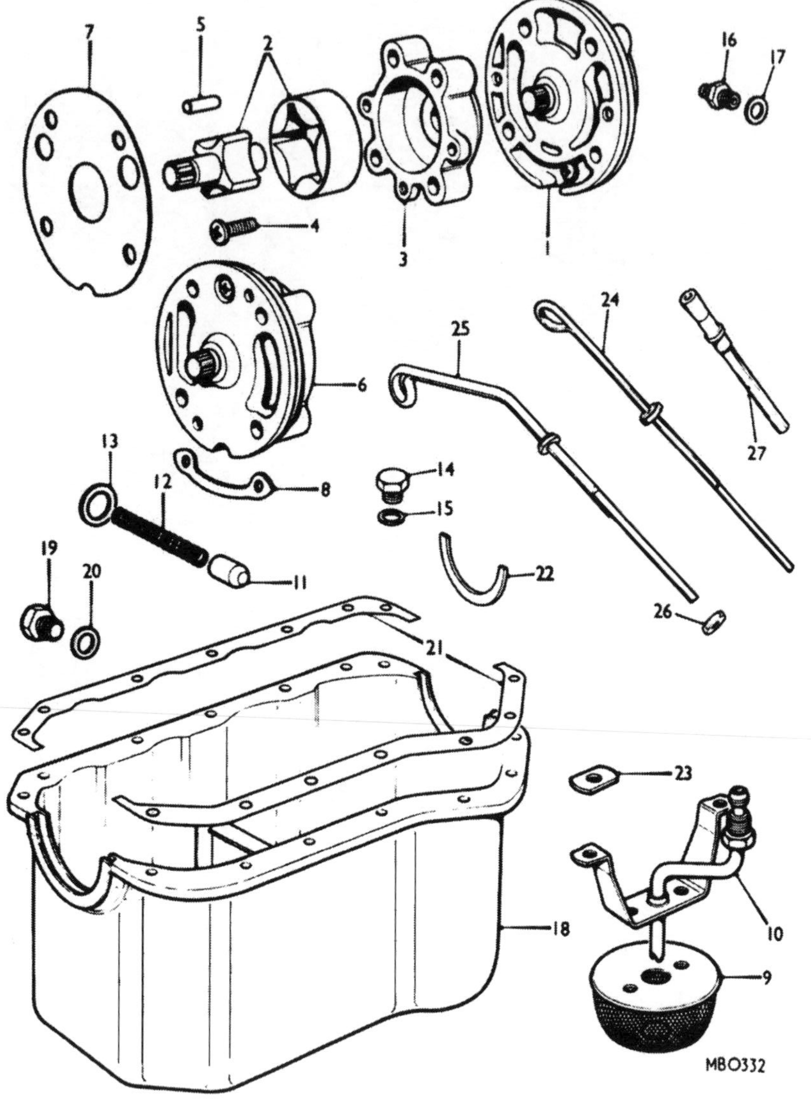

AUSTIN-HEALEY SPRITE MK. 3 AND MK. 4 & MG MIDGET MK. 2 AND MK. 3

NO.	PART NO.	DESCRIPTION	QTY	CHANGE POINT	REMARKS
		ENGINE UNIT-1275cc,12CC,12CD,12CE,12CJ AND 12V-continued			
	12G 1127	PUMP ASSEMBLY-OIL	NLA	Use prior to 12G 1924	Use 12G 1924
2	27H 8807	Shaft and rotor	NLA		
4	27H 8808	Screw	NLA		
	12G 1924	PUMP ASSEMBLY-OIL	NLA	(E)12CC/Da/h16926 TO(+)	Use 12G 2790
2	27H 8807	Shaft and rotor	NLA	(E)12CD/Da/H356	
3	37H 3365	Cover	1	TO(+)	
5	37H 3367	Dowel	2	(E)12CE/Da/H101	
1	12G 2790	Pump-oil	1	TO(+) (E)12CJ/Da/H2120 TO(+) (E)12V/-/101 ON	Alternative to 12G 1128
6	12G 1128	PUMP-OIL(CONCENTRIC)	1		Alternative to 12G 2790
7	12G 730	Gasket-pump to crankcase	1		
	BH 604131	Screw-pump to crankcase	4		
8	12G 926	Washer-lock	1		
9	2A 668	Strainer-oil	1		
10	12A 451	Pipe-oil suction	1		
	HZS 404	Screw-bracket to strainer	2		
	LWN 404	Washer-shakeproof	2		
	HZS 404	Screw-bracket to bearing cap	2		
	LWN 404	Washer-shakeproof	2		
11	12H 865	Valve-oil release	1		
12	6K 853	Spring-valve	1		
13	6K 431	Washer(copper)	1		
14	2K 4994	Plug-oil priming	1		
15	6K 464	Washer(copper)	1		
16	2A 269	Union-oil pressure	1		
17	6K 464	Washer	1		

(+) Change point not available.

AUSTIN-HEALEY SPRITE MK. 3 AND MK. 4 & MG MIDGET MK. 2 AND MK. 3

ENGINE UNIT-1275cc,12CC,12CD,12CE,12CJ AND 12V-continued

NO.	PART NO.	DESCRIPTION	QTY	CHANGE POINT	REMARKS
18	12G 976	Sump-oil	1		
19	88G 257	Plug-drain	1		
20	6K 638	Washer(copper)	1		
21	GEG 528	Gasket-sump to crankcase	1		
22	12G 3016	Seal-oil-main bearing cap-front	1		
	12G 1009	Seal-oil-main bearing cap-rear	1		
	HZS 404	Screw-sump to crankcase	14		
23	2K 5197	Washer	14		
24	12G 175	ROD ASSEMBLY-OIL DIPPER	1	(E)12CC/Da/101 TO(+) (E)12CE/Da/H101 TO(+) (E)12V/586F/101 TO(+) (E)12V/588F/101 TO(+) (E)12V/778F/101 ON	
25	12G 1779	ROD ASSEMBLY-OIL DIPPER	1	(E)12CD/Da/H101 TO(+) (E)12CJ/Da/H21201 TO(+) (E)12V/587Z/101 TO(+) (E)12V/671Z/101 ON	
26	AEC 671	Washer(rubber)	1		
27	12G 107	Tube-oil dipper rod(Nylon)	1		

(+) Change point not available.

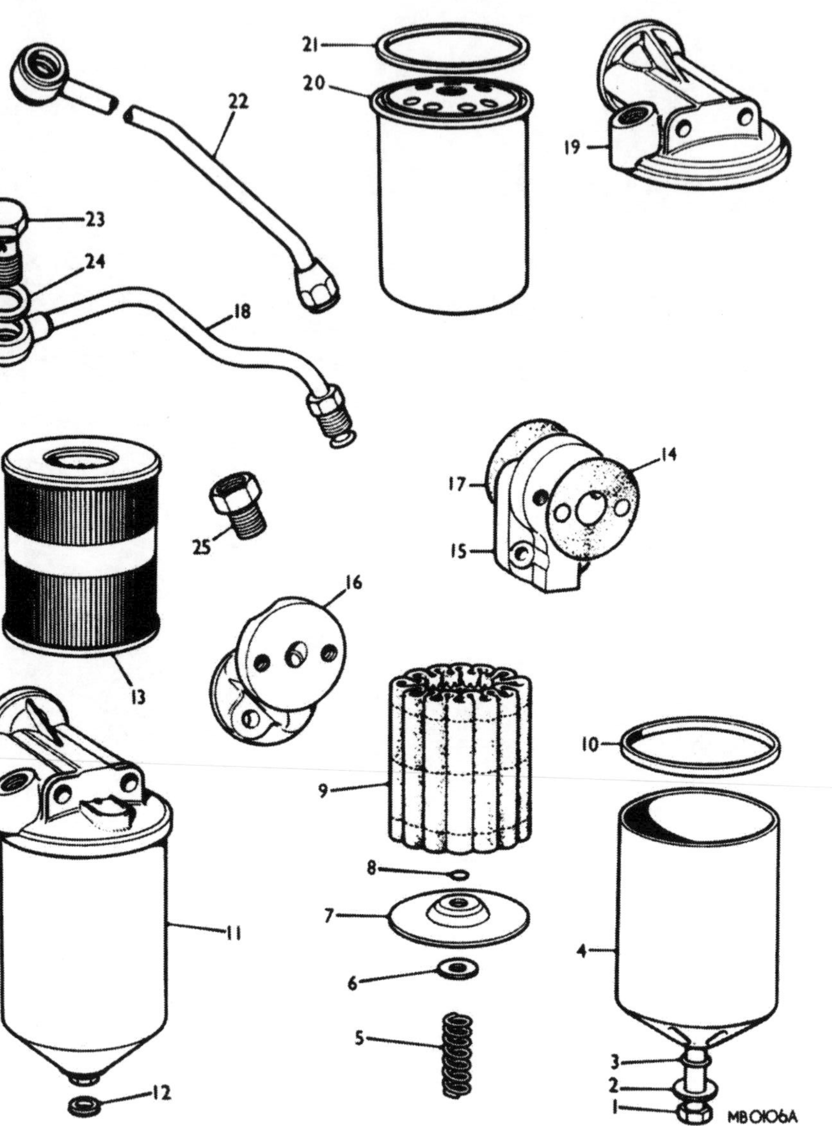

AUSTIN-HEALEY SPRITE MK. 3 AND MK. 4 & MG MIDGET MK. 2 AND MK. 3

ENGINE UNIT-1275cc,12CC,12CD,12CE,12CJ AND 12V-continued

NO.	PART NO.	DESCRIPTION	QTY	CHANGE POINT	REMARKS
	NSP	FILTER ASSEMBLY-OIL (PUROLATOR)	1		
1	37H 689	Bolt-centre	1		
2	17H 1172	Collar-centre-bolt	1		
3	17H 1173	Seal-centre-bolt	1		
4	17H 1169	Sump(steel)	1		
5	7H 25	Spring-pressure plate	1		
	PWN 106	Washer-plain-pressure plate	1		
6	7H 28	Seal-pressure plate	1		
7	17H 1148	Plate-pressure	1		
8	27H 2573	Circlip-centre-bolt	1		
9	GFE 103	Element(felt)	1		
10	12A 1591	Seal-sump to head	1		
11	12A 1726	FILTER ASSEMBLY-OIL (PUROLATOR)	1		
1	37H 689	Bolt-centre	1		
	PWN 106	Washer-centre bolt	1		
12	17H 2281	Seal-centre bolt	1		
8	27H 2573	Circlip-centre bolt	1		
7	17H 1148	Plate-pressure	1		
5	7H 25	Spring-pressure plate	1		
6	7H 28	Seal-pressure plate	1		
	PWN 106	Washer-plain	1		
13	GFE 103	Element(paper)	1	Use prior to DISPOSABLE TYPE FILTER	
10	12A 1591	Seal-sump to head	1		
	HCZ 630	Bolt-filter to adaptor	2		
	LWZ 206	Washer-spring	2		
14	88G 402	Gasket-filter to adaptor	1		
15	AEA 657	Adaptor-filter to crankcase	1		12CC,12CE,12V/586F,12V/588F
16	12G 1647	Adaptor-filter to crankcase $	1		12CD,12CJ,12V/587Z
17	88G 402	Gasket-adaptor to crankcase	1		
	CHS 613	Stud-adaptor to crankcase	2		12CD,12CJ,12V/587Z
	51K 371	Nut-stud	2		12CJ,12V/587Z
	LWZ 206	Washer-spring	2		
18	12G 2004	Pipe-filter to crankcase	1		12CC,12CE,12V/586F,12V/588F
18	12G 1646	Pipe-filter to crankcase	1		12CD,12CJ,12V/587Z

$ This item is subject to safety regulations.

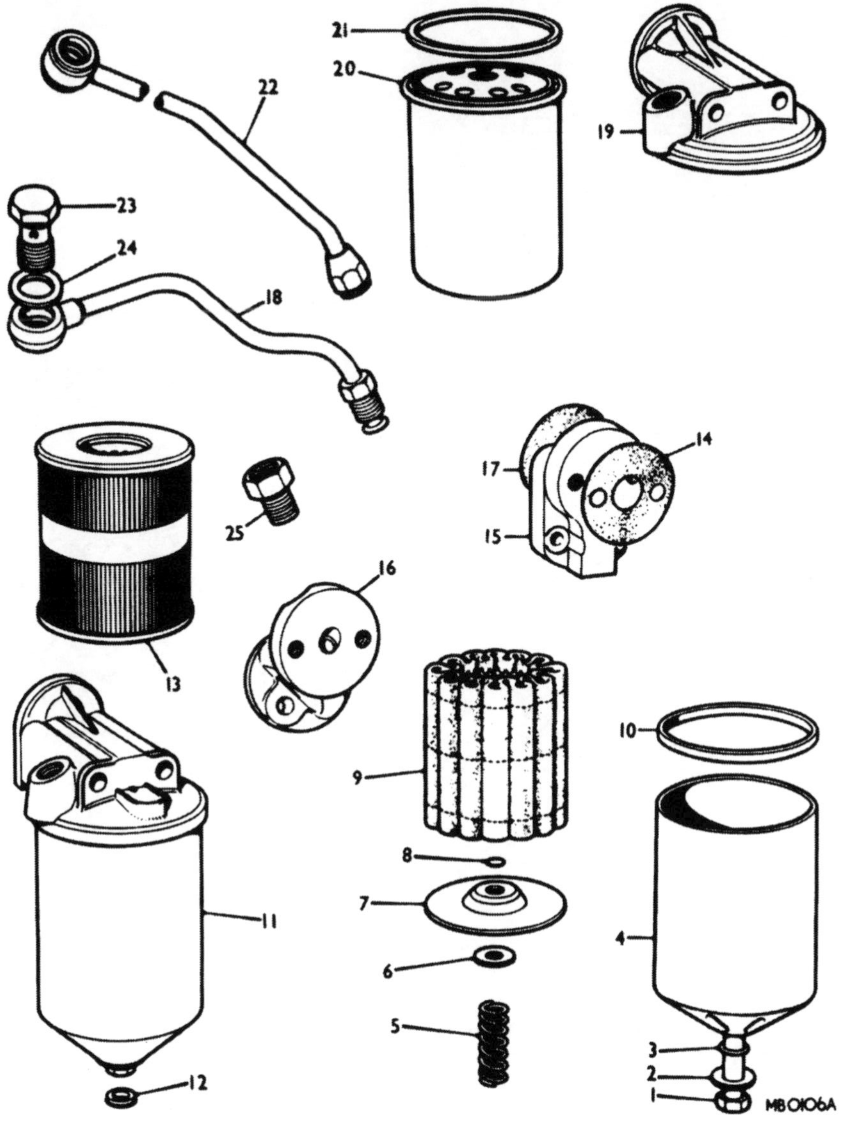

AUSTIN-HEALEY SPRITE MK. 3 AND MK. 4 & MG MIDGET MK. 2 AND MK. 3

NO.	PART NO.	DESCRIPTION	QTY	CHANGE POINT	REMARKS
		ENGINE UNIT-1275cc,12CC,12CD,12CE,12CJ AND 12V-continued			
19	37H 7078	Head-filter	1	(E)12CE/Da/H10309 TO(+) (E)12CJ/-/30847 TO(+) (E)12V/588F/101 TO(+) (E)12V/587Z/101 TO(+) (E)12V/588F/101 TO(+) (E)12V/671Z/101 TO 13811 (E)12V/778F/101 TO 392	
	12A 2032	Head-filter	1	(E)12V/671Z/13812 ON (E)12V/778F/393 ON	
	SH 506091	Screw-head to crankcase	2		Use with filter HEAD 12A 2032
	WA 110061	Washer	2		
	12A 2035	Gasket-filter	1		
20	GFE 139	Cartridge(disposable)-oil filter	NLA	(E)12CE/10309 TO(+) (E)12CJ/30847 TO(+) (E)12V/-/101 ON	Use GFE 148
20	GFE 148	Cartridge(disposable)oil filter	1		
21	37H 6073	Seal-cartridge to head	1		
22	88G 538	Pipe-filter to crankcase	1		
	WL 600061	Washer-spring	2		
17	88G 402	Gasket-filter to crankcase	1		
23	2A 715	Screw-banjo union	11		
24	12A 1768	Washer(copper)	1		
	AED 172	Washer	1		
25	TCZ 106	Connection-pipe to filter	1		

(+) Change point not available.

MB0106A

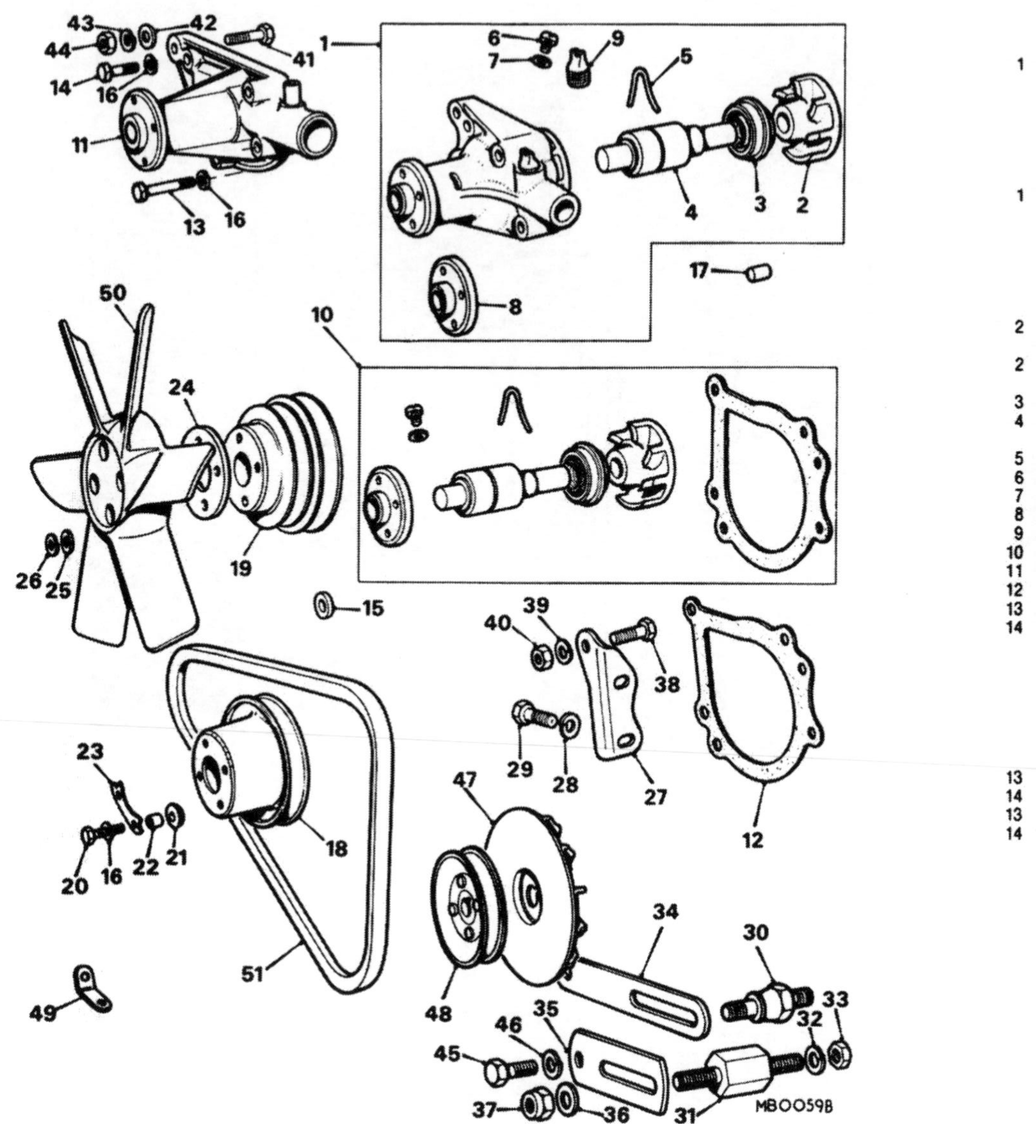

AUSTIN-HEALEY SPRITE MK. 3 AND MK. 4 & MG MIDGET MK. 2 AND MK. 3

ENGINE UNIT-1275cc,12CC,12CD,12CE,12CJ AND 12V-continued

NO.	PART NO.	DESCRIPTION	QTY	CHANGE POINT	REMARKS
1	GWP 101	PUMP ASSEMBLY-WATER	NLA	Use prior to GWP 102	Use GWP 132 with bottom hose GRH 508 (with heater) or AHA 8750 (less heater) and clip GHC 913 1 off.
1	GWP 102	PUMP ASSEMBLY-WATER	NLA	(E)12CD/Da/h1745 TO(+) (E)12CE/Da/H874 TO(+) (E)12CJ/Da/H21201 TO(+) (E)12V/-/101 ON	Use GWP 132
2	2A 664	Vane	1		Use with water pump GWP 101
2	12G 1773	Vane	1		Use with water pump GWP 102
3	88G 446	Seal	1		
4	12A 1802	Bearing(with spindle)	1		Use with GWP 101
5	2A 778	Wire-bearing locating	1		
6	53K 1433	Screw-lubricating point	1		Use with pump GWP 101
7	2K 4974	Washer(fibre)	1		Use with pump GWP 101
8	8G 733	Hub-pulley	1		
9	2A 243	Adaptor-by-pass	1		
10	8G 2570	KIT-REPAIR-WATER PUMP	1		
11	GWP 132	Pump-water	1		
12	88G 215	Gasket-water pump	1		
13	HZS 515	Screw-pump to crankcase-long	2	(E)12CC/Da/H101 TO(+) (E)12CE/Da/H101 TO(+) (E)12V/586F/101 TO(+) (E)12V/588F/101 TO(+) (E)12V/778F/101 ON	
14	HZS 510	Screw-pump to crankcase-short	2	(E)12CC/Da/H101 TO(+) (E)12CE/Da/H101 TO(+) (E)12V/586F/101 TO(+) (E)12V/588F/101 TO(+) (E)12V/778F/101 ON	
13	BH 605161	Screw-pump to crankcase-long	1	(E)12CD/Da/101 TO(+) (E)12CJ/Da/21201 TO(+) (E)12V/587Z/101 TO(+) (E)12V/671Z/101 ON	
14	BH 605111	Screw-pump to crankcase-short	1	(E)12CD/Da/101 TO(+) (E)12CJ/Da/21201 TO(+) (E)12V/587Z/101 TO(+) (E)12V/671Z/101 ON	
13	HZS 515	Screw-pump to crankcase-long	1	(E)12CD/Da/101 TO(+) (E)12CJ/Da/21201 TO(+) (E)12V/587Z/101 TO(+) (E)12V/671Z/101 ON	
14	HZS 510	Screw-pump to crankcase-short	1	(E)12CD/Da/101 TO(+) (E)12CJ/Da/21201 TO(+) (E)12V/587Z/101 TO(+) (E)12V/671Z/101 ON	

AUSTIN-HEALEY SPRITE MK. 3 AND MK. 4 & MG MIDGET MK. 2 AND MK. 3

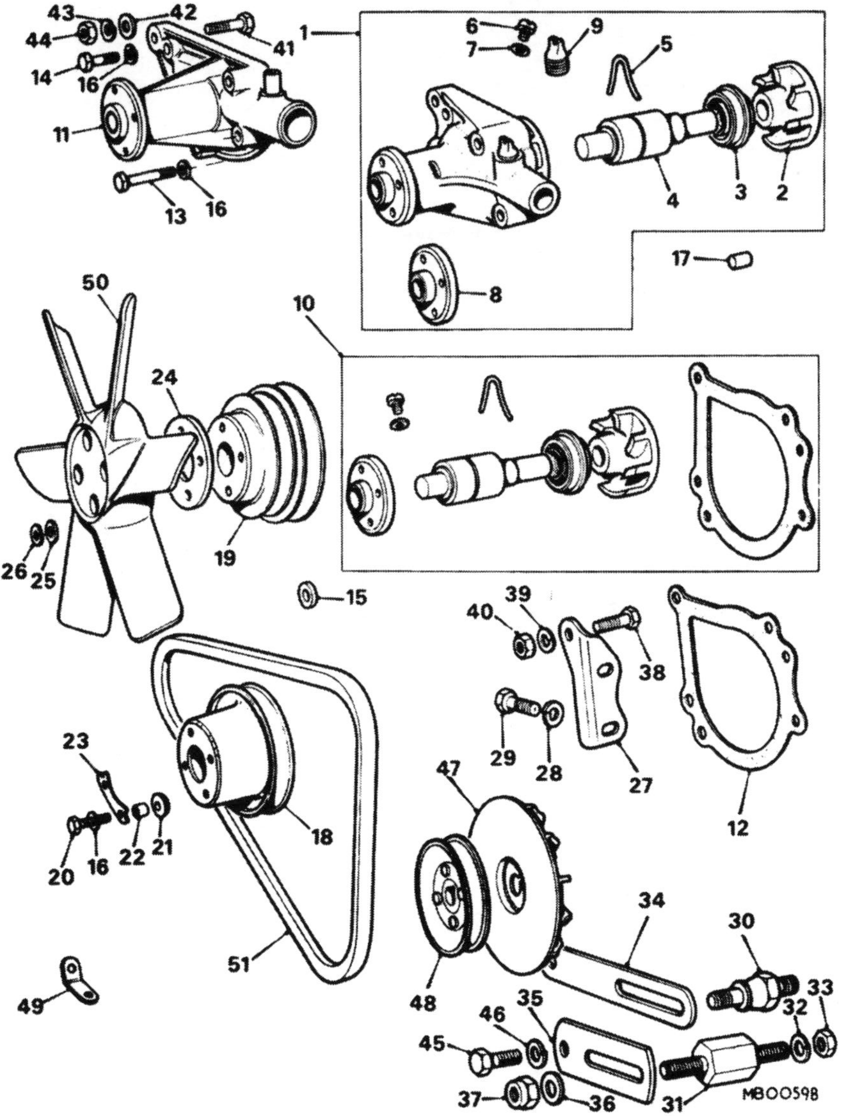

AUSTIN-HEALEY SPRITE MK. 3 AND MK. 4 & MG MIDGET MK. 2 AND MK. 3

ENGINE UNIT-1275cc,12CC,12CD,12CE,12CJ AND 12V-continued

NO.	PART NO.	DESCRIPTION	QTY	CHANGE POINT	REMARKS
15	12H 1581	Piece-distance	1		
16	LWZ 305	Washer-spring	4		
17	12A 1344	Dowel	NLA		
17	12G 2077	Dowel-water pump	2		Use when GWP 102 is fitted
18	2A 601	Pulley-fan and water pump	1		12CC,12CE,12V/586,12V/588F
19	12G 1542	Pulley-fan and water pump	1		12CD,12CJ,12V/587Z
20	SH 604101	Screw-fan to water pump	4	(E)12CC/Da/H101 TO H16300 (E)12CE/Da/H101 TO H898	
21	12H 1060	Grommet-fan mounting	4		
22	12H 1062	Piece-distance	4		
23	12H 1388	Washer-lock	2		
20	HZS 411	Screw-fan to water pump	4	(E)12CE/Da/H899 TO(+) (E)12V/586F/101 TO(+) (E)12V/588F/101 TO(+) (E)12V/778F/101 ON	
24	AEG 560	Piece-distance	1		
25	WA 106041	Washer-plain	4		
26	WL 600041	Washer-spring	4		
20	HZS 411	Screw-fan to water pump	4	(E)12CD/Da/101 TO(+) (E)12CJ/Da/H21201 TO(+) (E)12V/587Z/101 TO(+) (E)12V/671Z/101 ON	
25	WA 106041	Washer-plain	4		
26	WL 600041	Washer-spring	4		

(+) Change point not available.

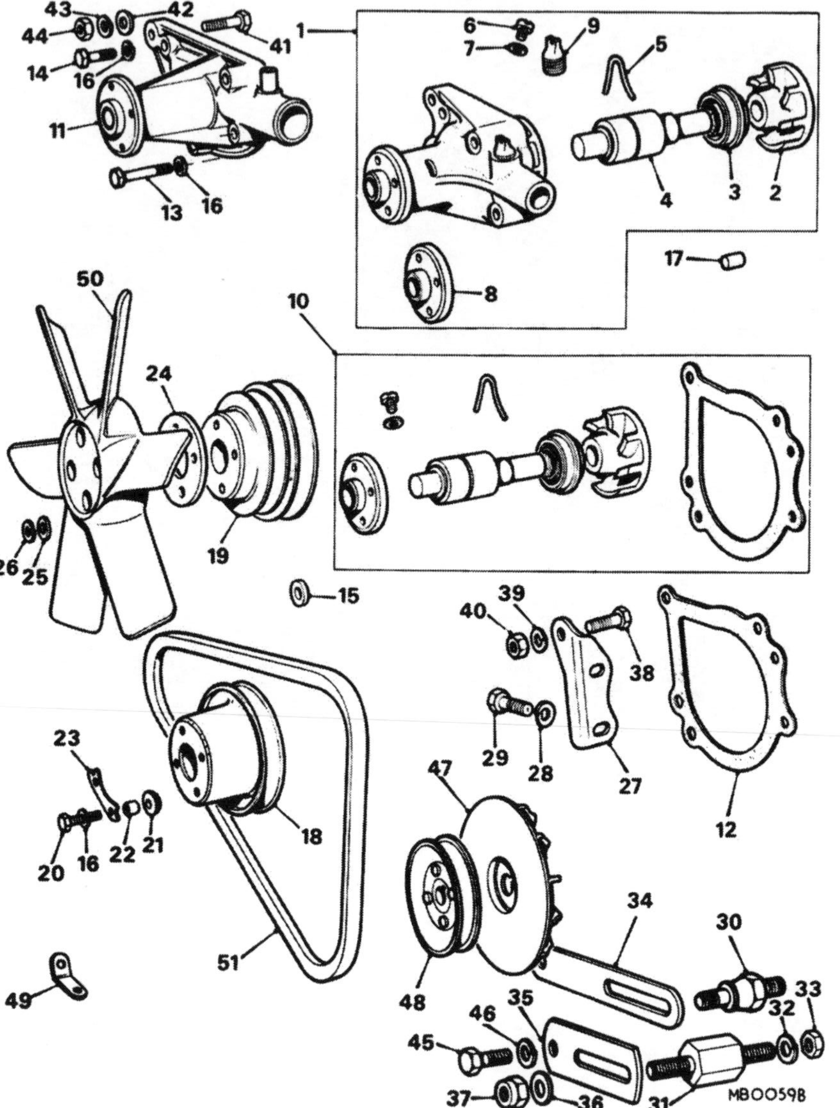

AUSTIN-HEALEY SPRITE MK. 3 AND MK. 4 & MG MIDGET MK. 2 AND MK. 3

NO.	PART NO.	DESCRIPTION	QTY	CHANGE POINT	REMARKS
		ENGINE UNIT-1275cc 12CC,12CD,12CE,12CJ AND 12V-continued			
27	12A 526	Bracket-dynamo rear	1		
28	LWZ 305	Washer-spring	2		
29	SH 605061	Screw	2		
30	12G 314	Pillar-dynamo adjusting link	1		12CC,12CE,12CJ, 12V
31	12G 1650	Pillar-dynamo adjusting link	1		12CD
32	WL 600061	Washer-spring	1		
33	NT 606041	Nut	1		
34	AEA 679	Link-dynamo adjusting	NLA		12CC,12CE,12CJ, 12V
35	12G 1642	Link-dynamo adjusting	1		12CD
36	1B 8806	Washer-plain	1		
37	LNZ 206	Nut	1		
38	SH 605101	Screw-dynamo to bracket	1		
38	SH 605111	Screw-dynamo to bracket	1		When cross-flow radiator is fitted
39	LWN 305	Washer-spring	1		
40	LNZ 205	Nut	1		
41	BH 605141	Screw-dynamo to water pump	1		
42	GHF 301	Washer-plain	2		
43	LWZ 305	Washer-spring	1		
44	LNZ 205	Nut	1		
45	SH 505051	Screw-dynamo to adjusting link	1		
46	LWZ 305	Washer-spring	1		
47	17D 11	Fan-dynamo	1		
48	12G 2102	Pulley-dynamo	1		
49	AHC 579	Clip-radiator capillary tube	1		
50	12G 1597	Fan-6 blade(platic)	1		
21	12H 1060	Grommet-fan mounting	4		
22	12H 1062	Piece-distance-fan to water pump	4		
23	12H 1388	Washer-lock	2		
51	GFB 120	Belt-fan(wedge-type)	1	(E)12CC/Da/H101 TO(+) (E)12CE/Da/101 TO(+)	
51	GFB 186	Belt-fan	1	(E)12V/586F/101 ON	
51	GFB 121	Belt-fan-32.25" dia. $	1	(E)12CD/Da/H101 TO(+) (E)12CJ/Da/H21201 TO(+)	
51	GFB 197	Belt-fan-33" dia.	NLA	(E)12V/587Z/101 TO(+) (E)12V/588F/101 TO 3192 (E)12V/671Z/101 TO 12845	Use GFB 253.
51	GFB 253	Belt-fan	1		
51	GFB 193	Belt-fan-32" dia.	1	(E)12V/588F/3193 TO(+) (E)12V/671Z/12846 ON (E)12V/778F/101 ON	

$ This item is subject to safety regulations

(+) Change point not available.

ILLUSTRATION NOT USED

AUSTIN-HEALEY SPRITE MK. 3 AND MK. 4 & MG MIDGET MK. 2 AND MK. 3

NO.	PART NO.	DESCRIPTION	QTY	CHANGE POINT	REMARKS
		ENGINE SERVICE KITS-1098cc-10CC			
	GEG 102	SET-GASKET-ENGINE DECARBONIZING	1		
	GEG 201	SET-GASKET-SUPPLEMENTARY	1	(E)10CC/Da/101 TO H37548 AND L25599	Use with geg 102 for engine complete overhaul
	GEG 239	SET-GASKET-SUPPLEMENTARY	1	(E)10CC/Da/H37549 and L25600 ON	

ILLUSTRATION NOT USED

AUSTIN-HEALEY SPRITE MK. 3 AND MK. 4 & MG MIDGET MK. 2 AND MK. 3

NO.	PART NO.	DESCRIPTION	QTY	CHANGE POINT	REMARKS
		ENGINE SERVICE KITS-1275cc-12CC,12CD,12CE,12CJ and 12V			
	GEG 126	SET-GASKET-ENGINE DECARBONIZING	1	Use prior to GEG 1140	Supply also 8 off valve oil seal AEG 327. Use with GEG 225 for engine complete overhaul
	GEG 1140	SET-GASKET-ENGINE DECARBONIZING	1	(E)12V/-/101 ON	Supply also 8 off valve oil seal AEG 327. Use with GEG 225 for engine complete overhaul
	GEG 225	SET-GASKET-SUPPLEMENTARY	1		Use with GEG 126 or GEG 1140 for engine complete overhaul

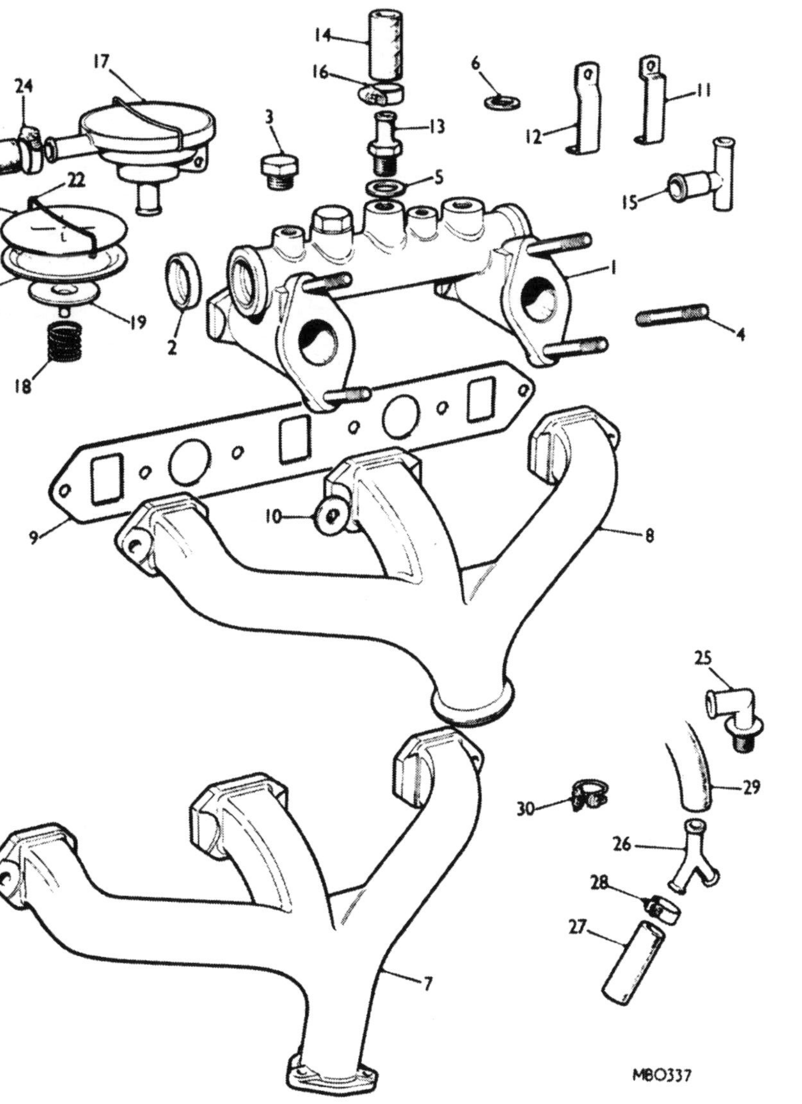

AUSTIN-HEALEY SPRITE MK. 3 AND MK. 4 & MG MIDGET MK. 2 AND MK. 3

ENGINE UNIT-MANIFOLDS-1275cc,12CC,12CD,12CE,12CJ AND 12V.

NO.	PART NO.	DESCRIPTION	QTY	CHANGE POINT	REMARKS
1	12G 583	MANIFOLD ASSEMBLY-INLET	1	(E)12CC/Da/h101 TO 16300 (E)12CE/Da/H101 TO 3400(less 3201 TO 3300)	
2	AEA 635	Plug-welch	2		
3	ADP 210	Plug-screwed	1		
4	CHS 2620	Stud-carburetter	4		
1	12G 1450	MANIFOLD ASSEMBLY-INLET $	1	(E)12CD/Da/101 TO(+) (E)12CE/Da/H3401 TO(+)(plus 3201 TO 3300) (E)12V/586F/101 TO(+) (E)12V/588F/101 TO(+) (E)12V/778F/101 ON	
2	AEA 635	Plug-welch	2		
4	CHS 2620	Stud-carburetter	NLA		
3	ADP 210	Plug-screwed	1		
1	12G 1450	MANIFOLD ASSEMBLY-INLET	1	(E)12CJ/Da/H21201 TO(+) (E)12V/587Z/101 TO (+) (E)12V/671Z/101 ON	For 12CJ engine SUPPLY 1 off plug ADP 205 and 1 off washer -PLAIN PWZ 105.
2	AEA 635	Plug-core	2		
3	ADP 210	Plug-screwed	1		
	CLS 2620	Stud-carburetter	NLA		
3	12H 1734	Plug-induction manifold	1		
3	ADP 210	Plug-inlet and exhaust manifold	1		
5	1B 3664	Washer-plug	1		
6	2K 4954	Washer(fibre)	1		
7	12G 1581	Manifold-exhaust	1		
8	12G 420	Manifold-exhaust	1		
9	GEG 601	Gasket-manifold to cylinder head	1		
10	12A 1211	Washer-clamping-manifold stud	4		
	PWZ 105	Washer-plain-manifold	2		
	BNN 105	Nut-manifold stud	6		
	53K 507	Stud-exhaust manifold to down pipe	3		
	ZCS 404	Screw-heater rail clip to inlet manifold	1		
	PWZ 104	Washer-plain	1		
	LWZ 204	Washer-spring	1		
	CHS 2408	Stud-heater rail clip to inlet manifold	1		
	LWZ 204	Washer-spring	1		
	NH 604041	Nut	1		

$ This item is subject to safety regulations.

(+) Change point not available

AUSTIN-HEALEY SPRITE MK. 3 AND MK. 4 & MG MIDGET MK. 2 AND MK. 3

NO.	PART NO.	DESCRIPTION	QTY	CHANGE POINT	REMARKS
		ENGINE UNIT-CLOSED CIRCUIT BREATHING-1275cc,12CC,12CD,12CE,12CJ AND 12V.			
		CLOSED-CIRCUIT BREATHING (VENTED THROUGH INLET MANIFOLD)			
11	12G 609	Bracket-support-control valve	1	(E)12CC/Da/101 TO (+) (E)12CE/Da/101 TO(+) (E)12V/586F/101 TO(+) (E)12V/588F/101 TO(+) (E)12V/778F/101 ON	
12	12G 1654	Bracket-support-control valve	1	(E)12CD/Da/101 TO(+) (E)12CJ/Da/H21201 TO(+) (E)12V/587Z/101 TO (+) (E)12V/671Z/101 ON	
5	1B 3664	Washer-adaptor to manifold	1		
	ZCS 405	Bolt-bracket to manifold	1		
	LWZ 304	Washer-spring	1		
13	12H 1405	Adaptor-one way-breather hose	1		
14	12H 1407	Hose-adaptor to control valve	1		
15	12H 2457	Adaptor-two way-breather hose	1		
14	12G 1656	Hose-adaptor to control valve	1		
16	HCS 407	Clip	2		
17	13H 5191	VALVE ASSEMBLY-BREATHER CONTROL	1		
18	27H 7756	Spring-top	1		
19	27H 7757	Sub-assembly of plunger	1		Use with 13H 3609.
19	37H 3686	Sub-assembly of plunger	1		Use with 13H 5191.
20	27H 7758	Diaphragm	1		
21	27H 7759	Plate-valve cover	1		
22	27H 7760	Clip-spring	1		
	SH 604061	Bolt-bracket to breather valve	1		
	LWZ 304	Washer-spring	1		
	NH 604041	Nut	1		
23	12A 1052	Hose-control valve to cylinder front cover	NLA		Use 37H 7085 M.
23	37H 7085 M	Hose-control valve to cylinder front cover-bulk metres	1		
24	HCS 507	Clip	2		
		CLOSED-CIRCUIT BREATHING (VENTED THROUGH CARBURETTERS)			
25	12H 2958	Adaptor-sensing control	1		
26	12G 2134	Connection-'Y'piece	1		
27	12G 2126	Hose-carburetter to'Y'piece	2		
28	ACH 5854	Clip	4		
29	12G 2127	Hose-'Y'piece to seperator	1		
30	GHC 507	Clip	2		

(+) Change point not available

MB0107A

AUSTIN-HEALEY SPRITE MK. 3 AND MK. 4 & MG MIDGET MK. 2 AND MK. 3

ENGINE UNIT-EXHAUST EMISSION CONTROL-1275cc,12CD,12CJ,12V

NO.	PART NO.	DESCRIPTION	QTY	CHANGE POINT	REMARKS
1	12G 2370	Manifold-air $	1		
2	13H 4358	Valve-check $	1		
3	12G 1649	Connection-valve to air pump $	1		
	GHC 709	Clip-connection	2		
4	1H 5452	Clip-connection-air manifold	2	(E)12CJ/Da/H21201 TO(+) (E)12V/587Z/101 TO(+) (E)12V/671Z/101 ON	
5	12G 1696	CLEANER ASSEMBLY-AIR (PLASTIC) $	1		
6	37H 2498	Element $	1		
7	37H 2533	Washer $	1		Use with 12H 2454
7	37H 2499	Washer $	1		Use with 12G 1696
8	37H 3460	Nut-lock $	1		
	MCZ 605	Screw-air cleaner bracket to pump	3		Required when plastic air cleaner is used to replace steel type
9	12H 2479	Connection-air cleaner to pump	1		
	HCS 116	Clip-connection	2		
10	13H 4322	Pump-air	NLA		USA only. Obtainable from Lucas depots in New York and Los Angeles
11	13H 4705	Belt-air pump $	1		
	HBZ 528	Bolt-pump to water outlet elbow	1		
	PWZ 105	Washer-plain	1		
	LWZ 305	Washer-spring	1		
	NH 605041	Nut	1		

(+) Change point not available

$ This item is subject to safety regulations

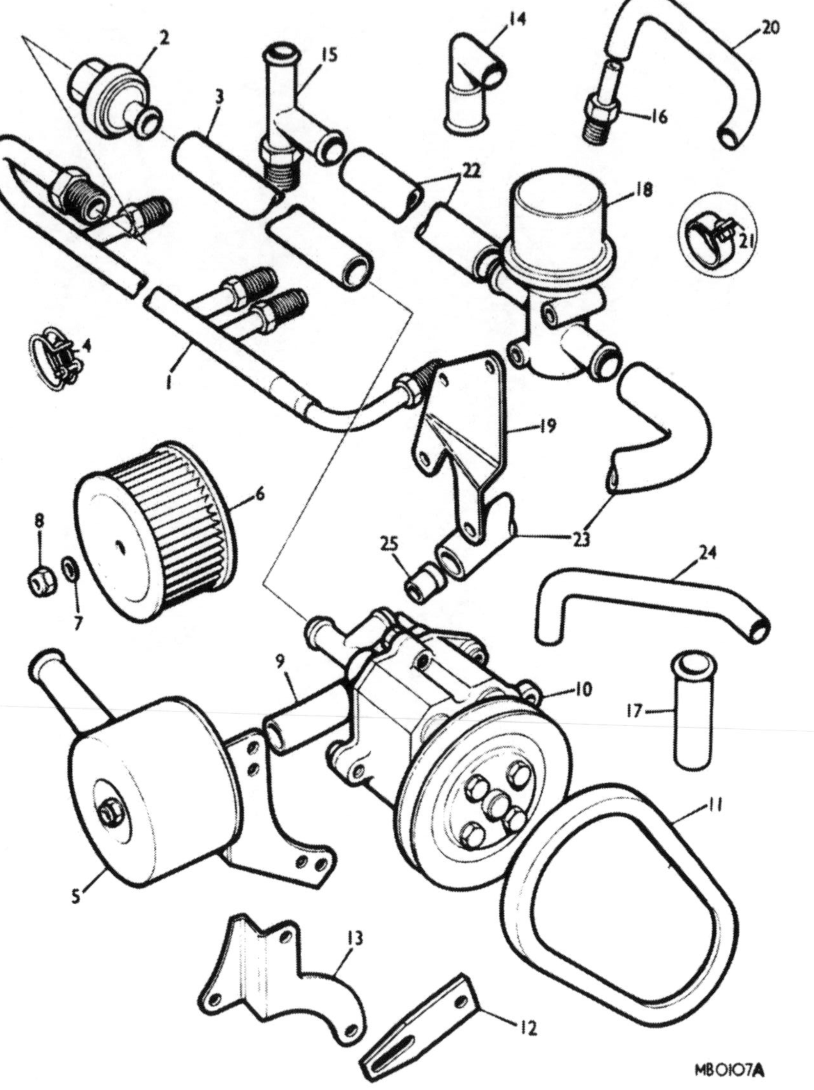

AUSTIN-HEALEY SPRITE MK. 3 AND MK. 4 & MG MIDGET MK. 2 AND MK. 3

NO.	PART NO.	DESCRIPTION	QTY	CHANGE POINT	REMARKS
		ENGINE UNIT-EXHAUST EMISSION CONTROL-1275cc,12CD,12CJ,12V CONTINUED			
12	12G 1641	Link-adjusting-air pump $	NLA		
13	12G 1639	Bracket-adjusting link $	1		
	HZS 509	Screw-adjusting link to bracket	1		
	LWZ 305	Washer-spring	1		
	ZCS 507	Screw-adjusting link to pump	1		
	PWZ 105	Washer-plain	1		
	LWZ 305	Washer-spring	1		
		ADAPTOR			
14	12H 2958	Sensing control	1		When carburetter ventilation is fitted
15	12H 2457	Inlet-manifold $	1		
16	12H 241	Inlet manifold sensing $	1		
17	12H 2729	Inlet manifold emmission valve	NLA	(E)12CJ/Da/H21201 TO(+) (E)12V/587Z/101 TO(+) (E)12V/671Z/101 ON	
18	13H 6189	Valve-gulp $	1		
	LWZ 304	Washer-spring	2		
	NH 604041	Nut-bolt	2		
		CONNECTION			
20	12G 1455	Sensing control $	1		
22	13H 3276	Valve to inlet manifold $	1		
23	12G 1648	Pump to valve $	1		
24	12G 1569	Valve to sensing control	1	(E)12CJ/Da/H21201 TO(+) (E)12V/587Z/101 TO(+) (E)12V/671Z/101 ON	
25	12G 1797	Restrictor-pump to gulp valve$	1		
	GHC 709	Clip-connection-pump to valve	2		
	HCS 116	Clip-connection-valve to inlet manifold	2		

(+) Change point not available

$ This item is subject to safety regulations

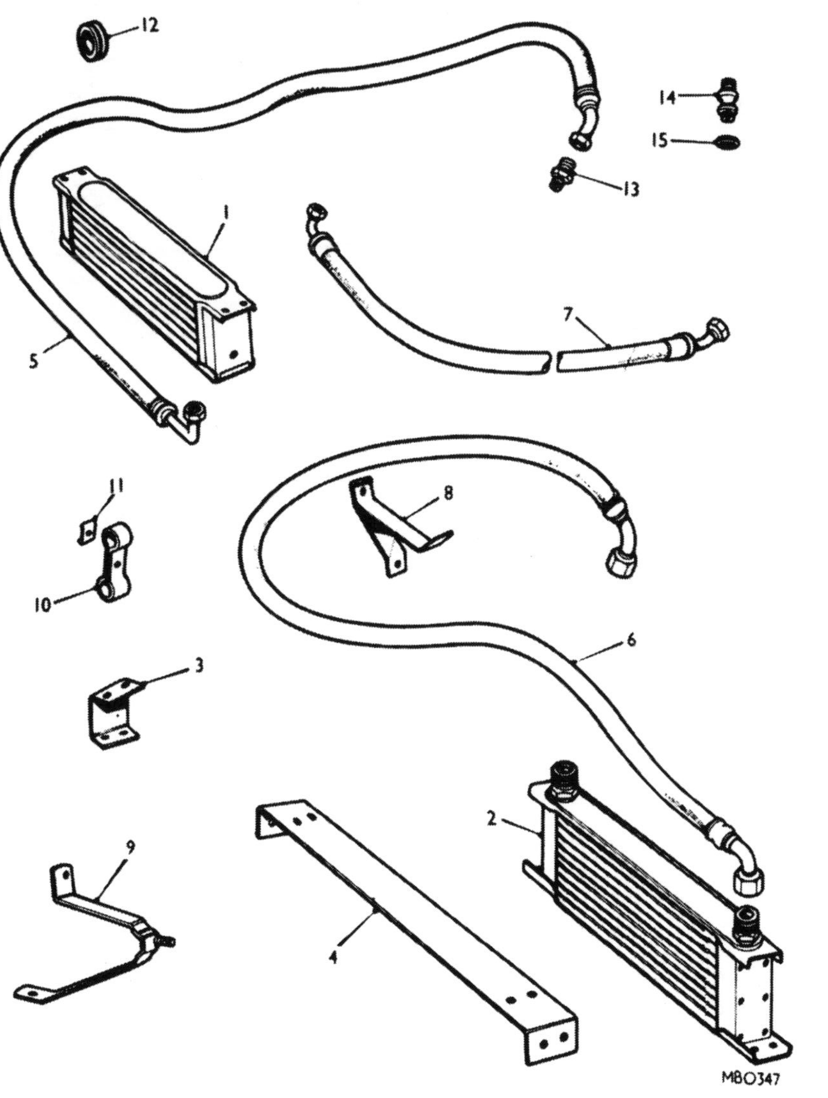

AUSTIN-HEALEY SPRITE MK. 3 AND MK. 4 & MG MIDGET MK. 2 AND MK. 3

NO.	PART NO.	DESCRIPTION	QTY	CHANGE POINT	REMARKS
		OIL COOLER-OPTIONAL EXTRA-ALL VERSIONS-EXCEPT 1500			
1	ARA 205	Cooler-oil	NLA	(C)H-AN8-38829 TO 64734 (C)G-AN3-24788 TO 52389	
2	ARH 186	Cooler-oil	1	(C)H-AN9-64735 TO 85286 (C)H-AN10-852 TO 86803 (C)A-AN10-86804 TO 87824 (C)G-AN4-52390 TO 74885 (C)G-AN5-74886 TO 154100	
3	AHA 7550	Bracket-cooler support	2	(C)H-AN8-38829 TO 64734 (C)G-AN3-25788 TO 52389	
4	AHA 8386	Bracket-cooler support	NLA	(C)H-AN9-64735 TO 85286 (C)H-AN10-852 TO 86803 (C)A-AN10-86804 TO 87824 (C)G-AN4-52390 TO 74885 (C)G-AN5-74886 TO 154100	
	PMZ 410	Screw	4		
	HZS 404	Screw	4		
	LWZ 204	Washer-spring	8		
	NH 604041	Nut	8		
	PWZ 104	Washer-plain	2		

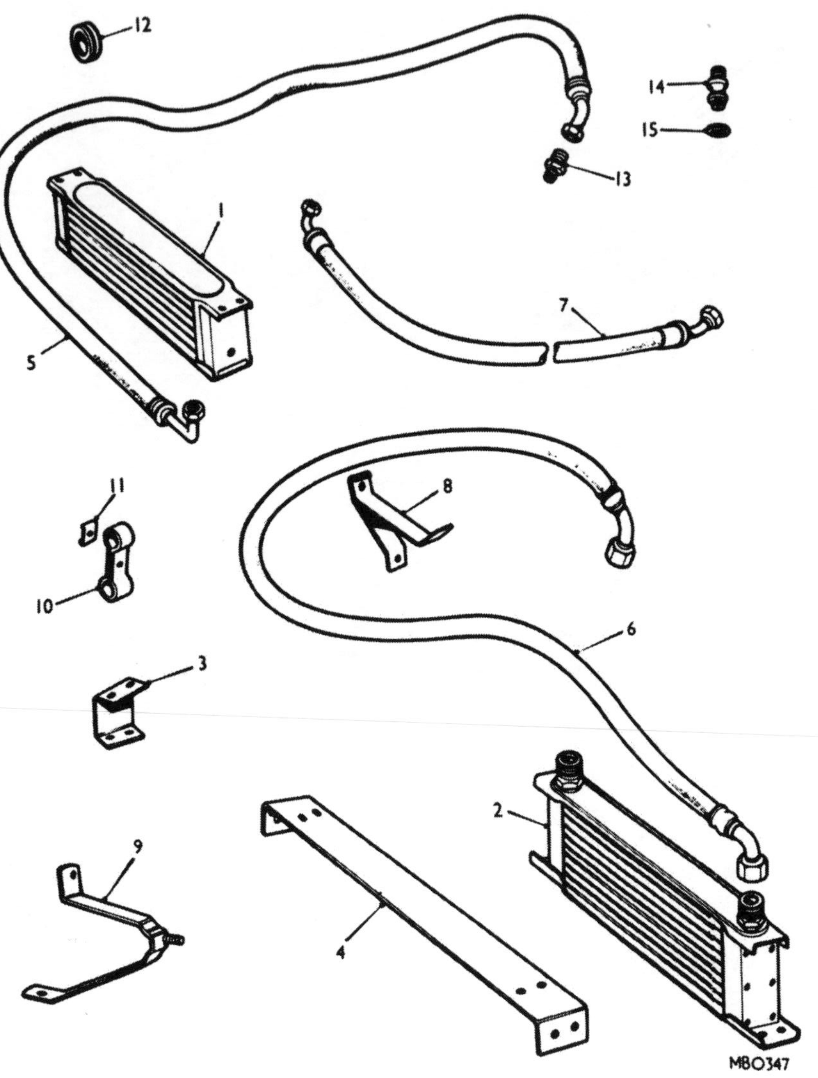

AUSTIN-HEALEY SPRITE MK. 3 AND MK. 4 & MG MIDGET MK. 2 AND MK. 3

OIL COOLER-OPTIONAL EXTRA-ALL VERSIONS-continued

NO.	PART NO.	DESCRIPTION	QTY	CHANGE POINT	REMARKS
5	AHA 7549	Hose-flexible-cooler to filter and block-1089mm(42.875")	2		
7	AHA 8778	Hose-flexible-cooler to filter -851mm(33.5")	1		Use when cross-FLOW RADIATOR IS FITTED
7	AHA 8777	Hose-flexible-cooler to block-1143mm(45")	1		
8	AHA 7914	Bracket-hose support	NLA		Use with hoses AHA 8384 and AHA 8385
9	AHA 8779	Bracket-hose support	1		Use with hoses AHA 8777 and AHA 8778
	HZS 404	Screw	2		
	LWZ 204	Washer-spring	2		
	FNZ 104	Nut	2		
	HZS 407	Screw-bracket to wheelarch	1		
	LWZ 204	Washer-spring	1		
	FNZ 104	Nut	1		
	PMZ 408	Screw-bracket to drain channel	1		
	LWZ 204	Washer-spring	1		
10	AHH 6865	Strap-hose(rubber)	NLA		
11	AHH 6866	Plate-strap	A/R		
11	AHA 8390	Plate-strap	NLA		
12	AHA 8401	Grommet-hose	4		
13	AHA 6423	Adaptor-union-oil-filter	1		
14	AHA 6424	Adaptor-union-cylinder block	1		
15	12A 1768	Washer-adaptor-cylinder block	1		

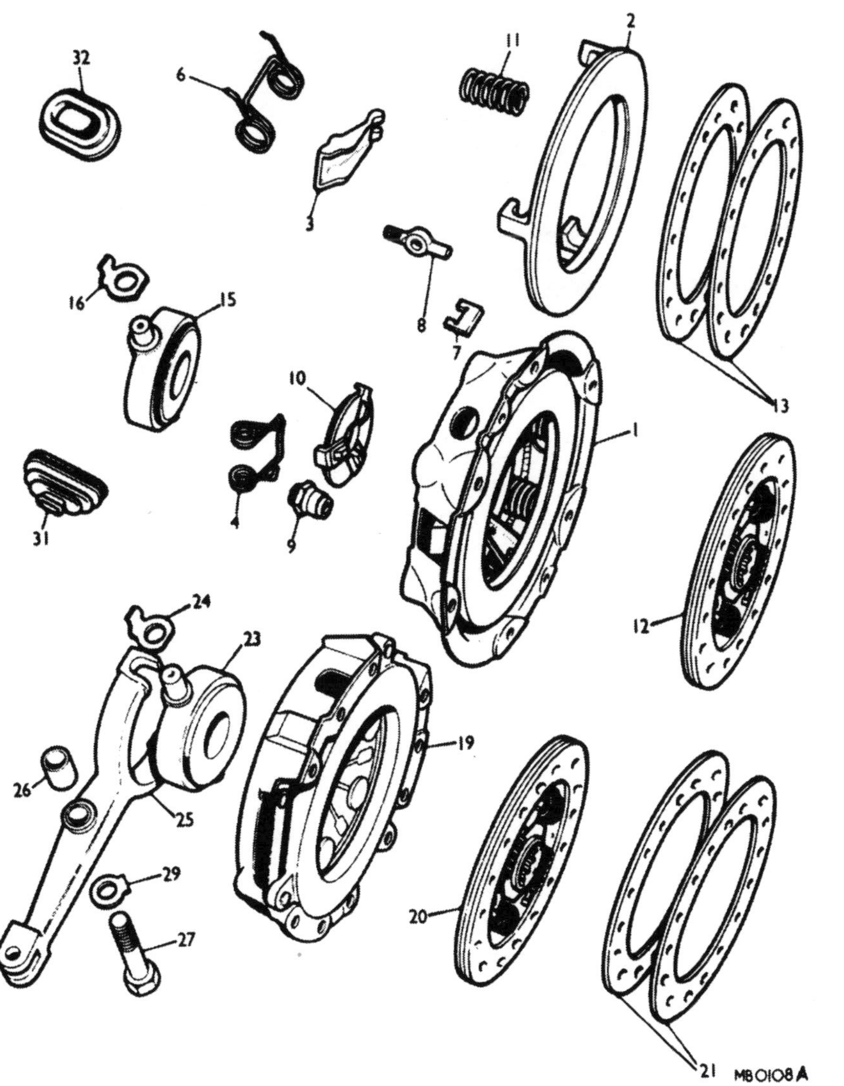

AUSTIN-HEALEY SPRITE MK. 3 AND MK. 4 & MG MIDGET MK. 2 AND MK. 3

NO.	PART NO.	DESCRIPTION	QTY	CHANGE POINT	REMARKS
		CLUTCH-ALL VERSIONS			
		CLUTCH COMPONENTS 1098cc(10CC)			
1	GCC 114	COVER ASSEMBLY-CLUTCH	1		
2	7H 3057	Plate-pressure	1		
3	7H 3209	Lever-release	3		
74	7H 3009	Retainer-lever	3		
6	7H 3008	Spring-anti-rattle	3		
7	7H 3060	Strut-release lever	3		
8	7H 3207	Eyebolt	3		
9	17H 2721	Nut-eyebolt	3		
10	7H 3043	Plate-thrust	1		
11	13H 989	Spring-pressure plate(Red)	6		
12	GCP 103	PLATE ASSEMBLY-DRIVEN	1		
13	8G 8347	Lining and rivets	NLA		
15	GRB 102	Bearing-release	1		
16	13H 783	Retainer-bearing to clutch withdrawal lever	1		
	HZS 506	Screw-clutch to flywheel	6		
	LWZ 305	Washer-spring	6		
		CLUTCH COMPONENTS 1275cc (12CC,12CD,12CE,12CJ,12V)			
19	GCC 115	Cover-clutch	1		
20	GCP 181	PLATE ASSEMBLY-DRIVEN	1		
21	18G 8231	Lining and rivets	1SET		
23	GRB 107	Bearing-clutch release	1		
24	13H 783	Retainer-bearing	2		
	HZS 506	Screw-clutch to flywheel	6		
	LWZ 305	Washer-spring	6		
		CLUTCH WITHDRAWAL LEVER-1098 AND 1275cc			
25	22G 168	LEVER ASSEMBLY-CLUTCH WITHDRAWAL	1		
26	2A 3006	Bush	1		
27	2A 3289	Bolt-lever to gearbox front cover-RHD	1		
27	22G 136	Bolt-lever to gearbox front cover-LHD	1		
	LWN 305	Washer-spring	1		
29	2K 5813	Washer-lOck	NLA		
	NH 605041	Nut	1		
31	22H 1337	Cover-dust-lever	1		
32	2A 5076	Cover-dust-gearbox case	1		

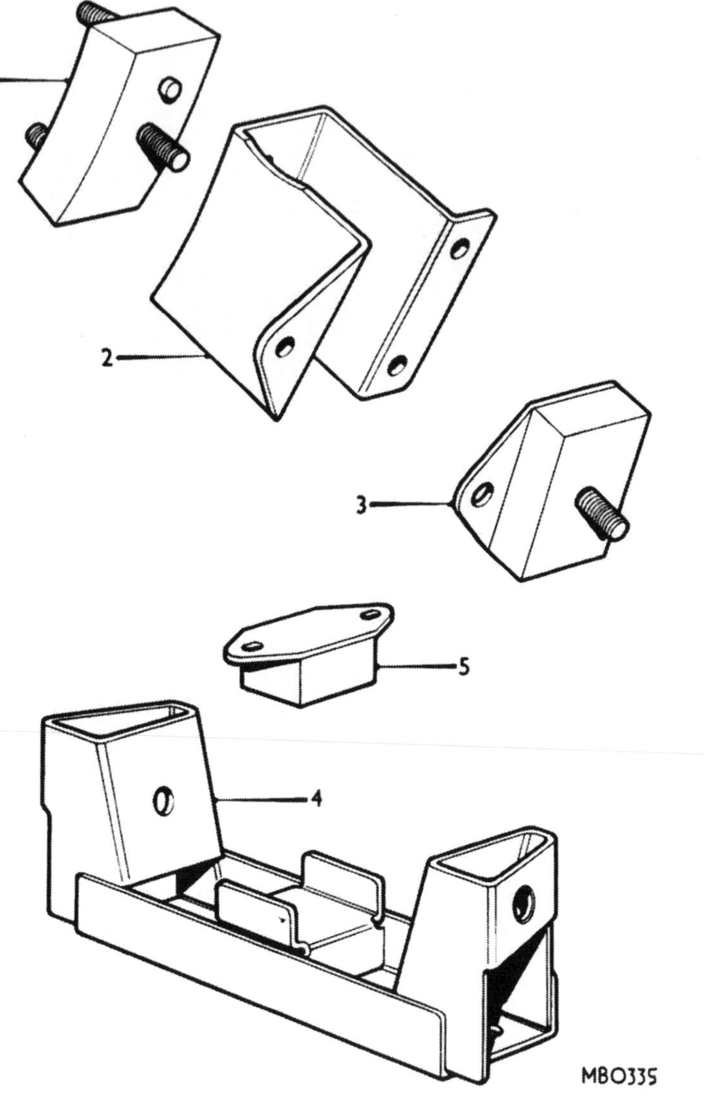

AUSTIN-HEALEY SPRITE MK. 3 AND MK. 4 & MG MIDGET MK. 2 AND MK. 3

ENGINE MOUNTINGS-ALL VERSIONS-EXCEPT 1500

NO.	PART NO.	DESCRIPTION	QTY	CHANGE POINT	REMARKS
1	AHA 5484	Mounting-front	2		
	NH 605041	Nut	2		
	LWZ 305	Washer-spring	4		
	FNZ 106	Nut	2		
	WA 110061	Washer-plain	2		
	LWZ 306	Washer-spring	2		
		BRACKET-FRONT MOUNTING			
2	2A 5570	RH	1		Except USA and Canada
	2A 5571	LH	1		
	2A 5570	RH	1	Use prior to CHA 218/9	USA and Canada
	2A 5571	LH	1		
	CHA 218	RH	1	(C)G-AN5-143355 TO 154100	
	CHA 219	LH	1		
	HZS 505	Screw	5		
	HZS 506	Screw	1		
	PWZ 105	Washer-plain	6		
	LWZ 305	Washer-spring	6		
3	AHA 9307	Mounting-rear	2		
	FNZ 106	Nut	2		
	LWZ 206	Washer-spring	2		
	SH 505061	Screw	4		
	LWZ 205	Washer-spring	4		
4	2A 5552	Plate-rear mounting support	1	Use prior to CHA 276(USA and Canada only)	
	WA 110061	Washer-plain-support plate	2		
	LWZ 206	Washer-spring-support plate	2		
	HZS 506	Screw	2		
	PWZ 205	Washer-plain	2		
	WL 600051	Washer-spring	2		
5	2A 5420	Tie rubber-rear mounting	1	Use prior to (C)G-AN5-146369 (USA and Canada ONLY)	
	SH 505061	Screw-tie rubber to gearbox	2		
	PWZ 105	Washer-plain-tie rubber to gearbox	2		
	WL 600051	Washer-spring-tie rubber to gearbox	2		
	CHA 276	Plate-rear mounting support	1	(C)G-AN5-146370 TO 154100(USA and Canada only)	
	HBZ 630	Bolt-support plate	2		
	WA 110061	Washer-plain-support plate	2		
	WL 600061	Washer-spring-support plate	2		
	CHA 260	Bracket assembly-engine restraint	1		
	CHA 263	Bracket-front-engine restraint	1		
	BHH 1540	Tube-engine restraint	1		
	53K 1389	Bolt-tube to front bracket	1		
	PWZ 105	Washer-plain-tube to front bracket	2		
	LNZ 105	Stiff nut-tube to front bracket	1		
	FNZ 106	Nut-tube to bracket assembly	2		
	LWZ 206	Washer-spring-tube to bracket assembly	1		
	1G 8781	Buffer-tube to bracket assembly	2		
	CHA 279	Strap-gearbox steady	1		
	BHA 4790	Strap-steady(rubber)	1		
	HZS 508	Screw	2		
	WL 600051	Washer-spring	2		
	WA 108051	Washer-plain	2		
	BHH 879	Spacer	2		

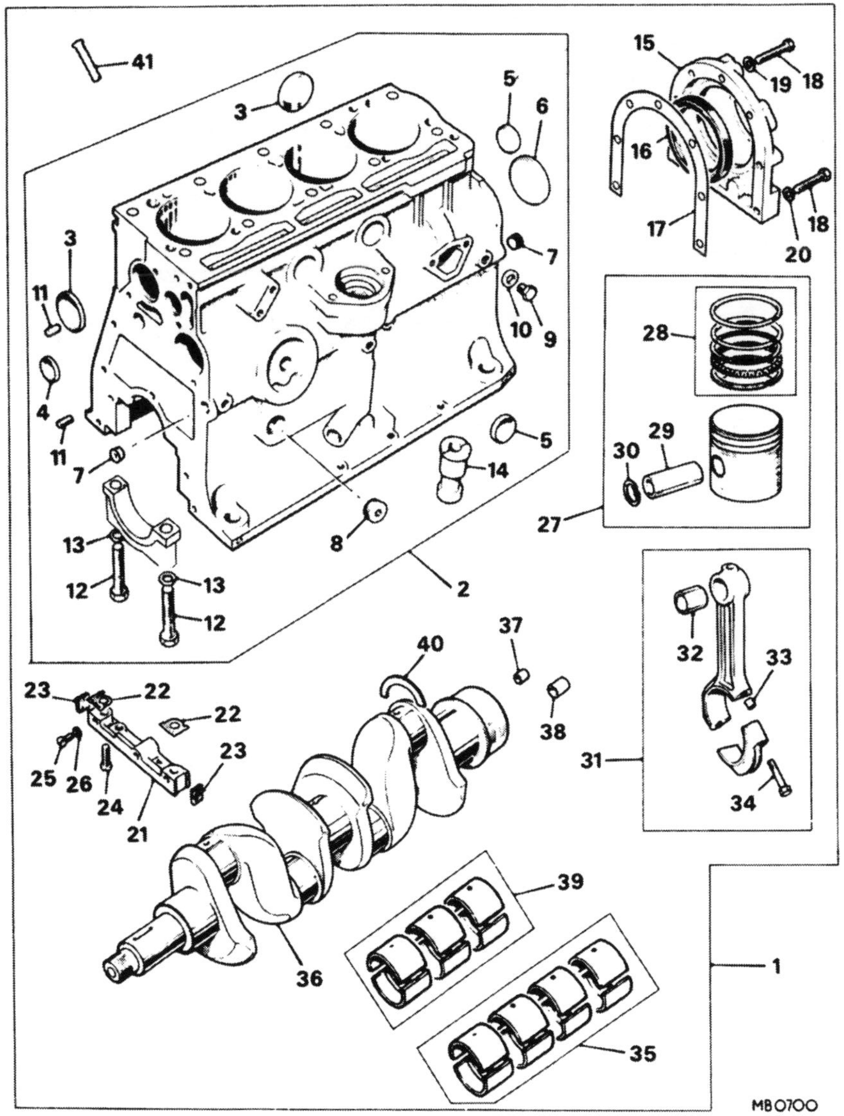

AUSTIN-HEALEY SPRITE MK. 3 AND MK. 4 & MG MIDGET MK. 2 AND MK. 3

NO.	PART NO.	DESCRIPTION	QTY	CHANGE POINT	REMARKS
		ENGINE UNIT-1500			
1	UKC 5955	ENGINE UNIT-SHORT-HC	1		
1	UKC 5956	ENGINE UNIT-SHORT-LC	1		
2	UKC 5957	ENGINE UNIT-SHORT	1		Canada and USA Less California.
	UKC 5958	ENGINE UNIT-SHORT	1		California.
		PLUG			
3	144688	Core	4		
4	144687	Core	1		
5	144686	Core	3		
6	148353	Core	1		
7	118632	Screwed	2		
8	116516	Screwed	1		
9	101022	Screw	4		
10	500469	Washer	4		
11	DP 514	Dowel	2		
12	HB 1024	Bolt-bearing cap	6		
13	WL 210	Washer	6		
14	131786	Bush-oil pump shaft	1		
15	156530	HOUSING-OIL SEAL-REAR	1		
16	143456	Seal-oil	1		
17	105321	Gasket-housing	1		
18	HU 809	Screw	7		
19	500469	Washer	1		
20	WL 208	Washer-lock	6		
21	151134	Block sealing-front	1		
22	150022	Gasket-block	2		
23	36234	Piece-filler	2		
24	100501	Screw	2		
25	PT 805	Screw	2		
26	WL 208	Washer-lock	2		

MB0700

AUSTIN-HEALEY SPRITE MK. 3 AND MK. 4 & MG MIDGET MK. 2 AND MK. 3

NO.	PART NO.	DESCRIPTION	QTY	CHANGE POINT	REMARKS
		ENGINE UNIT-1500-continued			
		PISTON ASSEMBLY-ENGINE SET (9.0:1 COMPRESSION RATIO)			
27	BHM 1058	Standard	1		
27	BHM 1058 20	.020"(.508mm) O/S	1		
		PISTON ASSEMBLY-ENGINE SET (7.5:1 COMPRESSION RATIO)			
27	BHM 1059	Standard	1		
27	BHM 1059 20	.020"(.508mm) O/S	1		
		PISTON ASSEMBLY-ENGINE SET (7.5:1 COMPRESSION RATIO)			USA and Canada TO 1976
27	BHM 1066	Standard	1		USA and Canada TO 1976
27	BHM 1066 20	.020"(.508mm) O/S	1		USA and Canada TO 1976
		PISTON ASSEMBLY-ENGINE SET 9.0:1 COMPRESSION RATIO			USA and Canada Federal 1976 Only.
27	BHM 1058	Standard	1		USA and Canada Federal 1976 Only.
27	BHM 1058 20	.020"(.508mm)O/S	1		USA and Canada Federal 1976 Only.
		PISTON ASSEMBLY-ENGINE SET (7.5:1 compression ratio)			USA California Federal 1976 and 1977. 1977 ON.
27	BHM 1066	Standard	1		USA California Federal 1976 and 1977. 1977 ON.
27	BHM 1066 20	.020"(.508mm)O/S	1		USA California Federal 1976 and 1977. 1977 ON.
		RING-PISTON-ENGINE SET			
28	BHM 1060	Standard	1		
28	BHM 1060 20	.020"(.508mm) O/S	1		
29	146485	Pin-gudgeon	4		
30	508978	Circlip-gudgeon pin	8		
31	146454	ROD-CONNECTING	4		
32	119813	Bush-small end	4		
33	107401	Dowel	8		
34	UKC 2598	Bolt	8		
		BEARING-CONNECTING ROD ENGINE SET			
35	BHM 1057	Standard	1		
35	BHM 1057 10	.010"(.254mm) U/S	1		
35	BHM 1057 20	.020"(.508mm) U/S	1		
35	BHM 1057 30	.030"(.762mm) U/S	1		
36	RKC 918	Crankshaft	1		
37	127883	Dowel	1		
38	105143	Bush-1st motion shaft	1		
		BEARING-MAIN-ENGINE SET			
39	BHM 1056	Standard	1		
39	BHM 1056 10	.010"(.254mm) U/S	1		
39	BHM 1056 20	.020"(.508mm) U/S	1		
39	BHM 1056 30	.030"(.762mm) U/S	1		
40	144195	Washer-thrust-crankshaft	2		
41	121831	Tube-oil-dipper rod	1		

MB0701

NO.	PART NO.	DESCRIPTION	QTY	CHANGE POINT	REMARKS
		ENGINE UNIT-1500-continued			
1	312188	Camshaft	1		
2	105114	Plate-locating	1		
3	HU 807	Screw	2		
4	WL 208	Washer	2		
5	121530	Pedestal-distributor	1		
6	104939	Gasket-.006"(.152mm)	A/R		] Alternative sizes
6	125252	Gasket-.020"(.508mm)	A/R		
7	HN 2008	Nut	2		
8	WL 208	Washer	2		
9	HB 816	Bolt	1		
10	HN 2008	Nut	1		
11	WL 208	Washer	1		
12	104860	Gear-distributor and oil pump drive	1		
13	104861	Shaft-oil pump drive	1		
14	500974	Pin	1		
15	35960	Gear-camshaft	1		
16	36411	Plate-locking	1		
17	100500	Screw	2		
18	105131	Chain-timing	1		
19	119389	Gear-crankshaft	1		
20	105115	Key-pulley and gear	1		
21	145275	Shim-thrust-.004"(.102mm)	A/R		] Alternative sizes
21	145276	Shim-thrust-.006"(.152mm)	A/R		
22	119390	Deflector-oil	1		
23	43752	Anchor plate-tensioner	1		
24	RP 504	Rivet	2		
25	33214	Pin-tensioner	1		
26	42425	Tensioner	1		
27	WP 18	Washer-plain	2		
28	PC 7	Pin-cotter	2		

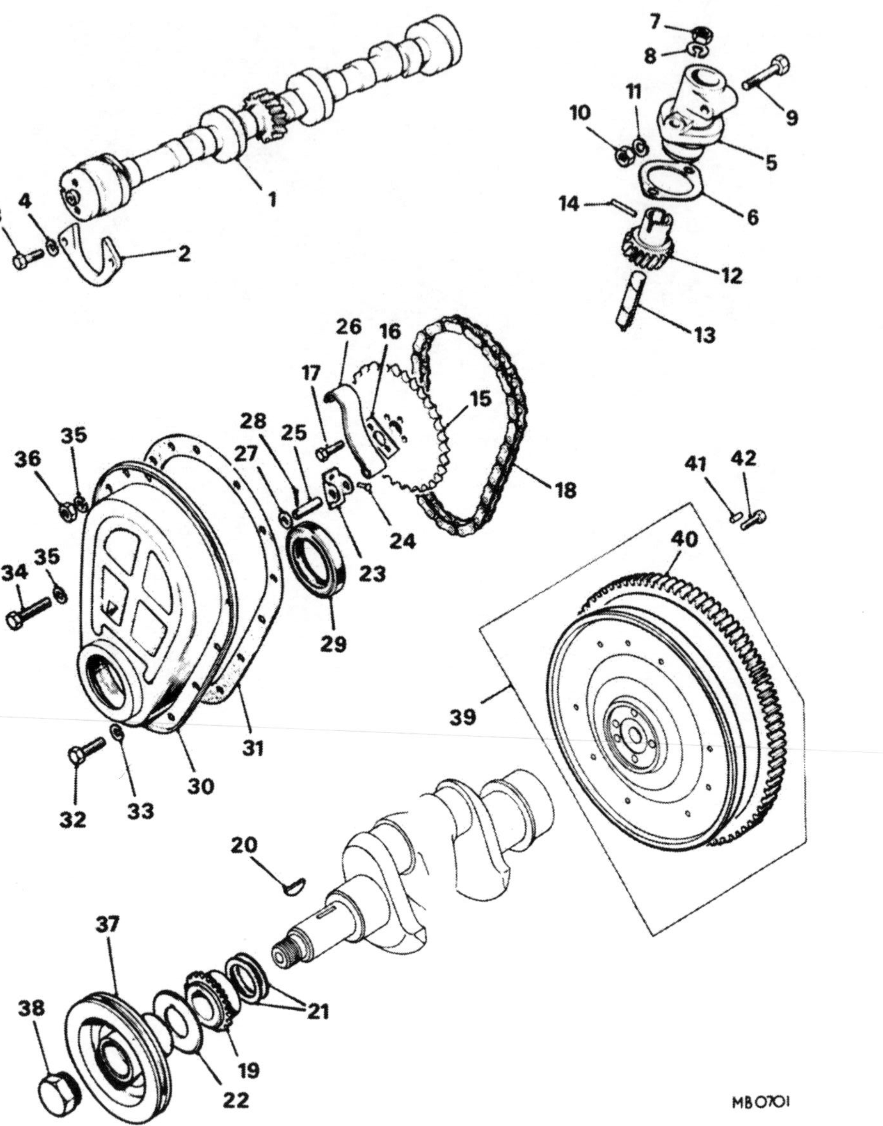

AUSTIN-HEALEY SPRITE MK. 3 AND MK. 4 & MG MIDGET MK. 2 AND MK. 3

ENGINE UNIT-1500-continued

NO.	PART NO.	DESCRIPTION	QTY	CHANGE POINT	REMARKS
29	UKC 1110	Seal-oil-timing cover	1		
30	217790	Cover-timing	1		
31	211126	Gasket	1		
32	PT 803	Screw	5		
33	WL 208	Washer-lock	5		
34	HU 807	Screw	6		
35	WL 208	Washer-lock	7		
36	HN 2008	Nut	1		
37	217789	Pulley-crankshaft	1		
43	TKC 1425	Pulley-crankshaft	1		USA and Canada.
38	155357	Nut	1		
39	TKC 1840	FLYWHEEL	1		
40	201350	Gear-starter ring	1		
41	UKC 1938	Dowel	3		
42	UKC 4254	Bolt	4		

AUSTIN-HEALEY SPRITE MK. 3 AND MK. 4 & MG MIDGET MK. 2 AND MK. 3

MB0699

NO.	PART NO.	DESCRIPTION	QTY	CHANGE POINT	REMARKS
		ENGINE UNIT-1500-continued			
		STUD			
1	121217	Cylinder head	10		
1	119758	Cylinder head	2		USA and Canada To 1976
1	121217	Cylinder head	8		
1	119758	Cylinder head	2		USA-Canada Federal
1	105121	Cylinder	8		
1	119758	Cylinder head	2		USA California
1	121217	Cylinder head	8		
3	101962	Distributor pedestal	2		
3	101962	Petrol pump	2		
3	101962	Cylinder block-front	1		
4	112907	Cylinder block-rear	3		
5	DP 610	Dowel-cylinder block-rear	1		
6	DP 616	Dowel-cylinder block-rear	1		
7	201344	Plate-gearbox mounting	1		
8	HU 806	Screw	7		
9	WL 208	Washer	7		
10	215372	Plate-engine-front	1		
10	TKC 1830	Plate-engine-front	1		USA and Canada.
11	215350	Gasket-plate	1		
8	HU 806	Screw	3		
9	WL 208	Washer	3		
12	132107	Piston-oil-relief valve	1		
13	131535	Spring	1		
14	6K 433	Washer-copper	1		
15	107246	Plug	1		
	143943	Adaptor-oil pressure gauge	1		
17	GFE 119	FILTER-OIL	1		
18	132098	'O'ring-sealing	1		
19	510451	Ring-sealing	1		
20	CHA 289	Adaptor-oil filter	1		LHD
21	157409	Ring-sealing	1		LHD
22	CHA 330	Bolt-adaptor	1		LHD
23	TRS 1114	'O'ring	1		LHD
24	TKC 1974	PUMP AND STRAINER-OIL	1		
25	TKC 2006	Strainer-oil	1		
26	155371	Nut	1		
27	HB 722	Bolt	3		
28	WL 221	Washer	3		
29	213863	Sump-oil	1		
30	114774	Plug-sump-drain	1		
31	GEG 517	Gasket-sump	1		
32	MA 805	Screw	12		
33	HU 805	Screw	4		
34	WL 208	Washer-lock	4		
35	134933	ROD-OIL DIPPER	1		
36	32307	Seal-felt	1		
37	129077	Plug-cylinder drain	1		
38	WF 511	Washer	1		
39	158941	Liner-cylinder block	A/R		

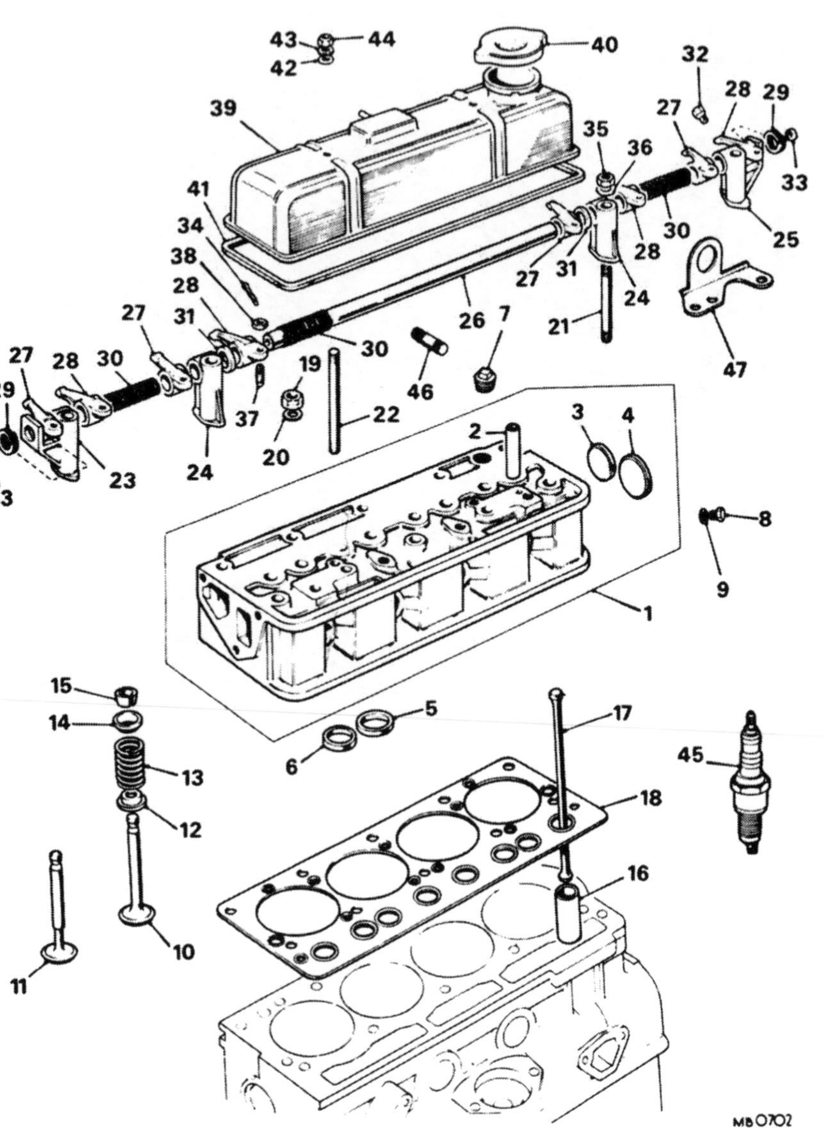

AUSTIN-HEALEY SPRITE MK. 3 AND MK. 4 & MG MIDGET MK. 2 AND MK. 3

ENGINE UNIT-1500-continued

NO.	PART NO.	DESCRIPTION	QTY	CHANGE POINT	REMARKS
1	TKC 1155	HEAD ASSEMBLY-CYLINDER	1		
1	TKC 1409	HEAD ASSEMBLY-CYLINDER	1		USA and Canada to 1976
1	TKC 2748	HEAD-ASSEMBLY-CYLINDER	1		Federal 1976 on
1	TKC 1409	HEAD ASSEMBLY-CYLINDER	1		USA Canada California 1976
2	58923	Guide-valve	8		
1	TKC 3239	HEAD ASSEMBLY-CYLINDER	1		] USA-Canada 1977 ON
2	UKC 4902	Guide-valve	8		
3	144686	Plug-core-1.25"(31.75mm)dia.	1		
4	144648	Plug-core-1.625"(41.28mm)dia.	1		
5	UKC 2335	Insert-valve seat-inlet	A/R		
6	UKC 2334	Insert-valve seat-exhaust	A/R		
7	114774	Plug-screwed	1		
8	101022	Screw-rocker oil feed	1		
9	500469	Washer-copper	1		
10	UKC 2460	Valve-inlet	4		
11	144965	Valve-exhaust	4		
	153886	Valve-exhaust	4		USA and Canada.
	157510	Collar-lower	8		
12	105118	Collar-lower	8		USA and Canada
	157476	Spring-valve-inner	8		
13	157229	Spring-valve-outer	8		
14	111870	Collar-upper	8		
15	106663	Cotter-valve	8PRS		
16	143552	Tappet	8		
17	157508	Push-rod	8		
18	GEG 373	Gasket-cylinder head	1		
19	110748	Nut-cylinder head stud	10		
20	WP 9	Washer	10		
21	132495	Stud-rocker pedestal	4		
22	105123	Stud-rocker cover	2		USA-Canada to 1977.
22	UKC 7851	Stud-rocker cover	2		USA-Canada 1977 ON

AUSTIN-HEALEY SPRITE MK. 3 AND MK. 4 & MG MIDGET MK. 2 AND MK. 3

NO.	PART NO.	DESCRIPTION	QTY	CHANGE POINT	REMARKS
		ENGINE UNIT-1500-continued			
		PEDESTAL-ROCKER			
23	144973	No.1	1		
24	144974	Intermediate	2		
25	144975	No.4	1		
26	144962	Shaft-rocker	1		
27	109024	Rocker-No.1,3,5,7	4		
28	109023	Rocker-No.2,4,6,8	4		
29	105322	Spring-spacing-No.1 and 8 rockers	2		
30	105120	Spring-spacing-No.2 and 3, 4 and 5,6 and 7 rockers	3		
31	146914	Washer-plain	2		
32	104859	Screw-shaft locating	1		
33	137811	Plug-shaft	2		
34	PC 10	Pin-cotter	1		
35	HN 2009	Nut-rocker pedestal	4		
36	WP 184	Washer	4		
37	109495	Screw-rocker adjusting	8		
38	57110	Nut-lock	8		
39	214814	Cover-valve rocker	1		
40	138176	Cap-oil-filler	1		
39	TKC 1466	Cover-valve rocker	1		USA and Canada TO 1977.USA-Canada 1977 ON.
	TKC 3238	Cover-value rocker	1		
40	UKC 3652	Cap-oil-filler	1		
41	GEG 414	Gasket	1		
42	WF 508	Washer-fibre	2		
43	WP 8	Washer-plain	2		
44	TN 3208	Nut-Nyloc	2		
	148090	"O" Ring-rocker cover	2		USA-Canada 1977 ON
	147738	Washer-"O" Ring	2		
	147737	Nut	2		
45	N 12 Y	Plug-sparking	4		
46	105124	Stud-manifold-exhaust	2		
46	144070	Stud-manifold-exhaust	2		USA and Canada
46	105125	Stud-manifold-inlet and exhaust	6		
47	142649	Bracket-lifting eye-rear	1		
47	UKC 3653	Bracket-lifting eye-rear	1		USA and Canada

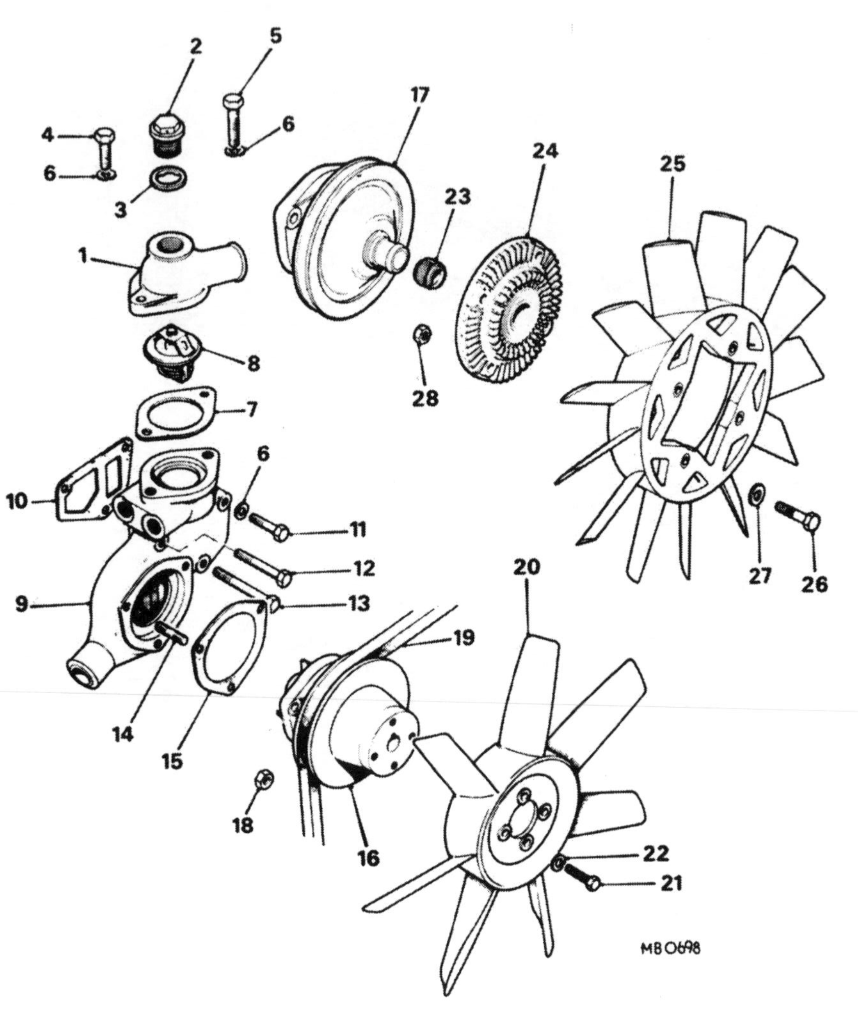

AUSTIN-HEALEY SPRITE MK. 3 AND MK. 4 & MG MIDGET MK. 2 AND MK. 3

ENGINE UNIT-1500-continued.

NO.	PART NO.	DESCRIPTION	QTY	CHANGE POINT	REMARKS
1	CHA 343	Elbow-water outlet	1		
	CHA 595	Elbow-water outlet	1		USA-Canada 1975 when fitted refer to TSB 75-A-6
	CHA 641	Elbow-water outlet	1		USA-Canada 1976 ON
2	ARA 2634	Plug	1		
3	TRS 1418	Washer-plug	1		
4	CHA 440	Screw-special-.3125"UNF x 1.25"	1		
5	CHA 441	Screw-special-.3125"UNF x 1"	1		
6	WL 208	Washer-lock	2		
7	GTG 103	Gasket	1		
8	GTS 104	Thermostat 82C	1		
8	GTS 106	Thermostat 88C	1		Cold climates.
9	144297	Body-water pump	1		
10	138702	Gasket-body to cylinder	1		
11	HB 818	Bolt	1		
12	HB 819	Bolt	1		
13	HB 822	Bolt	1		
6	WL 208	Washer	3		
14	101962	Stud-water pump	3		
15	138701	Gasket-pump to body	1		
16	GWP 128	Water pump assembly	1		
17	UKC 774	Water pump assembly	1		USA-Canada.
18	HN 2008	Nut-water pump	3		
19	GFB 248	Fan-belt	1		
19	CHA 328	Fan-belt	1		USA-Canada.
20	311702	Fan(Orange)	1		
20	309141	Fan(Green)	1		Hot climates.
21	SH 604061	Screw	4		
22	WL 600041	Washer	4		
23	UKC 759	Ring-Tolerance	1		
24	UKC 3532	Coupling-fan drive	1		
25	RKC 92	Fan	1		USA-Canada.
26	BH 604121	Bolt	4		
27	WA 106041	Washer	4		
28	NH 604041	Nut	4		
	11K 2846	Adaptor-thermal transmitter	1		
	AED 172	Washer-adaptor(copper)	1		

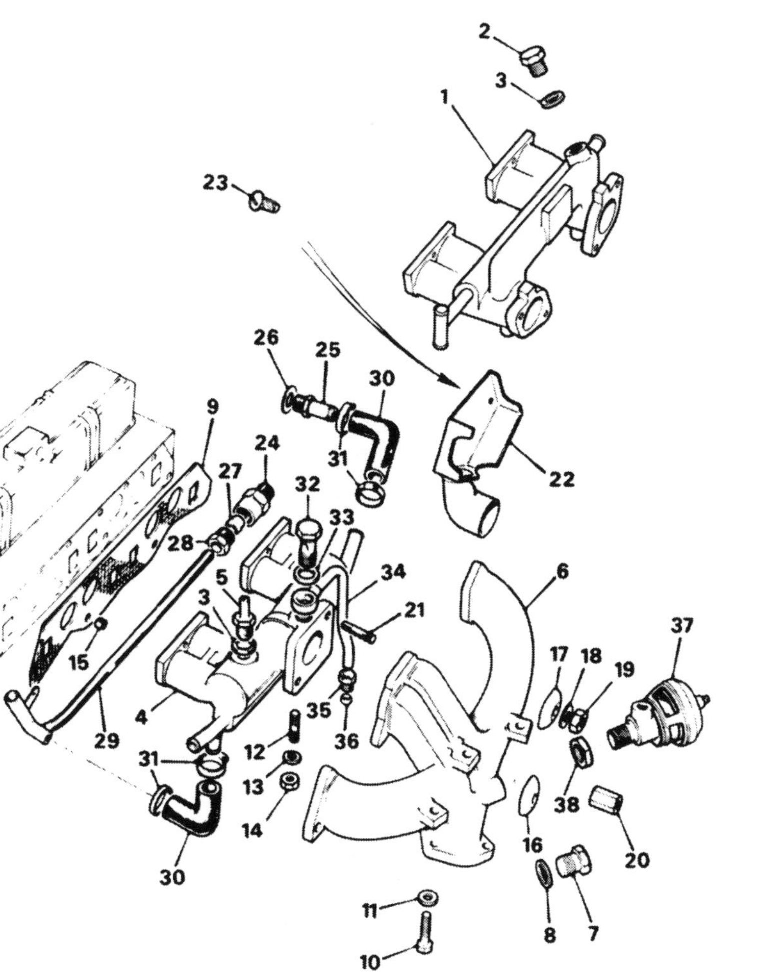

AUSTIN-HEALEY SPRITE MK. 3 AND MK. 4 & MG MIDGET MK. 2 AND MK. 3

ENGINE UNIT-1500-continued.

NO.	PART NO.	DESCRIPTION	QTY	CHANGE POINT	REMARKS
1	RKC 723	Manifold-inlet	1		
2	122132	Plug-blanking	1		
3	WF 513	Washer-plug(Fibre)	1		
4	TKC 285	Manifold-inlet	1		
5	159942	Adaptor	1		USA-Canada. TO 1977
3	WF 524	Washer(fibre)	1		
6	CHA 256	Manifold-exhaust	1		
7	ADP 212	Plug	1		
8	AEC 699	Washer-sealing	1		
9	GEG 648	Gasket-manifold to head	1		
10	BH 505131	Bolt-inlet to exhaust manifold	2		
11	WF 8	Washer-bolt	2		
12	TD 861	Stud-inlet to exhaust manifold	1		
13	WL 208	Washer-lock	1		USA and Canada. TO 1977
14	HN 2008	Nut	1		
15	DS 2512	Dowel-spring	2		
16	137845	Clamp	2		
17	58258	Clamp	4		
18	WP 36	Washer-plain	8		
19	100498	Nut	6		
20	CHA 360	Nut-manifold clamping	2		
21	105745	Stud-carburetter	4		
21	129383	Stud-carburetter	2		USA and Canada. TO 1977.
22	CHA 323	Pre-heater	1		
	CHA 503	Pre-heater	1		California to 1977.
23	UKC 4090	Screw-drive	4		
24	101343	Adaptor-water pump to heater rail	1		
25	138530	Adaptor-water pump to manifold hose	1		
26	WF 524	Washer-adaptor	1		
27	TL 11	Sleeve	1		
28	101302	Nut-tube	1		
29	212935	Pipe-water pump to inlet manifold-rear	1		
30	149699	Hose-inlet manifold to pipe and adaptor	2		
31	GHC 507	Clip-hose	4		
32	UKC 1846	Bolt-banjo	1		
33	UKC 2284	Washer	2		
34	UKC 1813	Pipe-manifold to valve	1		USA and Canada TO 1977.
35	UKC 1413	Nut-tube	1		
36	TL 11	Olive	1		
37	TKC 1470	Valve-EGR	1		
38	160108	Nut-lock	1		
		ENGINE GASKET SETS			
	GEG 1212	Set-gasket-decarbonizing	1		
	RTC 1760	Set-gasket-decarbonizing	1		USA and Canada.
	GEG 279	Set-gasket-supplementary	1		

ILLUSTRATION NOT USED

AUSTIN-HEALEY SPRITE MK. 3 AND MK. 4 & MG MIDGET MK. 2 AND MK. 3

ENGINE UNIT 1500-USA-CANADA 1977 ON

NO.	PART NO.	DESCRIPTION	QTY	CHANGE POINT	REMARKS
1	UKC 8119	MANIFOLD INLET	1		California
1	UKC 7916	MANIFOLD-INLET	1		Federal and Canada
2	154053	Plug-core	1		
3	159942	Adaptor	1		] California
4	WF 513	Washer-fibre	1		
5	RKC 3056	Manifold-exhaust	1		
6	ADP 212	Plug	1		
7	AEC 699	Washer-plug	1		
8	GEG 648	Gasket-manifold to head	1		
9	BH 505131	Bolt-inlet to exhaust manifold	2		
10	WA 108051	Washer-bolt	2		
11	SH 605091	Screw-inlet to exhaust manifold	2		
10	WA 108051	Washer-plain	2		
12	WL 600051	Washer-lock	2		
13	DS 2512	Dowel-spring	2		
14	137845	Clamp	2		
15	58258	Clamp	4		
16	WP 36	Washer-plain	8		
17	100498	Nut-clamp	6		
18	CHA 360	Nut-clamp	2		
19	129383	Stud-carburetter	2		
20	CHA 503	Pre-heater	1		
21	AU 614081	Screw-drive	2		
22	UKC 4209	Adaptor-water pump body	1		
23	101343	Adaptor-water pump to heater rail	1		
24	212935	Pipe-water pump to inlet Manifold rear	1		
25	101302	Nut-tube	1		
26	TL 11	Sleeve	1		
27	149699	Hose-manifold to pipe adaptor	1		
28	UKC 7375	Hose-water pump to manifold	1		
29	GHC 507	Clip-hose	4		
30	SK 604031	Screw-blanking-manifold	1		

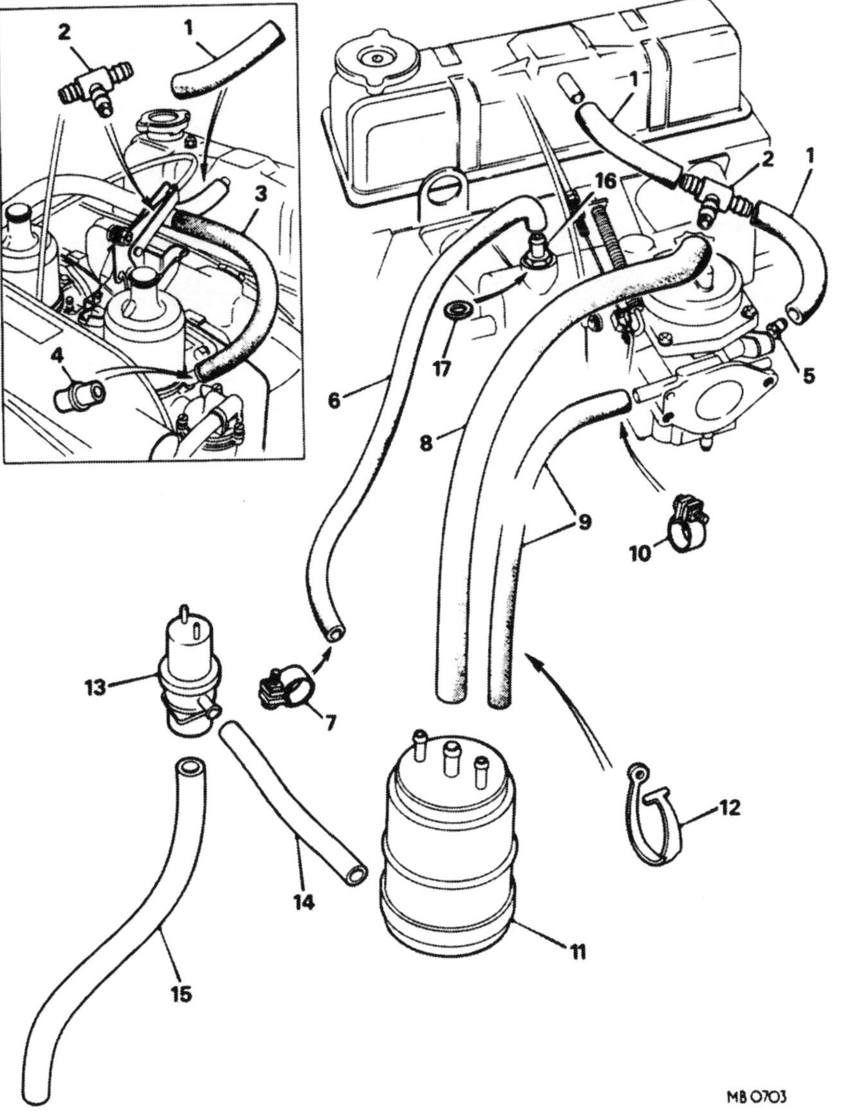

AUSTIN-HEALEY SPRITE MK. 3 AND MK. 4 & MG MIDGET MK. 2 AND MK. 3

ENGINE UNIT-1500-EMISSION CONTROL-1974.

NO.	PART NO.	DESCRIPTION	QTY	CHANGE POINT	REMARKS
1	154220	Hose-rocker cover to'T'piece	1		Not USA and Canada.
2	154211	'T'piece	1		
3	154935	Hose-'T'piece to carburetter adaptor	2		
4	154934	Adaptor-hose	2		
1	154220	Hose-rocker cover to'T'piece	1		USA and Canada.
2	154211	'T'piece	1		
1	154220	Hose-'T'piece to carburetter	1		
5	154210	Restrictor-carburetter hose	1		
6	CHA 380	Hose-adaptor to anti-run-on valve	1		
7	BHH 185	Clip-hose	2		
8	AHA 9666	Hose-'T'piece to carbon canister	1		
	154209	Restrictor	1		
9	CHA 401	Hose-carburetter to carbon canister	1		
10	88G 308	Clip-carburetter end	1		
11	13H 8511	Canister-carbon	1		
	AHH 9658	Strap-canister	1		
	PMZ 316	Screw-strap	1		
	LNZ 203	Nut-screw	1		
12	13H 6107	Strap-pipe retaining	1		
13	12H 4295	Valve-anti-run-on	1		
14	CHA 384	Hose-valve to carbon canister	1		
	GHC 913	Clip-hose	1		
15	CHA 404	Hose-valve to atmosphere	1		
16	159942	Adaptor-manifold	1		
17	WF 524	Washer	1		

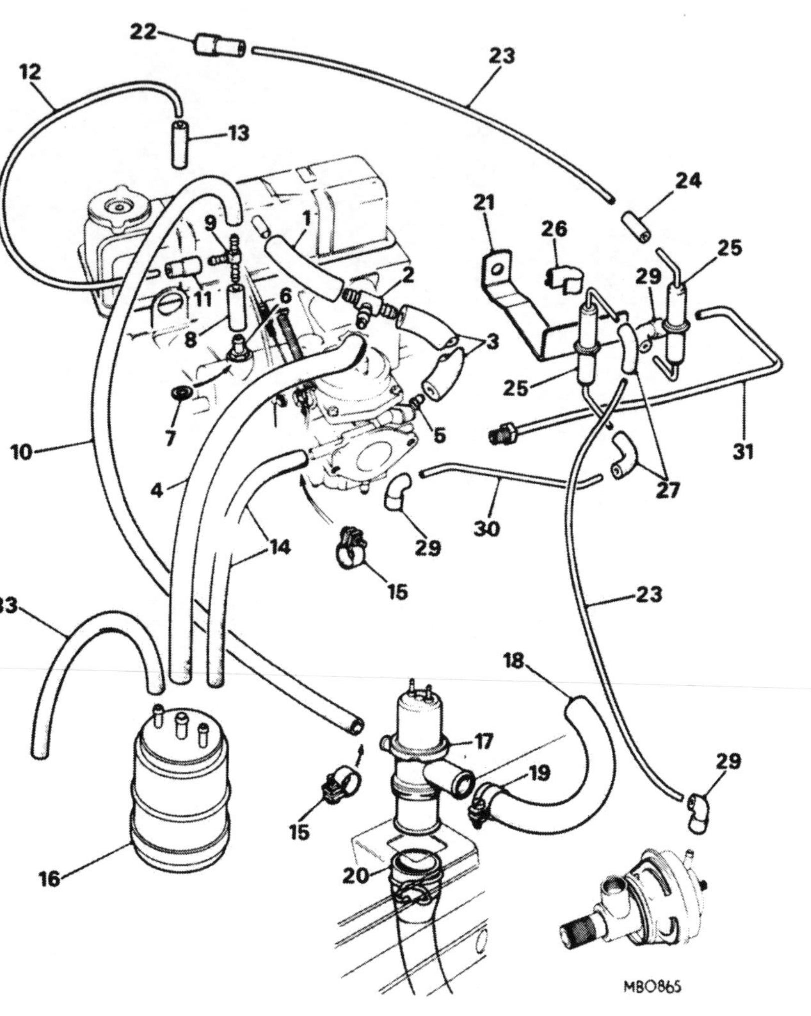

AUSTIN-HEALEY SPRITE MK. 3 AND MK. 4 & MG MIDGET MK. 2 AND MK. 3

ENGINE UNIT-1500 EMISSION BREATHER-1975 TO 1977.

NO.	PART NO.	DESCRIPTION	QTY	CHANGE POINT	REMARKS
1	154220	Hose-rocker cover to'T'piece	1		
2	154211	'T'piece	1		
3	216924	Hose-'T'piece to carburetter	1		
4	AHA 9666	Hose-'T'piece to carbon cannister	1		
5	154209	Restrictor	1		
6	159942	Adaptor-manifold	1		
7	WF 524	Washer-adaptor	1		
8	120331	Hose-adaptor to'T'piece	1		
9	UKC 3649	'T'piece	1		
10	120331	Hose-'T'piece to anti-run-on valve-1975	1		
10	AAU 2748 M	Hose-'T'piece to anti run on valve-1976 ON	1		
11	UKC 1905	Hose-'T'piece to diverter valve pipe	1		
12	UKC 1925	Pipe-hose to diverter valve	1		
13	117400	Sleeve-pipe	1		
14	CHA 401	Hose-carburetter to carbon cannister	1		
15	88G 308	Clip-hose	1		
16	13H 8511	Cannister-carbon	1		
17	12H 4295	Valve-anti run on	1		
18	CHA 384	Hose-valve to cannister-1975	1		
18	CHA 556	Hose-valve to cannister-1976 ON	1		
19	GHC 913	Clip-hose	2		
20	CHA 404	Hose-valve to atmosphere-1975	1		
20	CHA 557	Hose-valve to atmosphere-1976on	1		
21	UKC 1925	Bracket-fuel trap mounting	1		
22	131211	Sleeve	1		
23	37H 4229 M	Pipe-vacuum-distributor	1		
24	156608	Sleeve	1		
25	156607	Fuel trap	2		
26	156712	Clip-fuel trap	2		
27	149380	Sleeve	2		
30	37H 4229 M	Pipe-metal to carb	1		
29	152184	Sleeve	3		
23	37H 4229 M	Pipe-vacuum	1		
31	UKC 2130	'T'piece	1		
22	131211	Sleeve	1		
32	UKC 1905	Sleeve	1		
27	149380	Sleeve	1		
33	BHH 102	Hose-spilloff	1		

ILLUSTRATION NOT USED

AUSTIN-HEALEY SPRITE MK. 3 AND MK. 4 & MG MIDGET MK. 2 AND MK. 3

ENGINE UNIT-1500-EMISSION BREATHER-1977-ON

NO.	PART NO.	DESCRIPTION	QTY	CHANGE POINT	REMARKS
1	154220	Hose-rocker cover to breather Pipe	1		
2	TKC 3305	PIPE ASSEMBLY-BREATHER	1		
3	154220	Hose-pipe to carburettor	1		
4	154210	Restrictor-carburettor	1		
5	CHA 644	Hose-pipe to cannister	1		
6	154209	Restrictor-cannister	1		
7	CHA 401	Hose-carburetter to cannister	1		
8	159942	Adaptor-manifold	1		
9	WF 524	Washer-adaptor	1		
10	CHA 555	Hose-manifold to anti-run-on valve	1		California
11	12H 4295	Valve anti run-on	1		California
12	CHA 556	Hose-valve to cannister	1		California
13	GHC 913	Clip-hose	2		
14	CHA 557	Hose-valve to atmosphere	1		California
14	CHA 645	Hose-cannister to atmosphere	1		Federal-Canada
15	BHN 102	Hose-cannister spilloff	1		
16	TKC 3306	Valve-EGR	1		California
16	TKC 3320	Valve-EGR	1		Federal-Canada
17	160108	Nut-lock	1		
18	UKC 7722	PIPE ASSEMBLY-EGR VALVE TO ELBOW ADAPTOR	1		
19	TL 11	Sleeve	2		
20	UKC 1413	Nut	2		
21	UKC 7764	Elbow Adaptor	1		
22	UKC 7765	Nut-lock	1		
23	UKC 8544	Bracket-fuel trap	1		
24	156607	Trap-fuel	1/2		] 2 OFF California
25	156712	Clip-trap	1/2		
26	149380	Sleeve-Bent fuel trap	1/3		3 OFF California
27	156608	Sleeve-straight-fuel Trap	1		Federal-Canada
28	152184	Sleeve-bent-EGR-valve and Carburettor	2		
29	128262	Sleeve-bent-T piece	2		Federal-Canada
30	12B 2095	Sleeve-straight-T piece and Distributor	2		
29	128262	Sleeve-bent-distributor	1		Federal-California
31	37H 4229 M	Pipe-nylon-vacuum	A/R		
32	UKC 4294	PIPE ASSEMBLY-METAL	1		] California
33	TL 5	Sleeve	1		
34	UKC 4309	Nut	1		
35	UKC 8307	"T" Piece	1		Federal-Canada.

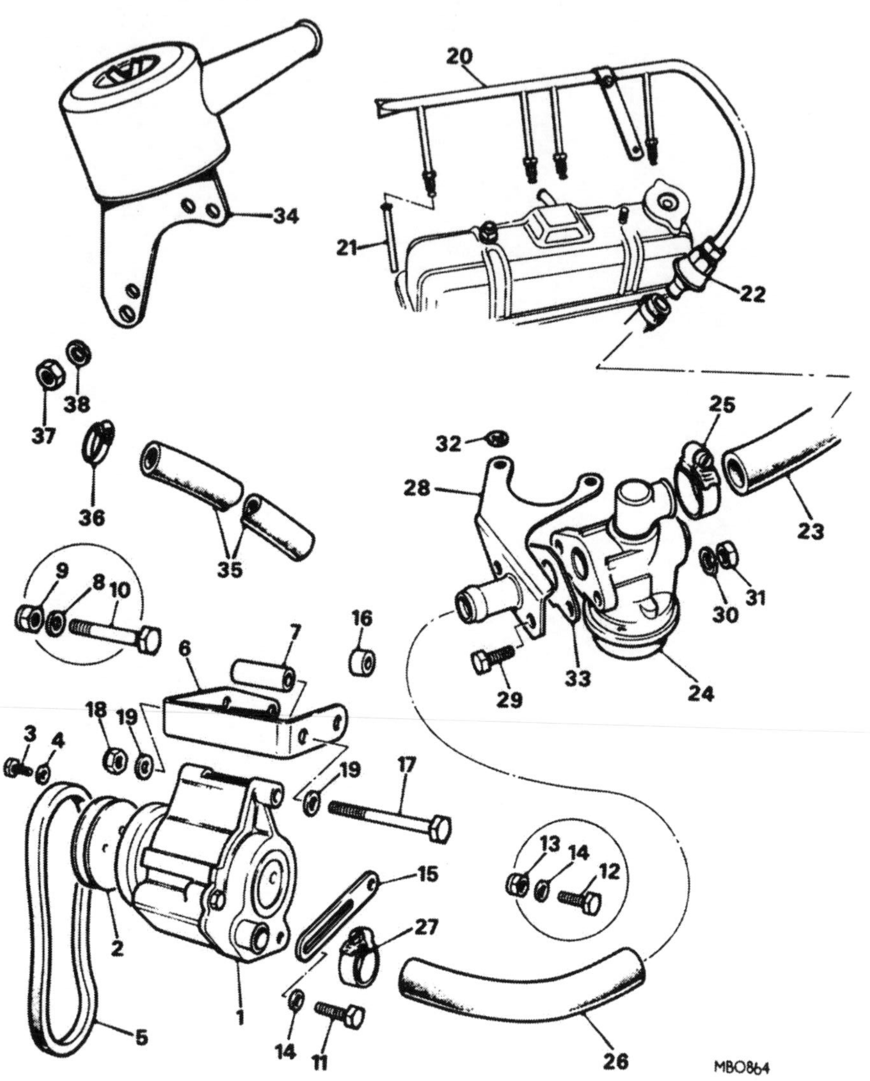

AUSTIN-HEALEY SPRITE MK. 3 AND MK. 4 & MG MIDGET MK. 2 AND MK. 3

AIR PUMP AND MANIFOLD-MIDGET 1500 TO 1977.

NO.	PART NO.	DESCRIPTION	QTY	CHANGE POINT	REMARKS
1	RKC 698	Pump-air	1		
2	UKC 3127	Pulley-air pump	1		
3	HU 755	Screw-pulley to pump	3		
4	WP 7	Washer	3		
5	TKC 1615	Belt-drive-air pump	1		
6	CHA 301	Bracket-mounting	1		
7	UKC 3128	Tube-distance	1		
8	WA 108051	Washer	2		
9	YN 2908	Nut-Nyloc	2		
10	HB 818	Bolt-bracket	2		
11	HB 821	Bolt	1		
12	HB 836	Bolt	2		
13	YN 2908	Nut-Nyloc	2		
14	WC 108051	Washer	3		
15	UKC 3131	Strap-tensioning-rear	2		
16	UKC 4073	Tube-distance-pump to bracket	1		
17	HB 841	Bolt-air pump and alternator to bracket	2		
18	YN 2908	Nut	2		
19	WA 108051	Washer	2		
20	TKC 1423	Manifold-air injection	1		
21	UKC 3120	Tube-air injection	4		
22	UKC 2643	Valve-non-return	1		
23	UKC 3123	Hose-valve to diverter valve	1		
24	TKC 1424	Valve-diverter	1		
25	CJ 3020	Clip-hose	2		
26	UKC 3126	Hose-valve to air pump	1		
27	CJ 3020	Clip-hose	2		
28	UKC 3124	Bracket-diverter valve	1		
29	HU 708	Screw	2		
30	WL 207	Washer	2		
31	HN 2007	Nut	2		
32	WM 95	Washer-bracket mounting	2		
33	UKC 2683	Gasket-diverter valve	1		
34	12G 1696	Cleaner-air-air pump	1		
35	12H 2479	Connection air pump to air cleaner	1		
36	GHC 709	Clip-connection	2		
37	MNZ 206	Nut-air cleaner	2		
38	WL 600041	Washer-spring	2		

ILLUSTRATION NOT USED

AUSTIN-HEALEY SPRITE MK. 3 AND MK. 4 & MG MIDGET MK. 2 AND MK. 3

AIR PUMP AND INJECTION PIPE-MIDGET-1500 1977 ON

NO.	PART NO.	DESCRIPTION	QTY	CHANGE POINT	REMARKS
1	RKC 3137	Pump-air	1		
2	UKC 3127	Pulley-pump	1		
3	HU 755	Screw-pulley to pump	3		
4	WP 7	Washer	3		
5	TKC 1615	Belt-drive-air pump	1		
6	CHA 301	Bracket-mounting	1		
7	UKC 3128	Tube-distance	1		
8	WA 108051	Washer	2		
9	YN 2908	Nut-nyloc	2		
10	HB 818	Bolt-bracket	2		
11	HB 821	Bolt	1		
12	HB 836	Bolt	2		
13	YN 2908	Nut-Nyloc	2		
14	WC 108051	Washer	3		
15	UKC 3131	Strap-tensioning-rear	2		
16	UKC 4073	Tube-distance-pump to bracket	1		
17	HB 841	Bolt-air pump and alternator To Bracket	2		
18	YN 2908	Nut-nyloc	2		
19	WA 108051	Washer	2		
20	TKC 3215	Pipe-air injection	1		
21	TL 11	Olive	1		
22	UKC 1413	Nut-tube	1		
23	UKC 2643	Valve-non-return	1		
24	UKC 3126	Hose-valve to air pump	1		
25	GHC 709	Clip-hose	2		
26	12G 1696	Cleaner-air-air pump	1		
27	37H 2498	Element			
28	12H 2479	Hose-air cleaner to air pump	1		
29	GHC 709	Clip-hose	2		
30	MNZ 206	Nut-air cleaner	2		
31	WL 600041	Washer-spring	2		

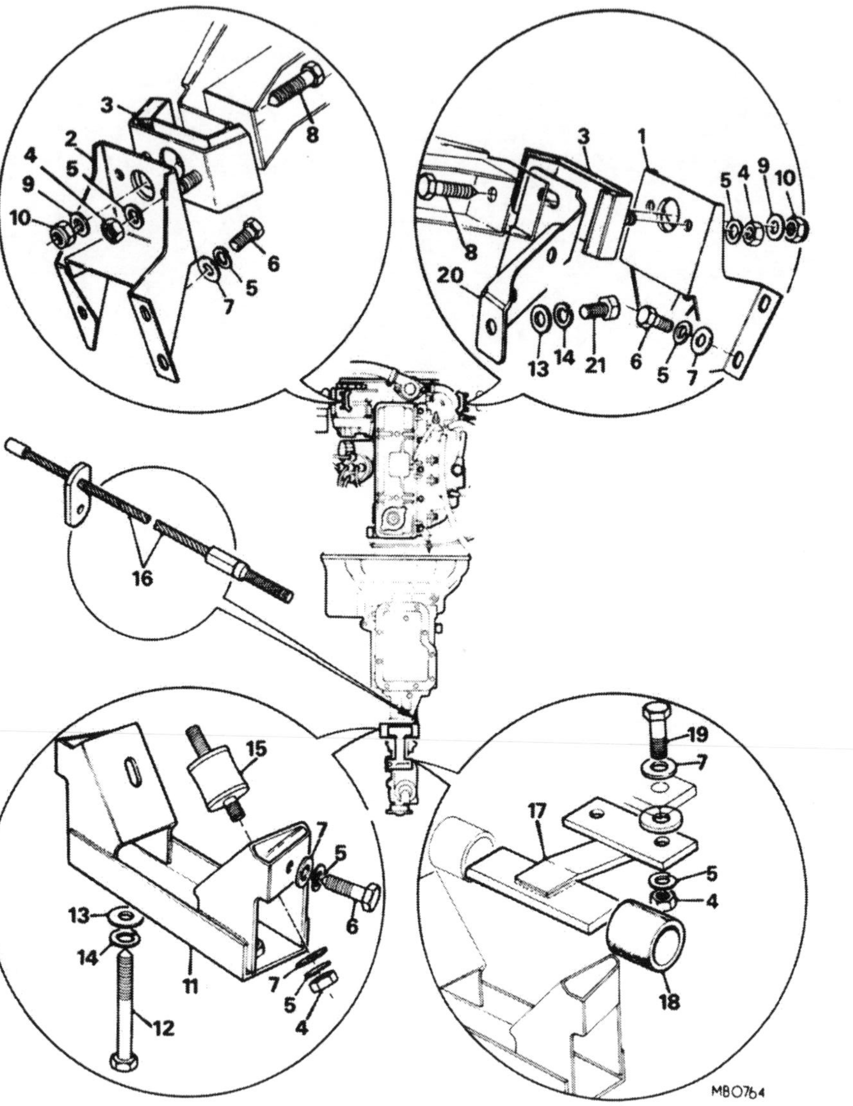

AUSTIN-HEALEY SPRITE MK. 3 AND MK. 4 & MG MIDGET MK. 2 AND MK. 3

ENGINE MOUNTINGS-MIDGET 1500.

NO.	PART NO.	DESCRIPTION	QTY	CHANGE POINT	REMARKS
1	CHA 257	Bracket-engine mounting-RH	1		
2	CHA 258	Bracket-engine mounting-LH	1		
3	CHA 280	Mounting(rubber)front	2	Use prior to CHA 565	
3	CHA 565	Mounting(rubber)front	2	(C)G-AN6-166304 ON	
4	NH 605041	Nut-mounting rubber to bracket	4		
5	WL 600051	Washer-locknut	4		
6	SH 605071	Screw-front mounting bracket to frame	6		
7	WA 108051	Washer-plain	6		
5	WL 600051	Washer-spring	6		
8	SH 606101	Screw-mounting rubber to engine-RH	1		
8	SH 606081	Screw-mounting rubber to engine-LH	1		
9	WC 110061	Washer-plain	2		
10	53K 1663	Nut	2		
11	CHA 266	Bracket-rear	1		
6	SH 605061	Screw-bracket to gearbox cover	2		
5	WL 600051	Washer-spring	2		
7	WA 108051	Washer-plain	2		
12	BH 606281	Bolt-support plate to crossmember	2		
13	WA 110061	Washer-plain	2		
14	WL 600061	Washer-spring	2		
15	122689	Mounting-engine-rear	2		Use CHA 615 in Pairs for this Application
15	CHA 615	Mounting-engine-rear	2	(C)G-AN6-176236 ON	
4	NH 605041	Nut-rear mounting	2		
7	WA 108051	Washer-plain	2		
5	WL 600051	Washer-lock	2		
16	CHA 483	Cable-engine restraint	1		USA and Canada.
17	CHA 487	Restraint-engine	1		
18	CHA 488	Rubber-engine restraint	2		
19	BH 605101	Bolt-restraint to gearbox	2		
7	WA 108051	Washer-plain	2		
5	WL 600051	Washer-spring	2		
4	NH 605041	Nut	2		
20	UKC 5254	Bar-tie-RH front	1		USA and Canada
21	SH 606061	Bolt-tie bar	1		USA and Canada
13	WA 110061	Washer-plain	1		USA and Canada
14	WL 600061	Washer-spring	1		USA and Canada

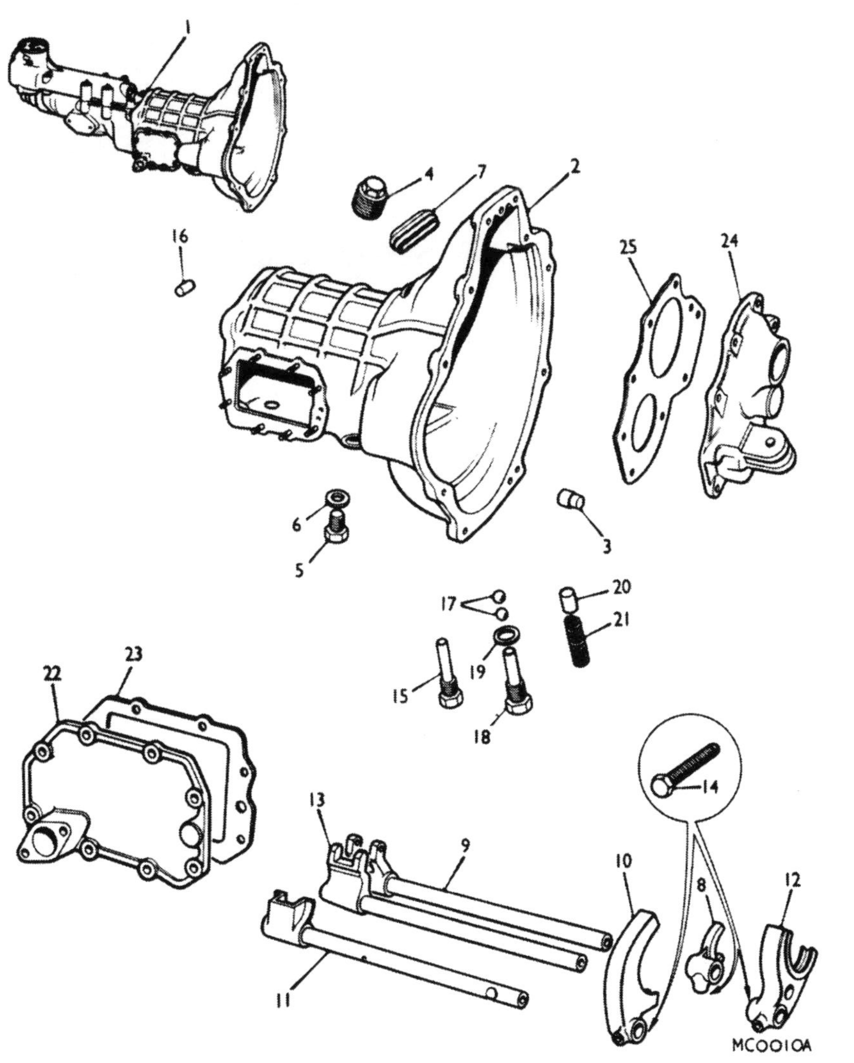

AUSTIN-HEALEY SPRITE MK. 3 AND MK. 4 & MG MIDGET MK. 2 AND MK. 3

GEARBOX-1098cc AND 1275cc.

NO.	PART NO.	DESCRIPTION	QTY	CHANGE POINT	REMARKS
1	38G 430 N	GEARBOX ASSEMBLY	1		Not USA and Canada
1	38G 430 N	GEARBOX ASSEMBLY	1	Use prior to 38G 514 N	USA and CANADA
1	38G 514 N	GEARBOX ASSEMBLY	1	(E)12V/587Z/L7591 TO(+) (E)12V/671Z/101 ON	USA and CANADA
2	38G 313	CASE ASSEMBLY	1		
3	1G 752	Dowel	1		
4	2K 5830	Plug-filler and drain	2		
5	6K 643	Plug-reverse plunger spring	1		
6	2K 4956	Washer-plug	1		
7	22G 199	Cover-dust-bell housing	1		
8	2A 3284	Fork-reverse	1		
9	22A 468	Rod-reverse fork	1		
10	22A 469	Fork-1st and 2nd speed	1		
11	22A 470	Rod-1st and 2nd speed fork	1		
12	22A 471	Fork-3rd and 4th speed	1		
13	22A 472	Rod-3rd and 4th speed fork	1		
14	2A 3492	Screw-locating fork	1		
	FNN 604	Nut	3		
	LWN 404	Washer-shakeproof	3		
15	2A 3028	Screw-locating-reverse shaft	1		
	LWN 204	Washer-spring	1		
16	2A 3110	Plunger-interlock	1		
17	BLS 110	Ball-interlock	1		
18	2A 3253	Plug-interlock ball hole	1		
19	2K 4956	Washer-plain	1		
20	2A 3108	Plunger-fork rod	3		
21	22G 327	Spring-plunger	3		
22	88G 214	Cover-side	1		
23	2A 3286	Gasket	1		
	LWZ 304	Washer-spring	8		
	NH 604041	Nut	8		
24	22G 118	Cover-front	1		
25	22G 165	Gasket	1		
	FNZ 104	Nut	7		
	LWN 304	Washer-spring	7		
	53K 1435	Screw-cover to case	3		
	LWN 204	Washer-spring	3		

(+) Change point not available.

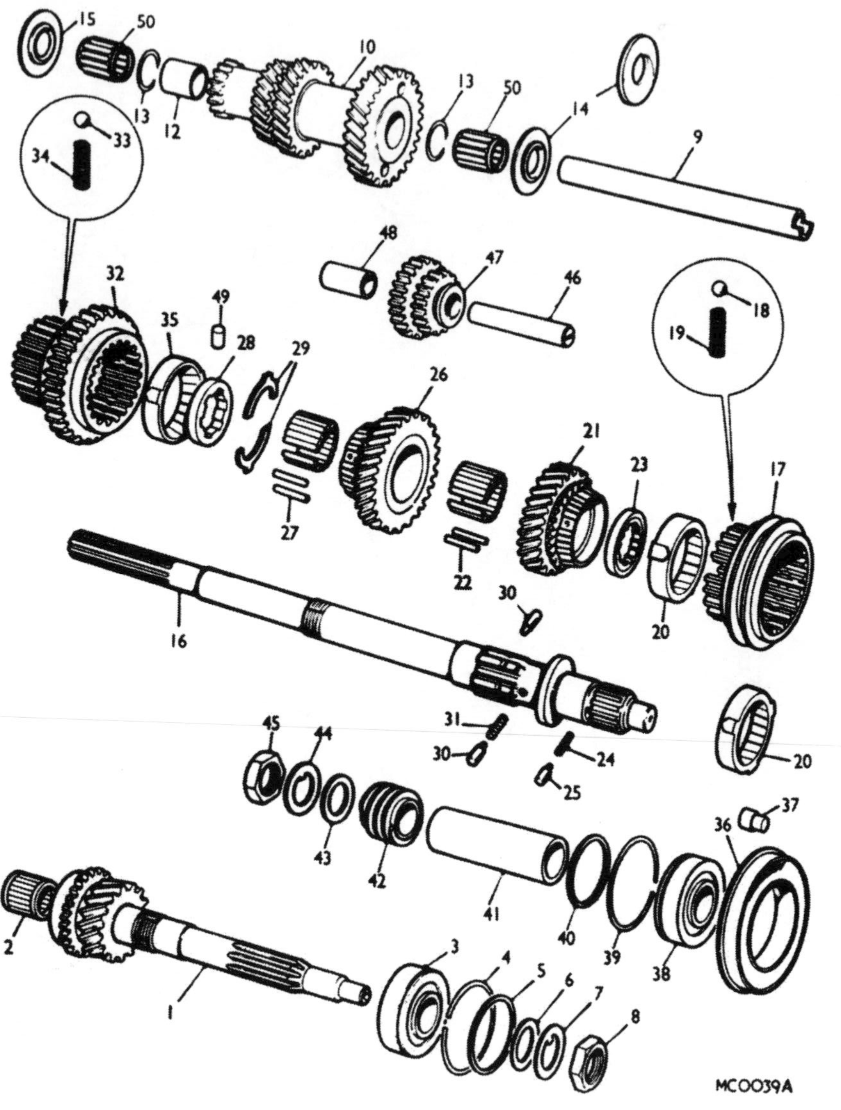

AUSTIN-HEALEY SPRITE MK. 3 AND MK. 4 & MG MIDGET MK. 2 AND MK. 3

GEARBOX-1098cc AND 1275cc-continued.

NO.	PART NO.	DESCRIPTION	QTY	CHANGE POINT	REMARKS
1	22G 172	Shaft-1st motion	1	See(1)foot of page	1098cc
1	22G 229	Shaft-1st motion	1	See(2)foot of page	1098cc and 1275cc
2	88G 409	Bearing-3rd motion shaft	1		
3	2A 3245	Bearing-ball-1st motion shaft	1		
4	6K 558	Ring-spring-bearing	1		
		WASHER-PACKING			
5	2K 8737	.004"(.1016mm)	A/R		
5	2K 8738	.006"(.1524mm)	A/R		
5	2K 8739	.010"(.254mm)	A/R		
7	2A 3035	Washer-lock	1		
8	2K 6677	Nut	1		
9	22G 673	Layshaft	1		
10	22G 76	Laygear	1	See(1)foot of page	1098cc
10	22G 1100	Laygear	1	See(2)foot of page	1098cc and 1275cc
50	88G 396	Bearing-needle roller	2		
12	22G 277	Piece-distance	1		
13	22G 278	Ring-spring	2		
		WASHER-THRUST			
14	2A 3024	Front	1		
15	2A 3024	Rear-.123" to .124"(3.12 to 3.14mm)	A/R		
15	2A 3025	Rear-.125" to .126"(3.17 to 3.20mm)	A/R		
15	2A 3026	Rear-.127" to .128"(3.33 to 3.25mm)	A/R		
15	2A 3027	Rear-.130" to .131"(3.30 to 3.32mm)	A/R		
16	22G 146	Shaft-3rd motion	1		
17	AEG 3009	SYNCHRONIZER ASSEMBLY-3RD AND 4TH SPEED	1		
18	BLS 107	Ball	1		
19	22A 367	Spring	3		
19	22G 317	Spring	3		
20	22G 220	Ring-baulk	2		

CHANGE POINTS:
(1):(E)10CC/Da/101 TO H4651 and L2355
(2):(E)10CC/Da/H4652 and L2356 ON.

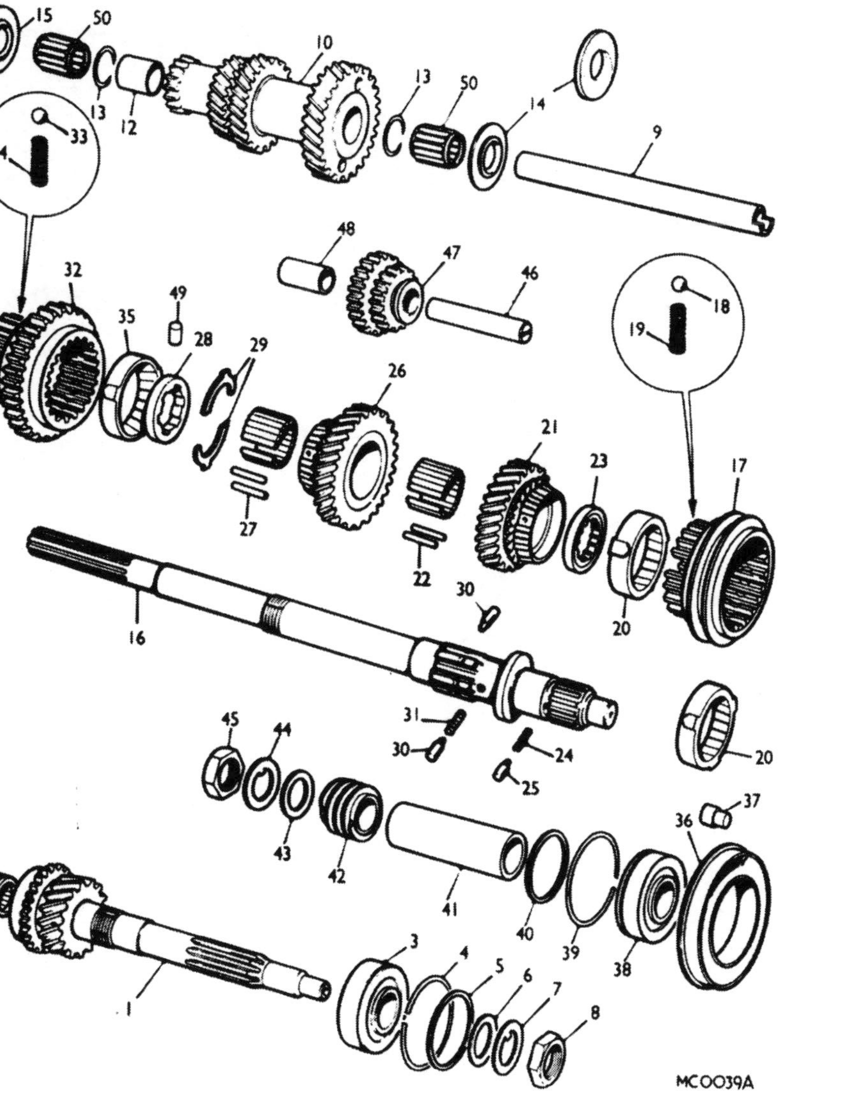

AUSTIN-HEALEY SPRITE MK. 3 AND MK. 4 & MG MIDGET MK. 2 AND MK. 3

GEARBOX-1098cc AND 1275cc-continued

NO.	PART NO.	DESCRIPTION	QTY	CHANGE POINT	REMARKS
21	22G 148	Gear-3rd speed	1	See(1)foot of page	1098cc
21	22G 1121	Gear-3rd speed	1	See(2)foot of page	1098cc and 1275cc
22	22G 149	Bearing-needle-roller	26		
23	22G 155	Collar-locking	1	See(1)foot of page	
23	22G 196	Collar-locking	1	See(2)foot of page	
25	22A 495	Peg	1		
24	22G 154	Spring	1		
26	22G 1120	Gear-2nd speed	1	See(2)foot of page	1098cc anD 1275cc
27	22G 149	Bearing-needle-roller	26		
28	22G 156	Collar-locking	1		
29	22G 157	Washer-locking collar	2		
30	22A 495	Peg-collar	2		
31	22G 154	Spring	1		
32	22G 257	1ST SPEED WHEEL-2ND SPEED SYNCHRONIZER ASSEMBLY	1	See(1)foot of page	1098cc
32	22G 1118	1ST SPEED WHEEL-2ND SPEED SYNCHRONIZER ASSEMBLY	1	See(2)foot of page	1098cc and 1275cc
33	BLS 107	Ball	3		
34	22A 367	Spring	2	See(1)foot of page	1098cc
34	22G 317	Spring	3	See(2)foot of page	1098cc and 1275CC
49	22G 89	Plunger	1		
35	22G 220	Ring-baulk	1		
36	22A 463	HOUSING ASSEMBLY-BEARING	1		
37	1G 3530	Peg-locating	1		
38	22A 465	Bearing-ball-3rd motion shaft	1		
39	6K 558	Ring-spring	1		
		WASHER-PACKING			
40	2K 8737	.004"(.1016mm)	A/R		
40	2K 8738	.006"(.1524mm)	A/R		
40	2K 8739	.010"(.254mm)	A/R		
41	22A 466	Piece-distance-3rd motion shaft	1		
42	2A 3371	Wheel-speedometer	1		
44	2A 3035	Washer-lock	1		
45	2K 6677	Nut	1		
46	88G 216	Shaft-reverse	1		
47	22A 453	WHEEL ASSEMBLY-REVERSE	1	See(1)foot of page	1098cc
47	22G 1114	WHEEL ASSEMBLY-REVERSE	1	See(2)foot of page	1098cc and 1275cc
48	2A 3282	Bush	1		

(+) Change point not available

CHANGE POINTS
(1) (E)10CC/Da/101 TO H4651 AND L2355 (2) (E)10CC/D9/H4652 AND L2356 TO (+)

AUSTIN-HEALEY SPRITE MK. 3 AND MK. 4 & MG MIDGET MK. 2 AND MK. 3

MCOO11C

GEARBOX-1098cc AND 1275cc-continued.

NO.	PART NO.	DESCRIPTION	QTY	CHANGE POINT	REMARKS
1	22A 474	EXTENSION ASSEMBLY-GEARBOX (WITH BUSH AND SEAL)	1		
2	2A 3325	Bush	1		
3	2A 3061	Seal-oil	1		
4	53K 528	Stud-remote control housing-short	NLA		
5	53K 535	Stud-remote control housing-long	6		
6	22A 475	Shaft-control	1		
7	22A 476	Lever-control	1		
8	1H 3101	Peg-lever locating	1		
	LWZ 304	Washer-spring-locating peg	1		
9	2A 3420	Pinion-speedometer	1		
10	22A 71	Bush-pinion	1		
11	2A 3385	Lever-selector-front	1		
12	2A 3468	Bush-selector	1		
	HBN 408	Screw	1		
	LWZ 204	Washer-spring-selector lever	1		
14	22A 480	Casing-remote control	1	See(1)foot of page	1098CC AND 1275cc
14	22G 671	Casing-remote control	1	See(2)foot of page	1275CC Not USA and Canada
14	22G 671	Casing-remote control	1	Use prior to 22G 2045	1275cc USA and Canada
14	22G 2045	Casing-remote control	1	(E)12V/587Z/L7591 TO(+) (E)12V/671Z/101 ON	
15	2A 3344	Gasket-casing to extension-front	1		
16	2A 3345	Gasket-casing to extension-rear	1		
17	2A 3388	Lever-selector-rear	1		
18	2A 3335	Screw	1		
	WL 600051	Washer-spring-screw-selector lever rear	1		
19	2A 3375	Shaft-remote control	1		Not USA and Canada
19	2A 3375	Shaft-remote control	1	Use prior to 22G 2046	USA and Canada
19	22G 2046	Shaft-remote control	1	(E)12V/587Z/L7591 TO(+) (E)12V/671Z/101 ON	
20	WKN 404	Key	2		
21	2K 8158	Plug-welch-remote control housing	2		
22	1G 3707	Plunger-reverse selector	1	See(1)foot of page	1098CC AND 1275CC
23	1G 3863	Spring	1		
22	22G 668	Plunger-reverse selector	1	See(2)foot of page	1275CC
23	22G 669	Spring-plunger	NLA		
24	2A 3378	Pin-locating-plunger	1	(+) Change point not available	
25	2A 3340	Cover-change speed tower-bottom	1		
26	2A 3341	Gasket	1		
	HZS 404	Screw-change speed tower	4		
	LWZ 204	Washer-spring	4		

CHANGE POINTS (1) (E)10CC/Da/101 TO (+) (E)12CC/Da/H101 TO 12410
(2) (E)12CC/Da/H12411 TO (+) (E)12CD/Da/H101 TO (+) (E)12CE/Da/H101 TO (+)
(E)12CJ/Da/H21201 TO (+) (E)12V/-/101 ON

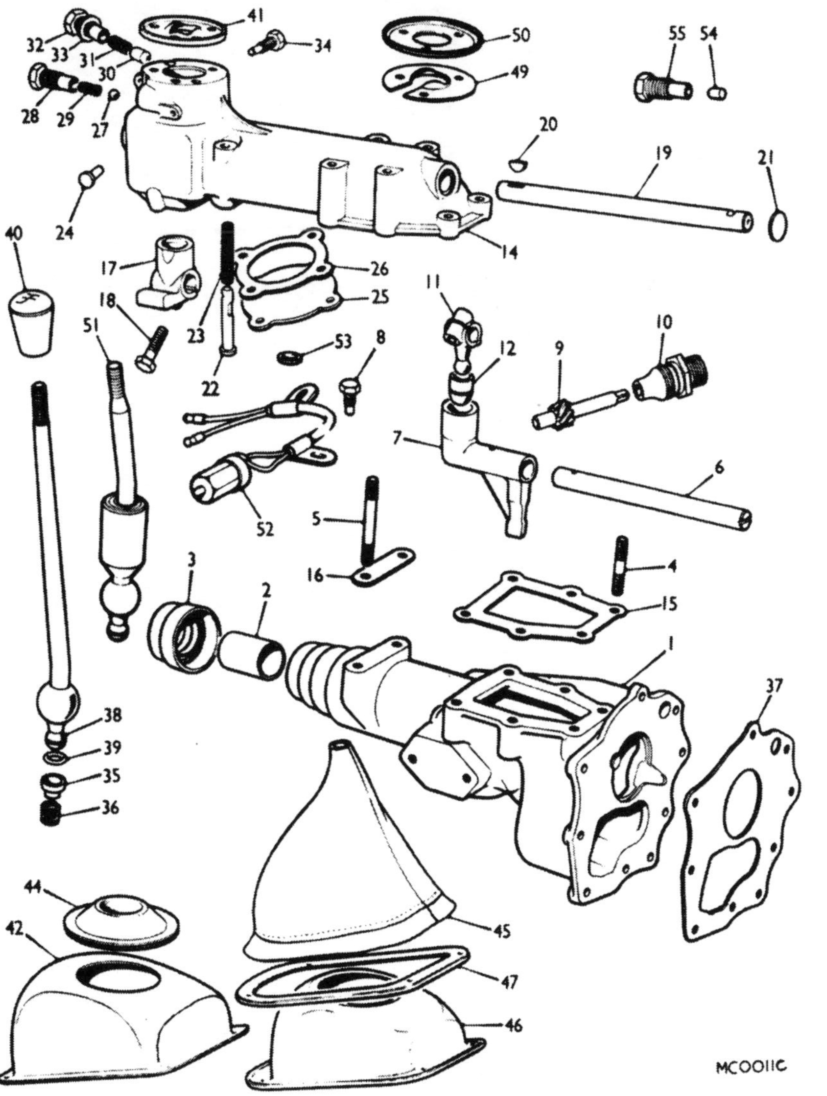

AUSTIN-HEALEY SPRITE MK. 3 AND MK. 4 & MG MIDGET MK. 2 AND MK. 3

GEARBOX-1098cc AND 1275cc-continued.

NO.	PART NO.	DESCRIPTION	QTY	CHANGE POINT	REMARKS
	NH 605041	Nut-stud-casing to extension	8		
	LWZ 305	Washer-spring	8		
27	BLS 110	Ball-reverse selector plunger	1		
54	22B 614	Plunger-reverse detent	1		Use together
55	22B 612	Plug-reverse detent	1		
29	22A 75	Spring	1		
30	22A 84	Plunger-control shaft damper	2		
31	AEG 3123	Spring	2		
32	22A 85	Cap-spring retaining	2		
33	AEG 3122	Washer-plain	2		
34	1H 3101	Peg-change speed lever locating	1		
	LWZ 304	Washer-spring-peg locating	1		
	HZS 405	Screw-change speed seat	3		
	LWZ 304	Washer-spring	3		
35	2A 3467	Button-thrust	1		
36	2A 3390	Spring-button	1		
37	22A 481	Gasket-extension to gearbox	1		
	HZS 407	Screw-extension to gearbox	9		
	LWN 304	Washer-spring	9		

AUSTIN-HEALEY SPRITE MK. 3 AND MK. 4 & MG MIDGET MK. 2 AND MK. 3

MCOOIIC

GEARBOX-1098cc AND 1275cc-continued.

NO.	PART NO.	DESCRIPTION	QTY	CHANGE POINT	REMARKS
38	22G 328	Lever-change speed	NLA	Use prior to 22G 1397	
39	TRS 710	Ring-lever(rubber)	1		
40	22G 110	Knob-lever $	1	Use prior to 22G 1860	
40	22G 1860	Knob-lever $	1	(C)G-AN5-105501 ON	
41	2A 3339	Cover-change speed lever seat	1	Use prior to AHA 9488	
42	BLA 768	Cover-remote control	1	Use prior to AHA 9488	
	PTZ 803	Screw	4	Use prior to AHA 9488	
44	ACA 5208	Grommet-change speed lever	1	Use prior to AHA 9488	
51	22G 1397	Lever-change speed	1	See(1)foot of page	
45	AHA 9488	Gaiter-gear lever	1	(C)H-AN10-85287 TO 86803 (C)A-AN10-86804 TO 87824 (C)G-AN5-74886 TO 123730	
45	CHA 69	Gaiter-gear lever	1	(C)G-AN5-123731 ON	
46	AHA 9486	Support-gaiter and turret seal	1	(C)H-AN10-85287 TO 86374 (C)G-AN5-74886 TO 90762	
46	AHA 9722	Support-gaiter and turret seal	1	(C)H-AN10-86375 TO 86803 (C)A-AN10-86804 TO 87824 (C)G-AN5-90763 ON	
47	AHA 9487	Retainer-gaiter support	1	See(1)foot of page	
	PTZ 805	Screw-retainer	4	See(1)foot of page	
50	22G 1518	Plate-retaining gaiter support	1	See(1)foot of page	
	HBZ 511	Bolt-gearbox to mounting plate	8/6		Quantity reduced at(C)G-AN5-146369.USA and Canada only
	HBZ 512	Bolt-gearbox to mounting plate	2	(C)G-AN5-146370 ON	USA and Canada only
	LWN 305	Washer-spring	8		
	NH 605041	Nut	3		
52	13H 4216	SWITCH ASSEMBLY-REVERSE LIGHT	1		1275cc engine
	PCR 409	Clip	1		
53	3H 693	Washer(copper)	A/R		
	ZCS 804	Screw-blanking	1		Use when reverse LIGHT SWITCH IS not fitted
53	3H 693	Washer-screw	1		Use when reverse LIGHT SWITCH IS not fitted

$ This item is subject to safety regulations.

CHANGE POINTS.
(1):(C)H-AN10-85287 TO 86803.(C)A-AN10-86804 TO 87824.(C)G-AN5-74886 ON.

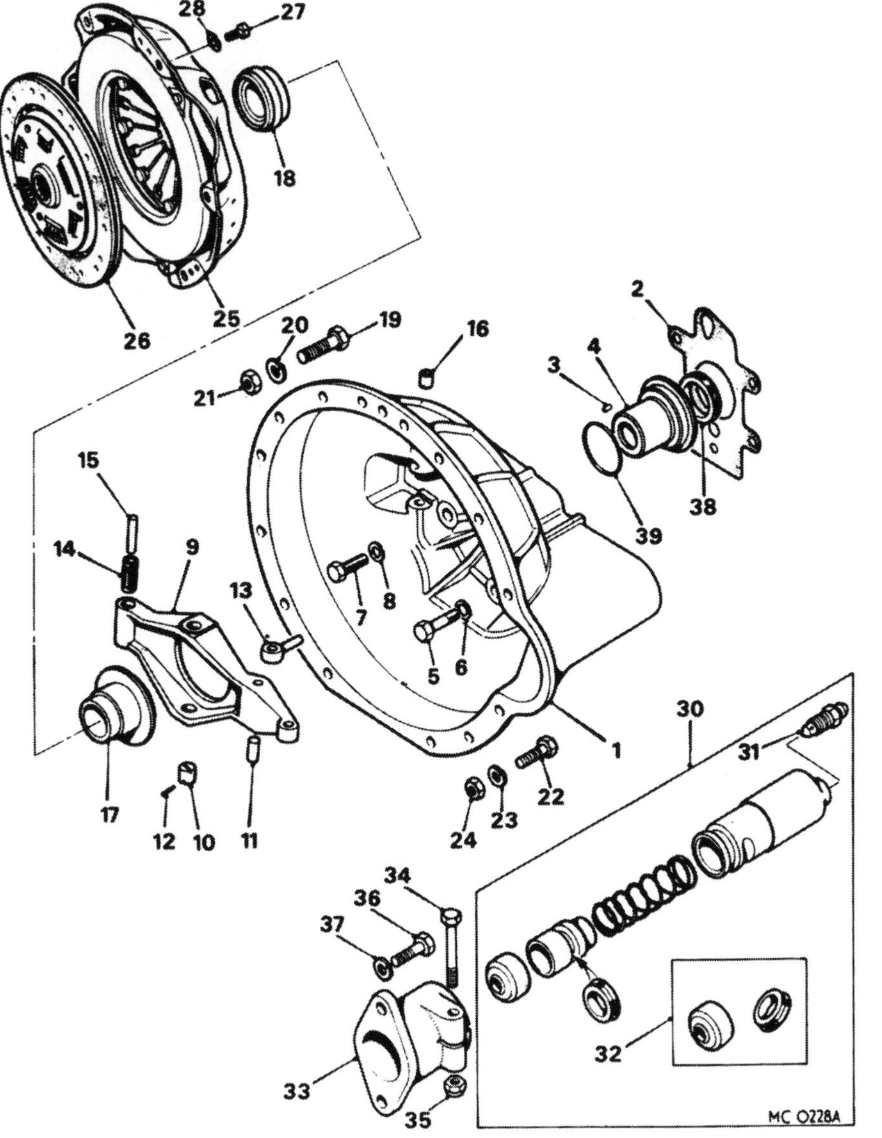

AUSTIN-HEALEY SPRITE MK. 3 AND MK. 4 & MG MIDGET MK. 2 AND MK. 3

NO.	PART NO.	DESCRIPTION	QTY	CHANGE POINT	REMARKS
		1500cc-GEARBOX ASSEMBLY-CLUTCH HOUSING AND LEVER-SELECTOR MECHANISM			
1	312151	Housing-clutch	1		
2	157690	Gasket	1		
3	DP 205	Dowel	1		
4	122566	Cover-front	1		
38	22G 2028	Seal-oil	1		
39	22G 1944	'O'ring	1		
5	156336	Bolt	1		
6	500464	Washer(copper)	1		
7	HU 909	Bolt	4		
8	WL 600061	Washer-spring	4		
9	207887	Lever-clutch operating	1		
10	112509	Plug-thrust	1		
11	112516	Pin	1		
12	DS 914	Dowel	2		
13	22B 65	Push-rod	1		
14	129412	Ring-tolerance	1		
15	129410	Pin	1		
16	129358	Bush	2		
17	139563	Sleeve	1		
18	GRB 207	Bearing-clutch release	1		
19	BH 605101	Bolt-clutch housing to engine	7		
19	BH 605111	Bolt-clutch housing to engine	1		
20	WL 600051	Washer-spring	11		
21	NH 605041	Nut	11		
22	132872	Bolt-dowel	1		
23	WL 600061	Washer	1		
24	NH 506041	Nut	1		
25	GCC 196	Cover-clutch	1		
26	GCP 230	Plate-clutch driven	1		
27	146176	Bolt-clutch to flywheel	6		
28	LWN 305	Washer	6		
30	DAM 73	Cylinder-clutch operating	1		
31	3H 554	Screw-bleeder	1		
32	BHM 7055	Kit-repair	1		
33	206175	Boss-operating cylinder	1		
34	HBZ 518	Bolt-cylinder retaining	1		
35	LNZ 205	Nut-bolt	1		
36	HNS 507	Screw-boss to housing	2		
37	WL 600051	Washer-spring	2		

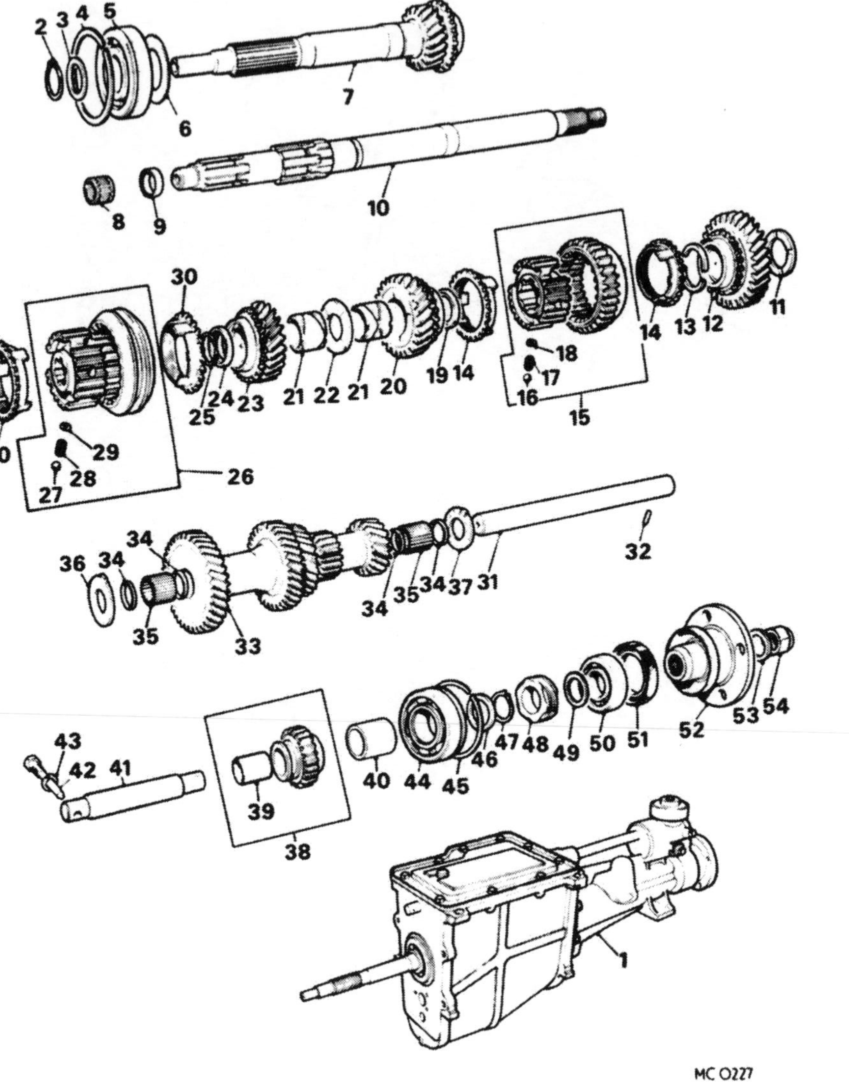

AUSTIN-HEALEY SPRITE MK. 3 AND MK. 4 & MG MIDGET MK. 2 AND MK. 3

NO.	PART NO.	DESCRIPTION	QTY	CHANGE POINT	REMARKS
		1500cc GEARBOX ASSEMBLY-CLUTCH HOUSING AND LEVER-SELECTOR MECHANISM-continued			
1	BHM 5003 N	GEARBOX ASSEMBLY	1		
2	CCN 116	Circlip	1		
3	22G 1869	Washer-packing	1		
4	112654	Ring-snap	1		
5	104433	Bearing-ball	1		
6	106365	Flinger-oil	1		
7	DAM 1005	Shaft-1st motion	1		
8	13H 9513	Bearing-needle roller	1		
9	DAM 739	Spacer-mainshaft	1		
11	22G 2210	Washer-1st speed gear	1		
10	DAM 738	Mainshaft	1		
12	22G 1641	Gear-1st speed	1		
13	137834	Collar	1PR		
14	150328	Cup-synchronizer	2		
15	22G 1975	SYNCHRONIZER ASSEMBLY-1ST AND 2ND SPEED	1		
16	BLS 108	Ball	3		
17	106388	Spring	3		
18	37948	Shim	A/R		
19	106262	Washer-2nd speed gear	1		
20	22G 1816	Gear-2nd speed	1		
21	147354	Bush-2nd and 3rd speed gear	2		
		WASHER-THRUST 2ND AND 3RD SPEED GEAR			
22	111422	3.86-3.9mm(.152-.154")	A/R		
22	149963	3.97-4.02mm(.156-.158")	A/R		
22	131843	4.07-4.13mm(.161-.163")	A/R		
22	156084	4.18-4.23mm(.165-.167")	A/R		
22	UKC 769	4.28-4.33mm(.169-.171")	A/R		

MC O227

AUSTIN-HEALEY SPRITE MK. 3 AND MK. 4 & MG MIDGET MK. 2 AND MK. 3

NO.	PART NO.	DESCRIPTION	QTY	CHANGE POINT	REMARKS
		1500cc GEAR BOX ASSEMBLY-CLUTCH HOUSING AND LEVER-SELECTOR MECHANISM-continued			
23	22G 1643	Gear-3rd speed	1		
24	159978	Washer-3rd speed gear	1		
25	112394	Circlip	1		
26	22G 1976	SYNCHRONIZER ASSEMBLY-3RD AND 4TH SPEED	1		
27	BLS 108	Ball	3		
28	104445	Spring	3		
29	37948	Shim	A/R		
30	150328	Cup-synchronizer	2		
31	144595	Layshaft	1		
32	DS 1908	Dowel	1		
33	22G 1818	Laygear	1		
34	119891	Ring-retaining	4		
35	119893	Needle-roller	50		
36	113229	Washer-thrust-front	1		
37	106270	Washer-thrust-rear	1		
	137532	Spring-laygear	1		
38	144580	GEAR-REVERSE-IDLER	1		
39	129862	Bush	1		
40	22G 1435	Piece-distance	1		
41	113071	Spindle-reverse idler	1		
42	106477	Screw-locating	1		
43	WL 600051	Washer-spring	1		
44	104433	Bearing-ball-centre	1		
45	112654	Ring-snap	1		
		WASHER-BEARING AND CIRCLIP			
46	155805	3.02-3.07mm(.119-.121")	A/R		Natural colour
46	155806	3.10-3.15mm(.122-.124")	A/R		Green
46	155807	3.18-3.23mm(.125-.127")	A/R		Blue
46	155808	3.25-3.30mm(.128-.130")	A/R		Orange
47	CCN 116	Circlip	1		
48	22G 1752	Wheel-speedometer(6 teeth)	1		
49	155756	Washer-rear bearing	1		
50	157732	Bearing-ball-rear	1		
51	22G 2353	Seal-oil-gearbox rear extension	1		
52	155755	Flange	1		
53	WA 116101	Washer-plain	1		
54	510618	Nut	1		

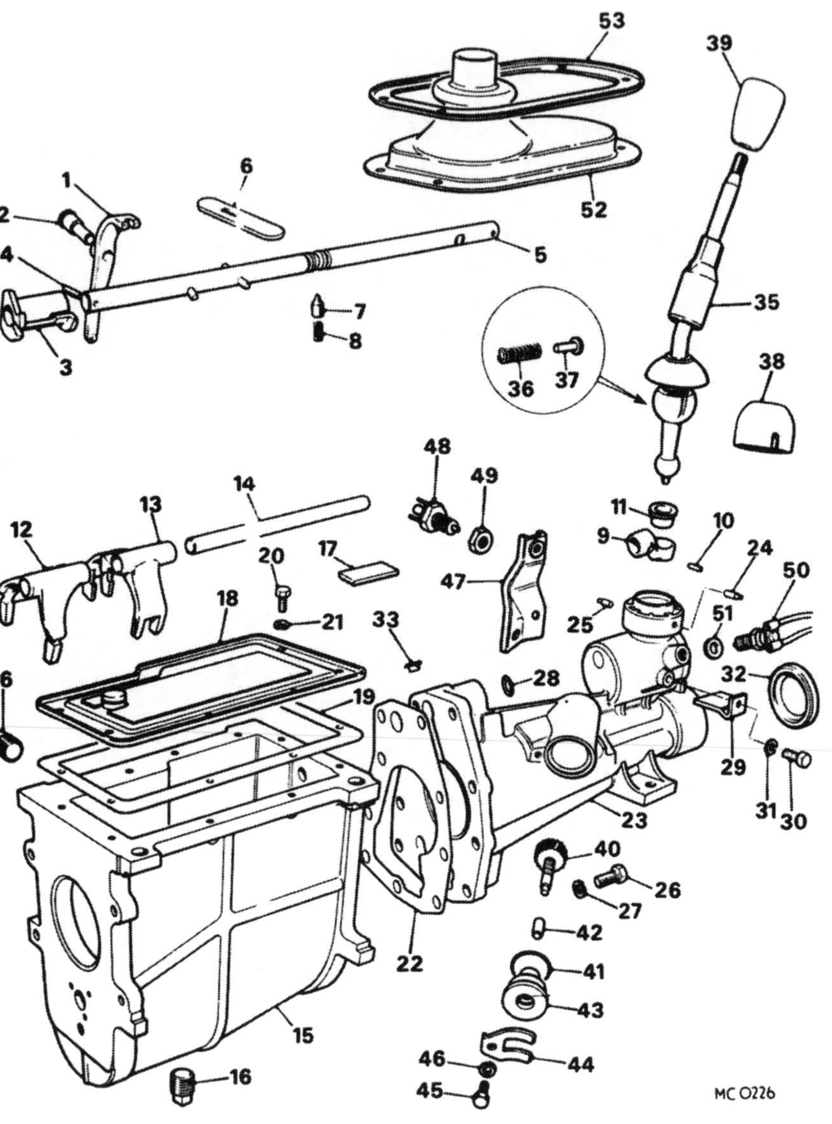

AUSTIN-HEALEY SPRITE MK. 3 AND MK. 4 & MG MIDGET MK. 2 AND MK. 3

1500cc GEARBOX ASSEMBLY-CLUTCH HOUSING AND LEVER-SELECTOR MECHANISM-continued

NO.	PART NO.	DESCRIPTION	QTY	CHANGE POINT	REMARKS
1	88G 582	Lever-reverse operating	1	(G)101 TO 5331	
2	22G 1412	Pin-pivot-lever	1	(G)101 TO 5331	
1	CHM 63	Lever-reverse operating	1	(G)5332 ON	See Technical Bulletin No.8
2	DAM 1714	Pin-pivot-lever	1	(G)5332 ON	See Technical Bulletin No.8
3	22G 1418	Spool-interlock	1		
4	RPS 1012	Pin-spool to shaft	1		
5	22G 2053	Shaft-gear selector	1		
6	22G 1419	Plate-interlock spool	1		
7	22G 1421	Plunger-detent	1		
8	22G 2198	Spring-plunger	1		
9	22G 2291	Yoke-gear lever	1		
10	RZS 1216	Pin-yoke to shaft	1		
11	22G 1424	Seat-gear lever	1		
12	22G 1584	Fork-3rd and 4th speed	1		
13	22G 1406	Fork-1st and 2nd speed	1		
14	22G 1408	Shaft-selector forks	1		
15	22G 1553	Case-gearbox	1		
16	114774	Plug-oil filler and drain	2		
17	153408	Magnet	1		
18	22G 1884	Cover-gearbox	1		
19	22G 1911	Gasket	2		
20	SH 604041	Screw	9		
21	WL 600041	Washer-spring	9		
22	22G 1420	Gasket-gearbox to extension	1		
23	DAM 1650	EXTENSION-GEARBOX	1		
24	22G 2276	Pin-long	1		
25	22G 2277	Pin-short	1		
26	SH 605081	Screw-extension to gearbox	8		
27	WL 600051	Washer-spring	8		
28	TRS 912	'O'ring-selector shaft	1		
29	22G 1425	Plate-reverse lift	1		
30	SH 604061	Screw	1		
31	WL 600041	Washer-spring	1		
32	22G 1422	Cover-end	1		
33	22G 1947	Plug-extension	1		

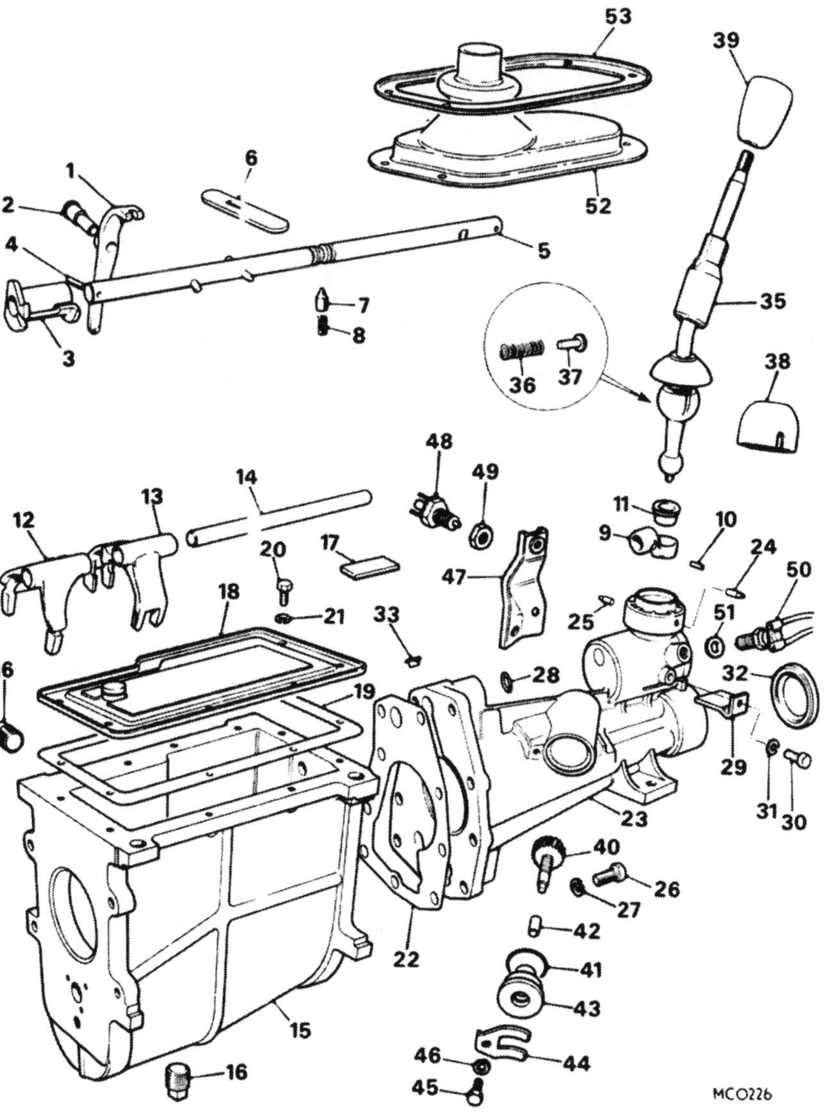

AUSTIN-HEALEY SPRITE MK. 3 AND MK. 4 & MG MIDGET MK. 2 AND MK. 3

1500cc GEARBOX ASSEMBLY-CLUTCH HOUSING AND LEVER-SELECTOR MECHANISM-continued

NO.	PART NO.	DESCRIPTION	QTY	CHANGE POINT	REMARKS
35	22G 2797	Lever-change speed	1		
37	22G 2286	Plunger-lever	1		
36	22G 2285	Spring-plunger	1		
38	22G 1434	Retainer-change speed lever	1		
39	22G 1755	Knob-change speed lever	1		
40	22G 2015	Pinion-speedometer(22 teeth)	1		
41	13H 2792	'O'ring	1		
42	22G 2202	Sleeve	1		
43	22G 1486	Bearing	1		
	CHM 1	Seal-oil	1		
44	22G 1711	Plate-retaining	1		
45	SH 604041	Screw	1		
46	WL 600041	Washer-spring	1		
47	22G 2052	Bracket-seat belt inhibitor switch	1	(C)G-AN6-154101 TO 159053	USA and Canada
48	22G 2047	Switch-inhibitor(seat belt)	1	(C)G-AN6-154101 TO 159053	USA and Canada
49	42H 1340	Locknut-switch	1	(C)G-AN6-154101 TO 159053	USA and Canada
50	13H 6084	Switch-reverse light	1		
51	WA 110061	Washer-switch	1		
52	CHA 431	Seal-change speed lever	1		
	CHA 466	Gaiter-lever	1		
53	AHA 9487	Retainer	1		
	PTZ 806	Screw	3		
	PTZ 805	Screw	1		
	DAM 518	Gaiter-gear selector shaft	1		Canada
	DAM 671	Clip-spring-rear	1		Canada
	DAM 1723	Clip-spring-front	1		Canada

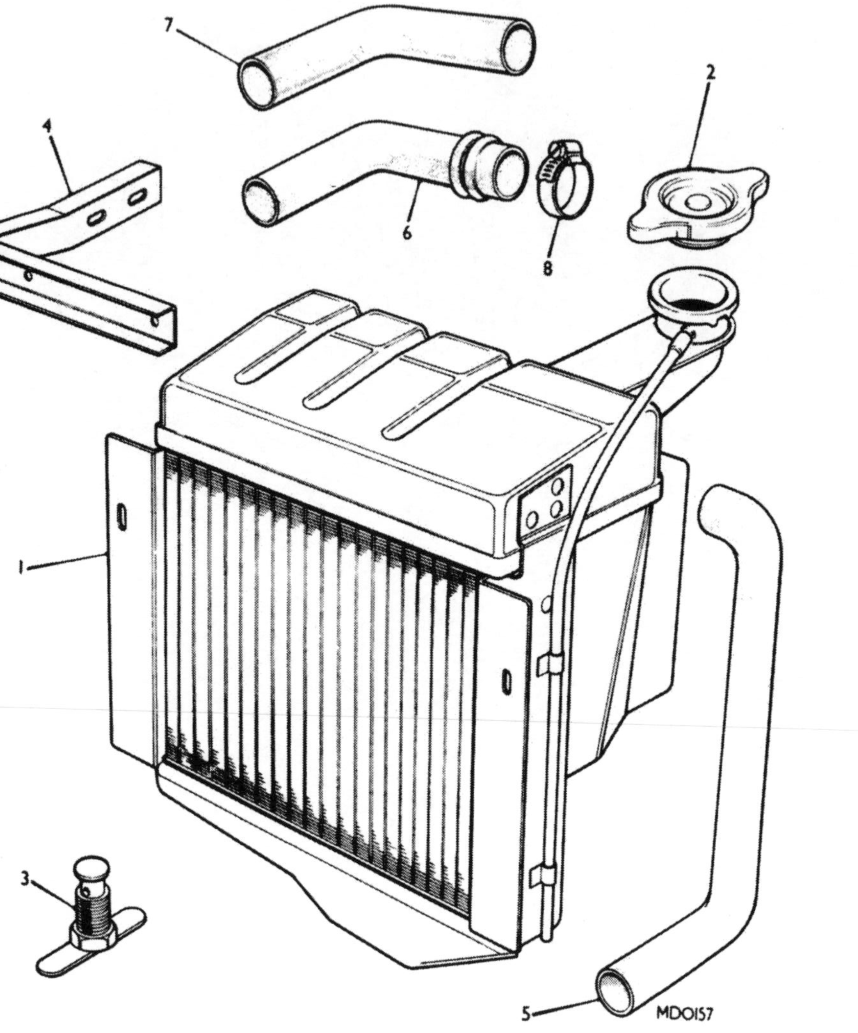

AUSTIN-HEALEY SPRITE MK. 3 AND MK. 4 & MG MIDGET MK. 2 AND MK. 3

NO.	PART NO.	DESCRIPTION	QTY	CHANGE POINT	REMARKS
		RADIATOR-VERTICAL FLOW-AND FITTINGS			
1	ARA 241	Radiator	1		Use prior to cross-flow radiator
2	GRC 101	Cap-filler	1		
3	88G 291	Tap-drain	1		
4	2A 5591	Bracket-radiator mounting-RH	1		
	2A 5592	Bracket-radiator mounting-LH	1		
	SH 604061	Screw-radiator to bracket	4		
	PWZ 104	Washer-plain	4		
	LWZ 304	Washer-spring	4		
	HZS 405	Screw-bracket to wheelarch	4		
	PWZ 204	Washer-plain	4		
	LWZ 204	Washer-spring	4		
5	AHA 8728	Hose-radiator to water pump	NLA	Use prior to AHA 8750 and GRH 508	Use when heater IS NOT FITTED.
5	GRH 315	Hose-radiator to water pump	1		Use with heater
5	AHA 8750	Hose-radiator to water pump	NLA	(E)12CE/Da/H874 TO(+)	Use when heater IS NOT Fitted.
5	GRH 508	Hose-radiator to water pump	1		Use with heater
6	GRH 313	Hose-radiator to outlet hose	1		1098CC
7	AHA 8726	Hose-radiator to outlet hose	1		1275CC
8	GHC 913	Clip-hose	A/R		
8	GHC 1217	Clip-hose	1		

(+) Change point not available.

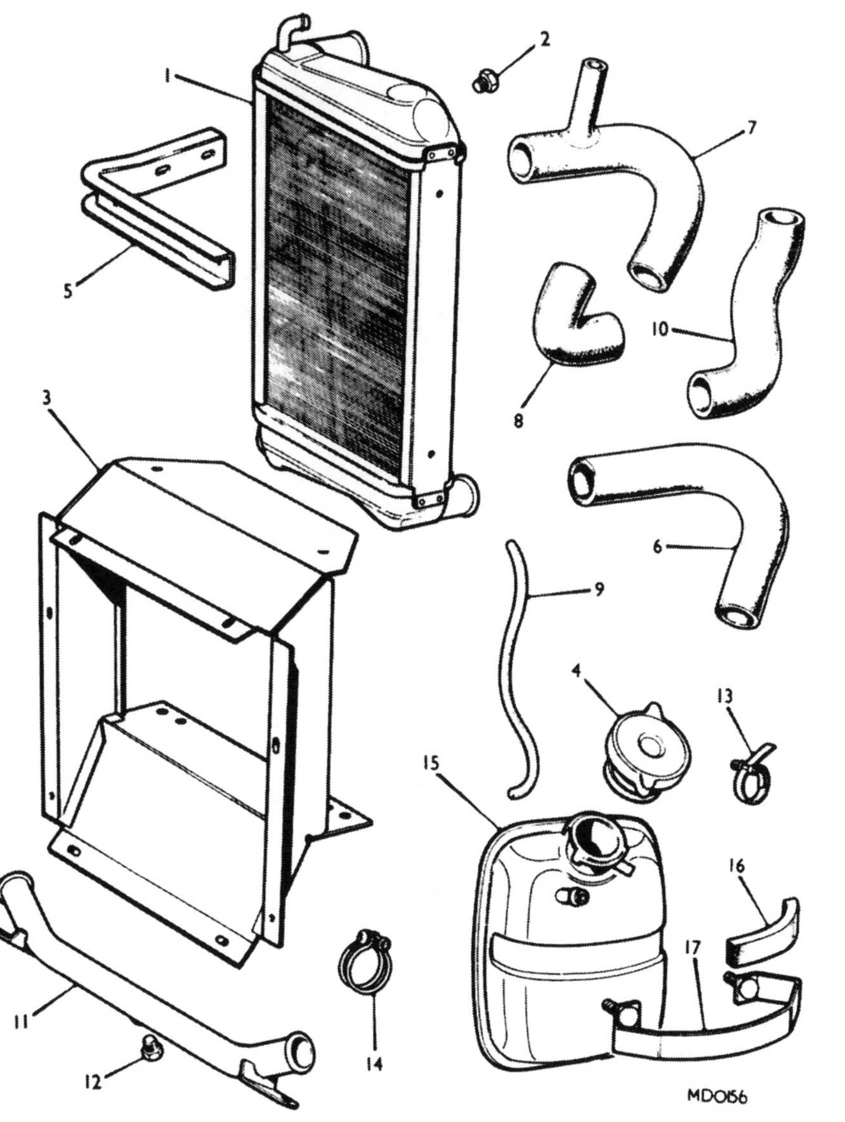

AUSTIN-HEALEY SPRITE MK. 3 AND MK. 4 & MG MIDGET MK. 2 AND MK. 3

RADIATOR-CROSS-FLOW AND FITTINGS-EXCEPT 1500

NO.	PART NO.	DESCRIPTION	QTY	CHANGE POINT	REMARKS
1	ARA 318	RADIATOR ASSEMBLY	1		
2	ARA 2404	Plug-filler	1		
3	AHA 8732	Cowl-radiator	1		
	HZS 504	Screw	4		
	LWZ 205	Washer	4		
	PMZ 308	Screw	4		
	PWZ 203	Washer-plain	4		
	LWZ 203	Washer-spring	4		
	HBZ 406	Screw	4		
	LWZ 204	Washer-spring	4		
	PWZ 104	Washer-plain	4		
4	GRC 110	Cap-filler	1		
5	2A 5591	Bracket-radiator mounting-RH	1		
	2A 5592	Bracket-radiator mounting-LH	1		
	SH 604061	Screw-radiator to bracket	2		
	PWZ 104	Washer-plain	2		
	LWZ 304	Washer-spring	2		
	HZS 405	Screw	4		
	PWZ 204	Washer-spring	4		
	LWZ 204	Washer-plain	4		
7	AHA 8742	Hose-radiator to water pump	1	Use prior to AHA 8749	
7	GRH 510	Hose-radiator to water pump	1	(E)12CD/-/H1745 TO(+) (E)12CE/-/(+)TO(+) (E)12CJ/Da/H21201 TO(+) (E)12V/-/101 ON	Was AHA 8749 Use when heater is fitted.
8	AHA 8730	Hose-radiator to lower tube	1		
9	GRH 1002 M	Hose-radiator to expansion tank 8"(21cm)	A/R		Supplied in 6 metre(19'8") lengths Was AHA 8738
10	GRH 509	Hose-radiator top	1		
11	AHA 8731	Tube-lower-radiator	1		
12	ARA 1618	Plug-drain	1		
13	21K 8341	Clip-hose-expansion tank to radiator	2		
14	GHC 709	Clip-hose-lower tube	1		
14	HCS 122	Clip-hose-water pump to radiator	A/R		
14	GHC 1217	Clip-hose-water pump to radiator	1		
15	ARH 250	Tank-expansion	1		
16	ACA 9872	Pad(rubber)	2		
17	AHA 8739	Strap-expansion tank	1		
	WL 600051	Washer-spring	2		
	PWZ 105	Washer-plain	2		
	NH 605041	Nut	2		

(+) Change point not available.

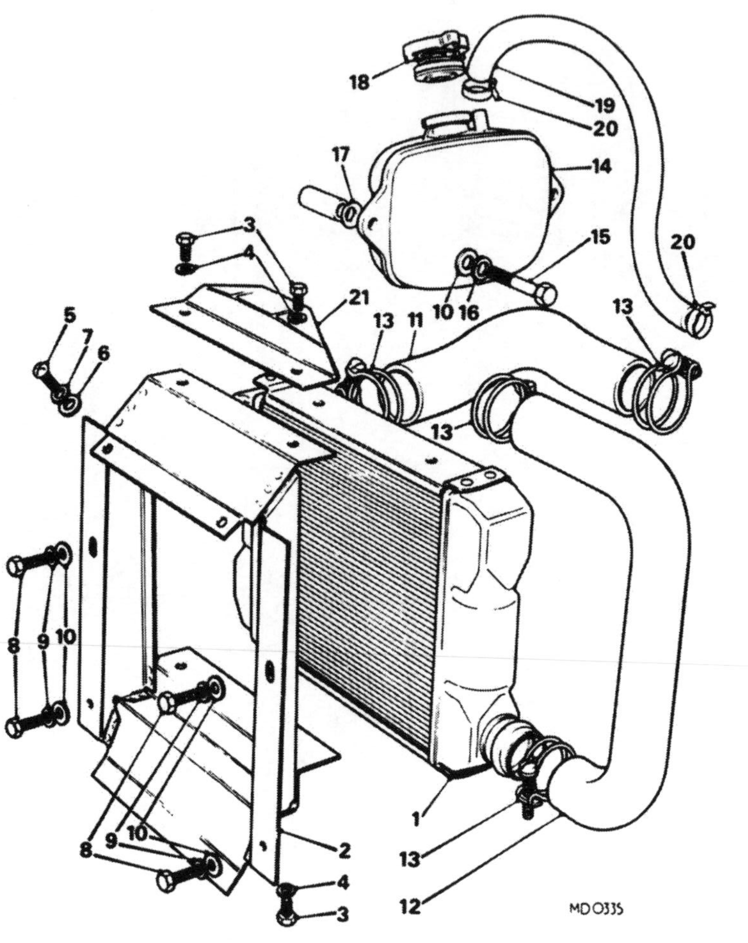

AUSTIN-HEALEY SPRITE MK. 3 AND MK. 4 & MG MIDGET MK. 2 AND MK. 3

RADIATOR-CROSS-FLOW AND FITTINGS-1500.

NO.	PART NO.	DESCRIPTION	QTY	CHANGE POINT	REMARKS
1	NRP 1028	Radiator	1		
2	CHA 281	Cowl-radiator	1		
3	SH 605041	Screw-radiator to cowl	4		
4	LWZ 205	Washer-spring	4		
5	PMZ 308	Screw-cowl fixing	2		
6	PWZ 203	Washer-plain	2		
7	WL 700100	Washer-spring	2		
8	SH 604061	Screw-cowl fixing	4		
9	WL 600401	Washer-spring	4		
10	WA 106041	Washer-plain	4	(C)G-AN6-154101 ON (EXCEPT USA and Canada) (C)G-AN6-154101 TO 166350 (USA and Canada ONLY)	
11	GRH 525	Hose-radiator-top	1		
12	GRH 534	Hose-radiator-lower	1		
13	GHC 1217	Clip-radiator hose	A/R		
14	ARA 326	Tank-expansion	1		
15	BH 604201	Bolt-expansion-tank fixing	2		
16	WL 600041	Washer-spring	2		
10	WA 106041	Washer-plain	2		
17	ACA 5374	Washer-countersunk	2		
18	GRC 110	Cap-filler	1		
19	GRH 1002 M	Hose-radiator to expansion tank 11"(279mm)long	A/R		Supplied in multiples of metres.
20	21K 8341	Clip-hose	2		
21	CHA 420	Guard-fan	1		

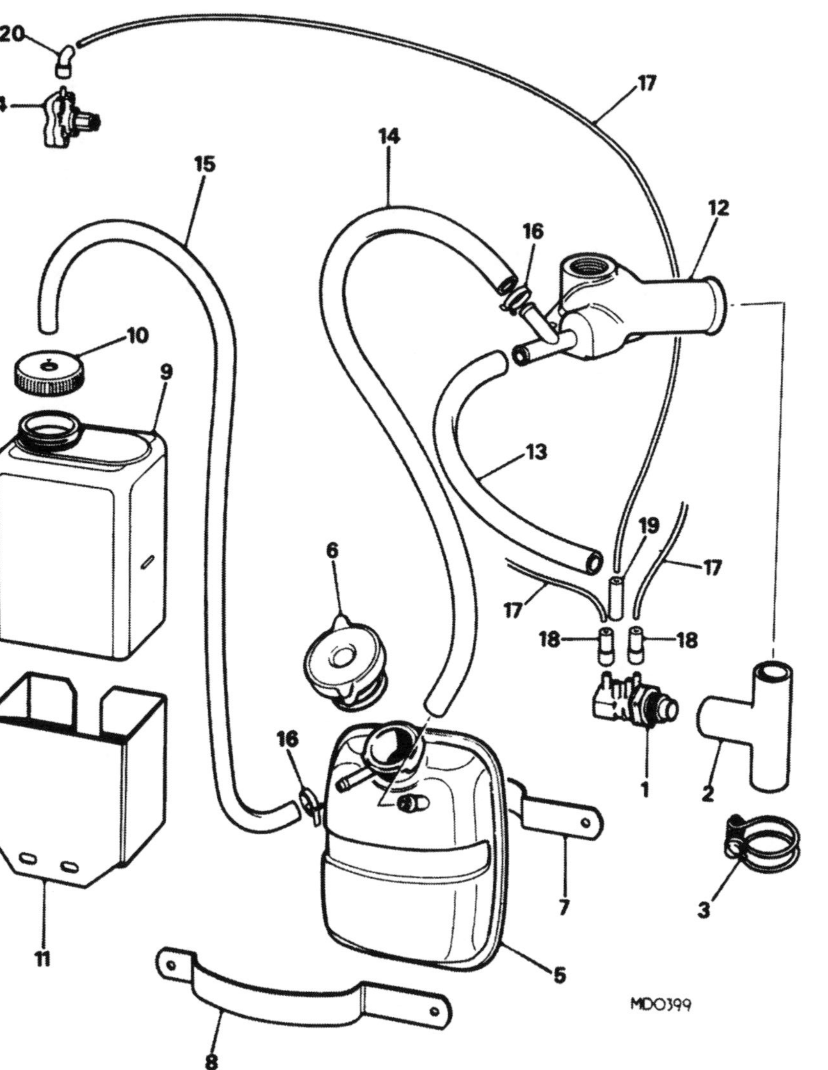

AUSTIN-HEALEY SPRITE MK. 3 AND MK. 4 & MG MIDGET MK. 2 AND MK. 3

RADIATOR-CROSS FLOW AND FITTINGS-1500-Continued.

NO.	PART NO.	DESCRIPTION	QTY	CHANGE POINT	REMARKS
		THE FOLLOWING PARTS REFER TO USA AND CANADA ONLY AND SHOULD BE USED IN ACCORDANCE WITH TSB 75-A-6.			
1	C 37430	Switch-thermo-vac	1		
2	158308	Adaptor 'T' piece	1		
3	CA 600254	Clip-adaptor	2		
4	AAU 2346	Valve-vented-carburetter	1		
5	URP 1148	Tank-expansion	1		
6	URP 1145	Cap-expansion tank	1		
7	CHA 590	Bracket-tank	1		Fitted in pairs.
8	CHA 591	Bracket-tank	1		
9	BHA 5239	Tank-spill	1		
10	CHA 582	Cap-spill tank	1		
11	CHA 585	Bracket	1		
12	CHA 595	Housing-thermostat	1	(C)G-AN6-154101 TO 166303 (USA and CANADA ONLY)	
		HOSE-WATER			
13	GRH 1002 M	Housing to radiator 11"long	1		
14	GRH 1002 M	Housing to expansion tank 23" long	1		
15	GRH 1001 M	Expansion tank to spill tank 23" long	1		
16	21K 8341	Clip-water hose	A/R		
		HOSE-VACUUM			
17	37H 4229 M	Thermo-vac to carburetter 44.5" long	1		
17	37H 4229 M	Thermo-vac to distributor 22" long	1		
17	37H 4229 M	Thermo-vac to vapour trap 40.5 long	1		
18	131211	Sleeve-straight	NLA		Use 12B 2095
18	12B 2095	Sleeve-straight	2		
19	117400	Sleeve-straight	1		
20	128262	Sleeve-right angle	1		
	AAU 2641	Gauge-temperature	1		

NOTE:-Part numbers listed with the suffix 'M'are supplied in mutiples of metres (39.37").

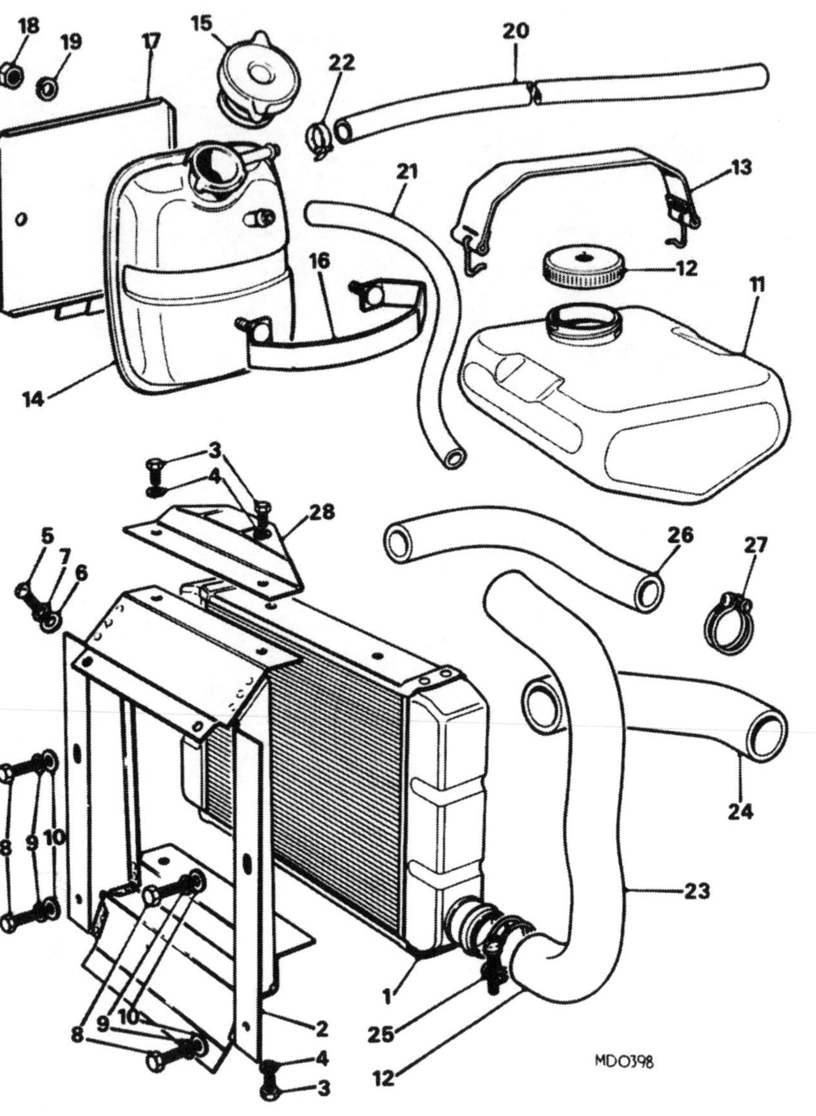

AUSTIN-HEALEY SPRITE MK. 3 AND MK. 4 & MG MIDGET MK. 2 AND MK. 3

RADIATOR-CROSS-FLOW AND FITTINGS-1500-continued.

NO.	PART NO.	DESCRIPTION	QTY	CHANGE POINT	REMARKS
1	NRP 1141	Radiator	1		
2	CHA 281	Cowl-radiator	1		
3	SH 605041	Screw-radiator to cowl	4		
4	LWZ 205	Washer-spring	4		
5	PMZ 308	Screw-cowl-top	2		
6	PWZ 203	Washer-plain	2		
7	WL 700100	Washer-spring	2		
8	SH 604061	Screw-cowl fixing	4		
9	WL 600040	Washer-spring	4		
10	WA 106041	Washer-plain	4		
11	CHA 434	Container-spill tank	1		
12	CHA 582	Cap-container	1		
13	CHA 458	Strap-container	1		
14	URP 1159	Tank-expansion	1	(C)G-AN6-166304 ON (USA and Canada ONLY)	
15	URP 1145	Cap-expansion tank	1		
16	AHA 8739	Clip-expansion tank to bracket	1		
17	CHA 609	Bracket-expansion tank	1		
18	NH 605041	Nut-bracket	2		
19	WL 600051	Washer-spring	2		
20	GRH 1001 M	Tube-overflow-23"long	1		
21	GRH 1002 M	Tube-housing to expansion tank 13"long	1		
22	21K 8341	CLIP-TUBE	A/R		
23	GRH 525	Hose-radiator-top	1		
24	CHA 603	Hose-radiator-lower	1		
25	GHC 1217	Clip-hoses	A/R		
26	CHA 616	Hose-outlet elbow to tank	1		
27	GHC 709	Clip-hose	2		
28	CHA 420	Guard-fan	1		

NOTE:
Part Nos.with the suffix letter'M'are supplied in multiples of metres(39.37").

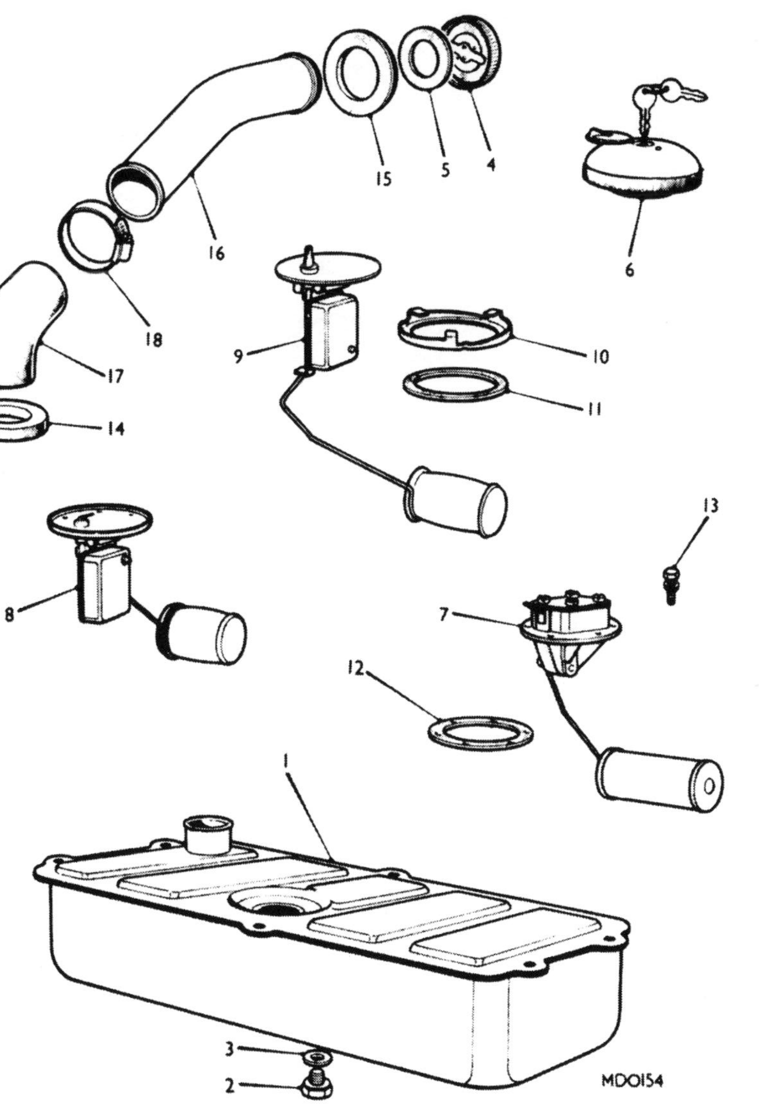

AUSTIN-HEALEY SPRITE MK. 3 AND MK. 4 & MG MIDGET MK. 2 AND MK. 3

FUEL TANK AND FITTINGS-NOT EVAPORATIVE LOSS CONTROL.

NO.	PART NO.	DESCRIPTION	QTY	CHANGE POINT	REMARKS
1	NRP 9	TANK ASSEMBLY-FUEL $	1	Use prior to NRP 8	Was ARA 114
2	ARH 672	Plug-drain	1		
3	ARA 967	Washer	1		
1	NRP 8	Tank-fuel(less gauge unit)$	1	(C)G-AN5-105501 TO 154100 (C)G-AN6-154101 TO 182000	Was ARC 84
2	ARH 672	Plug-drain	1		Use with ARC 84
3	ARA 967	Washer	1		
	NRP 1199	Tank-fuel	1	(C)G-AN6-182001 ON	
4	18G 8601	CAP ASSEMBLY-FILLER $	1		
5	27H 3573	Seal-filler cap $	1		
6	GSS 127	Cap-filler(locking)$	1		Optional extra.
7	21A 168	Unit-fuel gauge	NLA	Use prior to BHA 4711	
8	BHA 4711	Unit-fuel gauge	1	(C)H-AN9-72041 TO 85286 (C)H-AN10-85287 TO 86803 (C)A-AN10-86804 TO 87824 (C)G-AN4-60460 TO 74885 (C)G-AN5-74886 TO 105500	
9	BRA 960	Unit-fuel gauge	1	(C)G-AN5-105501 TO 154100 (C)G-AN6-154101 ON	
10	ARA 1501	Ring-locking	1		
11	ARA 1502	Ring-sealing	1		
12	2H 1082	Gasket	1		Use with unit 21A 168.
13	ARG 923	Screw-unit to tank(with washer)	6		
14	2A 2069	Ring-sealing-tank to floor	1		
	NH 605041	Nut	6		
	PWZ 105	Washer-plain	6		
	LWZ 405	Washer-shakeproof	6		
15	AHA 5445	Grommet-tank filler	1		
16	AHA 5662	Tube-filler $	1		Except 1500
17	AHA 5663	Hose-filler tube neck(rubber)$	1		
16	CHA 444	Tube-filler	1		1500
17	CHA 452	Tube-filler neck(rubber)	1		
18	GHC 1622	Clip	2		

$ This item is subject to safety regulations.

AUSTIN-HEALEY SPRITE MK. 3 AND MK. 4 & MG MIDGET MK. 2 AND MK. 3

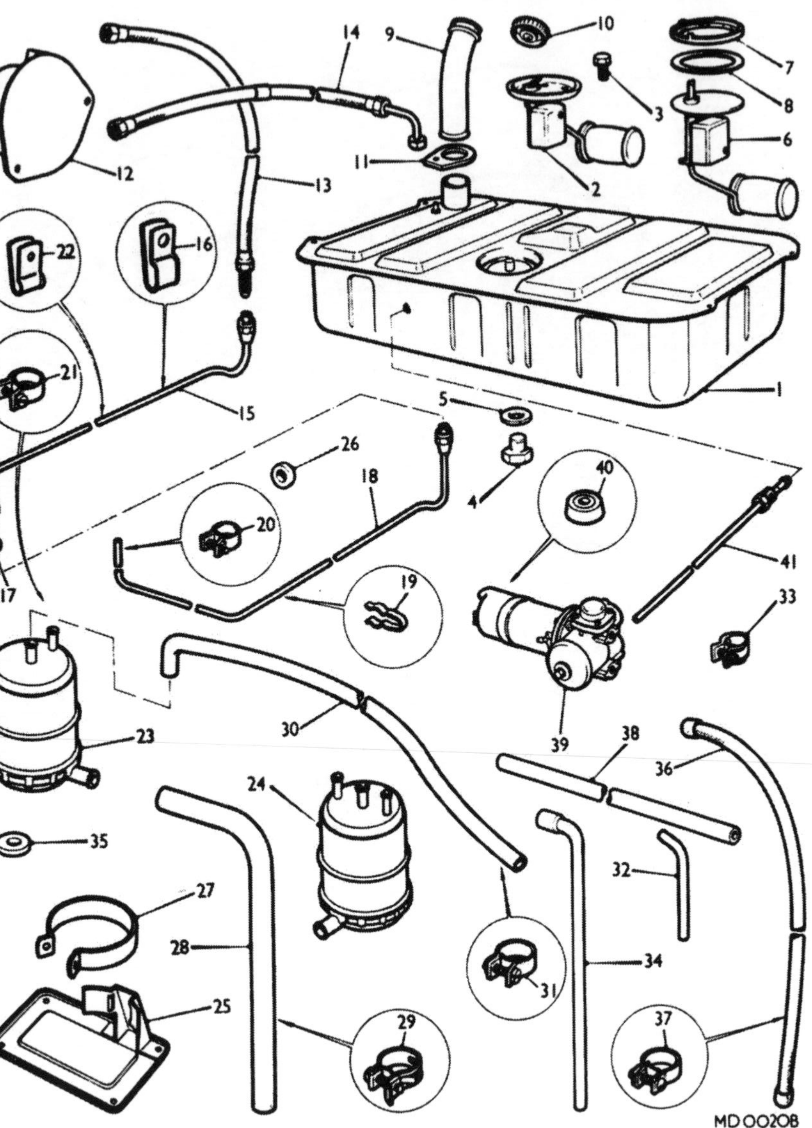

AUSTIN-HEALEY SPRITE MK. 3 AND MK. 4 & MG MIDGET MK. 2 AND MK. 3

FUEL TANK AND FITTINGS-EVAPORATIVE LOSS CONTROL EQUIPMENT.

NO.	PART NO.	DESCRIPTION	QTY	CHANGE POINT	REMARKS
1	ARA 373	Tank fuel-$	1	(C)G-AN5-74886 TO 105500	
2	BHA 4711	Unit-fuel gauge	1		
3	ARG 923	Screw	6		
1	NRP 6	Tank-fuel $	1	(C)G-AN5-105501 To 154100 (C)G-AN6-105501 TO 182000	Was ARC 86 Use with ARC 86 and ARA 373
4	ARH 672	Plug-drain	1		
5	ARA 969	Washer	1		
	NRP 1201	Tank-fuel	1	(C)G-AN6-182001 ON	
6	BRA 960	Unit-fuel gauge	1	(C)G-AN5-105501 TO 154100	
7	ARA 1501	Ring-locking	1		
8	ARA 1502	Ring-sealing	1	(C)G-AN6-154101 ON	
	AHA 5663	Filler neck(rubber)$	1	(C)G-AN5-74886 TO 113625	
9	AHA 9652	Tube-filler $	1		
	AHA 9941	Filler neck $	1	(C)G-AN5-113626 TO 154100	
	CHA 452	Filler-neck $	1	(C)G-AN6-154101 ON	
10	BHH 178	Cap-filler $	1	(C)G-AN6-154101 TO 166300	Except 1500. California
9	CHA 453	Tube-filler $	1	(C)G-AN6-160160 TO 166300 (California only)	
10	BHH 1663	Cap-filler $	1		
9	BHH 1883	Tube-filler	1	(C)G-AN6-166304 ON	Unleaded fuel
10	BHH 178	Cap-filler	1		
11	AHA 9653	Seal-vent pipe through floor	NLA		
12	ARH 302	Tank-vapour seperating $	1	Use prior to BHH 1626	
12	BHH 1626	Tank-vapour-separating $	1	(C)G-AN6-154101 ON	
	HZS 405	Screw-tank to wing valance	1		
	LWZ 204	Washer-spring	1		
	NH 604041	Nut	1		
	PWZ 204	Washer-plain	1		
13	BHH 196	Hose-vapour-separator tank to rear vapour pipe $	1	Use prior to BHH 1625	
13	BHH 1625	Hose-vapour-separator tank to rear vapour pipe $	1	(C)G-AN6-154101 TO 182000	
	LWZ 607	Washer-lock	1		
14	BHH 197	Hose-vapour-separator tank to petrol tank $	1	Use prior to CHA 378	
14	CHA 378	Pipe-vapour-separator tank to petrol tank $	1	(C)G-AN6-154101 TO 182000	
15	AHA 9668	Pipe-vapour-connection to separator tank connector	1		
	37H 7148 M	Pipe-vapour-intermediate-25"long	1	(C)G-AN6-182001 ON	
	37H 7148 M	Pipe-vapour-intermediate pipe To seperator tank flex-25"long	1		
	WF 600071	Washer-lock	1		
	NT 607041	Nut-pipe to floor	1		
	37H 6844 M	Hose-petrol tank to seperator tank 19"long	1		
	37H 6844 M	Hose-seperator tank to pipe 15"long	1		
	RFR 208	Ferrule(in boot floor)	1		

MD00208

AUSTIN-HEALEY SPRITE MK. 3 AND MK. 4 & MG MIDGET MK. 2 AND MK. 3

NO.	PART NO.	DESCRIPTION	QTY	CHANGE POINT	REMARKS
		FUEL TANK AND FITTINGS-EVAPORATIVE LOSS CONTROL EQUIPMENT-continued.			
16	AHH 7355	Clip-pipe to tank	1		
	PCR 407	Clip-pipe	3		
	LWZ 203	Washer-spring	1		
17	AHH 9662	Connector	1		
18	AHA 9666	Pipe-vapour-connector to elbow on canister	1		
19	6K 35	Clip	2		
	PMZ 310	Screw	1		
	PCR 407	Clip-vapour and brake pipe	2		
	PWZ 103	Washer-plain	1		
	LWZ 203	Washer-spring	1		
20	BHH 185	Clip-vapour pipe to elbow	1		
21	88G 308	Clip-elbow to canister	1		
22	AHA 8161	Clip-vapour pipe to canister support	1	Finished at (C)G-AN5-154100	
23	13H 6199	CANISTER ASSEMBLY-CARBON	1	(C)G-AN5-74886 TO 105500	
24	13H 5994	CANISTER ASSEMBLY-CARBON	1	(C)G-AN5-105501 TO 154100	
	37H 6101	Pad-filter	1		
24	13H 8511	Cannister-carbon	1	(C)G-AN6-154101 ON	
	BHH 102	Elbow-carbon cannister	1		
25	AHA 9333	Bracket-support-canister	NLA	Finished at (C)G-AN5-154100	
	PMZ 412	Screw-canister bracket bottom	1		
	PCR 409	Clip-pipe to bracket	1		
27	AHH 9658	Strap-canister	1		
	PMZ 316	Screw-strap	1		
	LNZ 103	Nut	1		
28	AHA 9670	Tube-breather-canister	1	Finished at (C)G-AN5-154100	
29	AHC 190	Clip-tube	1		
30	AHA 9607	Hose-canister to head cover	1		
31	AHC 234	Clip-hose	NLA		
32	AHA 9606	Pipe-overflow-carburetter	2	(C)G-AN5-74886 TO 105500	
33	BHH 185	Clip-pipe	2		
34	AHA 9608	Pipe-overflow	NLA	(C)G-AN5-105501 TO 154100	
21	88G 308	Clip-canister	1		
20	BHH 185	Clip-bundy pipe end	1		
	PCR 607	Clip-pipe to heater control screw	1		
35	AHH 8899	Washer-distance	1		
	37H 4760 M	PIPE-FUEL(FLEXIBLE)	A/R	Finished at (C)G-AN5-154100	
37	ACH 5854	Clip-flexible pipe	2		
38	AHA 7383	Pipe-carburetter to flexible pipe(straight)-244cm	NLA		Use 37H 7148 M
38	37H 7148 M	Pipe-carburetter to flexible pipe-244cm	1		
39	AUF 305	Pump-fuel	1		
40	AHH 6939	Spacer-pump bracket	1		

NOTE:-Part numbers with suffix 'm' are supplied in Multiples of Metres(39.37")

MDOO58A

AUSTIN-HEALEY SPRITE MK. 3 AND MK. 4 & MG MIDGET MK. 2 AND MK. 3

NO.	PART NO.	DESCRIPTION	QTY	CHANGE POINT	REMARKS
		FUEL PIPES AND FITTINGS			
1	AHA 7381	PIPE ASSEMBLY-TANK TO PUMP INLET FLEXIBLE PIPE $	1		Except USA and Canada
1	AHA 9556	PIPE ASSEMBLY-TANK TO PUMP INLET FLEXIBLE $	1		USA and Canada
2	ACA 5129	Nipple $	1		
3	ACA 5128	Nut $	1		
	37H 4760 M	PIPE-FUEL(FLEXIBLE) $	A/R		
4	37H 4760 M	Pump inlet 5"(13cm)	1		
5	37H 4760 M	Pump outlet 9"(23cm)	1		
7	37H 4760 M	Pipe to carburetter 10.5"(27cm)	1		
	37H 4760 M	Main feed filter to carburetter-7.5"(19cm)	1		
6	AHA 7383	Pipe-pump outlet to carburetter-244cm $	NLA		Use 37H 7148 M
8	12G 2409	Pipe-front to rear carburetter	1	Finished at (C)G-AN5-154100	
9	17H 8579 M	Pipe-pump breather-22"(56cm)	A/R		
10	ACH 5854	Clip-pump flexible pipes $	A/R		
11	6K 35	Clip-pipe to frame	2		
12	17H 9603	Clip-pipe to frame	3		
13	PCR 409	Clip-pump breather pipe to body	1		
	13H 320	Clip-vent pipe on pump	1		
14	BHA 4361	'T'piece-pump breather pipe	1		
15	AHH 8790	Tube-pump breather-22"(56cm)	NLA		Use with double-VENTED FUEL pump
16	BHA 4752	'T'piece	1		
15	47H 9545	Sleeve(PVC)-5"(12.7cm)	A/R		
17	AHA 7384	Bracket-pump mounting	1		
	NH 604041	Nut	2		
	PWZ 104	Washer-plain	2		
	LWZ 204	Washer-spring	2		
18	AHH 6708	Mounting-fuel pump(rubber)	1		
	HZS 405	Screw	2		
	LWZ 204	Washer-spring	2		
	NH 604041	Nut	2		
1	37H 7148 M	PIPE ASSEMBLY-TANK TO INTERMEDIATE HOSE-81.5" (207.07cm)$	1	(C)G-AN6-154101 ON	
2	ACA 5129	Nipple $	1		
3	ACA 5128	Nut $	1		
4	37H 7615 M	Hose-intermediate-10"(254mm)	1		Alternatives
4	37H 6844 M	Hose-intermediate-8"(203mm)	1		
6	CHA 397	Pipe-intermediate hose to pump hose	1		
	BRT 2805	Hose-pump inlet	1		

$ This item is subject to safety regulations

NOTE:
Part Nos.with the suffix letter 'M' are supplied in multiples of metres(39.37")

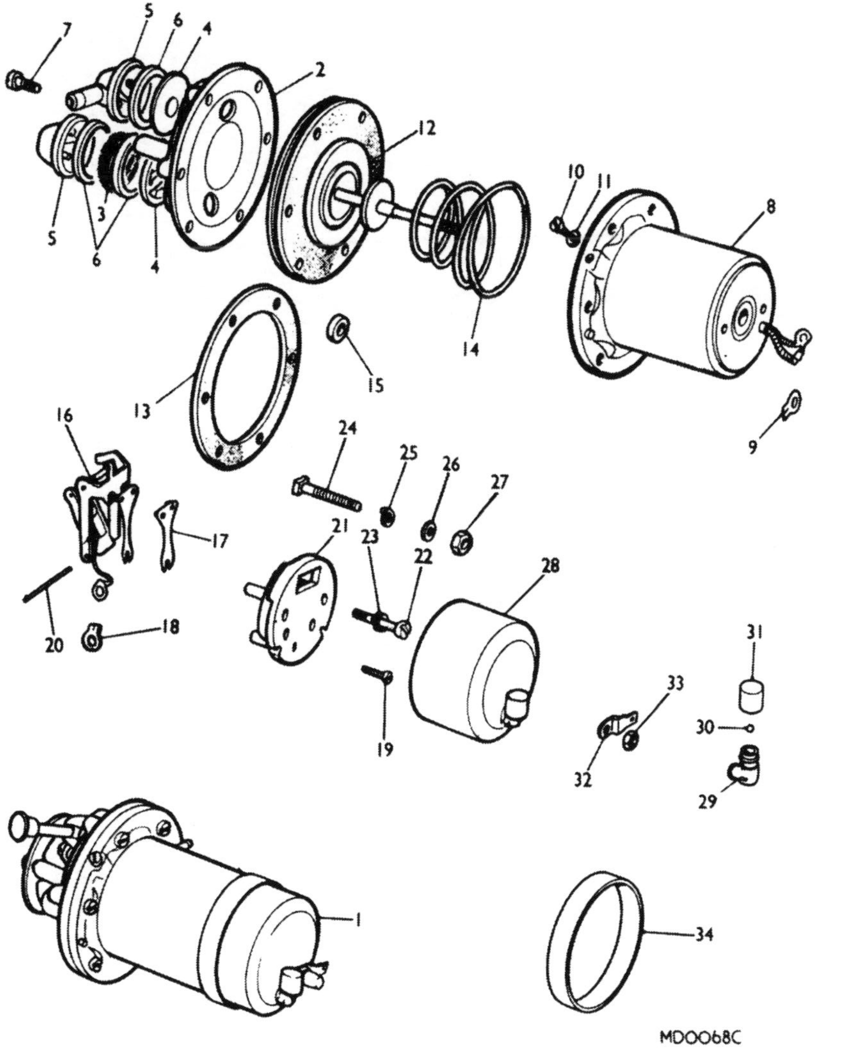

AUSTIN-HEALEY SPRITE MK. 3 AND MK. 4 & MG MIDGET MK. 2 AND MK. 3

NO.	PART NO.	DESCRIPTION	QTY	CHANGE POINT	REMARKS
		FUEL PUMP-EXCEPT MIDGET 1500.			
1	AUF 214	PUMP ASSEMBLY-FUEL	1		
2	AUB 613	Body	NLA		
3	AUB 617	Filter	1		
4	AUB 6062	Valve	2		
5	AUB 663	Banjo	2		
6	AUB 676	Washer-sealing	3		
7	AUA 1453	Screw-plate	2		
8	AUB 6080	Housing-coil	1		
10	AUA 699	Screw-earth	1		
11	AUA 585	Washer-spring	1		
12	AUB 6097	Diaphragm	1		
13	AUB 809	Washer-joint	1		
	LWZ 303	Washer-spring	1		
14	AUB 758	Spring-armature	NLA		
15	AUA 1433	Roller	1		
16	AUB 6106	ROCKER AND BLADE ASSEMBLY	1		
17	AUA 6036	Blade	1		
19	AUC 5047	Screw-blade	1		
20	AUA 1435	Spindle-contact breaker	1		
21	88G 534	Pedestal	1		
22	AUA 1459	Screw-pedestal to coil housing	2		
23	AUA 1863	Washer-spring	NLA		
24	AUA 1468	Screw-terminal	1		
25	AUA 1863	Washer-spring	NLA		
26	AUA 1662	Washer(lead)	1		
27	AUA 1661	Nut	1		
28	AUE 399	Cover and valve	1		
	LWZ 403	Washer-shakeproof	1		
32	AUA 692	Connector-Lucar	1		
33	AUA 878	Nut-cover	1		
34	AUB 716	Ring-sealing	1		

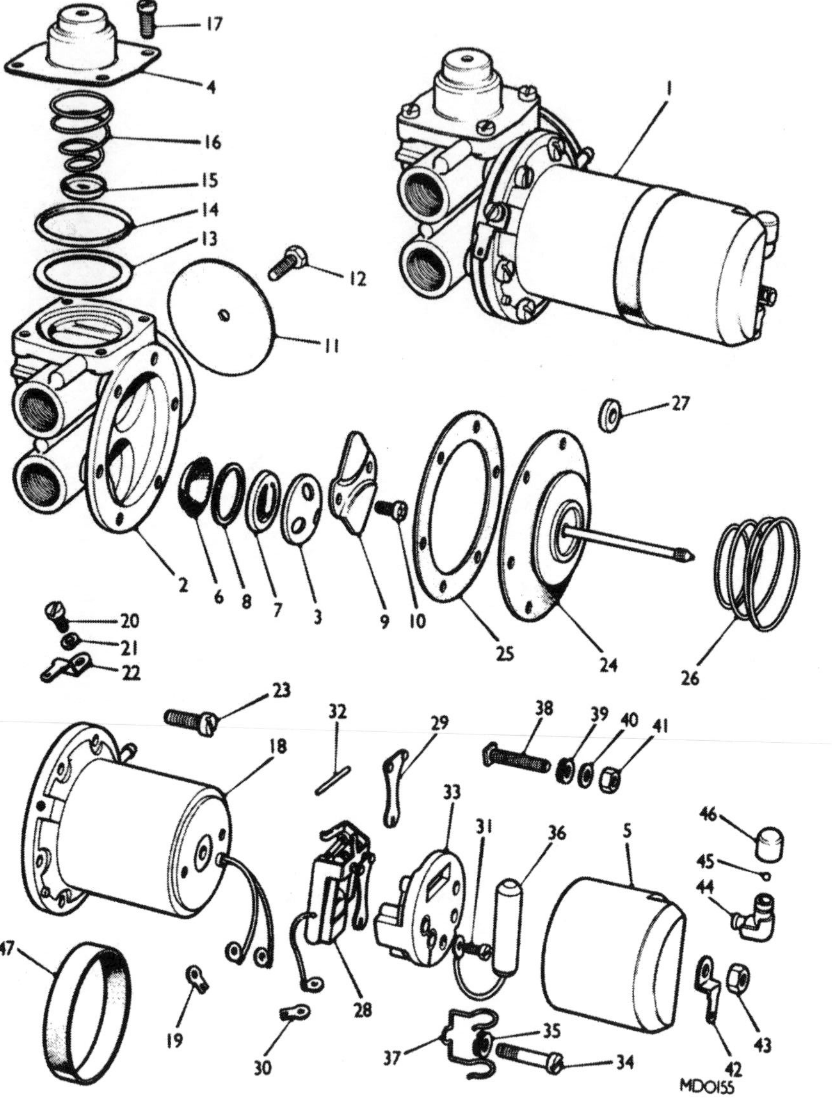

AUSTIN-HEALEY SPRITE MK. 3 AND MK. 4 & MG MIDGET MK. 2 AND MK. 3

NO.	PART NO.	DESCRIPTION	QTY	CHANGE POINT	REMARKS
		FUEL PUMP-RAC HOMOLOGATED			
1	AUF 305	PUMP ASSEMBLY-FUEL	1		
2	AUB 662	Body	NLA		
3	AUB 652	Cover-valve	NLA		
4	AUB 651	Cover-air bottle	NLA		
	AUB 656	Diaphragm(nylon)	1		
	AUB 657	Ring-sealing	1		
5	AUB 707	Cover-end	1		
6	AUB 617	Filter	1		
7	AUB 6062	Valve	2		
8	AUB 676	Washer-sealing	3		
9	AUB 653	Plate-valve cover clamp	1		
10	AUB 597	Screw-plate	NLA		
11	AUA 573	Gasket-side cover	1		
12	AJD 1042	Bolt-side cover	1		
	LWZ 303	Washer-spring	1		
13	AUB 795	Gasket-plate	1		
17	AJD 3803 Z	Screw-air bottle cover	4		
18	AUB 6080	Housing-coil	1		
20	AUA 699	Screw-earth	1		
21	AUA 585	Washer-spring	1		
22	AUA 692	Connector-Lucar	1		
23	AUB 660	Screw-oil housing to body	6		
24	AUB 6097	DIAPHRAGM ASSEMBLY	1		
25	AUB 849	Gasket	NLA		
26	AUB 759	Spring-armature	1		
27	AUB 794	Roller	11		
28	AUB 106	ROCKER AND BLADE ASSEMBLY	1		
29	AUA 6036	Blade	1		
31	AUC 5047	Screw-blade	1		
32	AUA 1435	Spindle-contact breaker	1		
33	88G 534	Pedestal	1		
34	AUA 1459	Screw-pedestal to coil housing	2		
35	AUA 1863	Washer-spring	NLA		
36	AUB 6079	Condenser	1		
37	AUA 5059	Clip-condenser	NLA		
38	AUA 1468	Screw-terminal	1		
39	AUA 1863	Washer-spring	NLA		
40	AUA 1662	Washer(lead)	1		
41	AUA 1661	Nut	1		
	LWZ 403	Washer-shakeproof	1		
42	AUA 692	Connector-Lucar	1		
43	AUA 878	Nut-end cover	1		
47	AUB 716	Ring-sealing	1		

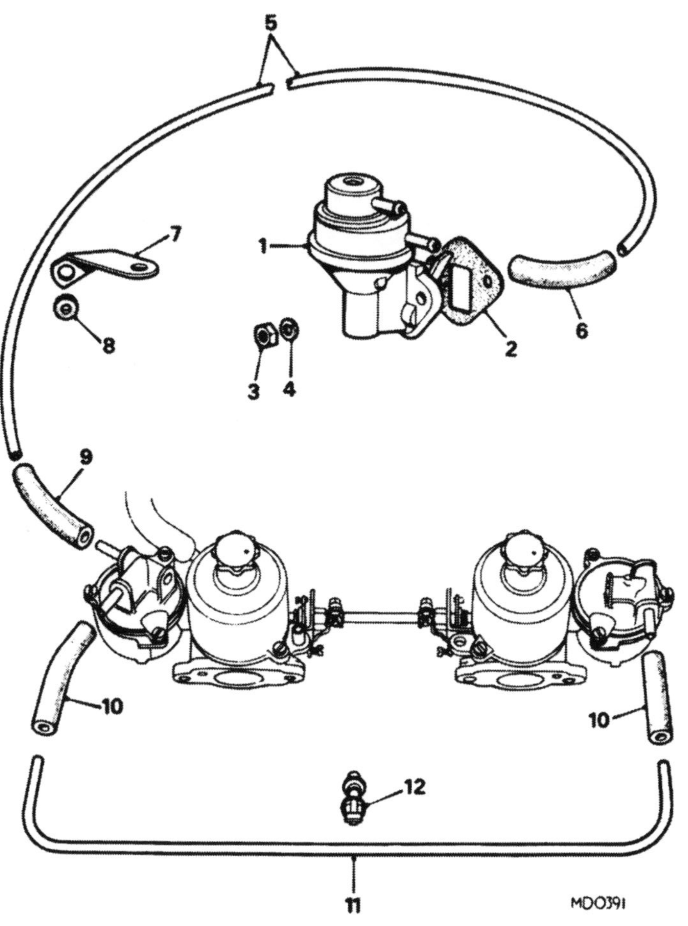

AUSTIN-HEALEY SPRITE MK. 3 AND MK. 4 & MG MIDGET MK. 2 AND MK. 3

FUEL PUMP AND FIXINGS-MIDGET 1500.

NO.	PART NO.	DESCRIPTION	QTY	CHANGE POINT	REMARKS
1	RKC 1624	Pump-fuel(AC Delco)	1		
1		Pump-fuel (AC Delco)	1		USA and Canada 1977 ON
2	138791	Gasket-fuel pump	1		
3	NH 605041	Nut	2		
4	WL 605091	Washer	2		
5	310221	Pipe-fuel pump to carburetter	1		
6	153300	Connector-pipe to pump	1		
7	155959	Bracket-pipe support	1		
8	630661	Grommet-bracket	1		
9	125170	Connector-pipe to carburetter	1		
10	120331	Connector-front and rear-fuel pipe	2		
11	UKC 4962	Pipe-fuel-front to rear carburetter	1		
12	UKC 3793	Clamp-pipe	1		
5	215997	Pipe-fuel-pump to carburetter	1		USA and Canada. TO 1977.
9	144938	Connector-fuel pipe	2		
5	TKC 3222	Pipe-fuel-pump to carburettor	1		USA and Canada 1977 ON
9	156952	Connector-fuel pipe	2		

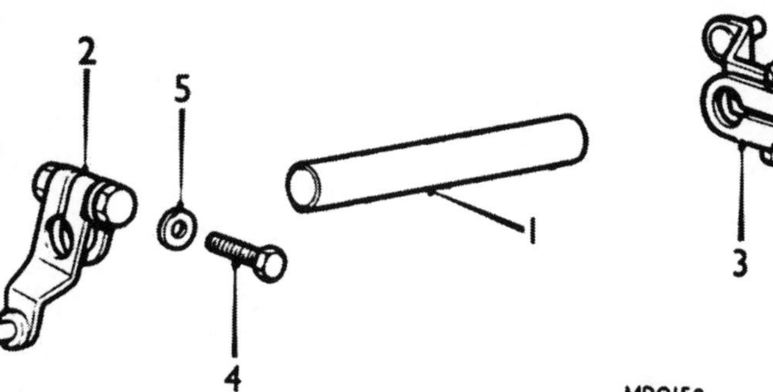

AUSTIN-HEALEY SPRITE MK. 3 AND MK. 4 & MG MIDGET MK. 2 AND MK. 3

NO.	PART NO.	DESCRIPTION	QTY	CHANGE POINT	REMARKS
		CARBURETTER INSTALLATION-NON VENTILATED TYPE-NOT USA AND CANADA			
	AUD 136	CARBURETTER INSTALLATION	NLA		Use front carburetter CUD 9029 with rear carburetter CUD 9030
1	AUC 1457	Rod-jet connecting	1	(E)10CC/Da/H101 TO 16300	
2	AUE 586	LEVER AND PIN ASSEMBLY-FRONT	2	(E)12CC/Da/H101 TO 16300	
3	AUE 587	LEVER AND PIN ASSEMBLY-REAR	2		
4	AJD 1042	Bolt	4		
5	AUC 8396	Washer-plain	4		
6	AJD 8012 Z	Nut	4		

AUSTIN-HEALEY SPRITE MK. 3 AND MK. 4 & MG MIDGET MK. 2 AND MK. 3

CARBURETTER INSTALLATION-NON VENTILATED TYPE-NOT USA AND CANADA -continued

NO.	PART NO.	DESCRIPTION	QTY	CHANGE POINT	REMARKS
	AUC 9268	CARBURETTER ASSEMBLY-FRONT	NLA		Use CUD 9029.
1	AUC 8700	Body	1		
2	AUC 8464	Pin-piston lifting	1		
3	AUC 1151	Spring-pin	1		
4	AUC 1250	Circlip-pin	NLA		Use AUD 4150.
4	AUD 4150	Circlip-pin	2		
5	AUD 9181	CHAMBER AND PISTON ASSEMBLY	1		
6	AUC 2057	Screw-needle locking	1		
7	AUC 8114	Cap and damper	1		
8	AUC 4900	Washer(fibre)	1		
9	AUC 4587	Spring-piston-Blue	1		
10	AUC 5156	Screw-chamber to body	2		
11	AUD 9141	JET ASSEMBLY	1		
12	AUD 2129	Nut	1		
13	AUD 2193	Washer	1		
14	AUD 2194	Gland	1		
15	AUD 2195	Ferrule	1		
16	AUC 8460	Bearing-jet	1		
17	AUC 8478	Washer-jet bearing(brass)	1		
18	AUC 2002	Screw-jet locking	1		
19	AUC 2114	Spring-jet locking	1		
20	AUC 8461	Screw-jet adjusting	1		
21	AUD 1242	NEEDLE-JET-Rich(H6)	1		
21	AUD 1478	NEEDLE-JET-Standard(AN)	1	(E)10CC/Da/H101 TO 16300	
21	AUD 1211	NEEDLE-JET-Weak(GG)	1	(E)12CC/Da/H101 TO 16300	
22	AUC 1310	Chamber-float	1		
23	AUC 1329	Washer-support	1		
24	AUD 2677	Grommet(rubber)	1		
25	AUC 1318	Washer(rubber)	1		
26	AUC 1317	Washer-plain	1		
27	AUD 2891	Bolt-float chamber to body	1		
28	AUD 9904	Float	1		
29	AUC 1152	Pin-hinge	1		
30	AUD 9255	Lid-float chamber	1		
31	AUC 8459	Gasket-lid	1		
32	AUD 9096	Needle and seat	1		
33	AUC 2175	Screw-lid	3		
	LWZ 303	Washer-spring	3		
34	AUC 1215	Plate-baffle	1		
35	AUC 8469	Spindle-throttle	1		
36	AUC 2169	Disc-throttle	1		
37	AUC 1358	Screw-disc	2		
38	AUC 1145	Lever-throttle return	1		
39	AUC 1400	Lever-lost motion	1		
40	AUC 1424	Nut-lever	1		
41	AUC 1206	Washer-tab	1		
42	AUC 8483	Screw-throttle stop	2		
43	AUC 2451	Spring-screw	2		
44	AUD 9004	Lever-and link-pick-up	1		
	PJZ 604	Screw-link to jet	1		
45	AUC 8456	Lever-cam	1		
46	AUC 8462	Spring-pick-up lever	1		
47	AUC 8463	Spring-cam lever	1		
48	AUC 1426	Bolt-pivot	1		
49	AUC 8473	Tube-pivot bolt	1		
50	AUC 8474	Washer-spring	1		
51	AUC 5032	Washer-distance	1		

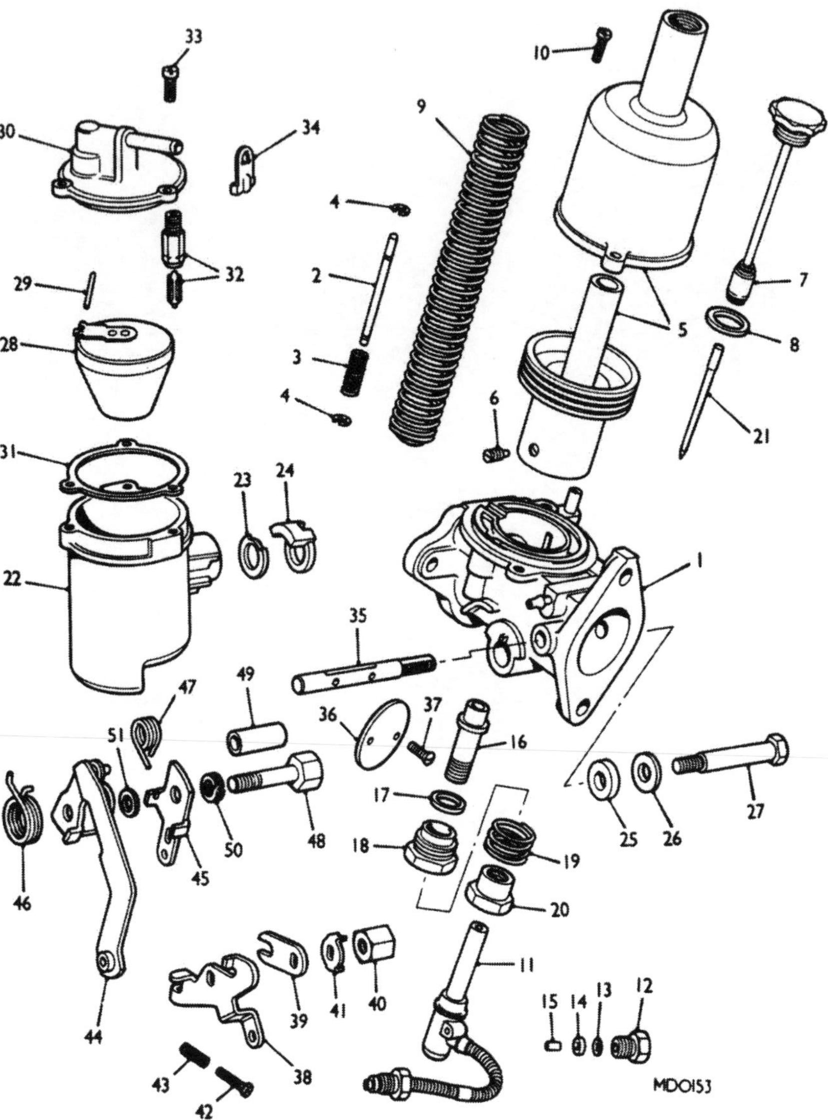

AUSTIN-HEALEY SPRITE MK. 3 AND MK. 4 & MG MIDGET MK. 2 AND MK. 3

CARBURETTER INSTALLATION-NON VENTILATED TYPE-NOT USA AND CANADA-continued

NO.	PART NO.	DESCRIPTION	QTY	CHANGE POINT	REMARKS
	AUC 9269	CARBURETTER ASSEMBLY-REAR	NLA		Use CUD 9030
1	AUC 8713	Body	NLA		
2	AUC 8464	Pin-piston lifting	1		
3	AUC 1151	Spring-pin	1		
4	AUC 1250	Circlip-pin	NLA		Use AUD 4150.
4	AUD 4150	Circlip-pin	2		
5	AUD 9181	CHAMBER AND PISTON ASSEMBLY	1		
6	AUC 2057	Screw-needle locking	1		
7	AUC 8114	Cap and damper	1		
8	AUC 4900	Washer(fibre)	1		
9	AUC 4587	Spring-piston-Blue	1		
10	AUC 5156	Screw-chamber to body	2		
11	AUD 9142	JET ASSEMBLY	1		
12	AUD 2120	Nut	1		
13	AUD 2193	Washer	1		
14	AUD 2194	Gland	1		
15	AUD 2195	Ferrule	1		
16	AUC 8460	Bearing-jet	1		
17	AUC 8478	Washer-jet bearing(brass)	1		
18	AUC 2002	Screw-jet locking	1		
19	AUC 2114	Spring-jet locking	1		
20	AUC 8461	Screw-jet adjusting	1		
21	AUD 1242	Needle-jet-rich(H6)	1		
21	AUD 1478	Needle-jet-standard(AN)	1	(E)10CC/Da/H101 TO 16300	
21	AUD 1211	Needle-jet-weak(GG)	1	(E)12CC/Da/H101 TO 16300	
22	AUC 1310	Chamber-float	1		
23	AUC 1329	Washer-support	1		
24	AUD 2676	Grommet(rubber)	1		
25	AUC 1318	Washer(rubber)	1		
26	AUC 1317	Washer-plain	1		
27	AUD 2891	Bolt-float chamber to body	1		
28	AUD 9904	Float	1		
29	AUC 1152	Pin-hinge	1		
30	AUD 9203	Lid-float chamber	1		
31	AUC 8459	Washer-lid	1		
32	AUD 9096	Needle and seat	1		
33	AUC 2175	Screw-lid	3		
	LWZ 303	Washer-spring	3		
34	AUC 1215	Plate-baffle	1		
35	AUC 8469	Spindle-throttle	1		
36	AUC 2169	Disc-throttle	1		
37	AUC 1358	Screw-disc	2		
38	AUD 2101	Lever-throttle return	1		
39	AUC 1400	Lever-lost motion	1		
40	AUC 1424	Nut-lever	1		
41	AUC 1206	Washer-tab	1		
42	AUC 8483	Screw-throttle stop	2		
43	AUC 2451	Spring-screw	2		
44	AUD 9005	Lever and link-pick-up	1		
	PJZ 604	Screw-link to jet	1		
45	AUC 1371	Lever-cam	1		
46	AUC 1375	Spring-pick-up lever	1		
47	AUC 1520	Spring-cam lever	1		
48	AUC 1426	Bolt-pivot	1		
49	AUC 8473	Tube-pivot bolt	1		
50	AUC 8474	Washer-spring	1		
51	AUC 5032	Washer-distance	1		

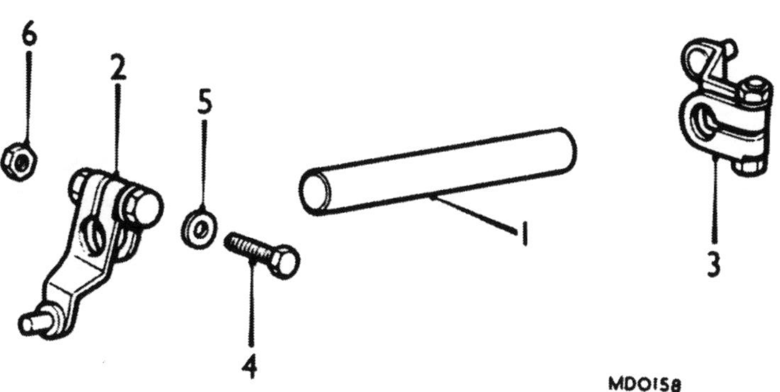

AUSTIN-HEALEY SPRITE MK. 3 AND MK. 4 & MG MIDGET MK. 2 AND MK. 3

CARBURETTER INSTALLATION-VENTILATED TYPE-NOT USA AND CANADA

NO.	PART NO.	DESCRIPTION	QTY	CHANGE POINT	REMARKS
	AUD 327	CARBURETTER INSTALLATION	NLA	(E)12CE/Da/h101 TO(+) (E)12V/586F/101 ON (E)12V/588F/101 ON	Use front carburetter CUD 9029 with rear carburetter CUD 9030
1	AUC 1457	Rod-jet connecting	1		
2	AUE 586	Lever and pin assembly-front	2		
3	AUE 587	Lever and pin assembly-rear	2		
4	AJD 1042	Bolt-lever	4		
5	AUC 8396	Washer-plain	4		
6	AJD 8012 Z	Nut	4		

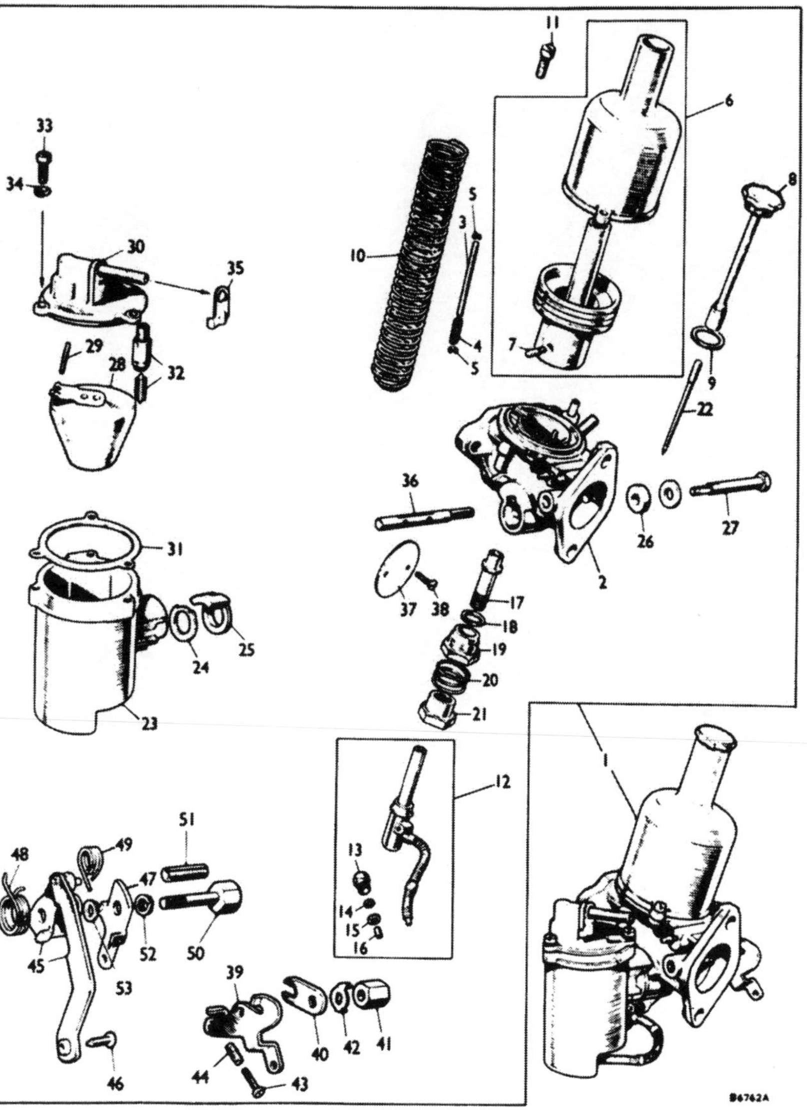

AUSTIN-HEALEY SPRITE MK. 3 AND MK. 4 & MG MIDGET MK. 2 AND MK. 3

CARBURETTER INSTALLATION-VENTILATED TYPE-NOT USA AND CANADA-CONTINUED

NO.	PART NO.	DESCRIPTION	QTY	CHANGE POINT	REMARKS
1	CUD 9029	CARBURETTER ASSEMBLY-FRONT	1	(E)12CE/Da/H101 TO(+) (E)12V/586F/101 ON (E)12V/588F/101 ON	
2	CUD 2316	Body	1		
3	AUC 8464	Pin-piston lifting	1		
4	AUC 1151	Spring-pin	1		
5	AUC 1250	Circlip-pin	NLA		Use AUD 4150.
5	AUD 4150	Circlip-pin	2		
6	AUD 9181	CHAMBER AND PISTON ASSEMBLY	1		
7	AUC 2057	Screw-needle locking	1		
8	AUC 8114	Cap and damper	1		
9	AUC 4900	Washer(fibre)	1		
10	AUC 4587	Spring-piston-Blue	1		
11	AUC 5156	Screw-chamber to body	2		
12	AUD 9141	JET ASSEMBLY	1		
13	AUD 2129	Nut	1		
14	AUD 2193	Washer	1		
15	AUD 2194	Gland	1		
16	AUD 2195	Ferrule	1		
17	AUC 8460	Bearing-jet	1		
18	AUC 8478	Washer-jet bearing(brass)	1		
19	AUC 2002	Screw-jet locking	1		
20	AUC 2114	Spring-jet locking	1		
21	AUC 8461	Screw-jet adjusting	1		
22	AUD 1242	Needle-jet-rich(H6)	1		
22	AUD 1478	Needle-jet-standard(AN)	1		
22	AUD 1211	Needle-jet-weak(GG)	1		
23	AUC 1310	Chamber-float	1		
24	AUC 1329	Washer-support	1		
25	AUD 2677	Grommet(rubber)	1		
26	AUC 1318	Washer(rubber)	1		
27	AUD 2891	Bolt-float chamber to body	1		
28	AUD 9904	Float	1		
29	AUC 1152	Pin-hinge	1		
30	AUD 9255	Lid-float chamber	1		
31	AUC 8459	Washer-lid	1		
32	AUD 9096	Needle and seat	1		
33	AUC 2175	Screw-lid	3		
34	LWZ 303	Washer-spring	3		
35	AUC 1215	Plate-baffle	1		
36	AUC 8469	Spindle-throttle	1		
37	AUC 2169	Disc-throttle	1		
38	AUC 1358	Screw-disc	2		
39	AUC 1145	Lever-throttle return	1		
40	AUC 1400	Lever-lost motion	1		
41	AUC 1424	Nut-lever	1		
42	AUD 3323	Washer-tab	1		
43	AUC 8483	Screw-throttle stop	2		
44	AUC 2451	Spring-screw	2		
45	AUD 9004	Lever and link-pick-up	1		
46	PJZ 604	Screw-link to jet	1		
47	AUC 8456	Lever-cam	1		
48	AUC 8462	Spring-pick-up lever	1		
49	AUC 8463	Spring-cam lever	1		
50	AUC 1426	Bolt-pivot	1		
51	AUC 8473	Tube-pivot bolt	1		
52	AUC 8474	Washer-spring	1		
53	AUC 5032	Washer-distance	1		

AUSTIN-HEALEY SPRITE MK. 3 AND MK. 4 & MG MIDGET MK. 2 AND MK. 3

CARBURETTER INSTALLATION-VENTILATED TYPE.NOT USA AND CANADA-continued.

NO.	PART NO.	DESCRIPTION	QTY	CHANGE POINT	REMARKS
1	CUD 9030	CARBURETTER ASSEMBLY-REAR	1		
2	AUD 9995	Body	NLA		
3	AUC 8464	Pin-piston lifting	1		
4	AUC 1151	Spring-pin	1		
5	AUC 1250	Circlip-pin	NLA		Use AUD 4150.
5	AUD 4150	Circlip-pin	1		
6	AUD 9181	CHAMBER AND PISTON ASSEMBLY	1		
7	AUC 2057	Screw-needle locking	1		
8	AUC 8114	Cap and damper	1		
9	AUC 4900	Washer(fibre)	1		
10	AUC 4587	Spring-piston-Blue	1		
11	AUC 5156	Screw-chamber to body	2		
12	AUD 9142	JET ASSEMBLY	1		
13	AUD 2129	Nut	1		
14	AUD 2193	Washer	1		
15	AUD 2194	Gland	1		
16	AUD 2195	Ferrule	1		
17	AUC 8460	Bearing-jet	1		
18	AUC 8478	Washer-jet bearing(brass)	1		
19	AUC 2002	Screw-jet locking	1		
20	AUC 2114	Spring-jet locking	1		
21	AUC 8461	Screw-jet adjusting	1		
22	AUD 1242	Needle-jet-rich(H6)	1		
22	AUD 1478	Needle-jet-standard(AN)	1		
22	AUD 1211	Needle-jet-weak(GG)	1	(E)12CE/Da/H101 TO	
23	AUC 1310	Chamber-float	1	(+)	
24	AUC 1329	Washer-support	1	(E)12V/586F/101 ON	
25	AUD 2676	Grommet(rubber)	1	(E)12V/588F/101 ON	
26	AUC 1318	Washer(rubber)	1		
27	AUD 2891	Bolt-float chamber to body	1		
28	AUD 9904	Float	1		
29	AUC 1152	Pin-hinge	1		
30	AUD 9203	Lid-float chamber	1		
31	AUC 8459	Washer-lid	1		
32	AUD 9096	Needle and seat	1		
33	AUC 2175	Screw-lid	3		
34	LWZ 303	Washer-spring	3		
35	AUC 1215	Plate-baffle	1		
36	AUC 8469	Spindle-throttle	1		
37	AUC 2169	Disc-throttle	1		
38	AUC 1358	Screw-disc	2		
39	AUD 2101	Lever-throttle return	1		
40	AUC 1400	Lever-lost motion	1		
41	AUC 1424	Nut-lever	1		
42	AUD 3323	Washer-tab	1		
43	AUC 8484	Screw-throttle stop	2		
44	AUC 2451	Spring-screw	2		
45	AUD 9005	Lever and link-pick-up	1		
46	PJZ 604	Screw-link to jet	1		
47	AUC 1371	Lever-cam	1		
48	AUC 1375	Spring-pick-up lever	1		
49	AUC 1520	Spring-cam lever	1		
50	AUC 1426	Bolt-pivot	1		
51	AUC 8473	Tube-pivot bolt	1		
52	AUC 8474	Washer-spring	1		
53	AUC 5032	Washer-distance	1		

AUSTIN-HEALEY SPRITE MK. 3 AND MK. 4 & MG MIDGET MK. 2 AND MK. 3

CARBURETTER INSTALLATION-VENTILATED TYPE.NOT USA AND CANADA-continued.
FRONT CARBURETTER FOR 12V/778F ENGINES ONLY

NO.	PART NO.	DESCRIPTION	QTY	CHANGE POINT	REMARKS
1	CUD 9296	CARBURETTER ASSEMBLY-FRONT	1		
3	AUC 8464	Pin-piston lifting	1		
4	AUC 1151	Spring-pin	1		
5	AUC 1250	Circlip-pin	NLA		Use AUD 4150.
5	AUD 4150	Circlip-pin	2		
6	AUD 9998	CHAMBER AND PISTON ASSEMBLY	1		
7	AUD 4250	Screw-needle locking	1		
8	AUC 8103	Cap and damper	1		
10	AUC 4587	Spring-piston-Blue	1		
11	AUC 5156	Screw-chamber to body	2		
12	AUD 9141	JET ASSEMBLY	1		
13	AUD 2129	Nut	1		
14	AUD 2193	Washer	1		
15	AUD 2194	Gland	1		
16	AUD 2195	Ferrule	1		
17	AUD 3410	Bearing-jet	1		
19	AUC 2002	Screw-jet locking	1		
20	AUC 2114	Spring-jet locking	1		
21	AUC 8461	Screw-jet adjusting	1		
22	CUD 1002	Needle-jet(AAC)	1		
22	AUD 3306	Spring-needle	1		
22	AUD 4288	Guide-needle	1		
23	AUC 1310	Chamber-float	1		
24	AUC 1329	Washer-support	1		
25	AUD 2677	Grommet(rubber)	1		
26	AUC 1318	Washer(rubber)	1	(E)12V/778F/101 ON	
27	AUD 2891	Bolt-float chamber to body	1		
28	AUD 9904	Float	1		
29	AUC 1152	Pin-hinge	1		
30	AUD 9255	Lid-float chamber	1		
31	AUC 8459	Washer-lid	1		
32	AUD 9095	Needle and seat	1		
33	AUC 2175	Screw-lid	3		
34	LWZ 303	Washer-spring	3		
36	AUC 8469	Spindle-throttle	1		
37	AUC 2169	Disc-throttle	1		
38	AUC 1358	Screw-disc	2		
39	AUC 1145	Lever-throttle return	1		
40	AUC 1400	Lever-lost motion	1		
41	AUC 1424	Nut-lever	1		
42	AUD 3323	Washer-tab	1		
43	AUC 8483	Screw-throttle stop	2		
44	AUC 2451	Spring-screw	2		
45	CUD 2686	Lever and link-pick-up	1		
46	PJZ 604	Screw-link to jet	1		
47	AUD 4410	Lever-cam	1		
48	AUC 8462	Spring-pick-up lever	1		
49	AUD 2431	Spring-cam lever	1		
50	AUC 1426	Bolt-pivot	1		
51	AUC 8473	Tube-pivot bolt	1		
	AUD 2430	Tube-pivot bolt-outer	1		
52	AUD 2429	Washer-spring	1		
53	AUD 2433	Washer-distance	1		

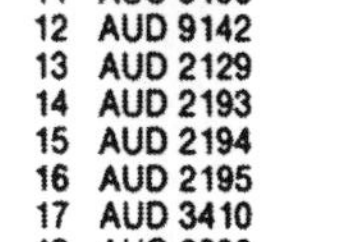
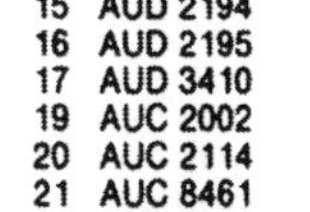
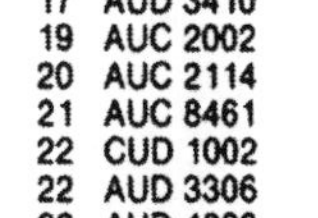
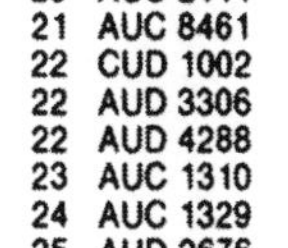
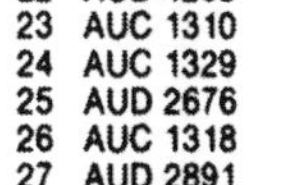

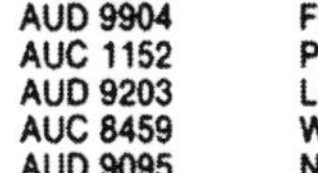
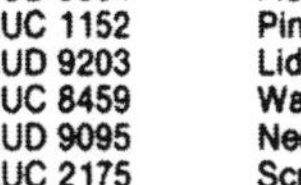

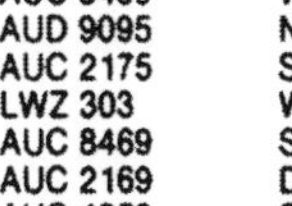
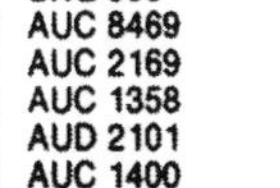
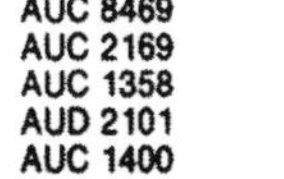

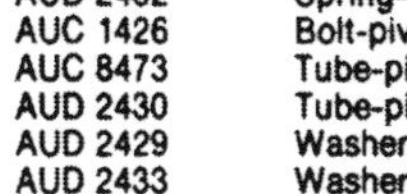
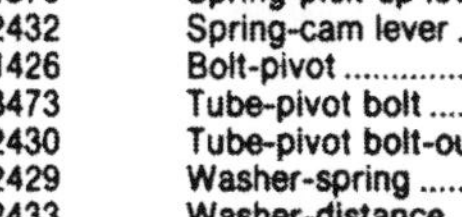
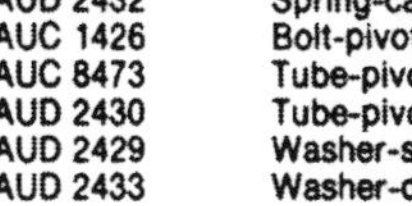
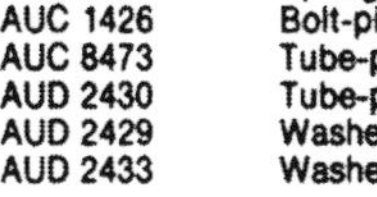
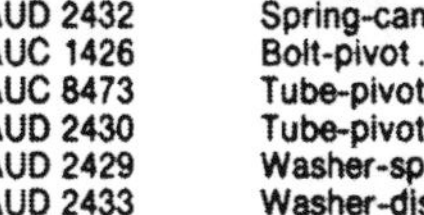
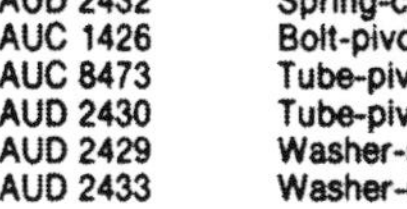
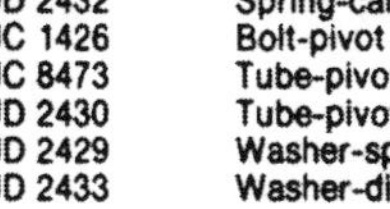
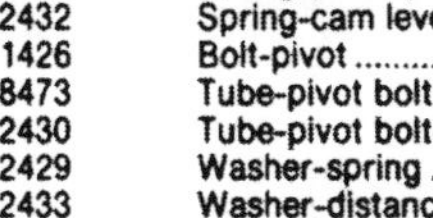
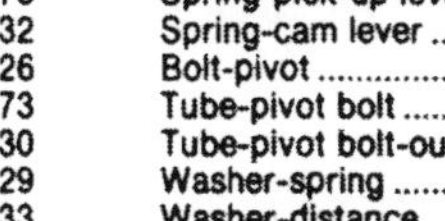
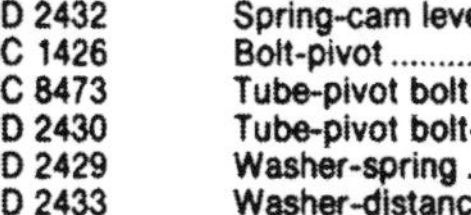
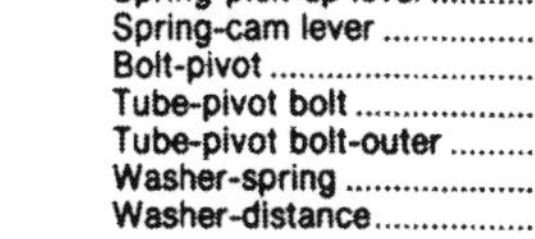
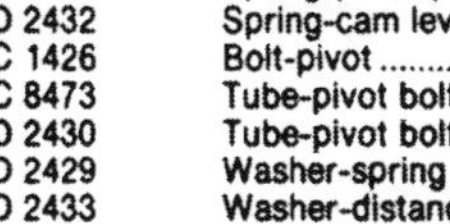
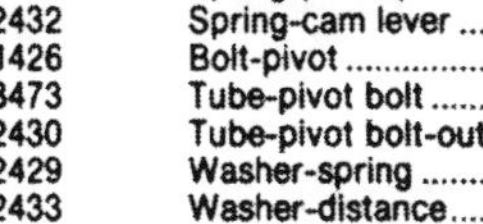
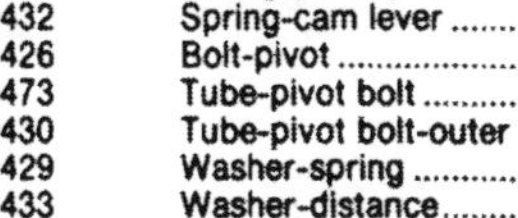
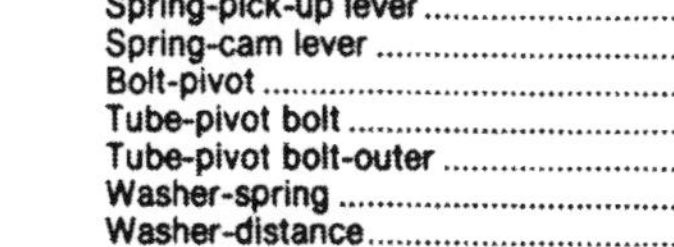
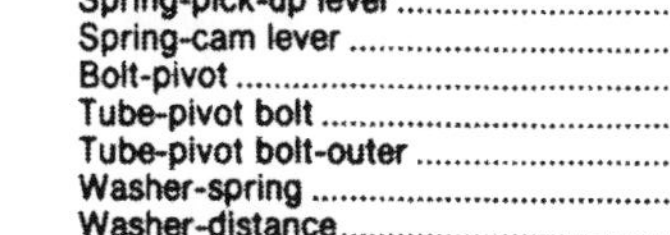
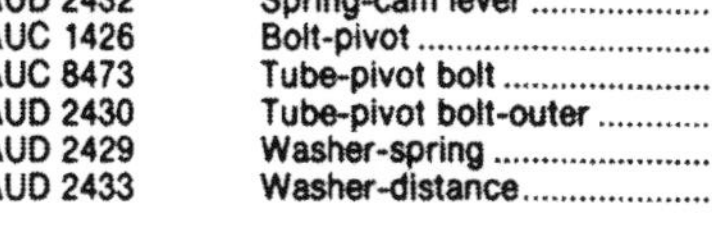

AUSTIN-HEALEY SPRITE MK. 3 AND MK. 4 & MG MIDGET MK. 2 AND MK. 3

CARBURETTER INSTALLATION VENTILATED TYPE.NOT USA AND CANADA-continued.
REAR CARBURETTER FOR
12V/778F ENGINES ONLY

NO.	PART NO.	DESCRIPTION	QTY	CHANGE POINT	REMARKS
1	CUD 9297	CARBURETTER ASSEMBLY-REAR	1		
2	AUD 9995	Body	NLA		
3	AUC 8464	Pin-piston lifting	1		
4	AUC 1151	Spring-pin	1		
5	AUC 1250	Circlip-pin	NLA		Use AUD 4150.
5	AUD 4150	Circlip-pin	1		
6	AUD 9998	CHAMBER AND PISTON ASSEMBLY	1		
7	AUD 4250	Screw-needle locking	1		
8	AUC 8103	Cap and damper	1		
10	AUC 4587	Spring-piston-Blue	1		
11	AUC 5156	Screw-chamber to body	2		
12	AUD 9142	JET ASSEMBLY	1		
13	AUD 2129	Nut	1		
14	AUD 2193	Washer	1		
15	AUD 2194	Gland	1		
16	AUD 2195	Ferrule	1		
17	AUD 3410	Bearing-jet	1		
19	AUC 2002	Screw-jet locking	1		
20	AUC 2114	Spring-jet locking	1		
21	AUC 8461	Screw-jet adjusting	1		
22	CUD 1002	Needle-jet(AAC)	1		
22	AUD 3306	Spring-needle	1		
22	AUD 4288	Guide-needle	1		
23	AUC 1310	Chamber-float	1		
24	AUC 1329	Washer-support	1		
25	AUD 2676	Grommet(rubber)	1		
26	AUC 1318	Washer(rubber)	1	(E)12V/778F/101 ON	
27	AUD 2891	Bolt-float chamber to body	1		
28	AUD 9904	Float	1		
29	AUC 1152	Pin-hinge	1		
30	AUD 9203	Lid-float chamber	1		
31	AUC 8459	Washer-lid	1		
32	AUD 9095	Needle and seat	1		
33	AUC 2175	Screw-lid	3		
34	LWZ 303	Washer-spring	3		
36	AUC 8469	Spindle-throttle	1		
37	AUC 2169	Disc-throttle	1		
38	AUC 1358	Screw-disc	2		
39	AUD 2101	Lever-throttle return	1		
40	AUC 1400	Lever-lost motion	1		
41	AUC 1424	Nut-lever	1		
42	AUD 3323	Washer-tab	1		
43	AUC 8484	Screw-throttle stop	2		
44	AUC 2451	Spring-screw	2		
45	CUD 2687	Lever and link-pick-up	1		
46	PJZ 604	Screw-link to jet	1		
47	AUD 4411	Lever-cam	1		
48	AUC 1375	Spring-pick-up lever	1		
49	AUD 2432	Spring-cam lever	1		
50	AUC 1426	Bolt-pivot	1		
51	AUC 8473	Tube-pivot bolt	1		
	AUD 2430	Tube-pivot bolt-outer	1		
52	AUD 2429	Washer-spring	1		
53	AUD 2433	Washer-distance	1		

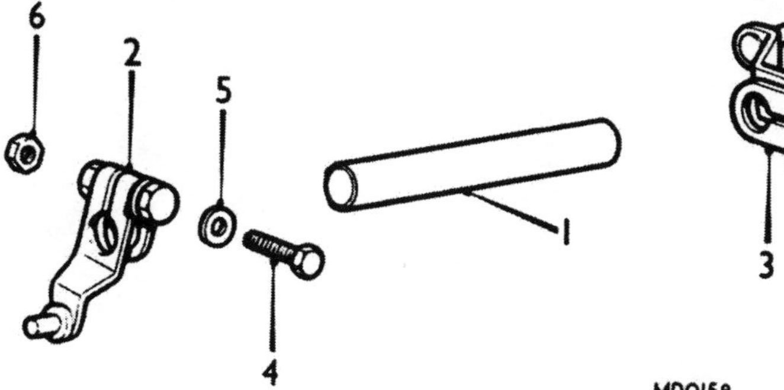

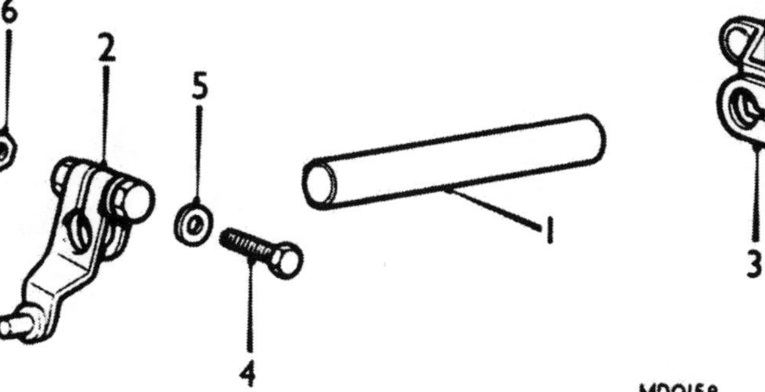

AUSTIN-HEALEY SPRITE MK. 3 AND MK. 4 & MG MIDGET MK. 2 AND MK. 3

CARBURETTER INSTALLATION-NON VENTILATED TYPE.USA AND CANADA.

NO.	PART NO.	DESCRIPTION	QTY	CHANGE POINT	REMARKS
	AUD 266	CARBURETTER INSTALLATION	NLA		Use front carburetter CUD 9031 with rear carburetter CUD 9032.
1	AUC 1457	Rod-jet connecting	1	(E)12CD/-/H101 TO 8700	
2	AUE 586	LEVER AND PIN ASSEMBLY-FRONT	2		
3	AUE 587	LEVER AND PIN ASSEMBLY-FRONT	2		
4	AJD 1042	Bolt	4		
5	AUC 8396	Washer-plain	4		
6	AJD 8012 Z	Nut	4		

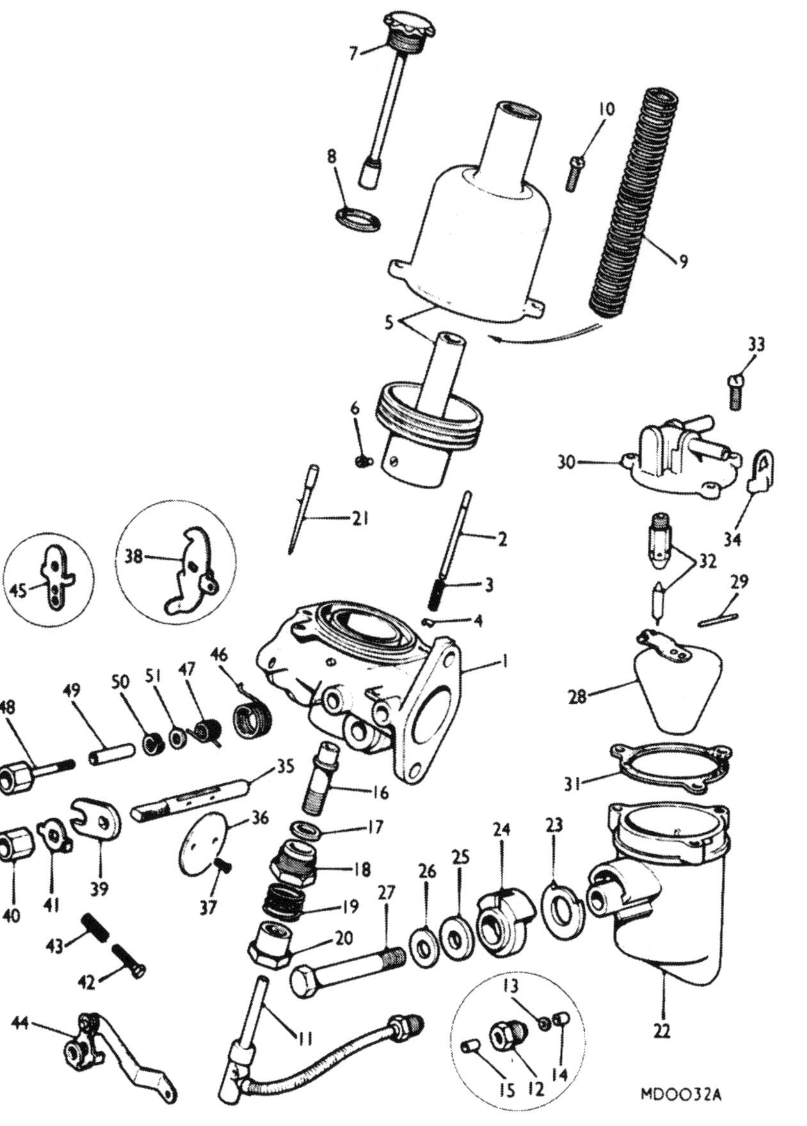

AUSTIN-HEALEY SPRITE MK. 3 AND MK. 4 & MG MIDGET MK. 2 AND MK. 3

CARBURETTER INSTALLATION,NON-VENTILATED TYPE-USA AND CANADA-continued

NO.	PART NO.	DESCRIPTION	QTY	CHANGE POINT	REMARKS
	AUC 9460	CARBURETTER ASSEMBLY-FRONT	NLA		Use CUD 9031.
1	AUD 9870	Body	NLA		
2	AUC 8464	Pin-piston lifting	1		
3	AUC 1151	Spring-pin	1		
4	AUC 1250	Circlip-pin	NLA		Use AUD 4150.
4	AUD 4150	Circlip-pin	2		
5	AUD 9181	CHAMBER AND PISTON ASSEMBLY	1		
6	AUC 2057	Screw-needle locking	1		
7	AUC 8114	Cap and damper	1		
8	AUC 4900	Washer(fibre)	1		
9	AUC 4587	Spring-piston-Blue	1		
10	AUC 5156	Screw-chamber to body	2		
11	AUD 9141	JET ASSEMBLY	1		
12	AUD 2129	Nut	1		
13	AUD 2193	Washer	1		
14	AUD 2194	Gland	1		
15	AUD 2195	Ferrule	1		
16	AUD 3101	Bearing-jet	1		
17	AUD 2987	Washer-jet centering	NLA		
18	AUC 2002	Screw-jet locking	1		
19	AUC 2114	Spring-jet locking	1		
	AUD 3235	Tab-locking	NLA		
20	AUD 3193	Screw-jet adjusting	NLA		
21	AUD 1242	Needle-jet-rich(h6)	1		
21	AUD 1478	Needle-jet-standard(an)	1		
21	AUD 1149	Needle-jet-weak(eb)	1	(E)12CD/-/H101 TO 8700	
22	AUC 1310	Chamber-float	1		
24	AUD 2677	Adaptor	1		
27	AUD 2891	Bolt-float chamber to body	1		
25	AUC 1318	Washer(rubber)	1		
23	AUC 1329	Washer-support	1		
28	AUD 9904	Float	1		
29	AUC 1152	Pin-hinge	1		
32	AUD 9096	Needle and seat	1		
30	AUD 9255	Lid-float chamber	1		
31	AJC 8459	Gasket-lid	1		
33	AUC 2175	Screw-lid	3		
	LWZ 303	Washer-spring	3		
34	AUC 1215	Plate-baffle	1		
35	AUC 8469	Spindle-throttle	1		
36	AUD 9876	Disc and valve-throttle	1		
37	AUC 1358	Screw-disc	2		
38	AUC 1145	Lever-throttle return	1		
39	AUC 1400	Lever-lost motion	1		
40	AUC 1424	Nut-lever	1		
41	AUC 1206	Washer-tab	1		
42	AUC 8483	Screw-fast idle	1		
43	AUC 2451	Spring-screw	1		
	AUD 3011	Screw-throttle stop	1		
44	AUD 9004	Lever and link-pick-up	1		
	PJZ 604	Screw-link to jet	1		
45	AUC 1371	Lever-cam	1		
46	AUC 8462	Spring-pick-up lever	1		
47	AUC 1520	Spring-cam lever	1		
48	AUC 1426	Bolt-pivot	1		
49	AUC 8473	Tube-pivot bolt	1		
50	AUC 8474	Washer-spring	1		
51	AUC 5032	Washer-distance	1		

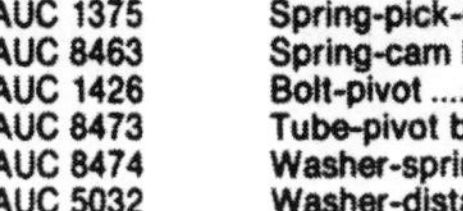
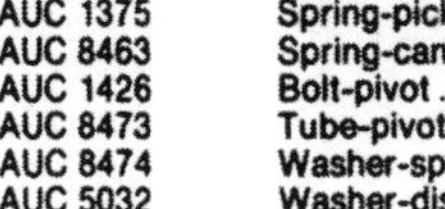
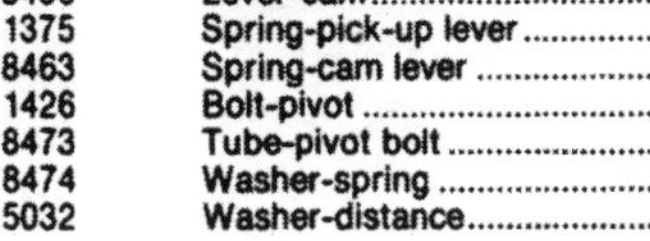
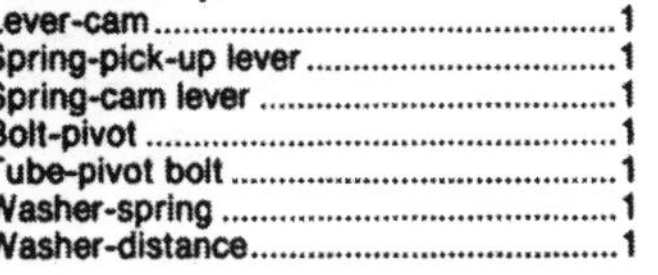

MDO153

AUSTIN-HEALEY SPRITE MK. 3 AND MK. 4 & MG MIDGET MK. 2 AND MK. 3

CARBURETTER INSTALLATION,NON VENTILATED TYPE-USA AND CANADA-continued

NO.	PART NO.	DESCRIPTION	QTY	CHANGE POINT	REMARKS
	AUC 9461	CARBURETTER ASSEMBLY-REAR	NLA		Use CUD 9032.
1	AUD 9871	Body	NLA		
2	AUC 8464	Pin-piston lifting	1		
3	AUC 1151	Spring-pin	1		
4	AUC 1250	Circlip-pin	NLA		Use AUD 4150.
4	AUD 4150	Circlip-pin	2		
5	AUD 9181	CHAMBER AND PISTON ASSEMBLY	1		
6	AUC 2057	Screw-needle locking	1		
7	AUC 8114	Cap and damper	1		
8	AUC 4900	Washer(fibre)	1		
9	AUC 4587	Spring-piston-Blue	1		
10	AUC 5156	Screw-chamber to body	2		
11	AUD 9861	JET ASSEMBLY	1		
12	AUD 2129	Nut	1		
13	AUD 2193	Washer	1		
14	AUD 2194	Gland	1		
15	AUD 2195	Ferrule	1		
16	AUD 3101	Bearing-jet	1		
17	AUD 2987	Washer-jet centering	NLA		
18	AUC 2002	Screw-jet locking	1		
19	AUC 2114	Spring-jet locking	1		
	AUD 3235	Tab-locking	NLA		
20	AUD 3193	Screw-jet adjusting	NLA		
21	AUD 1478	Needle-jet-standard(an)	1		
22	AUC 1310	Chamber-float	1	(E)12CD/-/H101 TO 8700	
24	AUD 2676	Adaptor	1		
27	AUD 2891	Bolt-float chamber to body	1		
25	AUC 1318	Washer(rubber)	1		
23	AUC 1329	Washer-support	1		
28	AUD 9904	Float	1		
29	AUC 1152	Pin-hinge	1		
32	AUD 9096	Needle and seat	1		
30	AUD 9203	Lid-float chamber	1		
31	AUC 8459	Gasket-lid	1		
33	AUC 2175	Screw-lid	3		
	LWZ 303	Washer-spring	3		
34	AUC 1215	Plate-baffle	1		
35	AUC 8469	Spindle-throttle	1		
36	AUD 9876	Disc and valve-throttle	1		
37	AUC 1358	Screw-disc	2		
38	AUD 2101	Lever-throttle return	1		
39	AUC 1400	Lever-lost motion	1		
40	AUC 1424	Nut-lever	1		
41	AUC 1206	Washer-tab	1		
42	AUC 8483	Screw-fast idle	1		
43	AUC 2451	Spring-screw	1		
	AUD 3011	Screw-throttle stop	1		
44	AUD 9005	Lever and link-pick-up	1		
	PJZ 604	Screw-link to jet	1		
45	AUC 8456	Lever-cam	1		
46	AUC 1375	Spring-pick-up lever	1		
47	AUC 8463	Spring-cam lever	1		
48	AUC 1426	Bolt-pivot	1		
49	AUC 8473	Tube-pivot bolt	1		
50	AUC 8474	Washer-spring	1		
51	AUC 5032	Washer-distance	1		

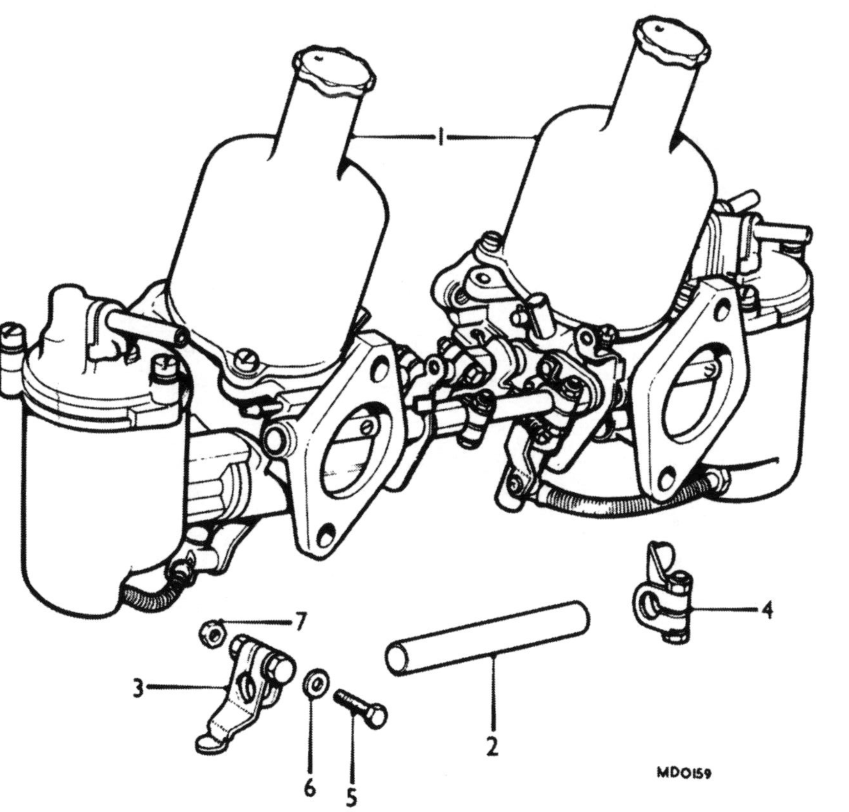

CARBURETTER INSTALLATION-VENTILATED TYPE-USA AND CANADA

NO.	PART NO.	DESCRIPTION	QTY	CHANGE POINT	REMARKS
	AUD 328	CARBURETTER INSTALLATION	NLA	(E)12CD/-/H8701 TO(+) (E)12CF/-/H101 TO(+) (E)12CG/-/H101 TO(+) (E)12CH/-/H101 TO(+)	Use front carburetter CUD 9031 with rear carburetter CUD 9032
1	AUD 404	CARBURETTER INSTALLATION	1 PR	(E)12CJ/Da/H21201 TO(+)	
	AUD 502	CARBURETTER INSTALLATION	NLA	(E)12V/587Z/101 TO(+)	Use front carburetter CUD 9180 with rear carburetter CUD 9181.
2	AUC 1457	Rod-jet connecting	1		
3	AUE 586	LEVER AND PIN ASSEMBLY-FRONT	1		
4	AUE 587	LEVER AND PIN ASSEMBLY-REAR	1		
	AUE 496	LEVER AND PIN ASSEMBLY-FRONT	1		
	AUE 685	LEVER AND PIN ASSEMBLY-REAR	1		
5	AJD 1042	Bolt	4		
6	AUC 8396	Washer-plain	4		
7	AJD 8012 Z	Nut	4		

(+) Change point not available.

AUSTIN-HEALEY SPRITE MK. 3 AND MK. 4 & MG MIDGET MK. 2 AND MK. 3

CARBURETTER INSTALLATION,VENTILATED TYPE-USA AND CANADA-continued

NO.	PART NO.	DESCRIPTION	QTY	CHANGE POINT	REMARKS
1	CUD 9031	CARBURETTER ASSEMBLY-FRONT	1		
2	CUD 2316	Body	1		
3	AUC 8464	Pin-piston lifting	1		
4	AUC 1151	Spring-pin	1		
5	AUC 1250	Circlip-pin	NLA		Use AUD 4150.
5	AID 4150	Circlip-pin	2		
6	AUD 9998	CHAMBER AND PISTON ASSEMBLY	1		
7	AUD 4007	Screw-needle locking	1		
8	AUC 8114	Cap and damper	1		
9	AUC 4900	Washer(fibre)	1		
10	AUC 4587	Spring-piston-Blue	1		
11	AUC 5156	Screw-chamber to body	2		
12	AUD 9141	JET ASSEMBLY	1		
13	AUD 2129	Nut	1		
14	AJD 2193	Washer	1		
15	AUD 2194	Gland	1		
16	AUD 2195	Ferrule	1		
17	AUD 3410	Bearing-jet	1		
18	AUD 2987	Washer-jet centering	NLA		
19	AUC 2002	Screw-jet locking	1		
20	AUC 2114	Spring-jet locking	1		
21	AUD 3235	Tab-locking	NLA		
22	AUD 3193	Screw-jet adjusting	NLA		
23	CUD 1002	Needle(AAC)	1	(E)12CD/-/H8701	
24	AUD 3306	Spring	1	TO(+)	
25	AUD 3836	Guide-needle	1	(E)12CF/-/H101 TO(+)	
26	AUC 1310	Chamber-float	1	(E)12CG/-/H101 TO(+)	
27	AUD 2677	Adaptor	1	(E)12CH/-/H101 TO(+)	
28	AUD 2891	Bolt-float chamber to body	1		
29	AUC 1318	Washer(rubber)	1		
30	AUC 1329	Washer-support	1	(+) Change point not available.	
31	AUD 9904	Float	1		
32	AUC 1152	Pin-hinge	1		
33	AUD 9096	Needle and seat	1		
34	AUD 9255	Lid-float chamber	1		
35	AUC 8459	Gasket-lid	1		
36	AUC 2175	Screw-lid	3		
37	LWZ 303	Washer-spring	3		
38	AUC 1215	Plate-baffle	1		
39	AUC 8469	Spindle-throttle	1		
40	AUD 9876	Disc and valve-throttle	1		
41	AUC 1358	Screw-disc	2		
42	AUC 1145	Lever-throttle return	1		
43	AUC 1400	Lever-lost motion	1		
44	AUC 1424	Nut-lever	1		
45	AUD 3323	Washer-tab	1		
46	AUC 8483	Screw-fast idle	1		
47	AUC 2451	Spring-screw	1		
48	AUD 3011	Screw-throttle stop	1		
49	AUD 9004	Lever and link-pick-up	1		
50	PJZ 604	Screw-link to jet	1		
51	AUC 1371	Lever-cam	1		
52	AUC 8462	Spring-pick-up lever	1		
53	AUC 1520	Spring-cam lever	1		
54	AUC 1426	Bolt-pivot	1		
55	AUC 8473	Tube-pivot bolt	1		
56	AUC 8474	Washer-spring	1		
57	AUC 5032	Washer-distance	1		

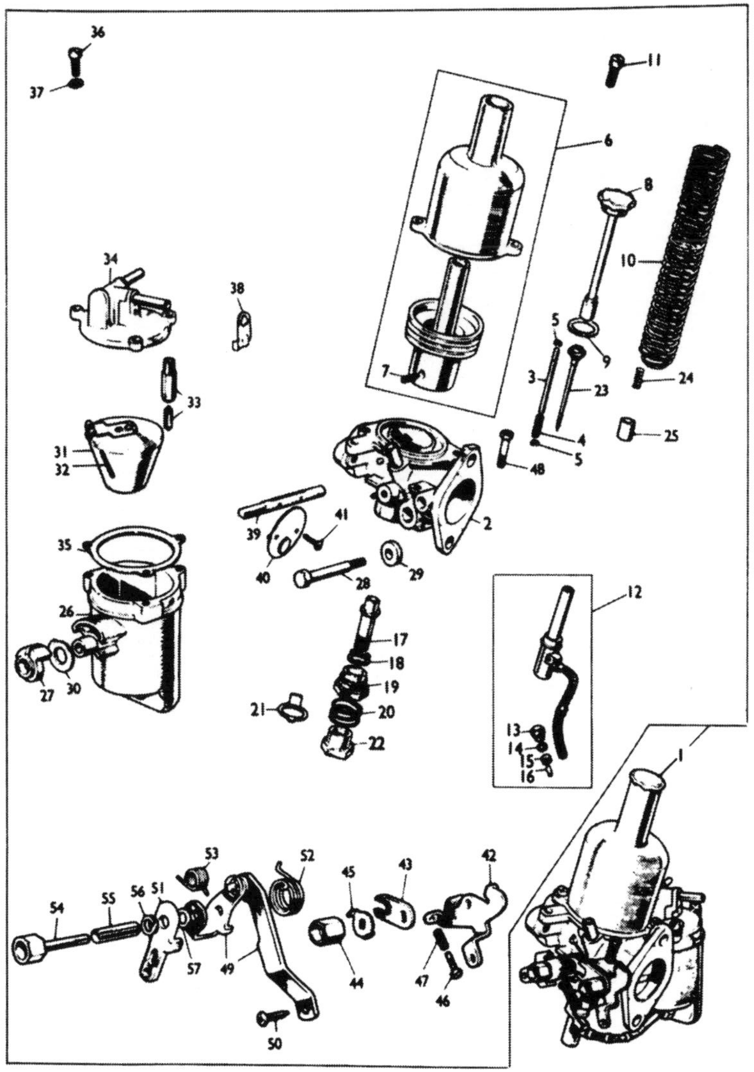

AUSTIN-HEALEY SPRITE MK. 3 AND MK. 4 & MG MIDGET MK. 2 AND MK. 3

CARBURETTER INSTALLATION-VENTILATED TYPE-USA AND CANADA-continued

NO.	PART NO.	DESCRIPTION	QTY	CHANGE POINT	REMARKS
1	CUD 9081	CARBURETTER ASSEMBLY-FRONT	1PR	(E)12CJ/Da/H21201 TO(+)	
2	CUD 2316	Body	1		
3	AUC 8464	Pin-piston lifting	1		
4	AUC 1151	Spring-pin	1		
5	AUC 1250	Circlip-pin	NLA		Use AUD 4150.
5	AUD 4150	Circlip-pin	2		
6	AUD 9998	CHAMBER/PISTON ASSEMBLY	1		
7	AUD 4007	Screw-needle locking	1		
8	AUC 8114	Cap and damper	1		
9	AUC 4900	Washer(fibre)	1		
10	AUC 4587	Spring-piston-Blue	1		
11	AUC 5156	Screw-chamber to body	2		
12	AUD 9860	JET ASSEMBLY	1		
13	AUD 2129	nUT	1		
14	AJD 2193	Washer	1		
15	AUD 2194	Gland	1		
16	AUD 2195	Ferrule	1		
17	AUD 3410	Bearing-jet	1		
19	AUC 2002	Screw-jet locking	1		
20	AUC 2114	Spring-jet locking	1		
21	AUD 3235	Tab-locking	NLA		
22	AUD 3193	Screw-jet adjusting	NLA		
23	CUD 1002	Needle(AAC)	1		
24	AUD 3306	Spring	1		
25	AUD 3836	Guide-needle	1		
26	AUC 1310	Chamber-float	1		
27	AUD 2677	Adaptor	1		
28	AUD 2891	Bolt-float chamber to body	1	(+) Change point not available	
29	AUC 1318	Washer(rubber)	1		
30	AUC 1329	Washer-support	1		
31	AUD 9904	Float	1		
32	AUC 1152	Pin-hinge	1		
33	AUD 9096	Needle and seat	1		
34	AUD 9207	Lid-float chamber	1		
35	AUC 8459	Gasket-lid	1		
36	AUC 2175	Screw-lid	3		
37	LWZ 303	Washer-spring	3		
38	AUC 1215	Plate-baffle	1		
39	AUC 8469	Spindle-throttle	1		
40	AUD 9876	Disc and valve-throttle	1		
41	AUC 1358	Screw-disc	2		
42	AUC 1145	Lever-throttle return	1		
43	AUC 1400	Lever-lost motion	1		
44	AUC 1424	Nut-lever	1		
45	AUD 3323	Washer-tab	1		
46	AUC 8483	Screw-fast idle	1		
47	AUC 2451	Spring-screw	1		
48	AUD 3011	Screw-throttle stop	1		
49	CUD 2686	Lever and link-pick-up	1		
50	PJZ 604	Screw	1		
51	AUD 3287	Lever-cam	1		
52	AUC 8467	Spring-pick-up lever	1		
53	AUD 2431	Spring-cam lever	1		
54	AUC 1426	Bolt-pivot	2		
55	AUC 8473	Tube-pivot bolt	2		
	AUD 2430	Tube-outer	2		
57	AUD 2433	Washer-distance	2		
	AUD 2429	Washer-skid	2		

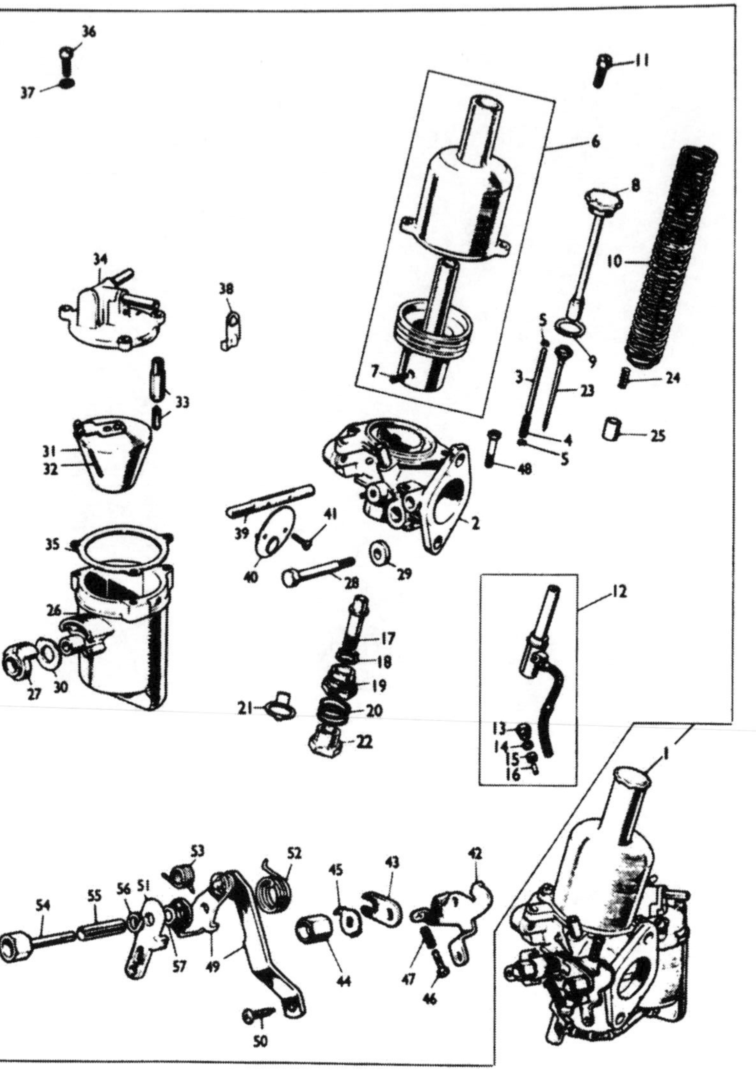

AUSTIN-HEALEY SPRITE MK. 3 AND MK. 4 & MG MIDGET MK. 2 AND MK. 3

NO.	PART NO.	DESCRIPTION	QTY	CHANGE POINT	REMARKS
		CARBURETTER INSTALLATION-VENTILATED TYPE-USA AND CANADA-continued			
1	CUD 9180	CARBURETTER ASSEMBLY-FRONT	1	(E)12V/587Z/101 TO(+)	
1	CUD 9236	CARBURETTER ASSEMBLY-FRONT	1	(E)12V/671Z/101 ON	
2	AUD 9990	Body	NLA		
3	AUC 8464	Pin-piston lifting	1		
4	AUC 1151	Spring-pin	1		
5	AUC 1250	Circlip-pin	NLA		Use AUD 4150.
5	AUD 4150	Circlip-pin	2		
6	AUD 9998	CHAMBER AND PISTON ASSEMBLY	1		
7	AUD 3308	Screrw-needle locking	1		
8	AUC 8114	Cap and damper	1		
9	AUC 4900	Washer(fibre)	1		
10	AUC 4587	Spring-piston-Blue	1	(E)12V/587Z/101 TO(+)	
11	AUC 5156	Screw-chamber to body	2		
12	AUD 9141	JET ASSEMBLY	1		
13	AUD 2129	Nut	1	(E)12V/671Z/101 ON	
14	AJD 2193	Washer	1		
15	AUD 2194	Gland	1		
16	AUD 2195	Ferrule	1		
17	AUD 3410	Bearing-jet	1		
19	AUC 2002	Screw-jet locking	1		
20	AUC 2114	Spring-jet locking	1		
21	AUD 3235	Tab-locking	NLA		
22	AUC 8461	Screw-jet adjusting	1		
23	CUD 1017	Needle(AAT)	1	(E)12V/587Z/101 TO(+)	
23	CUD 1026	Needle(ABC)	1	(E)12V/587Z/101 ON	

(+) Change point not available

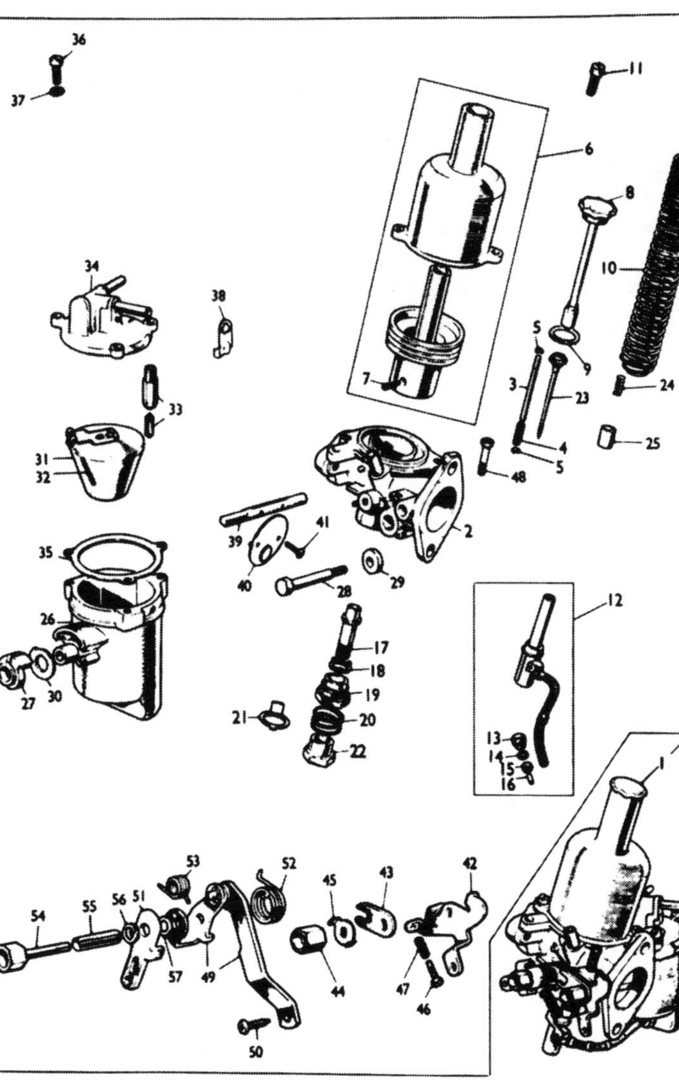

AUSTIN-HEALEY SPRITE MK. 3 AND MK. 4 & MG MIDGET MK. 2 AND MK. 3

CARBURETTER INSTALLATION-VENTILATED TYPE-USA AND CANADA-continued

NO.	PART NO.	DESCRIPTION	QTY	CHANGE POINT	REMARKS
24	AUD 3306	Spring	1		
25	AUD 3836	Guide-needle	1		
26	AUC 1310	Chamber-float	1		
27	AUD 2677	Adaptor	1		
28	AUD 2891	Bolt-float chamber to body	1		
29	AUC 1318	Washer(rubber)	1		
30	AUC 1329	Washer-support	1		
31	AUD 9904	Float	1		
32	AUC 1152	Pin-hinge	1		
33	AUD 9095	Needle and seat	1		
34	AUD 9207	Lid-float chamber	1		
35	AUC 8459	Gasket-lid	1		
36	AUC 2175	Screw-lid	3		
37	LWZ 303	Washer-spring	3		
39	AUC 8469	Spindle-throttle	1		
40	CUD 2799	Disc and valve-throttle	1	(E)12V/587Z/101	
41	AUC 1358	Screw-disc	2	TO(+)	
42	AUC 1145	Lever-throttle return	1	(E)12V/671Z/101 ON	
43	AUC 1400	Lever-lost motion	1		
44	AUC 1424	Nut-lever	1		
45	AUD 3323	Washer-tab	1		
46	AUC 8483	Screw-fast idle	1		
47	AUC 2451	Spring-screw	1		
48	AUD 3011	Screw-throttle stop	1		
49	CUD 2686	Lever and link-pick-up	1		
50	PJZ 604	Screw	1		
51	AUD 3287	Lever-cam	1		
52	AUC 8462	Spring-pick-up lever	1		
53	AUD 2431	Spring-cam lever	1		
54	AUC 1426	Bolt-pivot	2		
55	AUC 8473	Tube-pivot bolt	2		
	AUD 2430	Tube-outer	2		
57	AUD 2433	Washer-distance	2		
	AUD 2429	Washer-skid	2		

(+) Change point not available

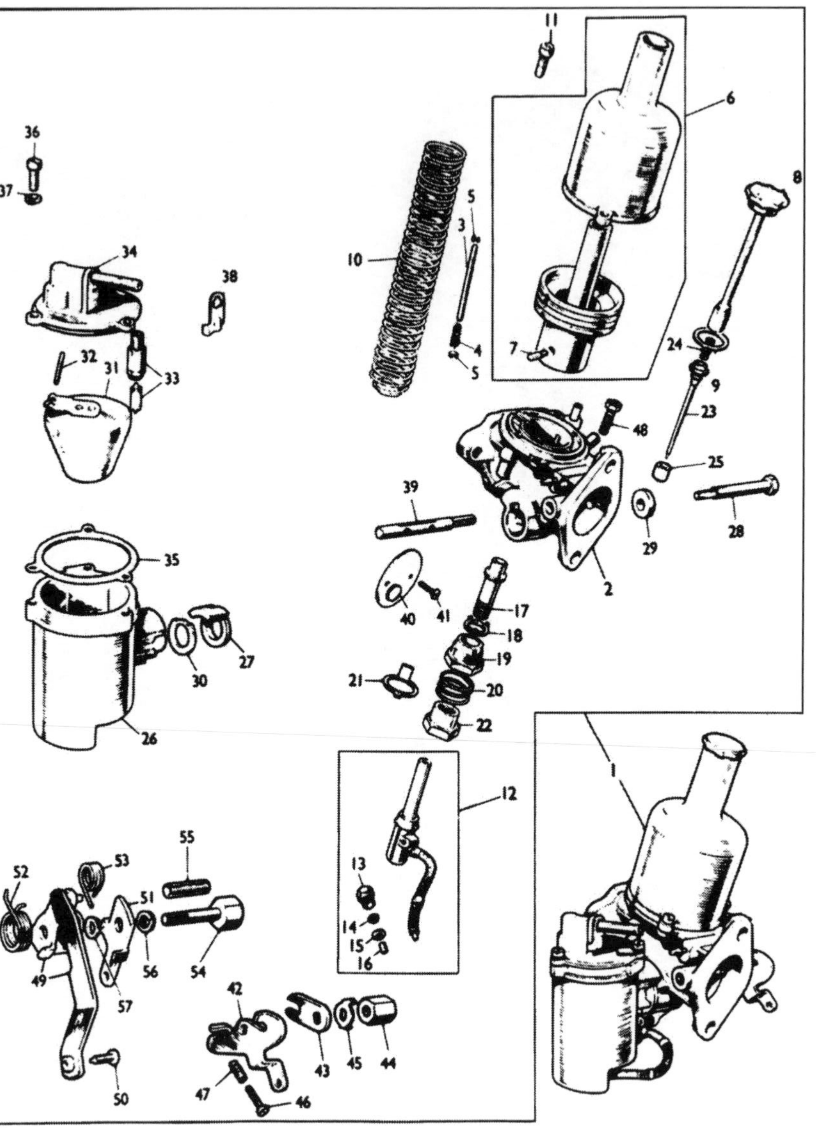

AUSTIN-HEALEY SPRITE MK. 3 AND MK. 4 & MG MIDGET MK. 2 AND MK. 3

CARBURETTER INSTALLATION-VENTILATED TYPE-USA AND CANADA-continued

NO.	PART NO.	DESCRIPTION	QTY	CHANGE POINT	REMARKS
1	CUD 9032	CARBURETTER ASSEMBLY-REAR	1		
2	CUD 2318	Body	1		
3	AUC 8464	Pin-piston lifting	1		
4	AUC 1151	Spring-pin	1		
5	AUC 1250	Circlip-pin	NLA		Use AUD 4150.
5	AUD 4150	Circlip-pin	2		
6	AUD 9998	CHAMBER AND PISTON ASSEMBLY	1		
7	AUD 4007	Screw-needle locking	1		
8	AUC 8114	Cap and damper	1		
9	AUC 4900	Washer(fibre)	1		
10	AUC 4587	Spring-piston-Blue	1		
11	AUC 5156	Screw-chamber to body	2		
12	AUD 9142	JET ASSEMBLY	1		
13	AUD 2129	Nut	1		
14	AUD 2193	Washer	1		
15	AUD 2194	Gland	1		
16	AUD 2195	Ferrule	1		
17	AUD 3410	Bearing-jet	1		
18	AUD 2987	Washer-jet centering	NLA		
19	AUC 2002	Screw-jet locking	1		
20	AUC 2114	Spring-jet locking	1		
21	AUD 3235	Tab-locking	NLA		
22	AUD 3193	Screw-jet adjusting	NLA	(E)12CD/-/H8701 TO(+)	
23	CUD 1002	Needle assembly(AAC)	1		
24	AUD 3306	Spring	1	(E)12CF/-/H101 TO(+)	
25	AUD 3836	Guide-needle	1	(E)12CG/-/H101 TO(+)	
26	AUC 1310	Chamber-float	1	(E)12CH/-/H101 TO(+)	
27	AUD 2676	Adaptor	1		
28	AUD 2891	Bolt-float chamber to body	1	(+) Change point not available	
29	AUC 1318	Washer(rubber)	1		
30	AUC 1329	Washer-support	1		
31	AUD 9904	Float	1		
32	AUC 1152	Pin-hinge	1		
33	AUD 9096	Needle and seat	1		
34	AUD 9203	Lid-float chamber	1		
35	AUC 8459	Gasket-lid	1		
36	AUC 2175	Screw-lid	3		
37	LWZ 303	Washer-spring	3		
38	AUC 1215	Plate-baffle	1		
39	AUC 8469	Spindle-throttle	1		
40	AUD 9876	Disc and valve-throttle	1		
41	AUC 1358	Screw-disc	2		
42	AUD 2101	Lever-throttle return	1		
43	AUC 1400	Lever-lost motion	1		
44	AUC 1424	Nut-lever	1		
45	AUD 3323	Washer-tab	1		
46	AUC 8483	Screw-fast idle	1		
47	AUC 2451	Spring-screw	1		
48	AUD 3011	Screw-throttle stop	1		
49	AUD 9005	Lever and link-pick-up	1		
50	PJZ 604	Screw-link to jet	1		
51	AUC 8456	Lever-cam	1		
52	AUC 1375	Spring-pick-up lever	1		
53	AUC 8463	Spring-cam lever	1		
54	AUC 1426	Bolt-pivot	1		
55	AUC 8473	Tube-pivot bolt	1		
56	AUC 8474	Washer-spring	1		
57	AUC 5032	Washer-distance	1		

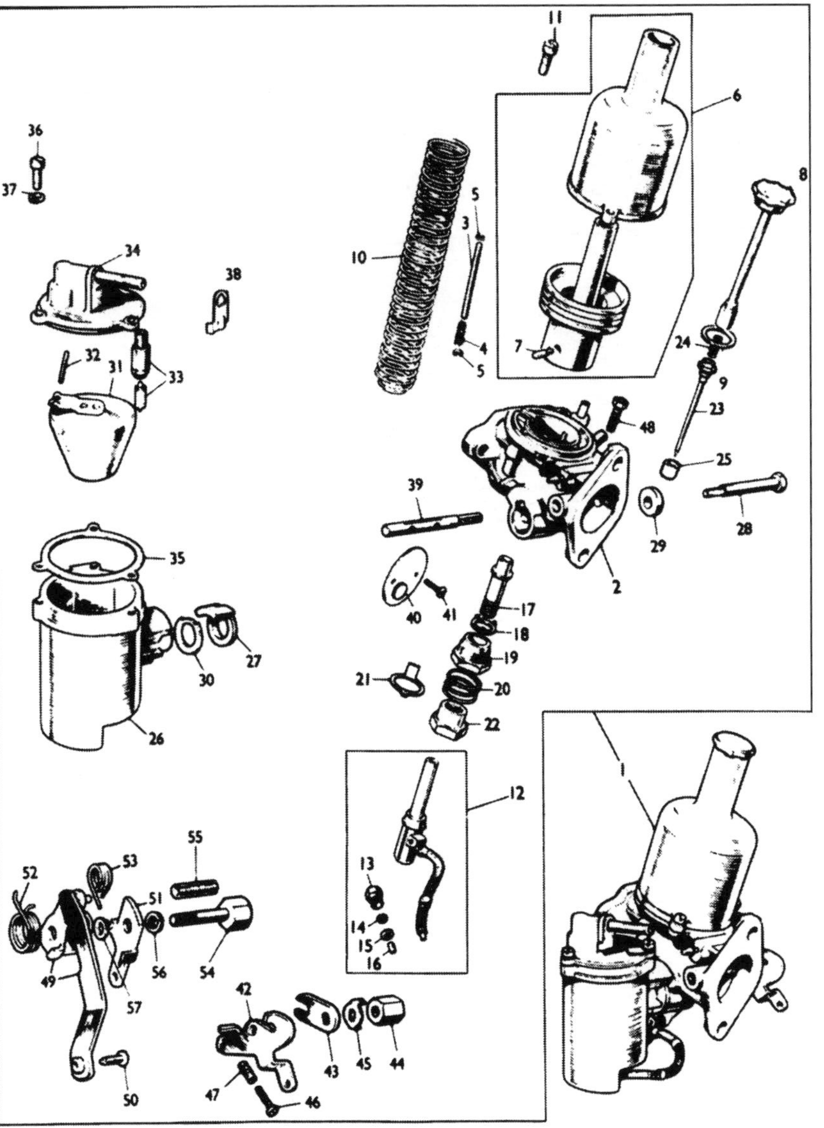

AUSTIN-HEALEY SPRITE MK. 3 AND MK. 4 & MG MIDGET MK. 2 AND MK. 3

CARBURETTER INSTALLATION-VENTILATED TYPE.USA AND CANADA-continued.

NO.	PART NO.	DESCRIPTION	QTY	CHANGE POINT	REMARKS
1	CUD 9082	CARBURETTER ASSEMBLY-REAR	1		
2	CUD 2318	Body	1		
3	AUC 8464	Pin-piston lifting	1		
4	AUC 1151	Spring-pin	1		
5	AUC 1250	Circlip-pin	NLA		Use AUD 4150.
5	AUD 4150	Circlip-pin	2		
6	AUD 9998	CHAMBER AND PISTON ASSEMBLY	1		
7	AUD 4007	Screw-needle locking	1		
8	AUC 8114	Cap and damper	1		
9	AUC 4900	Washer(fibre)	1		
10	AUC 4587	Spring-piston-Blue	1		
11	AUC 5156	Screw-chamber to body	2		
12	AUD 9142	JET ASSEMBLY	1		
13	AUD 2129	Nut	1		
14	AUD 2193	Washer	1		
15	AUD 2194	Gland	1		
16	AUD 2195	Ferrule	1		
17	AUD 3410	Bearing	1		
19	AUC 2002	Screw-jet locking	1		
20	AUC 2114	Spring-jet locking	1		
21	AUD 3235	Tab-locking	NLA		
22	AUD 3193	Screw-jet adjusting	NLA		
23	CUD 1002	Needle(AAC)	1	(E)12CJ/Da/H21201	
24	AUD 3306	Spring	1	TO(+)	
25	AUD 3836	Guide-needle	1		
26	AUC 1310	Chamber-float	1	(+) Change point not available	
27	AUD 2676	Adaptor	1		
28	AUD 289	Bolt-float chamber to body	1		
29	AUC 1318	Washer(rubber)	1		
30	AUC 1329	Washer-support	1		
31	AUD 9904	Float	1		
32	AUC 1152	Pin-hinge	1		
33	AUD 9096	Needle and seat	1		
34	AUD 9651	Lid-float chamber	1		
35	AUC 8459	Gasket-lid	1		
36	AUC 2175	Screw-lid	3		
37	LWZ 303	Washer-spring	3		
38	AUC 1215	Plate-baffle	1		
39	AUC 8469	Spindle-throttle	1		
40	AUD 9876	Disc and valve-throttle	1		
41	AUC 1358	Screw-disc	2		
42	AUD 2101	Lever-throttle return	1		
43	AUC 1400	Lever-lost motion	1		
44	AUC 1424	Nut-lever	1		
45	AUD 3323	Washer-tab	1		
46	AUC 8483	Screw-fast idle	1		
47	AUC 2451	Spring-screw	1		
48	AUD 3011	Screw-throttle stop	1		
49	CUD 2687	Lever and link-pick-up	1		
50	PJZ 604	Screw	1		
51	AUC 3288	Lever-cam	1		
52	AUC 1375	Spring-pick-up lever	1		
53	AUD 2432	Spring-cam lever	1		
54	AUC 1426	Bolt-pivot	1		
55	AUC 8473	Tube-pivot bolt	1		
	AUD 2430	Tube-outer	2		
57	AUD 2433	Washer-distance	2		
	AUD 2429	Washer-skid	1		

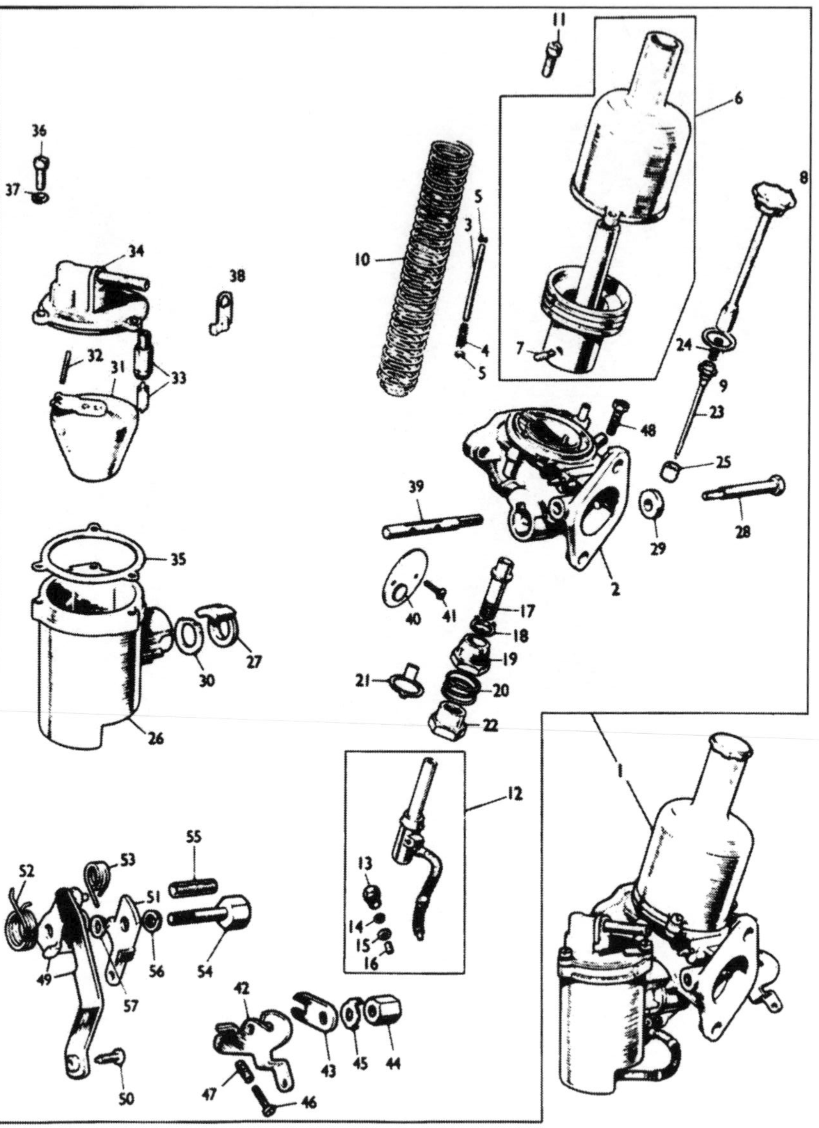

AUSTIN-HEALEY SPRITE MK. 3 AND MK. 4 & MG MIDGET MK. 2 AND MK. 3

CARBURETTER INSTALLATION-VENTILATED TYPE-USA AND CANADA-continued

NO.	PART NO.	DESCRIPTION	QTY	CHANGE POINT	REMARKS
1	CUD 9181	CARBURETTER ASSEMBLY-REAR	1	(E)12V/587Z/101 TO(+)	
1	CUD 9237	CARBURETTER ASSEMBLY-REAR	1	(E)12V/671Z/101 ON	
2	CUD 2318	Body	1		
3	AUC 8464	Pin-piston lifting	1		
4	AUC 1151	Spring-pin	1		
5	AUC 1250	Circlip-pin	NLA		Use AUD 4150.
5	AUD 4150	Circlip-pin	2		
6	AUD 9998	CHAMBER AND PISTON ASSEMBLY	1		
7	AUD 3308	Screw-needle locking	1		
8	AUC 8114	Cap and damper	1	(E)12V/587Z/101	
9	AUC 4900	Washer(fibre)	1	TO(+)	
10	AUC 4587	Spring-piston-Blue	1	(E)12V/671Z/101 ON	
11	AUC 5156	Screw-chamber to body	2		
12	AUD 9142	JET ASSEMBLY	1		
13	AUD 2129	Nut	1		
14	AUD 2193	Washer	1		
15	AUD 2194	Gland	1		
16	AUD 2195	Ferrule	1		
17	AUD 3410	Bearing	1		
19	AUC 2002	Screw-jet locking	1		
20	AUC 2114	Spring-jet locking	1		
21	AUD 3235	Tab-locking	NLA		
22	AUC 8461	Screw-jet adjusting	1		
23	CUD 1017	Needle(AAT)	1	(E)12V/587Z/101 TO(+)	
23	CUD 1026	Needle(ABC)	1	(E)12V/671Z/101 ON	

(+) Change point not available

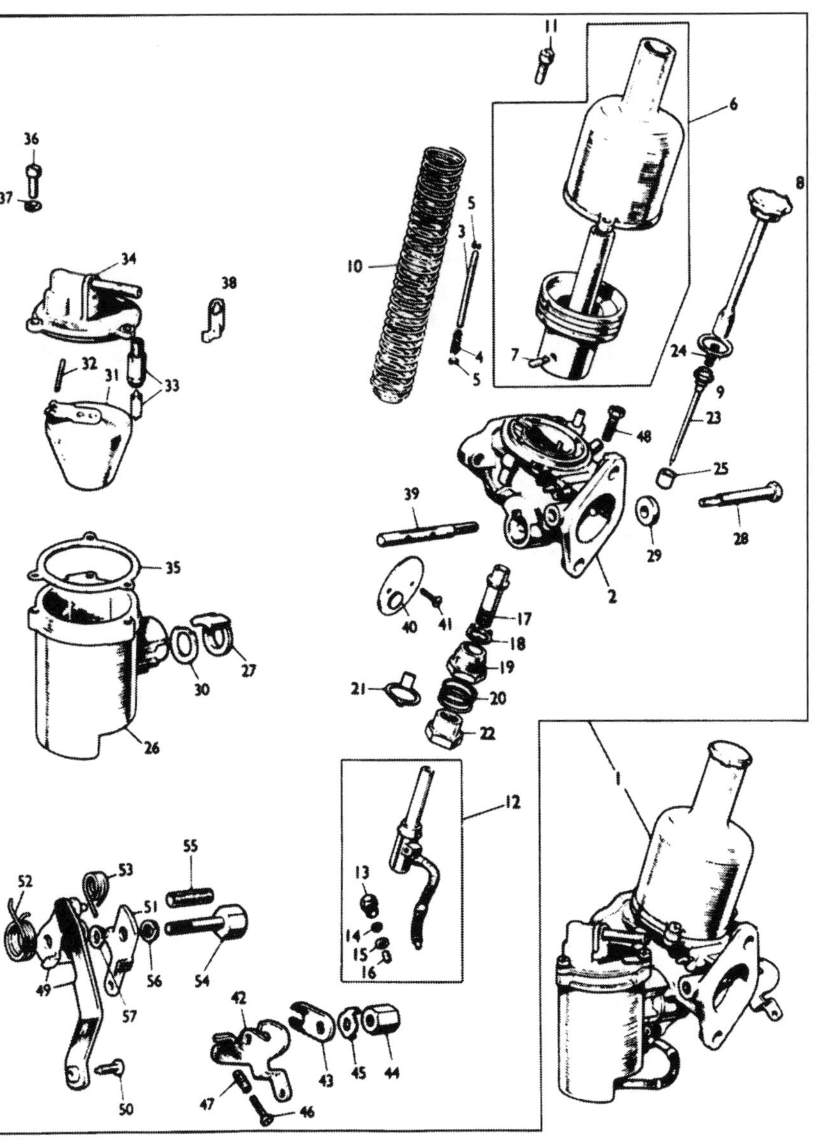

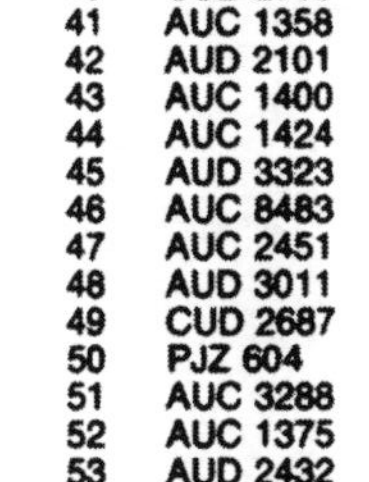

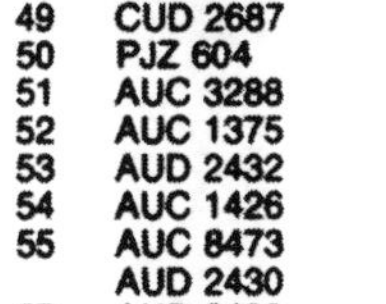

AUSTIN-HEALEY SPRITE MK. 3 AND MK. 4 & MG MIDGET MK. 2 AND MK. 3

CARBURETTER INSTALLATION-VENTILATED TYPE-USA AND CANADA-continued

NO.	PART NO.	DESCRIPTION	QTY	CHANGE POINT	REMARKS
24	AUD 3306	Spring	1		
25	AUD 3836	Guide-needle	1		
26	AUC 1310	Chamber-float	1		
27	AUC 2676	Adaptor	1		
28	AUD 289	Bolt-float chamber to body	1		
29	AUC 1318	Washer(rubber)	1		
30	AUC 1329	Washer-support	1		
31	AUD 9904	Float	1		
32	AUC 1152	Pin-hinge	1		
33	AUD 9095	Needle and seat	1		
34	AUD 9651	Lid-float chamber	1		
35	AUC 8459	Gasket-lid	1		
36	AUC 2175	Screw-lid	3		
37	LWZ 303	Washer-spring	3		
39	AUC 8469	Spindle-throttle	1		
40	CUD 2799	Disc and valve-throttle	1	(E)12V/587Z/101	
41	AUC 1358	Screw-disc	2	TO(+)	
42	AUD 2101	Lever-throttle return	1	(E)12V/671Z/101 ON	
43	AUC 1400	Lever-lost motion	1		
44	AUC 1424	Nut-lever	1		
45	AUD 3323	Washer-tab	1		
46	AUC 8483	Screw-fast idle	1		
47	AUC 2451	Spring-screw	1		
48	AUD 3011	Screw-throttle stop	1		
49	CUD 2687	Lever and link-pick-up	1		
50	PJZ 604	Screw	1		
51	AUC 3288	Lever-cam	1		
52	AUC 1375	Spring-pick-up lever	1		
53	AUD 2432	Spring-cam lever	1		
54	AUC 1426	Bolt-pivot	1		
55	AUC 8473	Tube-pivot bolt	1		
	AUD 2430	Tube-outer	2		
57	AUD 2433	Washer-distance	2		
	AUD 2429	Washer-skid	1		

(+) Change point not available

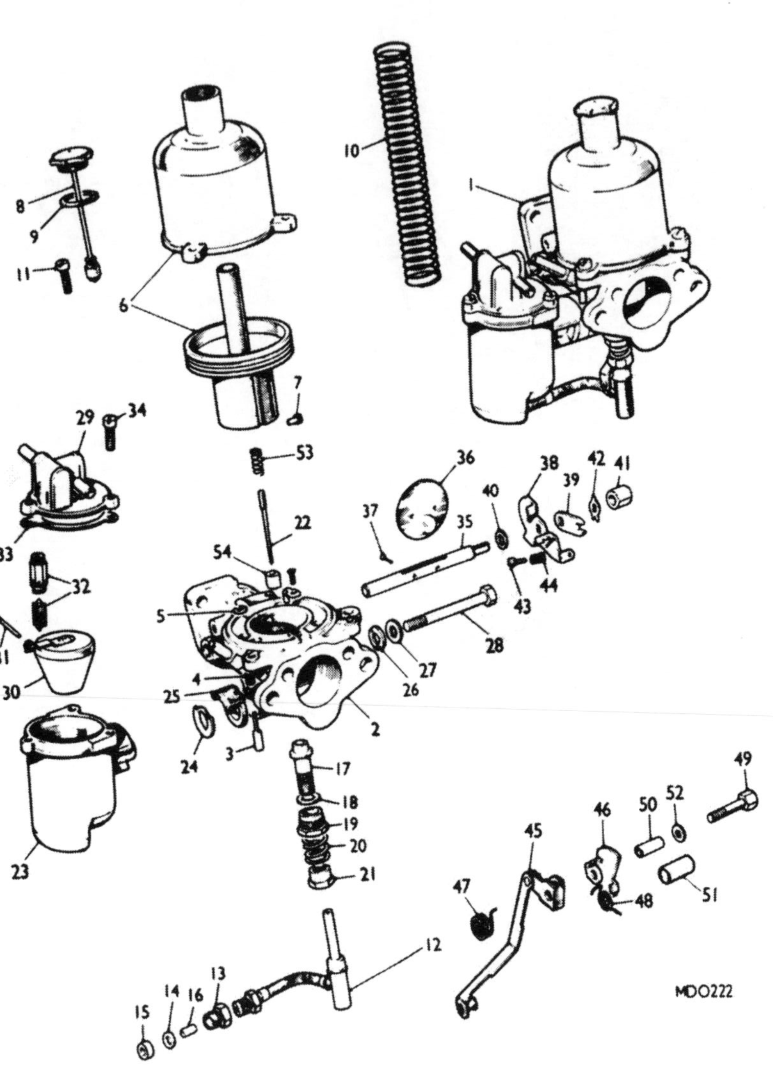

AUSTIN-HEALEY SPRITE MK. 3 AND MK. 4 & MG MIDGET MK. 2 AND MK. 3

CARBURETTER INSTALLATION-MIDGET 1500,NOT USA AND CANADA.

NO.	PART NO.	DESCRIPTION	QTY	CHANGE POINT	REMARKS
1	CUD 9334	CARBURETTER ASSEMBLY-FRONT	1		
3	AUC 1249	Pin-piston lifting	1		
4	AUC 1151	Spring-pin	1		
5	AUC 1250	Circlip-pin	NLA		Use AUD 4150.
5	AUD 4150	Circlip-pin	1		
6	AUD 9988	CHAMBER AND PISTON ASSEMBLY	1		
7	AUD 4252	Screw-needle locking	1		
8	AUC 8114	Cap and damper	1		
9	AUC 4900	Washer(fibre)	1		
10	AUC 4387	Spring-piston-Red	1		
11	AUC 2175	Screw-chamber to body	3		
12	AUD 9451	JET ASSEMBLY	1		
13	AUD 2129	Nut	1		
14	AUD 2193	Washer	1		
15	AUD 2194	Gland	1		
16	AUD 2195	Ferrule	1		
17	AUD 3414	Bearing-jet	1		
18	AUC 8478	Washer-jet bearing(brass)	1		
19	AUC 2002	Screw-jet locking	1		
20	AUC 2114	Spring-jet locking	1		
21	AUC 8461	Screw-jet adjusting	1		
22	CUD 1041	Needle-jet(ABT)	1		
53	AUD 3306	Spring-needle	1		
54	AUD 4288	Guide-needle	1		
23	AUD 2140	Chamber-float	1		
24	AUC 1329	Washer-support	1		
25	AUC 1316	Adaptor	1		
26	AUC 1318	Washer(rubber)	1		
28	AUD 3017	Bolt-float chamber fixing	1		
29	AUD 9257	Lid	1		
30	AUD 9904	Float	1		
31	AUC 1152	Pin-hinge	1		
32	AUD 9095	Needle and seat	1		
33	AUC 8459	Gasket-lid	1		
34	AUC 2175	Screw-lid	3		
	LWZ 303	Washer-spring	3		

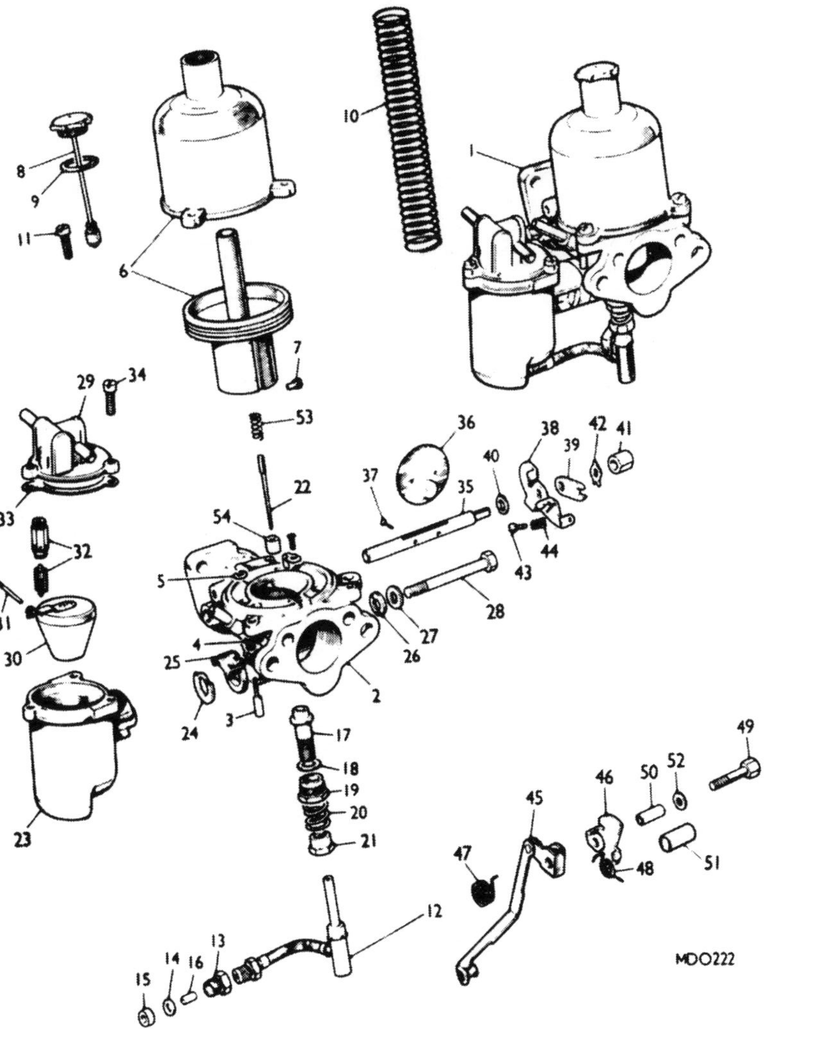

AUSTIN-HEALEY SPRITE MK. 3 AND MK. 4 & MG MIDGET MK. 2 AND MK. 3

NO.	PART NO.	DESCRIPTION	QTY	CHANGE POINT	REMARKS
		CARBURETTER INSTALLATION-MIDGET 1500,NOT USA AND CANADA-continued.			
35	AUC 1302	Spindle-throttle	1		
36	CUD 3070	Disc-throttle	1		
37	AUC 1358	Screw-disc	2		
38	AUD 4862	Lever-throttle return	1		
39	AUD 4939	Lever-lost motion	1		
40	AUC 2625	Washer-spacing	1		
41	AUC 1424	Nut-lever	1		
42	AUD 3323	Washer-tab	1		
43	AUD 4886	Screw-fast-idle	1		
	NH 604041	Nut-fast-idle	1		
44	AUC 2451	Spring-screw	1		
43	AUC 8483	Screw-throttle stop	1		
	AJD 8014 Z	Nut-throttle stop	1		
45	CUD 3073	Lever and link-pick-up	1		
	PTZ 605	Screw-link to jet	1		
46	AUD 4861	Lever-cam	1		
47	AUC 1375	Spring-pick-up lever	1		
48	AUC 2432	Spring-cam lever	1		
49	AUC 1426	Bolt-pivot	1		
50	AUC 8473	Tube-pivot bolt	1		
51	AUD 2430	Tube-outer	1		
52	AUD 2433	Washer-distance	1		
52	AUD 2429	Washer-skid	2		

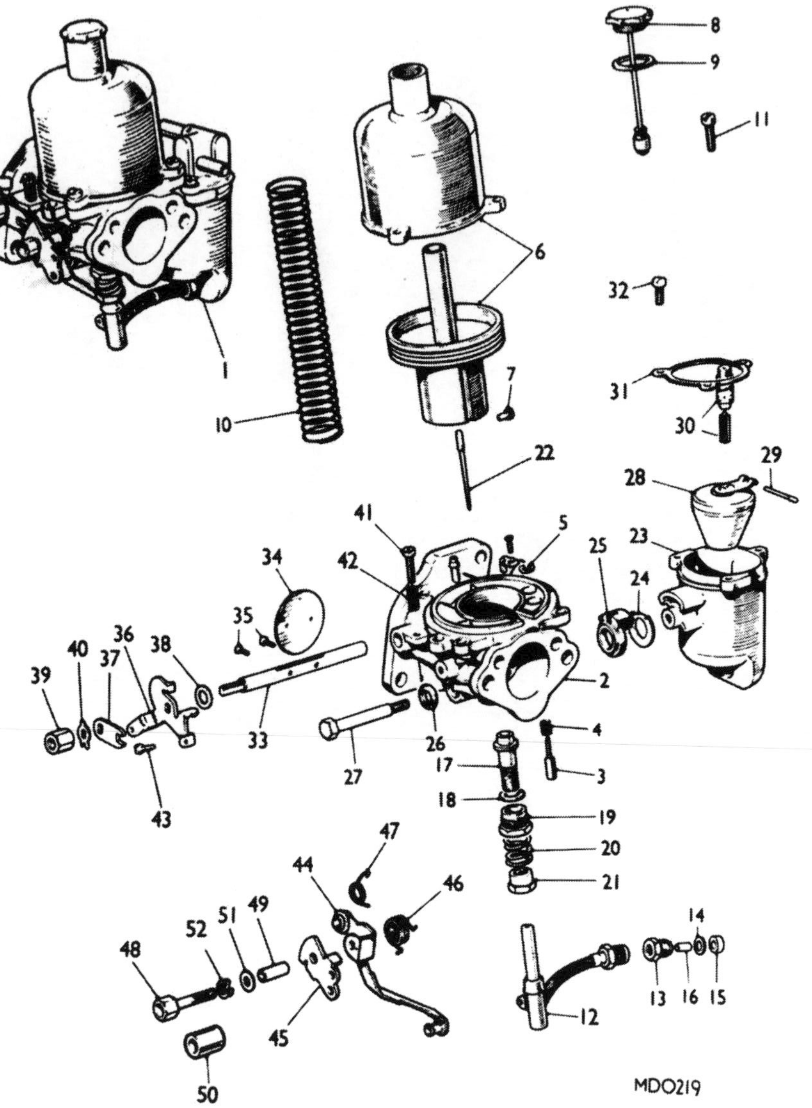

AUSTIN-HEALEY SPRITE MK. 3 AND MK. 4 & MG MIDGET MK. 2 AND MK. 3

NO.	PART NO.	DESCRIPTION	QTY	CHANGE POINT	REMARKS
		CARBURETTER INSTALLATION-MIDGET 1500,NOT USA AND CANADA-continued.			
1	CUD 9335	CARBURETTER ASSEMBLY-REAR	1		
3	AUC 1249	Pin-piston lifting	1		
4	AUC 1151	Spring-pin	1		
5	AUC 1250	Circlip-pin	NLA		Use AUD 4150.
5	AUD 4150	Circlip	1		
6	AUD 9988	CHAMBER AND PISTON ASSEMBLY	1		
7	AUD 4252	Screw-needle locking	1		
8	AUC 8114	Cap and damper	1		
9	AUC 4900	Washer(fibre)	1		
10	AUC 4387	Spring-piston-Red	1		
11	AUC 2175	Screw-chamber to body	3		
12	AUD 9450	JET ASSEMBLY	1		
13	AUD 2129	Nut	1		
14	AUD 2193	Washer	1		
15	AUD 2194	Gland	1		
16	AUD 2195	Ferrule	1		
17	AUD 3414	Bearing-jet	1		
18	AUC 8478	Washer-jet bearing(brass)	1		
19	AUC 2002	Screw-jet locking	1		
20	AUC 2114	Spring-jet locking	1		
21	AUC 8461	Screw-jet adjusting	1		
22	CUD 1041	Needle-jet(ABT)	1		
53	AUD 3306	Spring-needle	1		
54	AUD 4288	Guide-needle	1		
23	AUD 2140	Chamber-float	1		
24	AUC 1329	Washer-support	1		
25	AUC 1366	Adaptor	1		
26	AUC 1318	Washer(rubber)	1		
27	AUD 3017	Bolt-float chamber fixing	1		
	AUD 9254	Lid	1		
28	AUD 9904	Float	1		
29	AUC 1152	Pin-hinge	1		
30	AUD 9095	Needle and seat	1		
31	AUC 8459	Gasket-lid	1		
32	AUC 2175	Screw-lid	3		
	LWZ 303	Washer-spring	3		

AUSTIN-HEALEY SPRITE MK. 3 AND MK. 4 & MG MIDGET MK. 2 AND MK. 3

MDO219

NO.	PART NO.	DESCRIPTION	QTY	CHANGE POINT	REMARKS
		CARBURETTER INSTALLATION-MIDGET 1500,NOT USA AND CANADA-continued.			
33	AUC 1302	Spindle-throttle	1		
34	CUD 3070	Disc-throttle	1		
35	AUC 1358	Screw-disc	2		
36	AUD 4863	Lever-throttle return	1		
37	AUD 4939	Lever-lost motion	1		
38	AUC 2625	Washer-spacing	1		
39	AUC 1424	Nut-lever	1		
40	AUD 3323	Washer-tab	1		
41	AUD 4886	Screw-fast-idle	1		
	NH 604041	Nut-fast-idle	1		
42	AUC 2451	Spring-screw	1		
43	AUC 8483	Screw-throttle stop	1		
	AJD 8014 Z	Nut-throttle stop	1		
44	CUD 3072	Lever and link-pick-up	1		
	PTZ 605	Screw-link to jet	1		
45	AUD 4860	Lever-cam	1		
46	AUC 8462	Spring-pick-up lever	1		
47	AUD 2431	Spring-cam lever	1		
48	AUC 1426	Bolt-pivot	1		
49	AUC 8473	Tube-pivot bolt	1		
50	AUD 2430	Tube-outer	1		
51	AUD 2433	Washer-distance	1		
52	AUD 2429	Washer-skid	2		

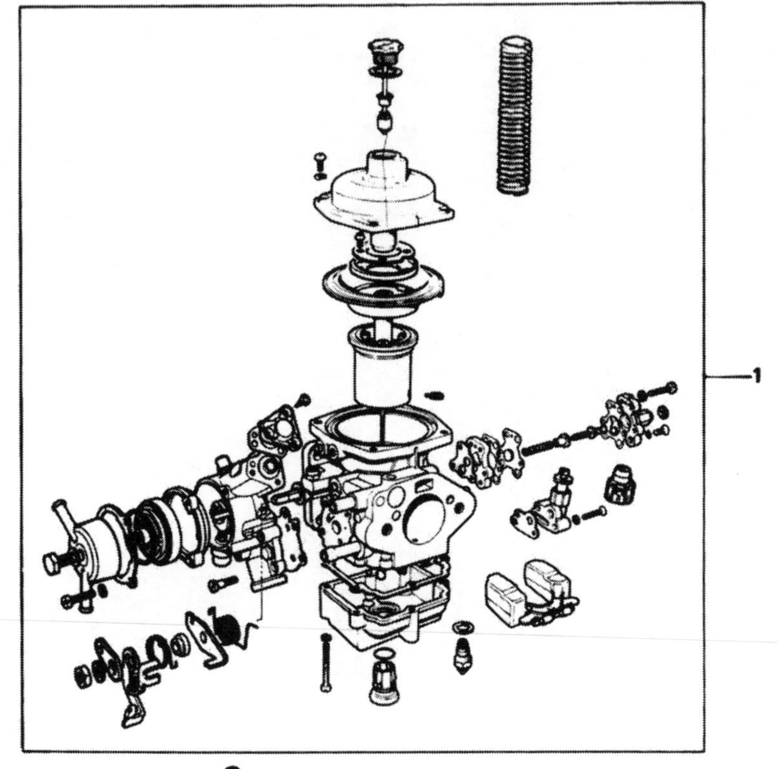

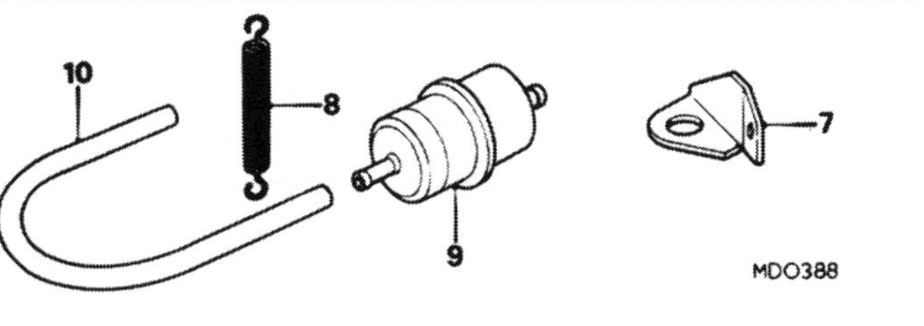

AUSTIN-HEALEY SPRITE MK. 3 AND MK. 4 & MG MIDGET MK. 2 AND MK. 3

NO.	PART NO.	DESCRIPTION	QTY	CHANGE POINT	REMARKS
		CARBURETTER ASSEMBLY-MIDGET 1500-USA AND CANADA.			
1	CHA 327	CARBURETTER ASSEMBLY	1		Federal.TO 1977
1	CHA 511	CARBURETTER ASSEMBLY	1		California TO 1977.
1	RKC 3169	CARBURETTER ASSY	1		Federal 1977 ON
	RKC 3170	CARBURETTER ASSY	1		California 1977 ON.
		KIT-CARBURETTER			
	BHM 1075	Needle and valve washer	1		
	BHM 1076	Gasket and sealing washer	1		Federal
	BHM 1080	Gasket and sealing washer	1		California
	BHM 1081	Gasket and sealing washer			
	BHM 1077	Emission(12,000 miles serivce)	1		
	BHM 1078	Emission(24,000 miles service)	1		

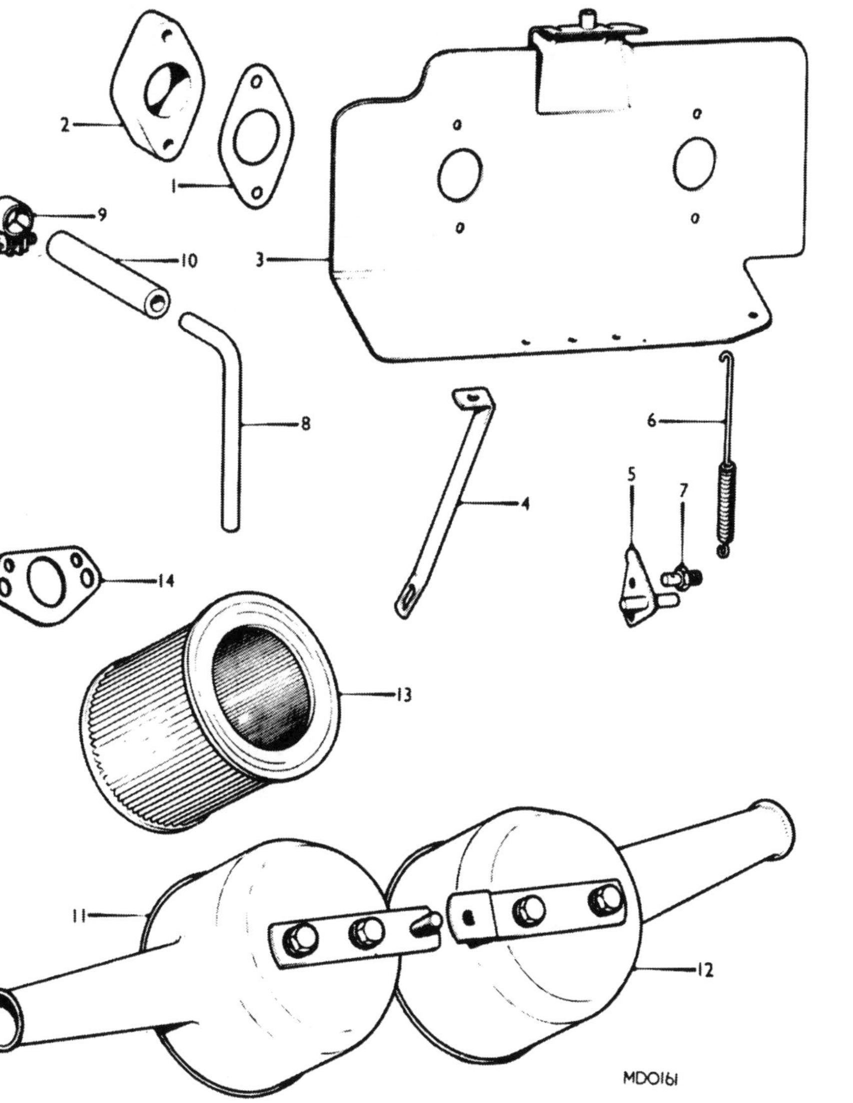

AUSTIN-HEALEY SPRITE MK. 3 AND MK. 4 & MG MIDGET MK. 2 AND MK. 3

CARBURETTER FITTINGS-HEAT SHIELD-AIR CLEANER-EXCEPT MIDGET 1500.

NO.	PART NO.	DESCRIPTION	QTY	CHANGE POINT	REMARKS
1	1G 2624	Gasket-carburetter and heat shield	6		
2	AEA 586	Piece-distance-insulating	2		
	FNZ 106	Nut	4		
	PWZ 206	Washer-plain	4		
3	12G 1460	Shield-heat	1		
4	AEG 558	Clip-rear	1		
	HZS 405	Screw-clip to shield	2		
	LWN 204	Washer-spring	2		
	NH 604041	Nut	2		
	HZS 407	Screw-clip to front cover	1		
	PWZ 104	Washer-plain	1		
	NH 604041	Nut	1		
	HZS 515	Screw-clip to rear mounting plate	1		
	PWZ 105	Washer-plain	1		
	LWZ 305	Washer-spring	1		
	LNZ 205	Nut	1		
5	AEA 597	Lever-throttle	1		
6	AEA 602	Spring-throttle return	1		
7	ACC 5062	Pin-clamp	1		
	PWZ 104	Washer-plain	1		
	NH 604041	Nut	1		
8	AHA 9606	Pipe-overflow	2		
9	88G 308	Clip-overflow pipes to carburetter	2		
10	AHH 9950	Connection-overflow pipe to carburetter	2		
9	88G 308	Clip-connection	4	(E)12CJ/Da/H21201	
	PCR 407	Clip-pipe to bracket	1	TO(+)	
	PMZ 308	Screw clip	1	(E)12V/587Z/101	
	PWZ 203	Washer-plain	1	TO(+)	
	LWZ 203	Washer-spring	1	(E)12V/671Z/101 ON	
11	AHA 8419	CLEANER ASSEMBLY-AIR-FRONT	1		
12	AHA 8420	CLEANER ASSEMBLY-AIR-REAR	1		
13	GFE 1004	Element-air cleaner	2		
	HCZ 536	Bolt-cleaner to carburetter	NLA		
	PWZ 105	Washer-plain	4		
	WL 600051	Washer-spring	4		
14	ACA 8014	Gasket-cleaner to carburetter	2		
	LNZ 205	Nut-front cleaner strap to rear cleaner strap	1		
	PWZ 205	Washer-plain	1		
	WL 600051	Washer-spring	1		

(+) Change point not available.

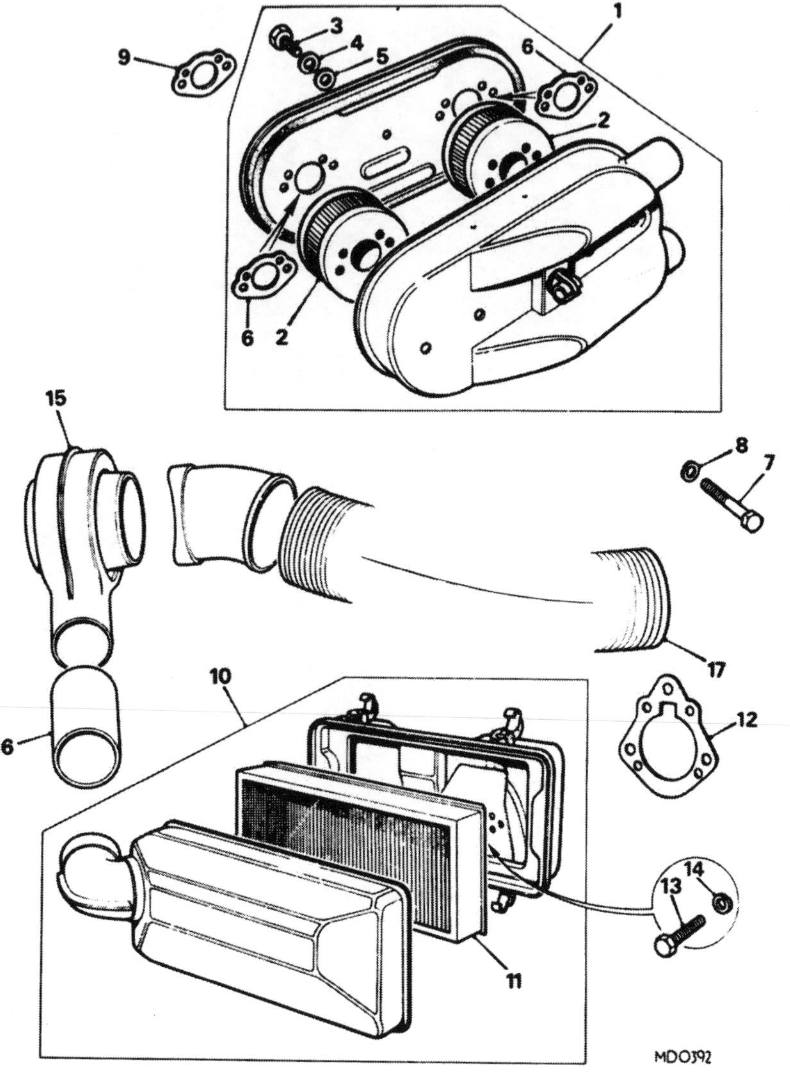

AUSTIN-HEALEY SPRITE MK. 3 AND MK. 4 & MG MIDGET MK. 2 AND MK. 3

AIR CLEANER AND SILENCER-MIDGET 1500.

NO.	PART NO.	DESCRIPTION	QTY	CHANGE POINT	REMARKS
1	TKC 1570	CLEANER ASSEMBLY-AIR	1		
2	GFE 1063	Element-air cleaner	2		
3	SH 604041	Bolt-base plate to body	1		
4	WL 600041	Washer-spring	1		
5	WA 106041	Washer-plain	1		
6	102488	Gasket-element to base plate	2		
7	HB 867	Bolt-air cleaner to carburetter	4		
8	WL 600051	Washer-spring	4		
9	102488	Gasket-air cleaner to carburetter	2		
10	CHA 295	CLEANER ASSEMBLY-AIR TO 1975	1		USA and Canada
10	CHA 554	CLEANER ASSEMBLY-AIR-1976 ON	1		USA and Canada
11	GFE 1060	Element	1		USA and Canada
12	148006	Gasket-air cleaner to carburetter	1		USA and Canada
13	SH 505071	Screw	2		USA and Canada
14	WL 600051	Washer	2		USA and Canada
15	BHH 1163	Compensator-air temperature	NLA		USA and Canada
16	CHA 379	Connection-compensator to air cleaner	1		USA and Canada
17	CHA 491	Connection-pre-heater to air temperature control device	1		Federal.

AUSTIN-HEALEY SPRITE MK. 3 AND MK. 4 & MG MIDGET MK. 2 AND MK. 3

CARBURETTER FITTINGS-HEAD SHIELD-MIDGET 1500-NOT USA AND CANADA

NO.	PART NO.	DESCRIPTION	QTY	CHANGE POINT	REMARKS
1	UKC 3009	Rod and lever connecting	1		
2	AUE 586	LEVER AND PIN ASSEMBLY-REAR	1		
3	AUE 587	LEVER AND PIN ASSEMBLY-FRONT	1		
4	AJD 1042	Bolt	2		
5	AUC 8396	Washer-plain	2		
6	AJD 8012 Z	Nut	2		
7	AUE 34	Pin-pivot-choke inner cable	1		
8	UKC 5374	Linkage-throttle	1		
9	SH 504051	Screw	2		
10	WL 600041	Washer-spring	2		
11	153957	Clip-bellcrank	2		
12	UKC 3272	Link-bellcrank to throttle lever	1		
13	UKC 3281	Bracket-anchor-spring link	1		
14	143747	Link-main throttle spring	1		
15	153959	Spring-main-throttle return	1		
16	145197	Spring-throttle return	2		
17	CHA 501	Heatshield	1		
18	UKC 2992	Gasket-carburetter	4		
19	SH 505091	Screw-carburetter to manifold	4		
20	WL 600051	Washer-spring	4		

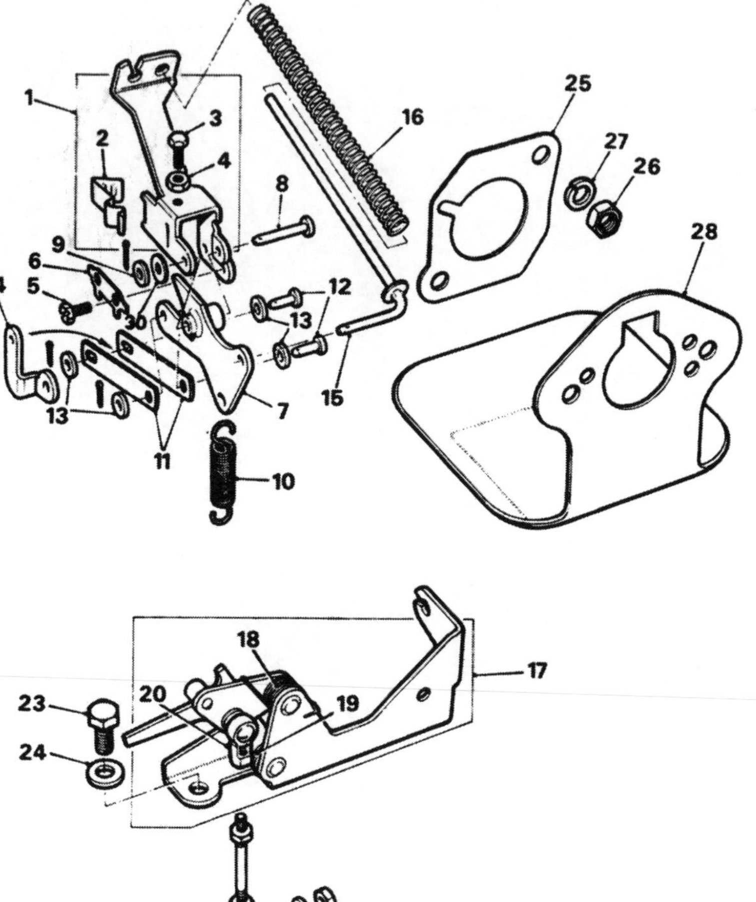

AUSTIN-HEALEY SPRITE MK. 3 AND MK. 4 & MG MIDGET MK. 2 AND MK. 3

CARBURETTER FITTINGS-MIDGET 1500 USA AND CANADA.

NO.	PART NO.	DESCRIPTION	QTY	CHANGE POINT	REMARKS
1	UKC 673	BRACKET ASSEMBLY-CABLE	1		
2	12B 2492	Clip-choke cable	1		
3	HU 504	Screw-adjusting	1		
4	HN 2005	Nut	1		
5	518528	Screw-bracket to carburetter	2		
6	518529	Washer-tab	1		
7	154117	Bellcrank	1		
8	PJ 8514	Pin-pivot	1		
9	WP 5	Washer-plain	1		Federal
10	UKC 4620	Spring-return-bellcrank	1		TO 1977
11	156572	Link-bellcrank to throttle lever	2		
12	PJ 8504	Pin-pivot	2		
13	WP 5	Washer-plain	4		
14	153417	Lever-throttle	1		
15	159123	Rod-spring retaining	1		
16	131368	Spring-return	1		
17	TKC 1832	BRACKET AND THROTTLE LEVER ASSEMBLY	1		
18	UKC 4222	Spring	1		
19	UKC 4223	Spring	1		
20	UKC 4131	Ball-end	1		
21	HN 2005	Nut	1		California
22	WL 205	Washer	1		Federal 1977 ON.
23	BH 505041	Bolt	2		
29	UKC 4415	ROD ASSY-LINK	1		
24	WA 108051	Washer	2		
25	UKC 490	Gasket-carburetter	1		
26	NH 605041	Nut-carburetter to manifold	2		
27	WL 600051	Washer-spring	2		
28	TKC 1990	Heatshield	1		

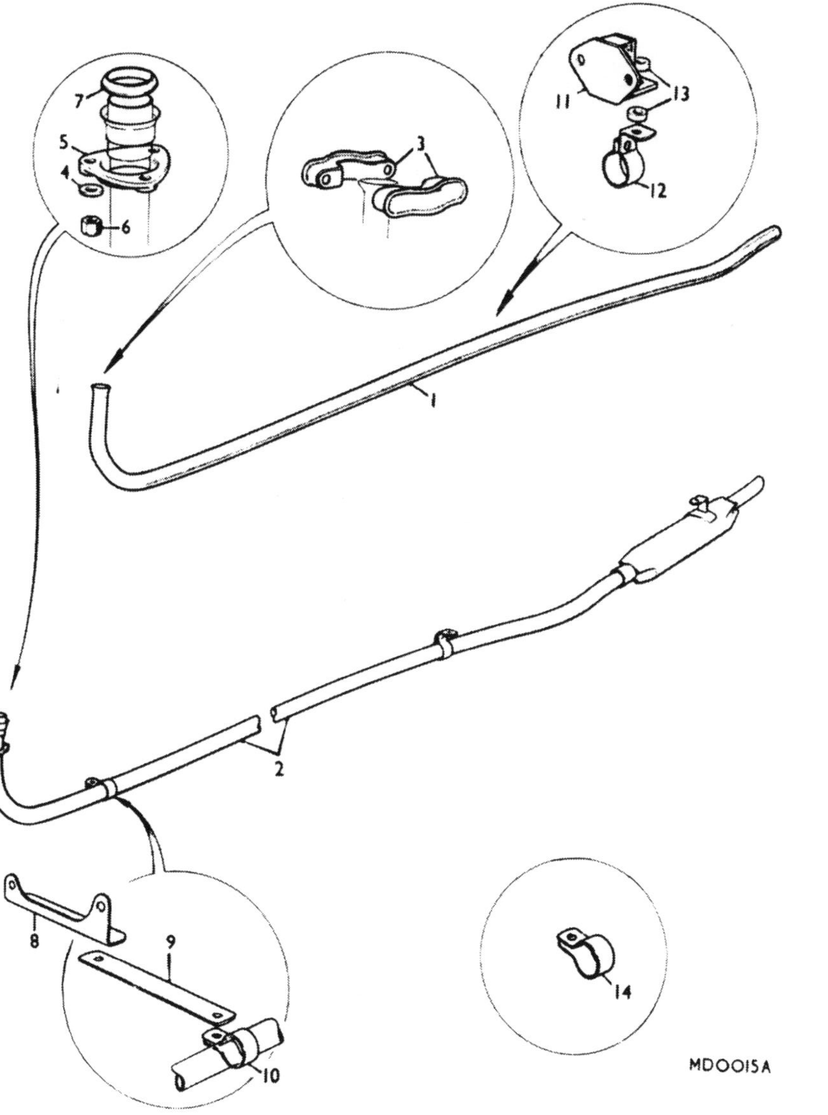

AUSTIN-HEALEY SPRITE MK. 3 AND MK. 4 & MG MIDGET MK. 2 AND MK. 3

EXHAUST SYSTEM-EXCEPT 1500

NO.	PART NO.	DESCRIPTION	QTY	CHANGE POINT	REMARKS
1	GEX 1306	Pipe-exhaust	1	Use prior to GEX 142	(E)10CC,12CC, 12CE,12V/586, 12V/588. 12CD.
	GEX 142	Exhaust system-complete	1	(C)G-AN5-139137 ON	
1	AHA 8688	Pipe-exhaust	1	Use prior to complete exhaust system ARA 333	
2	ARA 333	Exhaust system-complete	1	(E)12CD/Da/H101 TO(+)	
2	ARA 384	Exhaust system-complete (C$)	1	(E)12CJ/Da/H21201 TO(+) (E)12V/587Z/L101 TO(+)	
2	ARC 90	Exhaust system-complete (C$)	1	(E)12V/671Z/L101 TO (C)G-AN5-139772	
	GEX 142	Exhaust system-complete (C$)	1	(C)G-AN5-139773 TO 154100	
3	18G 8584	Clamp-pipe to manifold	2		Use when exhaust MANIFOLD 12G 420 IS FITTED.
	HZS 518	Screw	2		
4	2K 5806	Washer-plain	4		
	BNN 105	Nut	2		
	HBZ 510	Bolt	1		Use when exhaust MANIFOLD 12G 1581 IS FITTED.
	LWZ 305	Washer-spring	1		
4	12A 1211	Washer-special	2		
6	AHH 8382	Nut-special	3		
7	GEX 7193	Joint-exhaust down-pipe $ (C$)	1		
	WL 600051	Washer-spring	3		
8	GEX 7153	Bracket-pipe mounting	1	(+) Change point not available.	
9	GEX 7154	Strap-bracket to clip	1		
10	GEX 7072	Clip-pipe $	1		
	HZS 506	Screw-bracket to strap	1		
	HZS 507	Screw-strap to clip	1		
	PWZ 105	Washer-plain	1		
	LWZ 205	Washer-spring	2		
	NH 605041	Nut	2		
11	GEX 7155	Mounting-pipe $	1		
	HZS 505	Screw	2		
	WL 600051	Washer-spring	2		
12	GEX 7073	Clip-pipe $	1		
	HZS 509	Screw	1		
13	GEX 7250	Washer-insulation	2		
	LNZ 105	Locknut	1		
	HZS 407	Screw-clip to pipe	1		
	LWZ 204	Washer-spring	1		
	NH 604041	Nut	1		
14	GEX 7074	Clip-pipe to silencer	1		
	HZS 510	Screw	1		
	LWZ 305	Washer-spring	1		
4	12A 1211	Washer-special	2		
	NH 605041	Nut	1		

$ This item is subject to safety regulations.

NOTE:-
(C$) These parts comply with Californian State regulations when fitted on vehicles to which this list applies.

AUSTIN-HEALEY SPRITE MK. 3 AND MK. 4 & MG MIDGET MK. 2 AND MK. 3

EXHAUST SYSTEM-EXCEPT 1500-continued.

NO.	PART NO.	DESCRIPTION	QTY	CHANGE POINT	REMARKS
1	GEX 3365	Silencer	1	Use prior to GEX 3369	Except Europe.
2	GEX 7151	Bush-silencer support(rubber)	2		
3	GEX 7152	Spacer-bush	1		
	PWZ 205	Washer-plain	1		
	LNZ 205	Locknut fixing silencer	1		
4	ARA 281	Silencer	1		Europe.
	GEX 3369	Silencer	1	(C)H-AN10-85287 TO 86803 (C)A-AN10-86804 TO 87824 (C)G-AN5-74886 TO 139136	Except USA and Canada.
	HZS 506	Screw-rear exhaust mounting	4	(C)H-AN10-85287 TO 86803 (C)A-AN10-86804 TO 87824 (C)G-AN5-74886 ON	
	PWZ 105	Washer-plain	4		
	WL 600051	Washer-spring	4		
5	GEX 7168	Bracket-pipe-support-LH	1	Use prior to GEX 7364	
	GEX 7364	Bracket-pipe-support-LH	1	(C)G-AN5-138801 ON	
6	GEX 7155	Mounting-pipe-LH	1		
	HZS 505	Screw	2		
	WL 600051	Washer-spring	2		
	FNZ 105	Nut	2		
	HBZ 512	Bolt-clip to mounting	1		
7	GEX 7250	Washer-insulation	2		
	WL 600051	Washer-spring	1		
	FNZ 105	Nut	1		
8	GEX 7169	Bracket-pipe-support-RH	1	Use prior to GEX 7365	
	GEX 7365	Bracket-pipe-support-RH	1	(C)G-AN5-138801 ON	
9	GEX 7170	Clip-pipe-RH	1		
	HZS 506	Screw-clip to pipe	1		
	WL 600051	Washer-spring	1		
	FNZ 105	Nut	1		
10	GEX 7151	Bush-pipe-support-RH(rubber)	2		
11	GEX 7166	Spacer-bush	1		
	LNZ 105	Locknut	1		

AUSTIN-HEALEY SPRITE MK. 3 AND MK. 4 & MG MIDGET MK. 2 AND MK. 3

EXHAUST SYSTEM-1500.

NO.	PART NO.	DESCRIPTION	QTY	CHANGE POINT	REMARKS
1	GEX 161	Exhaust system complete (C$)	NLA	Use prior to GEX 164 (C)G-AN6-172237 ON	Use GEX 164
1	GEX 164	Exhaust system complete (C$)	1		
2	GEX 1618	Down pipe	1		Except California
3	CHA 287	Down pipe(with Catalyst) (C$)	1		California
4	CHA 471	Nut-down pipe to manifold	3		Except California
5	WL 600061	Washer-spring	3		
6	BH 606121	Bolt	3		
7	WL 600061	Washer-spring-Catalyst to manifold	3		California
8	UKC 4960	Nut	6		
9	GEG 742	Gasket-down pipe	1		
10	GEX 7470	Olive-coupling (C$)	1		Was GEX 7352
11	BH 605151	Bolt-coupling	3		
12	WL 600051	Washer-spring	3		
13	AHH 8382	Nut	3		
34	GEX 7203	Clip-saddle-support bracket	1	(C)G-AN6-160091 ON (California only) (C)G-AN6-162211 ON (Except California)	
34	GEX 7252	Clip-saddle-support bracket	1		
35	SH 605081	Screw	2		
36	WL 600051	Washer-spring	2		
37	NH 605041	Nut	2		
14	GEX 7073	Clip-intermediate	1		
15	HZS 407	Screw-clip to pipe	1		
16	WL 600040	Washer-spring	1		
17	NH 604041	Nut	1		
11	BH 605151	Screw-clip to mounting	1		
18	LNZ 105	Nut-lock	1		
19	GEX 7250	Washer-insulating	1		
20	WC 108051	Washer-plain	1		
21	GEX 7155	Bracket-mounting-intermediate	1		
22	HZS 505	Screw-mounting	2		
23	LWZ 205	Washer-spring	2		

NOTE:-(C$) These parts comply with Californian State regulations when fitted on vehicles to which this list applies.

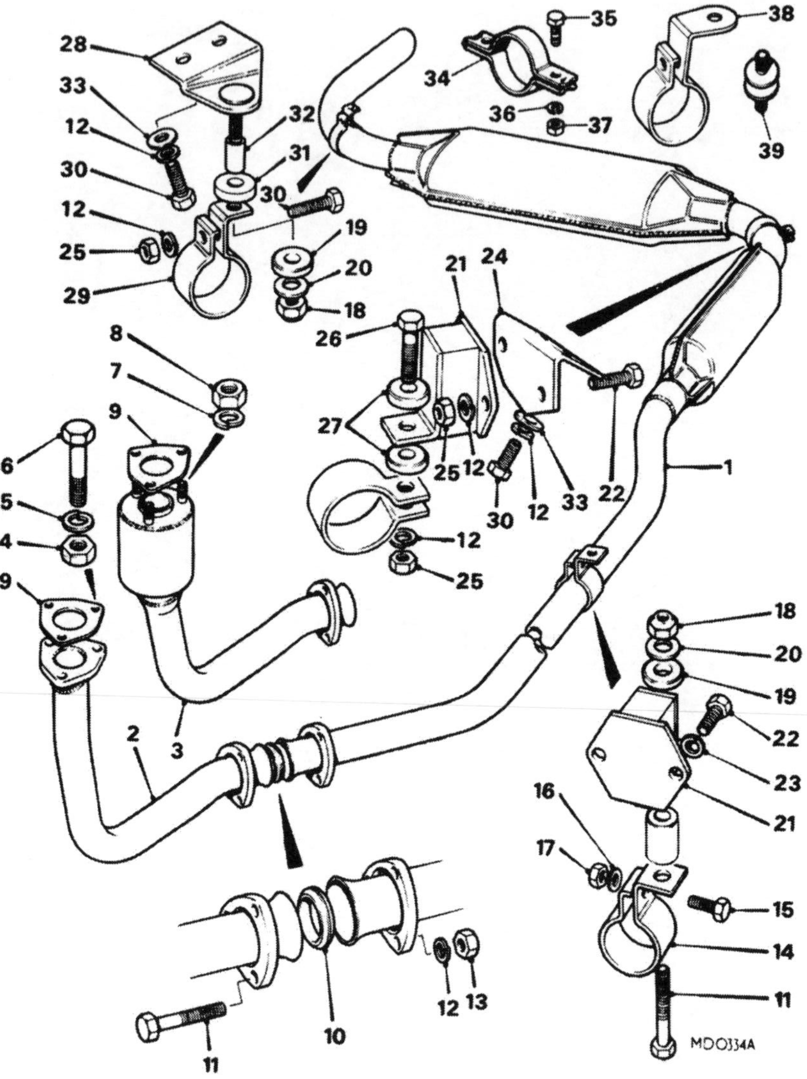

AUSTIN-HEALEY SPRITE MK. 3 AND MK. 4 & MG MIDGET MK. 2 AND MK. 3

NO.	PART NO.	DESCRIPTION	QTY	CHANGE POINT	REMARKS
		EXHAUST SYSTEM-1500-continued.			
24	GEX 7364	Bracket-pipe support-LH	1		
21	GEX 7155	Mounting-pipe-LH	1		
22	HZS 505	Screw-mounting	2		
12	WL 600051	Washer-spring	2		
25	FNZ 105	Nut	2		
26	HBZ 512	Bolt-clip to mounting	1		
27	GEX 7250	Washer-insulating	2		
12	WL 600051	Washer-spring	1		
25	FNZ 105	Nut	1		
28	GEX 7365	Bracket-pipe support-RH	1	(C)G-AN6-154101 TO 169791	
29	GEX 7170	Clip-pipe-RH	1	(C)G-AN6-154101 TO 169791	
38	GEX 7468	Clip-support	1	(C)G-AN6-169792 ON	
39	GEX 7251	Mounting(rubber)	1	(C)G-AN6-169792 ON	
27	GEX 7250	Washer-insulating	2	(C)G-AN6-169792 ON	
30	HZS 506	Screw-clip to pipe	1		
12	WL 600051	Washer-spring	1		
25	FNZ 105	Nut	1		
31	GEX 7151	Bush-pipe support-RH(rubber)	2	(C)G-AN6-154101 To 169791	
32	GEX 7166	Spacer-bush	1	(C)G-AN6-154101 To 169791	
18	LNZ 105	Nut-lock	1	(C)G-AN6-154101 To 169791	
30	HZS 506	Screw-rear mounting	4		
33	PWZ 105	Washer-plain	4		
12	WL 600051	Washer-spring	4		

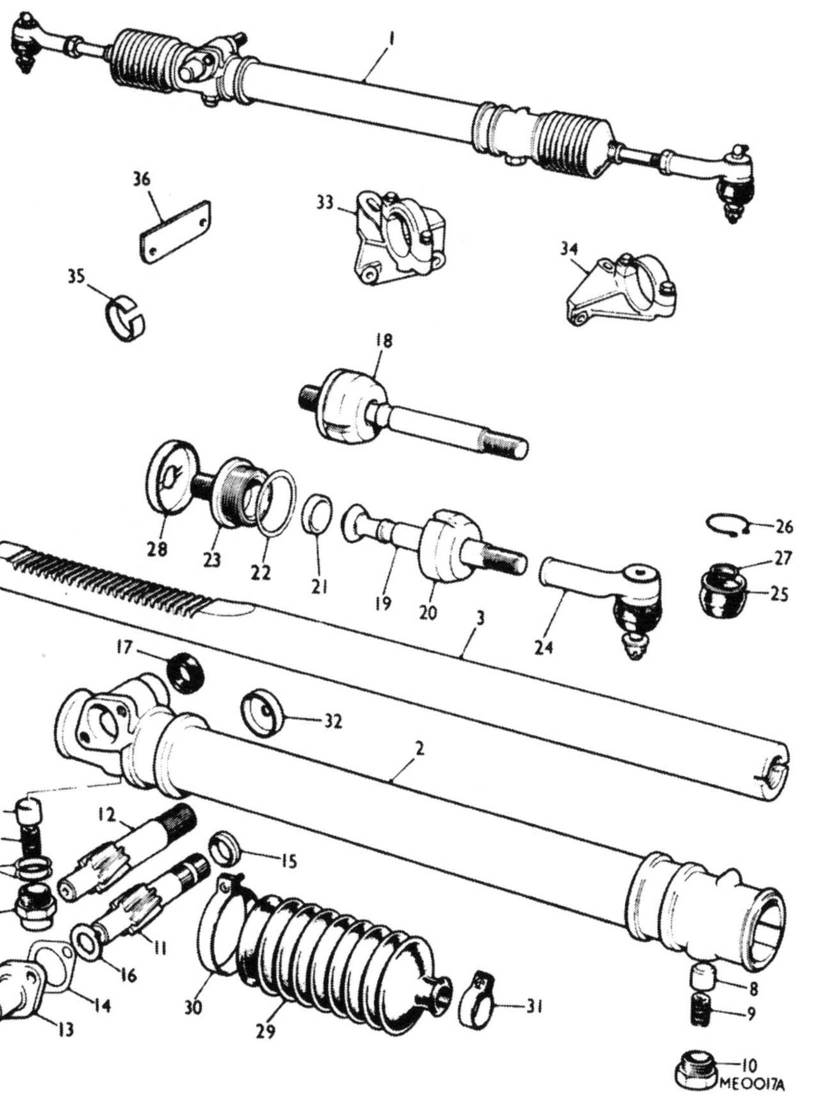

AUSTIN-HEALEY SPRITE MK. 3 AND MK. 4 & MG MIDGET MK. 2 AND MK. 3

STEERING RACK

NO.	PART NO.	DESCRIPTION	QTY	CHANGE POINT	REMARKS
1	ACG 6010	RACK ASSEMBLY-RHD	1	Use prior to BTA 1096	
	ACG 6009	RACK ASSEMBLY-LHD	1	Use prior to BTA 1097	
1	BTA 1096	RACK ASSEMBLY-RHD	NLA	(C)H-AN9-72529 TO 85286 (C)H-AN10-85287 TO 86803 (C)A-AN10-86804 TO 87824 (C)G-AN4-61166 TO 74885 (C)G-AN5-74886 TO See(1)foot of page	Use AHA 9956 RHD or AHA 9957 LHD with 1 off bracket AHA 9959,1 Off bracket AHA 9960,2 Off clamp AHA 9961, 1 off lever AHA 9957 and 1 off lever AHA 9958
	BTA 1097	RACK ASSEMBLY-LHD $	NLA	(C)H-AN9-72034 USA, 72529 except USA TO 85286 (C)H-AN10-85287 TO 86803 (C)A-AN10-86804 TO 87824 (C)G-AN4-60441 USA, 61166 except USA TO 74885 (C)G-AN5-74886 TO See(1)foot of page	
2	ACA 6019	Housing-LHD $	1	(C)H-AN8-38829 TO 64734 (C)H-AN9-64735 TO 85286 (C)H-AN10-85287 TO 86803(C)A-AN10-86804 TO 87824 (C)G-AN3-25788 TO 52389 (C)G-AN4-52390 TO 74885 (C)G-AN5-74886 TO See(1)foot of page	
3	ACA 6026	Rack $	1		
4	ACA 5244	Pad-damper $	1		
5	ACA 5248	Spring-pad $	1		
6	ACA 5245	Housing-pad $	1		
7	ACA 5249	Shim-housing-.003"(.08mm) $	A/R		
7	ACA 5275	Shim-housing-.010"(.25mm) $	A/R		
8	ACA 5284	Pad-secondary damper $	1		
9	ACA 5286	Spring-secondary damper $	1		
10	ACA 5285	Housing-secondary damper	1		

$ This item is subject to safety regulations

CHANGE POINTS
(1) (C)G-AN5-114486 USA (LESS 114352,114473,114475 TO 114480, 114526 TO 114541,114543 AND 114580 TO 114588)
(C)G-AN5-114642 NOT USA (LESS 114244,114332,114333,114361 TO 114365, 114377,114385,114398 TO 114406,114416 TO 114419,114446 TO 114472 AND 114483 TO 114486)

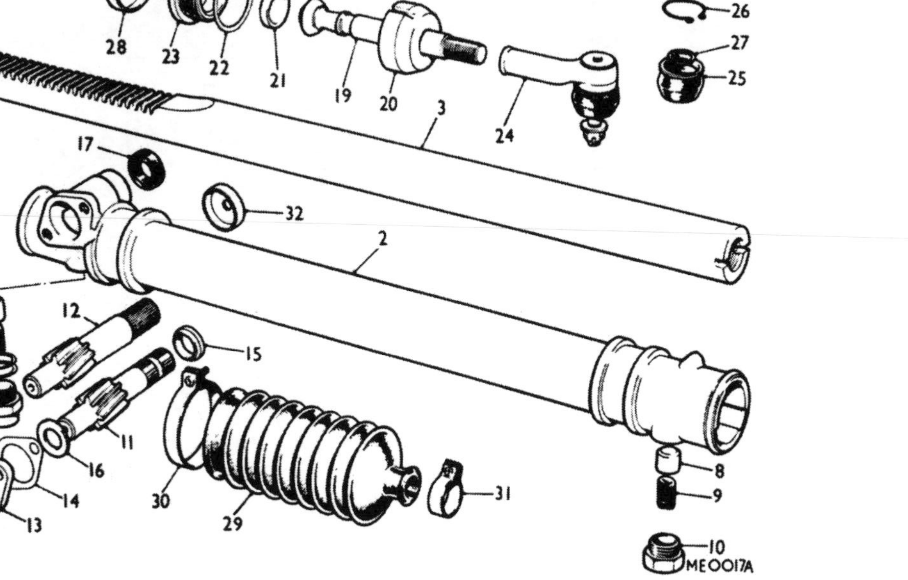

AUSTIN-HEALEY SPRITE MK. 3 AND MK. 4 & MG MIDGET MK. 2 AND MK. 3

NO.	PART NO.	DESCRIPTION	QTY	CHANGE POINT	REMARKS
		STEERING RACK-continued			
11	ACA 6028	Pinion-RHD	1	Use prior to BTA 942	
12	BTA 942	Pinion-RHD	1	(C)H-AN9-72529 TO 85286 (C)H-AN10-85287 TO 86803 (C)A-AN10-86804 TO 87824 (C)G-AN4-61166 TO 74885 (C)G-AN5-74886 TO SEE(1)foot of page	
	ACA 6027	Pinion-LHD	1	Use prior to BTA 941	
	BTA 941	Pinion-LHD $	1	(C)H-AN9-72034 USA, 72529 except USA TO 85286 (C)H-AN10-85287 TO 86803 (C)A-AN10-86804 TO 87824 (C)G-AN4-60441 USA, 61166 except USA TO 74885 (C)G-AN5-74886 TO See(1)foot of page	

$ This item is subject to safety regulations

CHANGE POINTS
(1).(C)G-AN5-114486 USA(LESS 114352,114473,114475 TO 114480,114526 TO 114541, 114543 AND 114580 TO 114588),(C)G-AN5-114642 Not USA(Less 114244,114332, 114333,114361 TO 114365,114377,114385,114398 TO 114406,114416 TO 114419, 114446 TO 114472 AND 114482 TO 114486)

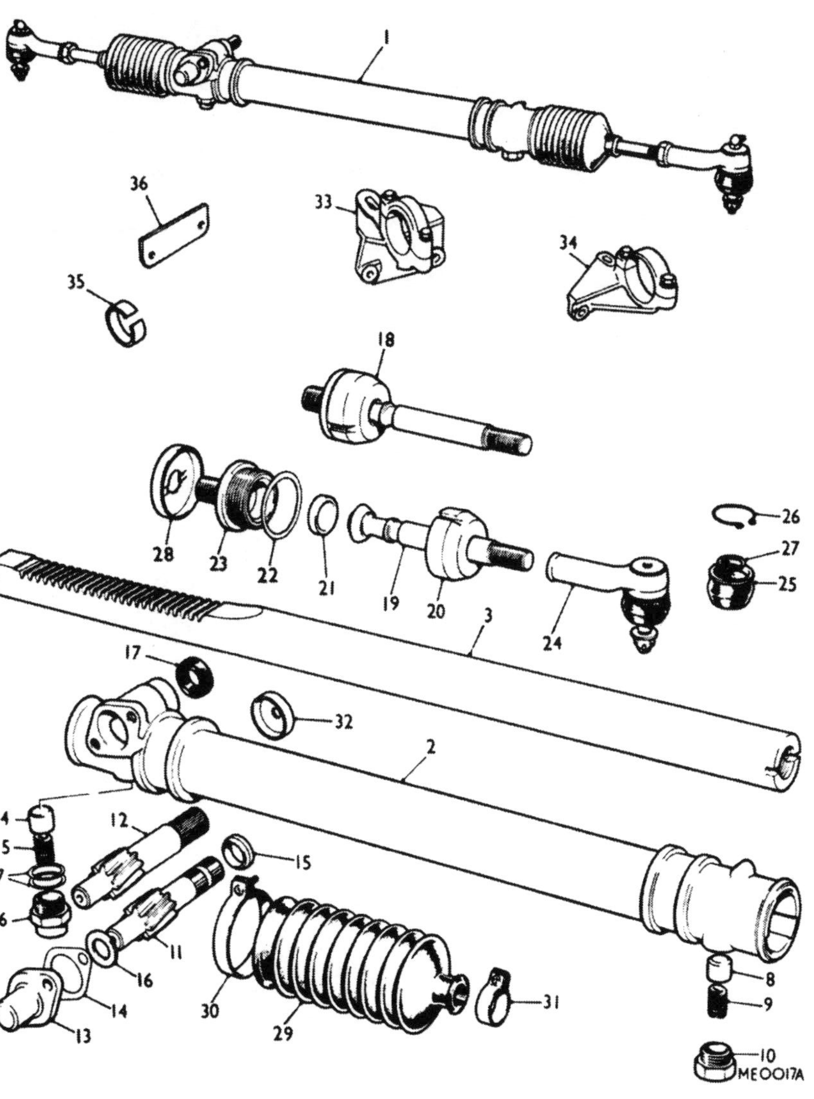

AUSTIN-HEALEY SPRITE MK. 3 AND MK. 4 & MG MIDGET MK. 2 AND MK. 3

STEERING RACK-continued.

NO.	PART NO.	DESCRIPTION	QTY	CHANGE POINT	REMARKS
13	ACA 5307	Bearing-pinion tail $	1	(C)H-AN8-38829 TO 64734	
		SHIM-TAIL BEARING		(C)H-AN9-64735 TO 85286	
14	ACA 5259	.076mm(.003") $	A/R	(C)H-AN10-85287 TO 86803	
14	ACA 5260	.127mm(.005") $	A/R	(C)A-AN10-86804 TO 87824	
14	ACA 5320	.245mm(.010") $	A/R	(C)G-AN3-25788 TO 52389	
	AJD 6155 Z	Screw-bearing to rack housing	2	(C)G-AN4-52390 TO 74885	
	LWZ 204	Washer-spring	2	(C)G-AN5-74886 TO see(1)foot of page	
15	ACA 5257	Washer-thrust-pinion-top $	1		
16	ACA 5258	Washer-thrust-pinion-bottom $	1		
17	ACA 5261	Seal-pinion	1	Use prior to BTA 9008	
	BTA 9008	Seal-pinion $	NLA	(C)H-AN9-72034 USA 72529 except USA TO 85286 (C)H-AN10-85287 TO 86803 (C)A-AN10-86804 TO 87824 (C)G-AN4-60441 USA 61166 except USA TO 74885 (C)G-AN5-74886 TO see(1)foot of page	

$ This item is subject to safety regulations.

CHANGE POINTS.
(1).(C)G-AN5-114486 USA(less 114352,114473,114475 TO 114480,114526 TO 114541, 114543 AND 114580 TO 114588).
(C)G-AN5-114642 NOT USA(less 114244,114332,114333,114361 TO 114365, 114377,114385,114398 TO 114406,114416 TO 114419,114446 TO 114472 AND 114482 TO 114486).

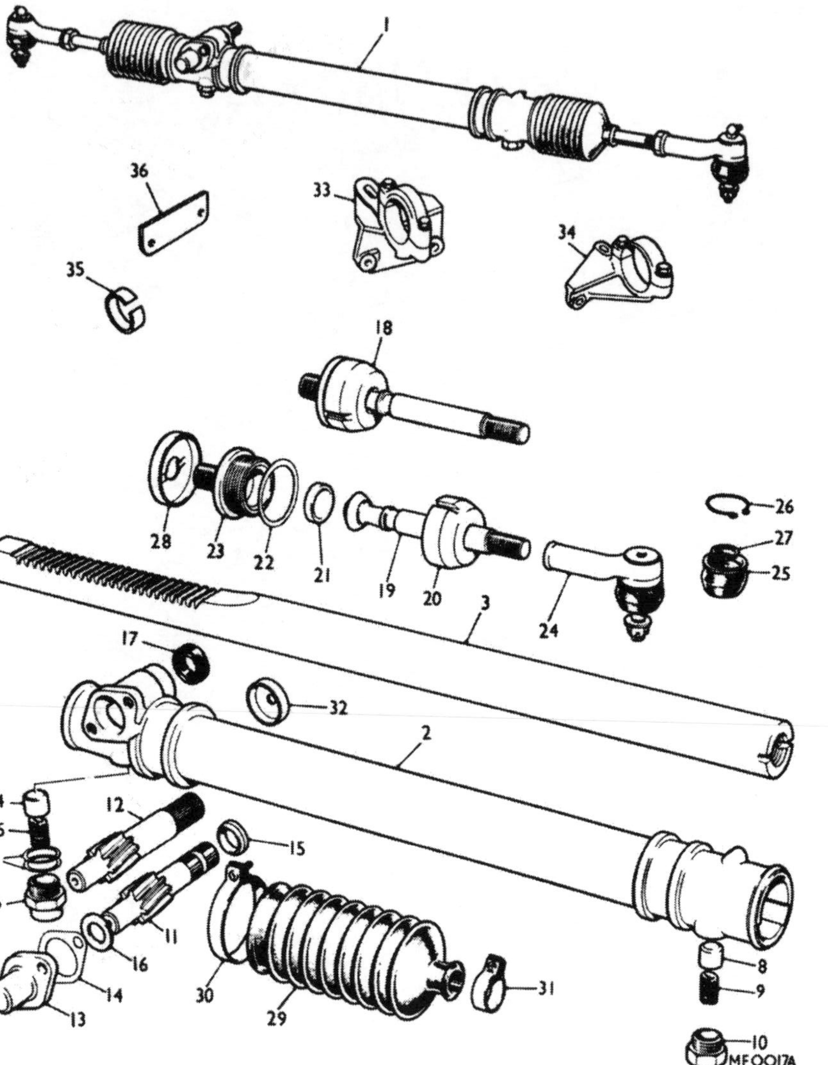

134

AUSTIN-HEALEY SPRITE MK. 3 AND MK. 4 & MG MIDGET MK. 2 AND MK. 3

NO.	PART NO.	DESCRIPTION	QTY	CHANGE POINT	REMARKS
		STEERING RACK-continued.			
18	ACA 6018	TIE-ROD ASSEMBLY $	NLA		Use component parts.
19	ACA 6015	Tie-rod $	2		
20	ACA 5304	Ball-housing-female $	2		
21	ACA 5246	Seat-ball $	2		
		SHIM			
22	ACA 6017	.002"(.061mm)$	A/R		
22	ACA 5301	.003"(.076mm) $	A/R		
22	ACA 5302	.005"(.127mm) $	A/R		
22	ACA 5303	.010"(.254mm) $	A/R		
23	ACA 6031	Ball housing-male $	2		
24	88G 414	SOCKET ASSEMBLY-BALL-OUTER $	2		
25	7H 3762	Boot $	2		
26	7H 3565	Clip-boot to body $	2	(C)H-AN8-38829 TO 64734 (C)H-AN9-64735 TO 85286 (C)H-AN10-85287 TO 86803 (C)A-AN10-86804 TO 87824 (C)G-AN3-25788 TO 52389 (C)G-AN4-52390 TO 74885 (C)G-AN5-74886 TO See(1)foot of page	
27	7H 3763	Ring-boot to ball pin	2		
	PWZ 107	Washer-plain	2		
	FNZ 407	Nut	2		
	ACH 6173	Washer-ball socket(fibre) $	2		
	NT 610041	Locknut	2		
28	ACA 5247	Washer-lock-ball housing $	2		
29	ACA 6029	Seal-rack housing $	2		
30	BMK 924	Clip-inner seal $	2		
31	3H 2963	Clip-outer seal $	2		
	UHN 305	Lubricator-rack	1		
	UHN 305	Lubricator-ball socket	2		
32	AHA 5496	Retainer-pinion oil seal	1		
33	AHA 5391	Bracket and cap-rack mounting-RH $	1		
34	AHA 5392	Bracket and cap-rack mounting-LH $	1		
35	2A 6128	Seating-mounting bracket-rack $	2		
36	AHA 8718	Packing-mounting bracket-rack(.79mm)	A/R		
	SH 605061	Screw-.75"(19.05mm)bracket	4		
	SH 605081	Screw-1"(25.4mm)bracket	2		
	WA 108051	Washer-plain	4		
	WL 600051	Washer-spring	6		

$ This item is subject to safety regulations.

CHANGE POINTS.
(1).(C)G-AN5-114486 USA(less 114352,114473,114475 TO 114480,114526 TO 1145411, 114543 AND 114580 TO 114588).
(C)G-AN5-114642 NOT USA(less 114244,114332,114333,114361 TO 114365, 114377,114385,114398 TO 114406,114416 TO 114419,114446 TO 114472 AND 114483 TO 114486).

MEO167

AUSTIN-HEALEY SPRITE MK. 3 AND MK. 4 & MG MIDGET MK. 2 AND MK. 3

STEERING RACK-continued.

NO.	PART NO.	DESCRIPTION	QTY	CHANGE POINT	REMARKS
1	AHA 9956	RACK ASSEMBLY-RHD $	1		
	AHA 9955	RACK ASSEMBLY-LHD $	1		
2	208375	Rack $	1		
3	37H 7336	Cap-screwed	1		
4	120946	Plunger	1		
5	37H 7560	Bush-pinion-upper	1		
6	127997	Bush-pinion-lower	1		
7	37H 7561	Washer-thrust-upper	1		
8	128000	Washer-thrust-lower	1		
9	37H 7562	Shim-pinion .005"(.127mm)	A/R		
9	37H 7341	Shim-pinion .010"(.26mm)	A/R		
10	133103	Plug-grease	1		
11	126765	Spring	1		
12	128004	Bellows-pinion side	1		
13	120948	Bellows	1		
14	120959	Shim-plunger .002"(.051mm)	A/R		
14	120949	Shim-plunger .004"(.102mm)	A/R		
14	37H 7342	Shim-plunger .010"(.26mm)	A/R	(C)G-AN5-114487	
	37H 7338	Nut-lock	1	ON USA(plus(1)foot	
16	GHC 507	Clip-bellows	2	OF PAGE)	
16	GHC 811	Clip-bellows	1	(C)G-AN5-114643	
17	37H 7339	Pinion-RHD	1	ON NOT USA (plus	
	37H 7340	Pinion-LHD	1	(2)foot of page)	
18	37H 7343	Spring	2		
19	37H 7344	Circlip	1		
20	37H 7345	'O'Ring $	1		
21	37H 7346	BALL JOINT ASSEMBLY-INNER $	2		
22	130031	Shim	A/R		
22	130032	Shim	A/R		
23	120957	Washer-tab	1		
24	BHA 5141	END ASSEMBLY-TIE-ROD $	2		
25	143992	Gaiter	2		
26	138869	Clip-gaiter	2		
	PWZ 106	Washer-plain	2		
	GHF 223	Nut	2		
27	AHA 9959	Bracket-rack mounting-RH $	1		
	AHA 9960	Bracket-rack mounting-LH $	1		
28	AHA 9961	Clamp-bracket $	2		
	HZS 506	Screw	4		
	SH 605081	Screw-pinion side	2		
	WL 600051	Washer-spring	6		

$ This item is subject to safety regulations.

CHANGE POINTS.
(1).114352,114473,114475 TO 114480,114526 TO 114541,114543 AND 114580 TO 114588.
(2).114244,114332,114333,114361 TO 114365,114377,114385,114398 TO 114406, 114416 TO 114419,114446 TO 114472 AND 114483 TO 114486.

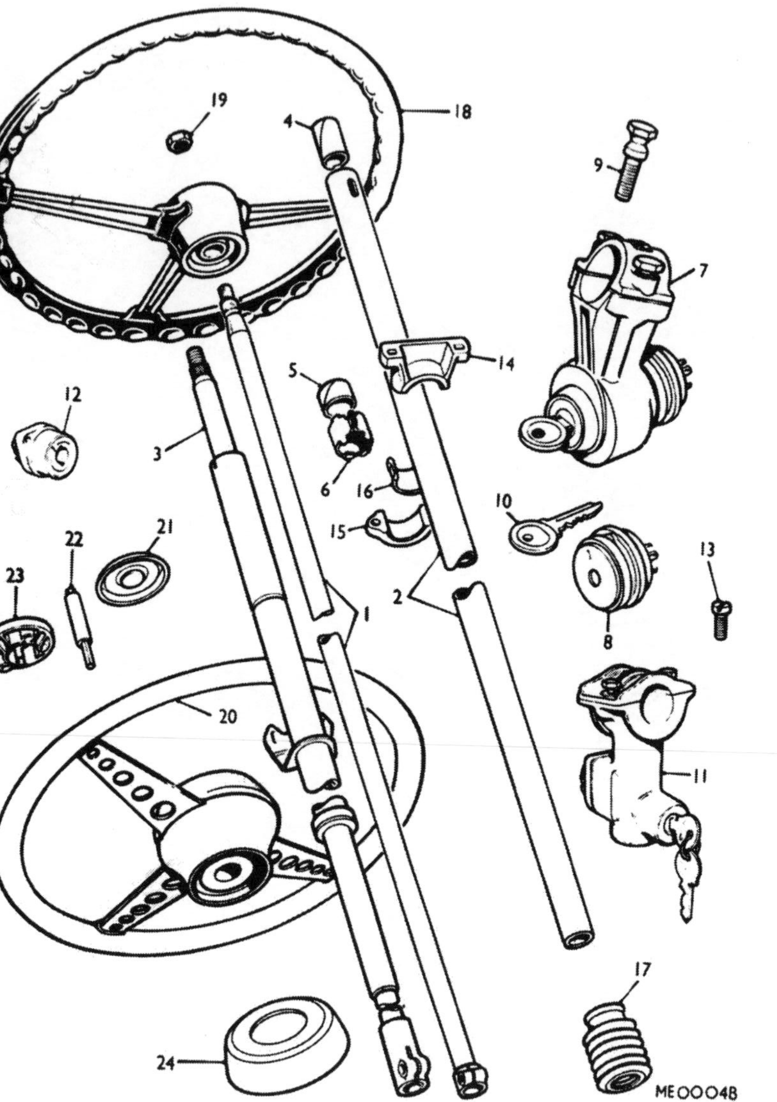

AUSTIN-HEALEY SPRITE MK. 3 AND MK. 4 & MG MIDGET MK. 2 AND MK. 3

STEERING COLUMN AND LOCK-EXCEPT N.AMERICA

NO.	PART NO.	DESCRIPTION	QTY	CHANGE POINT	REMARKS
1	17H 9185	Column-inner-RHD and LHD	1	Finished at (C)G-AN9-85286 (C)G-AN4-74885	Used when steering lock is fitted
1	27H 2359	Column-inner-RHD	1		
	27H 2361	Column-inner-LHD	1		
2	17H 9184	Tube-column-outer-RHD and LHD	1		When steering lock is fitted
2	27H 2358	Tube-column-outer-RHD	1		
1	37H 4769	Column-inner	1	(C)H-AN10-85287 TO 86803 (C)A-AN10-86804 TO 87824 (C)G-AN5-74886 TO 86766	When steering lock is not fitted
	37H 4766	Column-outer	1		
1	37H 4770	Column-inner	1	(C)H-AN10-85287 TO 86803 (C)A-AN10-86804 TO 87824 (C)G-AN5-74886 TO 105500	Used when steering lock is fitted.
2	37H 4771	Column-outer-RHD	NLA		
	37H 4772	Column-outer-LHD	1		
3	AHA 9792	Column complete-RHD $	1	(C)G-AN5-105501 TO 154100 (C)G-AN6-154101 TO 170989	Energy absorbing
3	CHA 558	Column complete-RHD $	1	(C)G-AN6-170990 ON	
	AHA 9882	Column complete-LHD $	1	(C)G-AN5-105501 TO 154100	
4	AHA 5893	Bush-top(felt)	1	(C)H-AN10-85287 TO 86803 (C)A-AN10-86804 TO 87824 (C)G-AN5-74886 TO 105500	
5	13H 569	Bush-bottom(felt)	1		
6	13H 568	Clip-bush retaining	1		
7	37H 5933	LOCK ASSEMBLY(WITH IGNITION SWITCH)	NLA	Use prior to BMK 2259	
8	27H 6237	Switch	1		
9	27H 9394	Bolt-shear	2		
11	BMK 2259	LOCK ASSEMBLY-STEERING COLUMN	1	(C)H-AN10-86766 TO 86803 (C)A-AN10-86804 TO 87824 (C)G-AN5-96273 TO 115925	
12	37H 5934	Switch	1		
13	37H 6967	Screw	1		
9	37H 5935	Bolt-shear	2		
11	BMK 2259	LOCK ASSEMBLY-STEERING COLUMN	1	(C)G-AN5-115926 ON	
	37H 7087	Switch	NLA		Use 37H 7708.
	37H 7708	Switch	1		
	51K 4001	Bolt-shear	2		

$ This item is subject to safety regulations

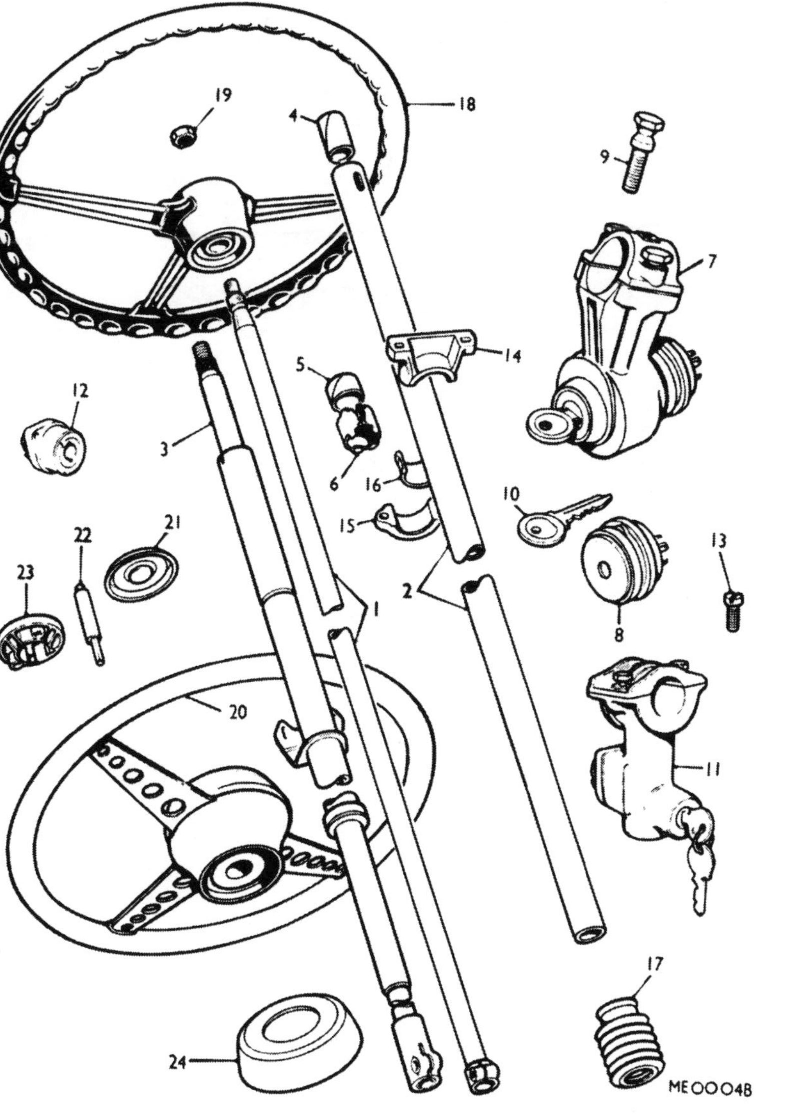

AUSTIN-HEALEY SPRITE MK. 3 AND MK. 4 & MG MIDGET MK. 2 AND MK. 3

STEERING COLUMN AND LOCK-EXCEPT N.AMERICA-continued

NO.	PART NO.	DESCRIPTION	QTY	CHANGE POINT	REMARKS
	53K 1013	Bolt-column tube to pinion clamping	1		
	LNZ 104	Nut	1		
15	2A 6133	Cap-bracket-column mounting	1		
	PWZ 104	Washer-plain	2		
	LWZ 204	Washer-spring	2		
16	37H 2966	Seating-column mounting bracket	1		
	HBZ 408	Screw	2		
	PWZ 104	Washer-plain	2		
	LWZ 204	Washer-spring	2		
17	AHA 5435	Seal-outer tube to footwell	NLA	Use prior to AHA 9801	
17	AHA 9801	Seal-column to toeboard	1	(C)G-AN5-105501 TO 154100	
	CHA 457	Seal-column to toeboard	1	(C)G-AN6-154101 TO 170989	
	CHA 559	Seal-column to toeboard	1	(C)G-AN6-170990 ON	
19	AHA 9193	Wheel-steering	1	(C)H-AN9-78731 TO 85286 (C)G-AN4-66224 TO 74885	
19	ACH 6001	Nut-wheel	1		
20	BHH 291	Wheel-steering	1	(C)H-AN10-85287 TO 86803 (C)A-AN10-86804 TO 87824 (C)G-AN5-74886 TO 123730	Prior to (C)H-AN10-86803 and (C)G-AN5-89515 use also horn push BHA 5043 Midget or BHA 5053 Sprite
	BHH 786	Wheel-steering	1	(C)G-AN5-123731 TO 135881	
	BHH 1307	Wheel-steering $	1	(C)G-AN5-135882 ON	
19	BHH 119	Nut-wheel $	1	(C)H-AN10-85287 TO 86803 (C)A-AN10-86804 TO 87824 (C)G-AN5-74886 ON	

$ This item is subject to safety regulations

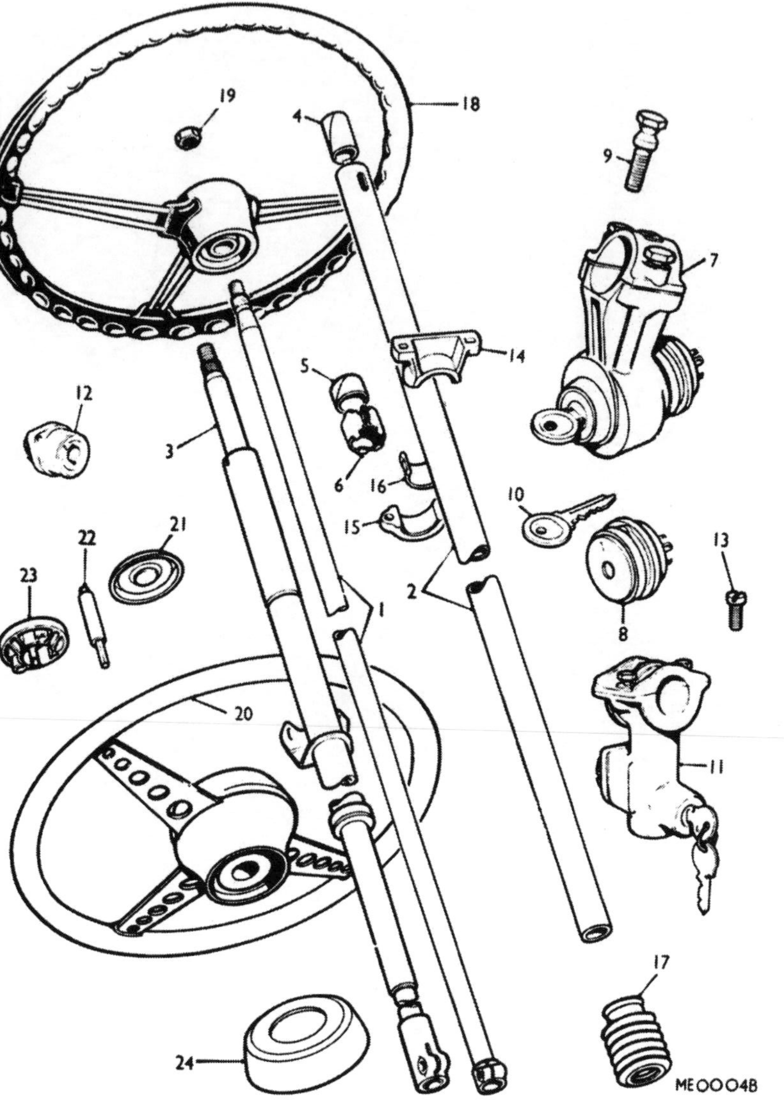

AUSTIN-HEALEY SPRITE MK. 3 AND MK. 4 & MG MIDGET MK. 2 AND MK. 3

STEERING COLUMN AND LOCK-EXCEPT N.AMERICA- continued

NO.	PART NO.	DESCRIPTION	QTY	CHANGE POINT	REMARKS
21	BHA 4979	Bezel and motif-Midget	1	(C)H-AN10-85287 TO 86302 (C)G-AN5-74886 TO 89514	
	BHA 5010	Bezel and motif-Sprite	1		
22	BHA 5041	Brush-horn push	1	(C)H-AN10-86303 TO 86803 (C)A-AN10-86804 TO 87824 (C)G-AN5-89515 ON	
23	BHA 5042	Slip-ring	1		
24	BHA 5043	Horn push-Midget	1	(C)H-AN10-86303 TO 86803 (C)A-AN10-86804 TO 87824 (C)G-AN5-89515 TO 105500	
24	BHA 5053	Horn push-Sprite	1		
24	BHA 5135	Horn push-Midget	1	(C)G-AN5-105501 TO 154100 (C)G-AN6-154101 TO 157172	
24	AAU 1161	Horn push	1	(C)G-AN6-157173 ON	

AUSTIN-HEALEY SPRITE MK. 3 AND MK. 4 & MG MIDGET MK. 2 AND MK. 3

STEERING COLUMN-COLLAPSIBLE TYPE-AND STEERING LOCKS-N.AMERICA

NO.	PART NO.	DESCRIPTION	QTY	CHANGE POINT	REMARKS
1	AHA 8496	Column-steering $	1	Use prior to AHA 9448	
1	AHA 9448	Column-steering $	1	(C)G-AN5-74886 TO 154100	
1	CHA 341	Column-steering $	1	(C)G-AN6-154101 ON	
2	AHA 8498	Wheel-steering $	1	Use prior to AHA 9194	
3	AHA 9194	Wheel-steering $	NLA	(C)H-AN9-78826 TO 85286 (C)G-AN4-67476 TO 74885	
4	AHH 8561	Nut-steering wheel $	1		
3	BHH 291	Wheel-steering $	1	(C)H-AN10-85287 TO 86803 (C)A-AN10-86804 TO 87824 (C)G-AN5-74886 TO 123730	
	BHH 786	Wheel-steering	1	(C)G-AN5-123731 TO 135881	
	BHH 1307	Wheel-steering $	1	(C)G-AN5-135882 ON	
4	BHH 119	Nut-steering wheel $	1	(C)H-AN10-85287 TO 86803 (C)A-AN10-86804 TO 87824 (C)G-AN5-74886 ON	
5	BHA 5041	Brush-horn push	1	(C)H-AN10-86303 TO 86803 (C)A-AN10-86804 TO 87824 (C)G-AN5-89515 TO 105500	
6	BHA 5042	Slip ring-horn push	1		
7	BHA 5043	Horn push	1		
7	BHA 5135	Horn push	1	(C)G-AN5-105501 TO 154100 (C)G-AN6-154101 TO 157172	
7	AAU 1161	Horn push	1	(C)G-AN6-157173 ON	
	HZS 506	Screw-column to bulkhead	5	Finished at (C)154100	
	PWZ 205	Washer-plain	5		
	PWZ 305	Washer-plain	5		
	LWZ 205	Washer-spring	5		
	FNZ 105	Nut	5		
	HZS 506	Screw-column to bulkhead	4	(C)G-AN6-154101 ON	
	PWZ 305	Washer-plain	8		
	LWZ 205	Washer-spring	4		
	FNZ 105	Nut	4		

$ This item is subject to safety regulations.

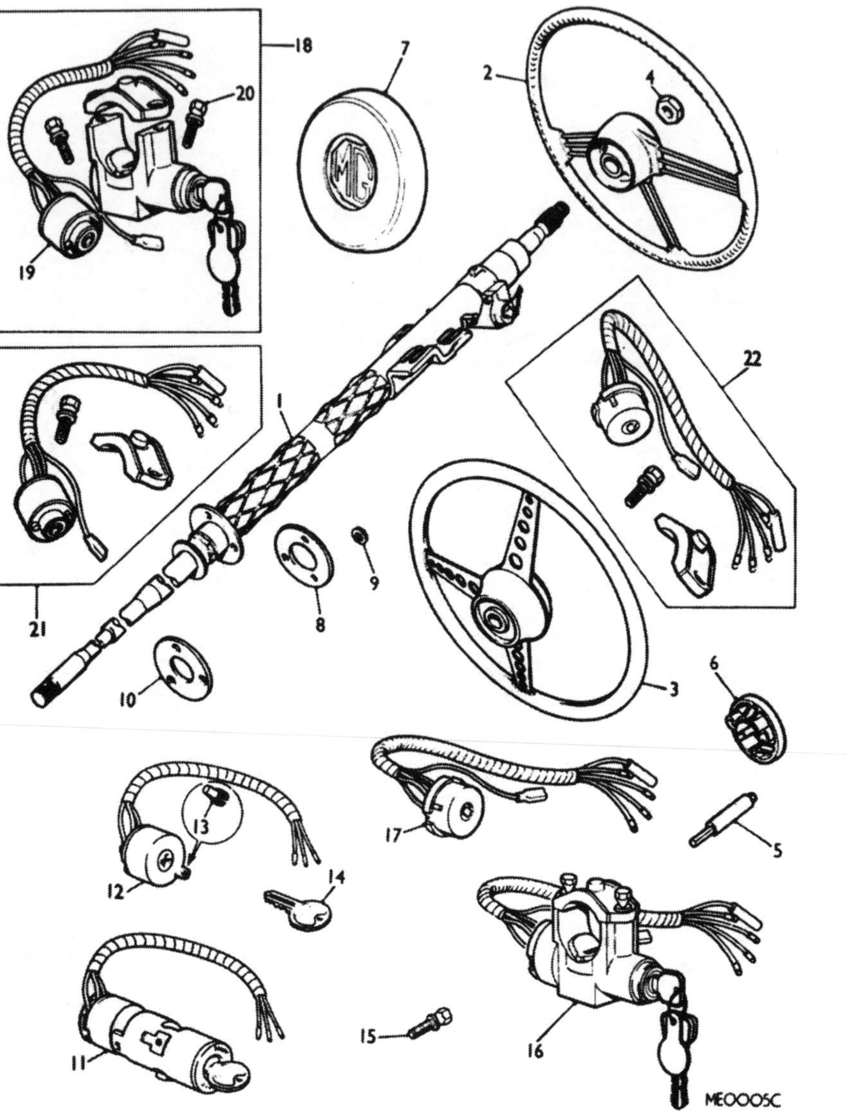

AUSTIN-HEALEY SPRITE MK. 3 AND MK. 4 & MG MIDGET MK. 2 AND MK. 3

STEERING COLUMN-COLLAPSIBLE TYPE-AND STEERING LOCKS-N.AMERICA-continued

NO.	PART NO.	DESCRIPTION	QTY	CHANGE POINT	REMARKS
	HZS 612	Screw-column to bulkhead	2		
	HZS 616	Screw-column to bulkhead	1		
	FNZ 106	Nut	3		
	LWZ 206	Washer-spring	3		
	PWZ 306	Washer-plain	6		
	HZS 507	Screw-column to floor	3		
	PWZ 205	Washer-plain	3		
	LWZ 205	Washer-spring	3		
8	AHA 8769	Ring-sealing-column flange to body	NLA	Finished at (C)G-AN5-154100	
9	53K 3159	Washer	3		
	53K 1013	Bolt-column to pinion clamp	1		
	LNZ 104	Nut-Aerotight	1		
10	AHA 8720	Seal-steering column to toe panel	1		
11	BHA 4715	LOCK ASSEMBLY(WITH IGNITION SWITCH)-USA FOR GERMANY $	1	Use prior to BHA 5050 and 18G 8901	
12	37H 4114	Switch $	NLA		
13	37H 4113	Screw-switch retaining $	1		
	BHA 5050	LOCK ASSEMBLY(WITH IGNITION SWITCH)$	NLA	(C)G-AN5-74886 TO 105500	Use 18G 8906.
17	BHA 5056	Switch $	1		
	18G 8901	KIT-STEERING LOCK	NLA		Use 18G 8905.
19	BHA 5070	Switch-lock	1		
20	51K 4001	Bolt-shear	2		
21	18G 8906	Kit-steering lock	1	(C)G-AN5-105501 TO 138800	Alternatives
22	18G 8905	Kit-steering lock	1		
18	18G 9120	KIT-STEERING LOCK $	1	(C)G-AN5-138801 TO 154100	
19	BHA 5294	Switch $	1		
18	18G 9119	Kit-steering lock $	1	(C)G-AN6-154101 ON	
19	BHA 5292	Switch $	1		

$ This item is subject to safety regulations.

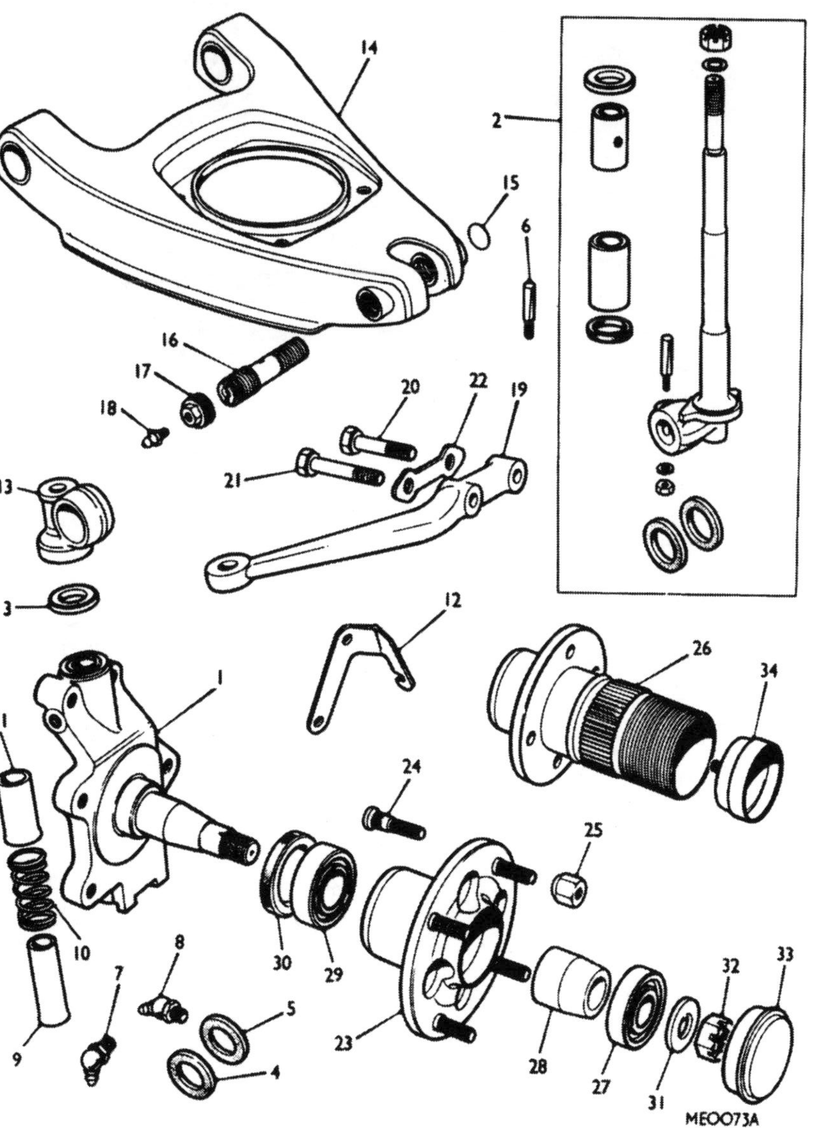

AUSTIN-HEALEY SPRITE MK. 3 AND MK. 4 & MG MIDGET MK. 2 AND MK. 3

FRONT SUSPENSION

NO.	PART NO.	DESCRIPTION	QTY	CHANGE POINT	REMARKS
	NSP	FRONT SUSPENSION ASSEMBLY	2		
1	BTA 744	Axle-swivel-RH $	1		
	BTA 745	Axle-swivel-LH $	1		
2	8G 4220	KIT-REPAIR-SWIVEL PIN AND BUSH $	2		
	FNZ 307	Nut-swivel pin	2		
3	2A 4006	Washer-thrust $	2		
4	2A 4206	Ring-large-fulcrum pin $	2		
5	2A 4205	Ring-small-fulcrum pin $	2		
6	51K 1769	Pin-cotter-fulcrum pin to swivel pin $	2		
	FNZ 103	Nut-cotter pin	2		
	LWZ 203	Washer-spring	2		
7	UHN 445	Lubricator-swivel axle-top	2		
8	UHN 490	Lubricator-swivel pin-bottom	2		
9	BTA 606	Tube-dust excluder-bottom $	2		
10	6K 653	Spring-dust excluder $	2		
11	2A 4010	Tube-dust excluder-top $	2		
12	BTA 792	Lockplate-brake hose-RH $	1	(C)H-AN8-62388 TO 64734 (C)H-AN9-64735 TO 85286 (C)H-AN10-85286 TO 86803 (C)A-AN10-86804 TO 87824 (C)G-AN3-50463 TO 52389 (C)G-AN4-52390 TO 74885 (C)G-AN5-74886 ON	
	BTA 793	Lockplate-brake hose-LH $	1		
13	2A 4005	Trunnion-suspension link $	2		
14	AHA 7029	LINK ASSEMBLY-LOWER $	2		
15	51K 3424	Plug-blanking-fulcrum pin small bush	2		
16	2A 4020	Pin-fulcrum $	2		
	51K 2751	Pin-cotter-fulcrum pin to swivel pin O/S $	2		
17	8G 589	Plug-screwed-fulcrum pin large bush $	2		
18	UHN 400	Lubricator	2		

$ This item is subject to safety regulations

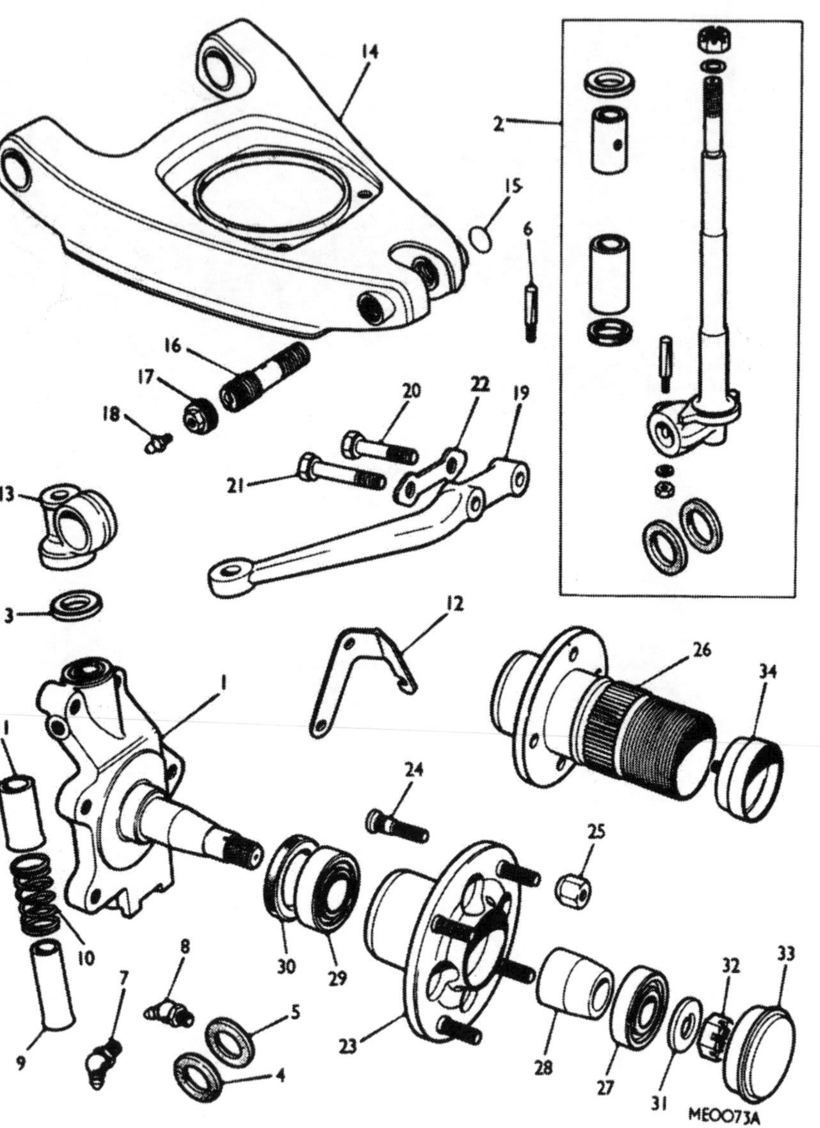

AUSTIN-HEALEY SPRITE MK. 3 AND MK. 4 & MG MIDGET MK. 2 AND MK. 3

FRONT SUSPENSION - continued

NO.	PART NO.	DESCRIPTION	QTY	CHANGE POINT	REMARKS
19	BTA 648	Lever-steering-RH $	1	Use prior to AHA 9957/8	
	BTA 649	Lever-steering-LH $	1		
19	AHA 9957	Lever-steering-RH $	1	(C)G-AN5-114487 ON USA(Plus(1)foot of page) (C)G-AN5-114643 ON Not USA(Plus(2) foot of page	
	AHA 9958	Lever-steering-LH $	1		
20	53K 1370	Screw-steering lever to swivel axle-short $	2		
21	ATA 4132	Screw-steering lever to swivel axle-long $	2		
22	2K 5377	Washer-lock $	2		
23	BTA 1254	HUB ASSEMBLY $	2		Disc wheels only
24	BTA 339	Stud-wheel $	8		
25	88G 577	Nut-wheel stud	8		
25	AHA 8785	Nut-wheel stud CP	8		
26	BTA 686	Hub-RH $	1		Wire wheels only
	BTA 687	Hub-LH $	1		
27	GHB 128	Bearing-hub-outer $	2		
28	88G 321	Piece-distance-bearing $	2		
29	GHB 129	Bearing-hub-inner $	2		
30	GHS 142	Seal-oil $	2		
31	2A 4003	Washer-bearing $	NLA		
32	51K 328	Nut-swivel axle	2		
33	2A 4067	Cap-grease retaining $	2		Disc wheels only
34	BTC 392	Cap-grease retaining $	2		Wire wheels only

$ This item is subject to safety regulations

CHANGE POINTS.
(1).114352,114473,114475 TO 114480,114526 TO 114541,114543 AND 114580 TO 114588
(2).114244,114332,114333,114361 TO 114365,114377,114385,114398 TO 114406, 114416 TO 114419,114446 TO 114472 AND 114483 TO 114486

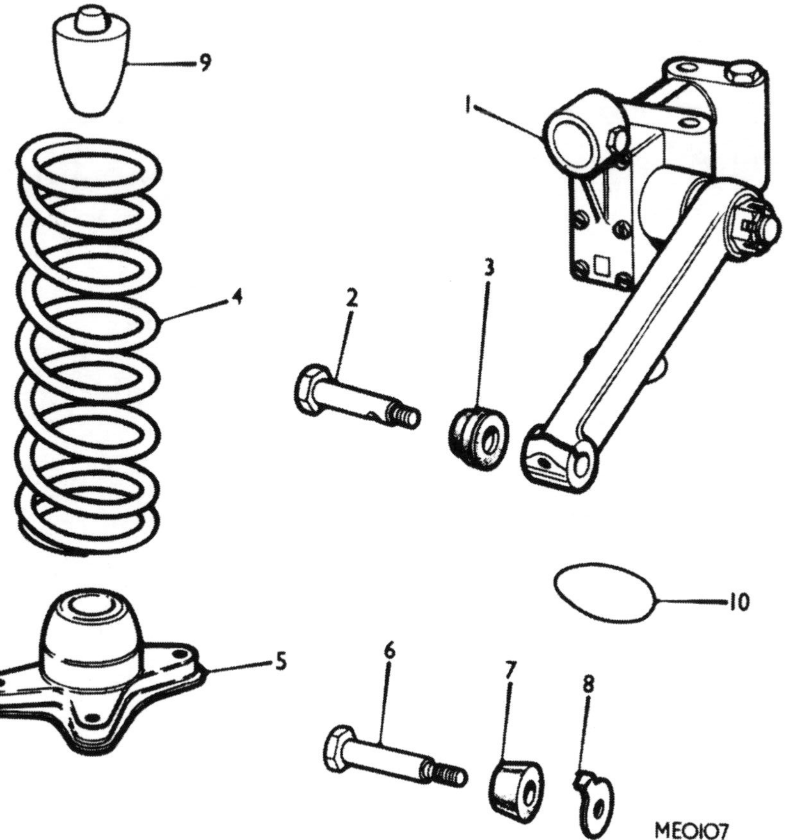

AUSTIN-HEALEY SPRITE MK. 3 AND MK. 4 & MG MIDGET MK. 2 AND MK. 3

FRONT SHOCK ABSORBERS

NO.	PART NO.	DESCRIPTION	QTY	CHANGE POINT	REMARKS
1	GSA 102	Absorber-shock-RH $	1		
	GSA 103	Absorber-shock-LH $	1		
	53K 1364	Screw-shock absorber to frame	6	Use prior to CHA 398	
	CHA 398	Bolt-shock absorber to frame	6	(C)G-AN6-154101 ON	
	WA 110061	Washer-plain	6		
	LWZ 306	Washer-spring	6		
2	2A 4028	Pin-fulcrum-shock absorber to trunnion $	2		
3	88G 274	Bearing $	4		
	FNZ 306	Nut-fulcrum pin	2		
	53K 1389	Bolt-clamping-fulcrum pin to shock absorber arm $	2		
	LWN 405	Washer-shakeproof	2		
4	2A 4214	Spring-road-coil	2	Use prior to CHA 129	
4	CHA 129	Spring-road-coil	2	(C)H-AN8-58381 N.America 60260 Not N.America TO 64734 (C)H-AN9-64735 TO 85286 (C)H-AN10-85287 TO 86803 (C)A-AN10-86804 TO 87824 (C)G-AN3-46042 N.America 47527 Not N.America TO 52389 (C)G-AN4-52390 TO 74885 (C)G-AN5-74885 TO 154100 (C)G-AN6-154101 TO 171477	
4	CHA 570	Spring-road-coil $	2	(C)G-AN6-171478 ON	
5	21A 137	Seat-spring $	2		
	53K 1368	Bolt-spring seat to lower link $	8		
	LNZ 205	Nut	8		Alternatives
	LNZ 105	Nut	8		Alternatives
	LWN 405	Washer-shakeproof	8		
6	2A 4272	Pin-fulcrum-lower link to frame $	4		
7	8G 621	Bearing-lower link $	8		
8	2A 4024	Washer-special-fulcrum pin $	4		
	GHF 223	Nut-fulcrum pin	4		Alternatives
	LNZ 106	Nut-fulcrum pin	4		Alternatives
9	AHA 6378	Buffer suspension	2		
10	2A 4082	Buffer rebound	2		

$ This item is subject to safety regulations

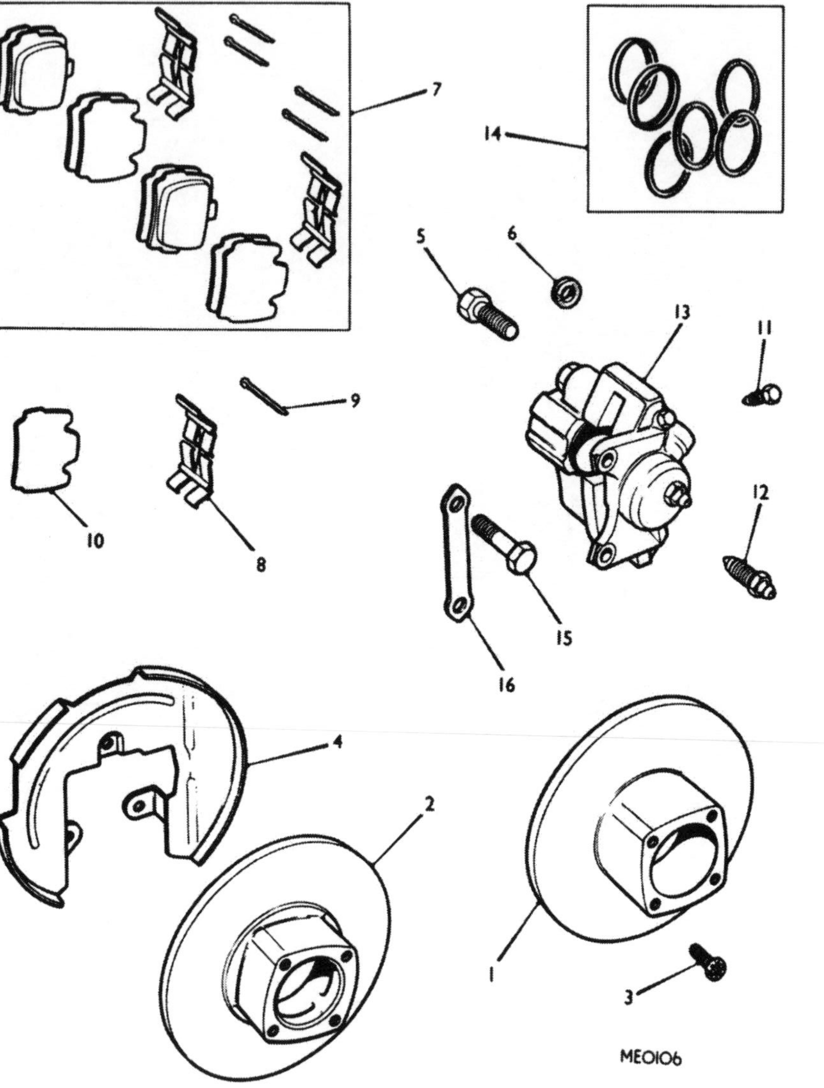

AUSTIN-HEALEY SPRITE MK. 3 AND MK. 4 & MG MIDGET MK. 2 AND MK. 3

NO.	PART NO.	DESCRIPTION	QTY	CHANGE POINT	REMARKS
		FRONT BRAKES			
1	BTA 383	Disc-brake $	2		Disc wheels only
2	BTA 469	Disc-brake $	2		Wire wheels only
3	BTA 370	Bolt-disc to hub $	8		
4	BTA 472	Cover-dust-brake disc-RH $	1		
	BTA 473	Cover-dust-brake-disc-LH $	1		
	HZS 503	Bolt	2		
	LWZ 505	Washer-shakeproof	2		
	BTA 653	UNIT ASSEMBLY-CALLIPER-LH	NLA		Use 17H 9438 with pad GBP 108 and shim 17H 2460
	BTA 652	UNIT ASSEMBLY-CALLIPER-RH	NLA		Use 17H 9439 with pad GBP 108 and shim 17H 2460
5	17H 8250	Bolt-bridge	4		
6	17H 7679	Seal-fluid channel $	2		
7	GBP 108	PAD ASSEMBLY	1SET		
8	17H 7963	Spring-pad retainer	2		
9	ZPS 524	Pin-split cotter	4		
10	17H 2460	Shim-pad	4		
11	17H 7917	Plug	2		
12	3H 2428	Screw-bleed	2		

$ This item is subject to safery regulations

AUSTIN-HEALEY SPRITE MK. 3 AND MK. 4 & MG MIDGET MK. 2 AND MK. 3

FRONT BRAKES- continued

NO.	PART NO.	DESCRIPTION	QTY	CHANGE POINT	REMARKS
	17H 9438	UNIT ASSEMBLY-CALLIPER(LESS PADS AND SHIMS)-LH $	1		
13	17H 9439	UNIT ASSEMBLY-CALLIPER(LESS PADS AND SHIMS)-RH $	1		
5	17H 8250	Bolt-bridge $	4		
6	17H 7679	Seal-fluid channel	2		
14	8G 8668	KIT-REPAIR-CALLIPER UNIT $	2		
7	GBP 108	PAD ASSEMBLY $	1SET		
8	17H 7963	Spring-pad retainer $	2		
9	ZPS 524	Pin-split cotter	4		
10	17H 2460	Shim-anti-squeal $	4		
	BTA 444	Bolt-calliper mounting	NLA		Use BTA 789 and BTC 114 together with 1 off lock plate BTA 792 RH or BTA 793 LH
15	BTA 789	Bolt-calliper mounting $	4	(C)H-AN8-62388 TO 64734 (C)H-AN9-64735 TO 85286 (C)H-AN10-85287 TO 86803 (C)A-AN10-86804 TO 87824 (C)G-AN3-50463 TO 52389 (C)G-AN4-52390 TO 74885 (C)G-AN5-74886 ON	
16	BTC 114	Washer-tab $	2		

$ This item is subject to safety regulations

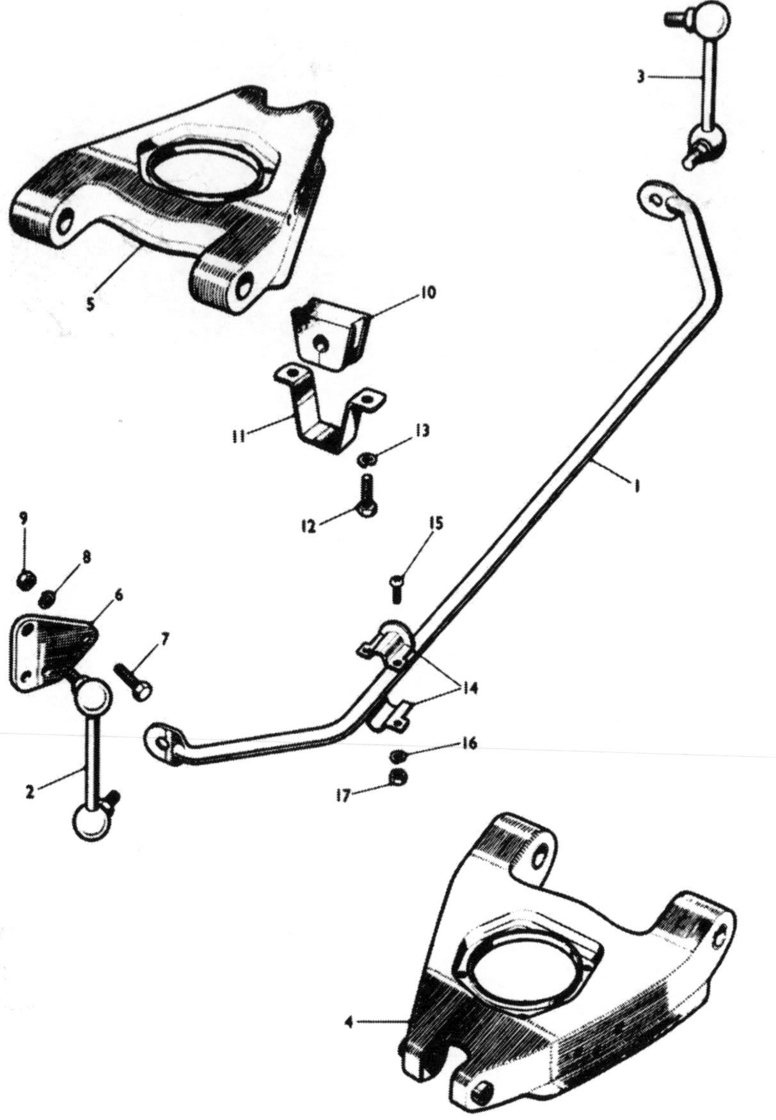

AUSTIN-HEALEY SPRITE MK. 3 AND MK. 4 & MG MIDGET MK. 2 AND MK. 3

ANTI-ROLL BAR

NO.	PART NO.	DESCRIPTION	QTY	CHANGE POINT	REMARKS
1	AHA 7013	Bar-anti-roll $	1		Optional extra, STANDARD FITMENT FOR UK FROM (C)G-AN5-138801 ON
2	AHA 7011	Link-anti-roll bar-RH $	1		
3	AHA 7012	Link-anti-roll bar-LH $	1		
4	AHA 7029	Link-lower $	2		
6	AHA 7028	Bracket-anti-roll bar link $	2		
7	HZS 506	Screw-bracket to lower link	6		
8	WL 600051	Washer-spring	6		
9	NH 605041	Nut	6		
10	AHH 6541	Bearing-anti-roll bar $	2		
11	1B 7356	Strap-bearing $	2		
12	HZS 505	Screw-strap to frame	4		
13	WL 600051	Washer-spring	4		
14	AHH 6546	Stop-end $	4		
15	PMZ 307	Screw-clamping-end stop	4		
16	LWZ 203	Washer-spring	4		
17	FNZ 103	Nut	4		

$ This item is subject to safety regulations

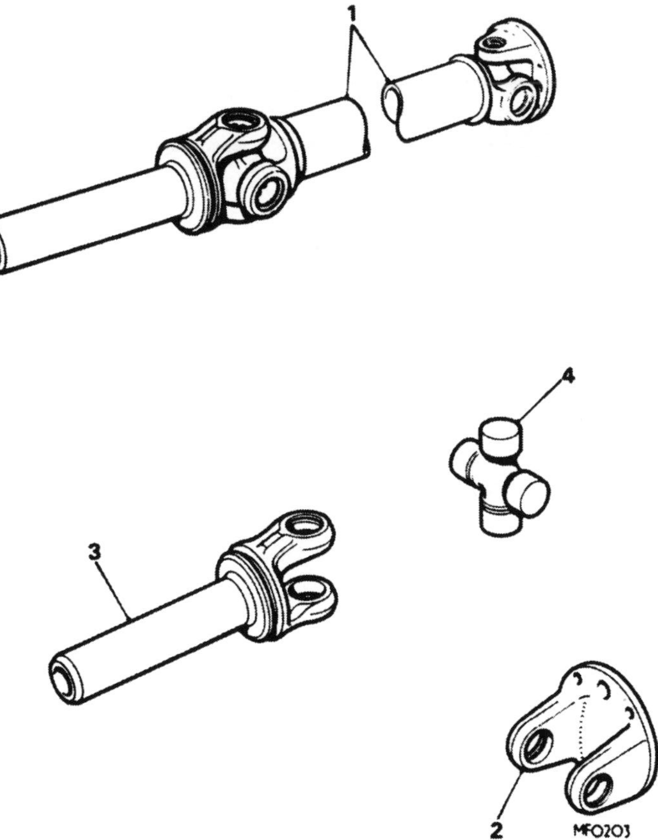

AUSTIN-HEALEY SPRITE MK. 3 AND MK. 4 & MG MIDGET MK. 2 AND MK. 3

NO.	PART NO.	DESCRIPTION	QTY	CHANGE POINT	REMARKS
		PROPELLER SHAFT			
1	AHA 9053	SHAFT ASSEMBLY-PROPELLER	1	Use prior to CHA 336	
2	17H 3828	Flange-yoke	1		
3	37H 4149	Sleeve-yoke	1		
4	GUJ 101	Journal	2		
1	CHA 336	SHAFT ASSEMBLY-PROPELLER	1	(C)G-AN6-154101 ON	
	37H 4973	Flange-yoke(slip joint)	1		
	17H 3828	Flange-yoke(fixed joint)	1		
	37H 8817	Sleeve-yoke	1		
	GUJ 101	Journal	2		
9	HBZ 510	Bolt-shaft to pinion flange	4		
10	LWZ 305	Washer-spring	4		
11	LNZ 105	Nut	4		Alternatives
11	LNZ 205	Nut	4		
	144961	Bolt-shaft to gearbox flange	4		
	53K 1663	Nut	4		

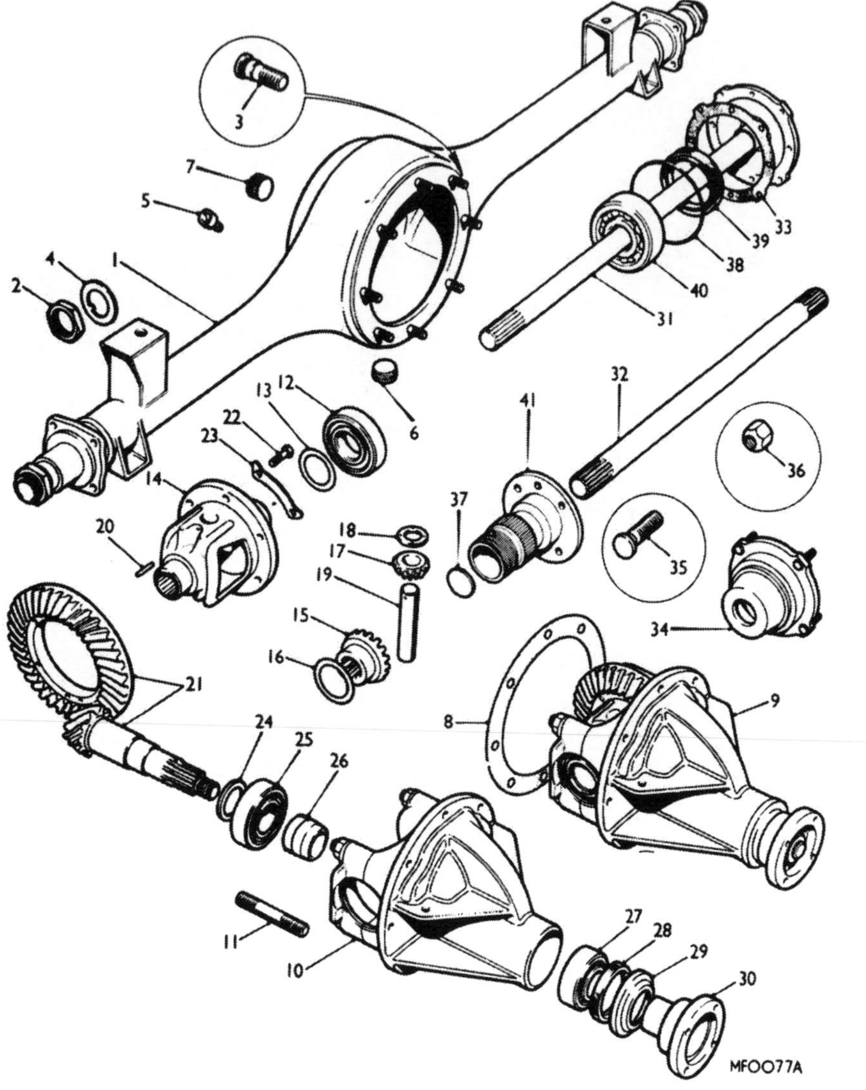

AUSTIN-HEALEY SPRITE MK. 3 AND MK. 4 & MG MIDGET MK. 2 AND MK. 3

NO.	PART NO.	DESCRIPTION	QTY	CHANGE POINT	REMARKS
		REAR AXLE			
	NSP	AXLE ASSEMBLY	1		
1	BTA 694	CASE ASSEMBLY	1	Use proir to DAM 2483/4	Disc wheels only
	BTA 695	CASE ASSEMBLY	1		Wire wheels only
2	2A 7103	Nut-bearing retaining-RHT	1		Not supplied With DAM 2483 And DAM 2484
	1G 3584	Nut-bearing retaining-LHT	1		
3	2A 7226	Stud-gear carrier	8		
	DAM 2483	Case	1	(C)G-AN6 182001 ON	Disc wheels only
	DAM 2484	Case	1		Wire wheels only
4	2A 7250	Washer-bearing retaining nut	2		
5	1H 3364	Breather	1		
6	6K 499	Plug-drain	1		
7	6K 499	Plug-filler	1		
8	2A 7027	Gasket-gear carrier to axle case	1		
	NH 605041	Nut-gear carrier to axle case	8		
	LWZ 305	Washer-spring	8		
9	BTA 550	DIFFERENTIAL ASSEMBLY-9x38 TEETH(4.22:1 RATIO)	1	Use prior to BTA 1222	
9	BTA 1222	DIFFERENTIAL ASSEMBLY-10x39 TEETH(3.90:1 RATIO)	1	(C)H-AN9-77591 TO 85286 (C)H-AN10-85287 TO 86803 (C)A-AN10-86804 TO 87824 (C)G-AN4-66226 TO 74885 (C)G-AN5-74886 ON	
10	BTA 549	CARRIER ASSEMBLY	1		
11	51K 886	Stud-bearing cap	4		
	PWZ 107	Washer-plain	4		
	LWN 307	Washer-spring	4		
	FNN 107	Nut	4		
12	2K 5943	Bearing-differential	2		
		WASHER-BEARING PACKING			
13	2K 7779	.002"(.050mm)	A/R		
13	ATA 7269	.003"(.067mm)	A/R		
13	2K 7778	.004"(.101mm)	A/R		
13	2A 7271	.010"(.254mm)	A/R		
14	ATA 7036	Cage-differential	1		
15	ATA 7037	Wheel-differential	2		
16	ATA 7039	Washer-thrust-differential wheel	2		
17	2A 7015	Pinion-differential	2		
18	2A 7062	Washer-thrust-differential pinion	2		
19	2A 7016	Pin-pinion	1		
20	6K 631	Peg-pinion pin	1		

AUSTIN-HEALEY SPRITE MK. 3 AND MK. 4 & MG MIDGET MK. 2 AND MK. 3

NO.	PART NO.	DESCRIPTION	QTY	CHANGE POINT	REMARKS
		REAR AXLE-continued			
21	BTA 539	CROWN WHEEL AND PINION-9x38 TEETH(4.22:1 RATIO)	1	Use prior to BTA 1223	
21	BTA 1223	CROWN WHEEL AND PINION-10x39 TEETH(3.90:1 RATIO)	1	(C)H-AN9-77591 TO 85286 (C)H-AN10-85287 TO 86803 (C)A-AN10-86804 TO 87824 (C)G-AN4-66226 TO 74885 (C)G-AN5-74886 ON	
22	ATA 7232	Bolt-crown wheel to differential cage	6		
23	ATA 7044	Washer-lock	3		
		WASHER-PINION THRUST			
24	ATA 7123	.130"(3.30mm)	1		One used of SELECTED SIZE
24	ATA 7124	.128"(3.25mm)	1		
24	ATA 7125	.126"(3.20mm)	1		
24	ATA 7126	.124"(3.15mm)	NLA		
24	ATA 7127	.122"(3.10mm)	1		
24	ATA 7128	.120"(3.05mm)	1		
24	ATA 7129	.118"(3.00mm)	1		
24	ATA 7130	.116"(2.95mm)	NLA		
25	ATA 7166	Bearing-inner-pinion	1		
26	BTA 532	Spacer-bearing	1		
27	BTB 440	Bearing-outer-pinion	1		
28	88G 320	Seal-oil	1		
29	1G 7439	Cover-dust	1		
30	ATA 7056	Flange-universal joint	1		
	FNN 612	Nut	1		
	LWZ 212	Washer-spring	1		
31	BTA 806	Shaft-axle	2		Disc wheels only
32	BTA 807	Shaft-axle	2		Wire wheels only
33	2A 7091	Gasket-shaft to hub	2		
34	2A 7087	HUB ASSEMBLY $	2		Disc wheels only
35	2A 7089	Stud-wheel $	8		
36	88G 577	Nut-wheel stud $	8		
36	AHA 8785	Nut-wheel stud-CP	8		
34	BTA 490	HUB ASSEMBLY $	2		Wire wheels only
35	BTA 492	Stud-wheel $	8		
41	BTA 688	Extension-hub-RH $	1		
	BTA 689	Extension-hub-LH $	1		
37	2K 8160	Plug-welch	2		
38	ATA 7225	Ring-oil seal	2		
39	GHS 147	Seal-oil	2		
40	GHB 130	Bearing-hub	2		

$ This item is subject to safety regulations.

MFO083A

AUSTIN-HEALEY SPRITE MK. 3 AND MK. 4 & MG MIDGET MK. 2 AND MK. 3

REAR BRAKES

NO.	PART NO.	DESCRIPTION	QTY	CHANGE POINT	REMARKS
1	BTA 566	Plate-brake-RH $	1	Use prior to 37H 8804/5	
	BTA 567	Plate-brake-LH $	1		
1	37H 8804	Plate-brake-RH $	1	(C)G-AN6-154101 ON	
	37H 8805	Plate-brake-LH $	1		
	HZS 507	Screw	8		
	LNZ 205	Locknut	8		
2	GBS 512	SHOE ASSEMBLY-BRAKE $	2STS	Use prior to GBS 625.	
3	18G 8329	Lining $	1BOX		
2	GBS 625	SHOE ASSEMBLY-BRAKE $	2STS	(C)G-AN6-154101 ON	
4	17H 7947	Spring-shoe return-cylinder end-RH $	1		
5	17H 7948	Spring-shoe return-cylinder end-LH $	1		
6	17H 7621	Spring-shoe return-adjuster end $	2		
7	17H 7618	Tappet $	4		
8	17H 7619	Wedge $	2		
9	GWC 1102	CYLINDER ASSEMBLY-WHEEL $	2	Finished at (C)G-AN5-154100	
10	17H 8399	Piston $	4		
11	17H 7623	Screw-bleed $	2		
12	8G 8797	KIT-REPAIR-WHEEL CYLINDER $	2		
9	GWC 1129	CYLINDER ASSEMBLY-WHEEL $	2	(C)G-AN6-154101 ON	
11	17H 7623	Screw-bleed $	2		
12	BHM 7054	Kit-repair $	2		
13	17H 7613	Washer-Belleville-wheel cylinder fixing $	2		
14	17H 7622	Circlip-wheel cylinder fixing $	2		
15	17H 2824	Lever-handbrake-RH $	1		
	17H 2825	Lever-handbrake-LH $	1		
16	17H 7612	Boot-handbrake lever $	2		
17	2A 7168	Drum-brake $	2		
	CMZ 410	Screw	4		
	FNZ 506	Nut	8		Wire wheels ONLY
18	BTA 493	Washer-tab $	4		
19	2A 7228	Plug-drum(rubber)	2		

$ This item is subject to safety regulations

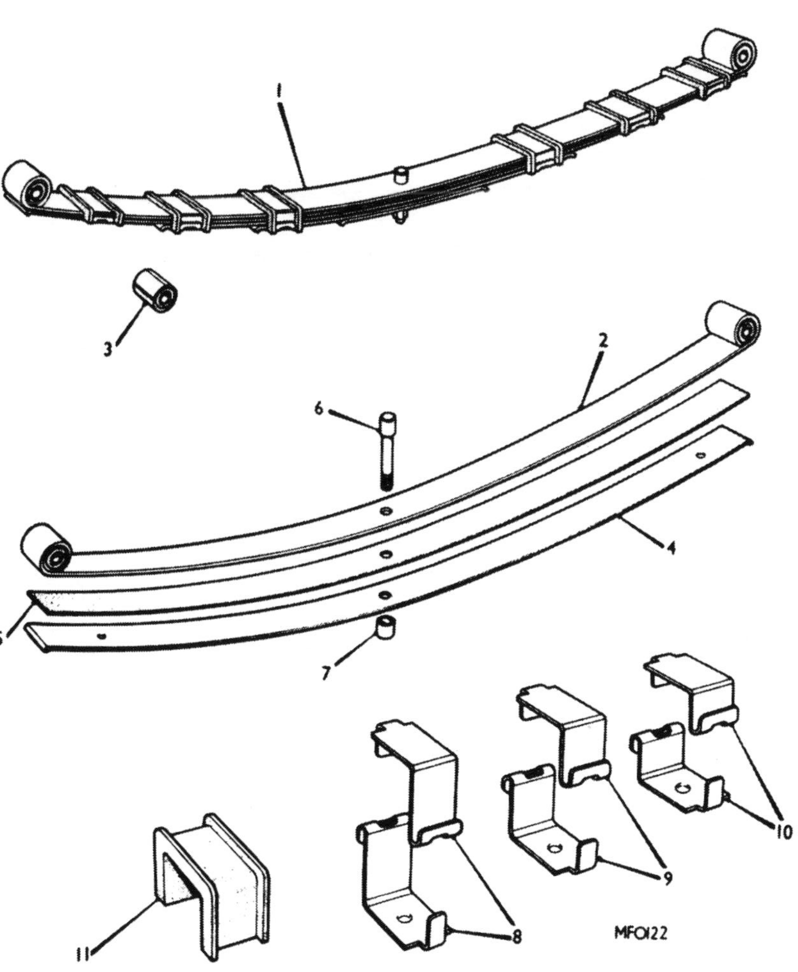

AUSTIN-HEALEY SPRITE MK. 3 AND MK. 4 & MG MIDGET MK. 2 AND MK. 3

NO.	PART NO.	DESCRIPTION	QTY	CHANGE POINT	REMARKS
		REAR SPRINGS			
1	AHA 7184	SPRING ASSEMBLY	2		
2	AHA 7807	LEAF ASSEMBLY-MAIN	NLA		
3	AAA 629	Bush	2		
5	AHA 7551 M	Strip-interleaf	A/R		Supplied in 23 metre(25 yards) lengths
6	AHA 7813	Toe-bolt	2	(C)H-AN8-38829	
7	ACA 5000	Piece-distance-toe-bolt	2	TO 64734	
	LNZ 105	Nut-toe-bolt	2	(C)G-AN3-25788	
8	AHA 7359	Clip-long	4	TO 52389	
9	AHA 7360	Clip-intermediate	4		
10	AHA 7361	Clip-short	4		
11	AHB 6707	Pad-clip	6		
1	AHA 8093	SPRING ASSEMBLY	2		
2	AHA 7807	LEAF ASSEMBLY-MAIN	NLA		
3	AAA 629	Bush	2		
5	AHA 7551 M	Strip-interleaf	A/R		Supplied in 23 metre (25yards) lengths
6	AHA 7813	Toe-bolt	2		
7	ACA 5000	Piece-distance-toe-bolt	2	(C)H-AN9-64735	
	NH 605041	Nut-toe-bolt	2	TO 85286	Alternatives
	LNZ 405	Stiffnut	2	(C)H-AN10-85287	
8	AHA 8308	Clip-long	2	TO 86803	
8	AHA 7359	Clip-intermediate-long	4	(C)A-AN10-86804 TO	
9	AHA 7360	Clip-intermediate-short	4	87824	
10	AHA 7361	Clip-short	4	(C)G-AN4-52390	
11	AHB 6707	Pad-clip-long	2	TO 74885	
11	AHA 8307	Pad-clip-long	NLA	(C)G-AN5-74886 TO	
11	AHB 6707	Pad-clip-intermediate-long	4	154100	
11	AHB 6707	Pad-clip-intermediate-short	4		
1	CHA 493	SPRING ASSEMBLY $	2	(C)G-AN6-154101 ON	

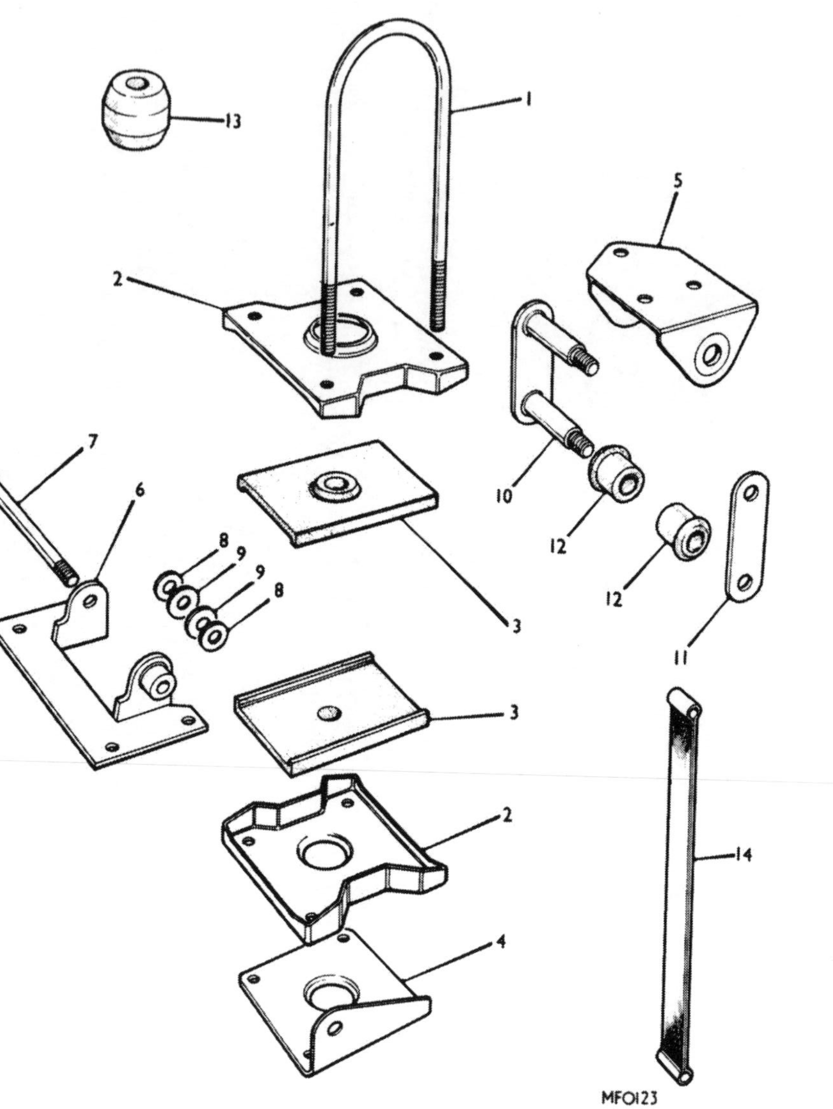

AUSTIN-HEALEY SPRITE MK. 3 AND MK. 4 & MG MIDGET MK. 2 AND MK. 3

NO.	PART NO.	DESCRIPTION	QTY	CHANGE POINT	REMARKS
		REAR SPRING FIXINGS			
1	AHA 8097	Clip-spring to axle	4		
	WA 110061	Washer-plain	8		
	GHF 223	Nut	8		
2	ACA 5139	Plate-locating	4		
3	ACA 5138	Pad-seating	4		
4	AHA 7172	Bracket-shock absorber link to spring-RH	1		
	AHA 7173	Bracket-shock absorber link to spring-LH	1		
5	AHA 7201	Bracket-spring	2		
	HZS 507	Screw	6	Finished at (C)G-AN5-154100	
	PWZ 105	Washer-plain	6		
	WL 600051	Washer-spring	6		
	LNZ 105	Nut	6		
	HZS 505	Screw	6	(C)G-AN6-154101 ON	
	WL 600051	Washer-spring	6		
6	AHA 7174	Mounting-spring-front $	2		
7	AHA 7180	Bolt-spring to front bracket $	2		
8	AHA 7178	Washer-distance	4		
9	AHA 7179	Washer-special	4		
	LWZ 207	Washer-spring	2		
	SH 606101	Screw	4		
	HZS 607	Screw	4	Use prior to HZS 614	
	HZS 614	Screw	NLA	(C)G-AN6-154101 ON	
	WA 110061	Washer-plain	4		
	LWZ 206	Washer-spring	8		
10	AHA 7686	Plate-shackle(with pin) $	2		
11	AHA 7687	Plate-shackle $	2		
12	AHA 7182	Bush-shackle	8		
	LWZ 206	Washer-spring	4		
	FNZ 106	Nut	4		
13	AHH 7074	Rubber-bump	2	Use prior to AHH 9158	
13	AHH 9158	Rubber-bump	2	(C)H-AN10-85309 TO 86803 (C)A-AN10-86804 TO 87824 (C)G-AN5-77979 ON	
14	AHH 5081	Strap-rebound	2	Use prior to BHH 989	
14	BHH 989	Strap-rebound	2	(C)G-AN6-154101 ON	
	HBZ 630	Bolt	2		
	PWZ 206	Washer-plain	4		
	LWZ 206	Washer-spring	4		
	FNZ 106	Nut	4		

$ This item is subject to safety regulations

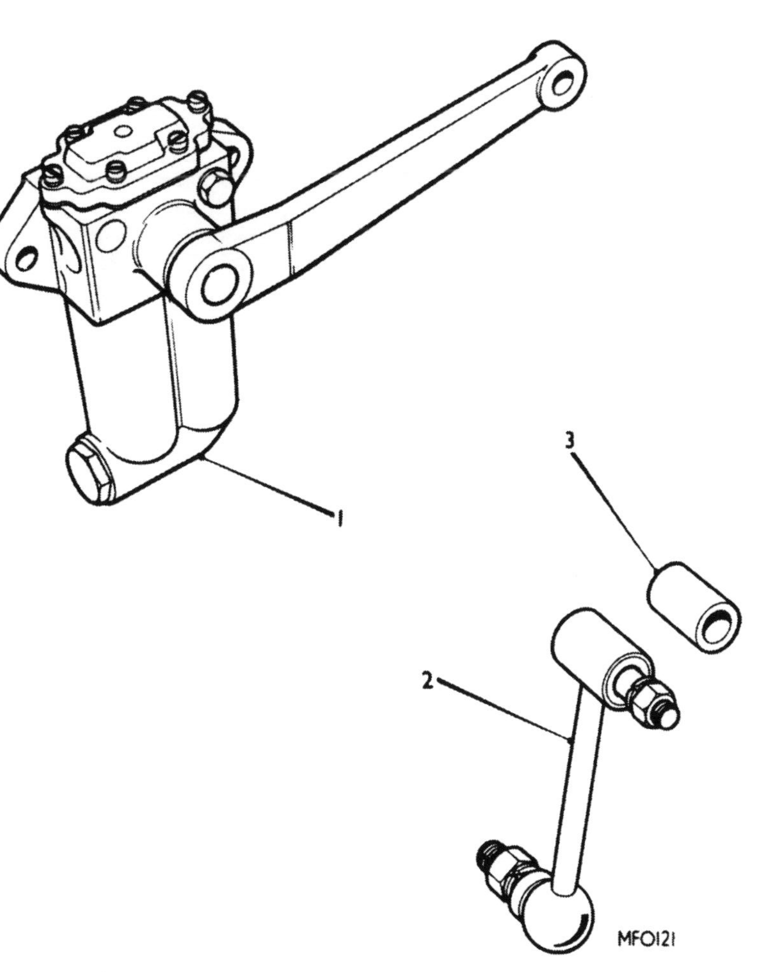

AUSTIN-HEALEY SPRITE MK. 3 AND MK. 4 & MG MIDGET MK. 2 AND MK. 3

REAR SHOCK ABSORBERS

NO.	PART NO.	DESCRIPTION	QTY	CHANGE POINT	REMARKS
1	GSA 149	SHOCK ABSORBER-REAR(LESS LINK)-RH	1		
	GSA 150	SHOCK ABSORBER-REAR(LESS LINK)-LH	1		
2	17H 9275	LINK ASSEMBLY $	2	Use prior to AAU 1949	
2	AAU 1949	LINK ASSEMBLY $	2	(C)G-AN6-157672 ON	
3	97H 222	Bush-link-top(rubber) $	2		
	FNZ 507	Nut	2		
	LWZ 307	Washer-spring	2		
	FNZ 508	Nut	2		
	LWZ 308	Washer-spring	2		
	HZS 612	Bolt	4		
	PWZ 206	Washer-plain	4		
	GHF 223	Nut	4		
	WA 110061	Washer-plain	4		
	LWZ 206	Washer-spring	4		

$ This item is subject to safety regulations

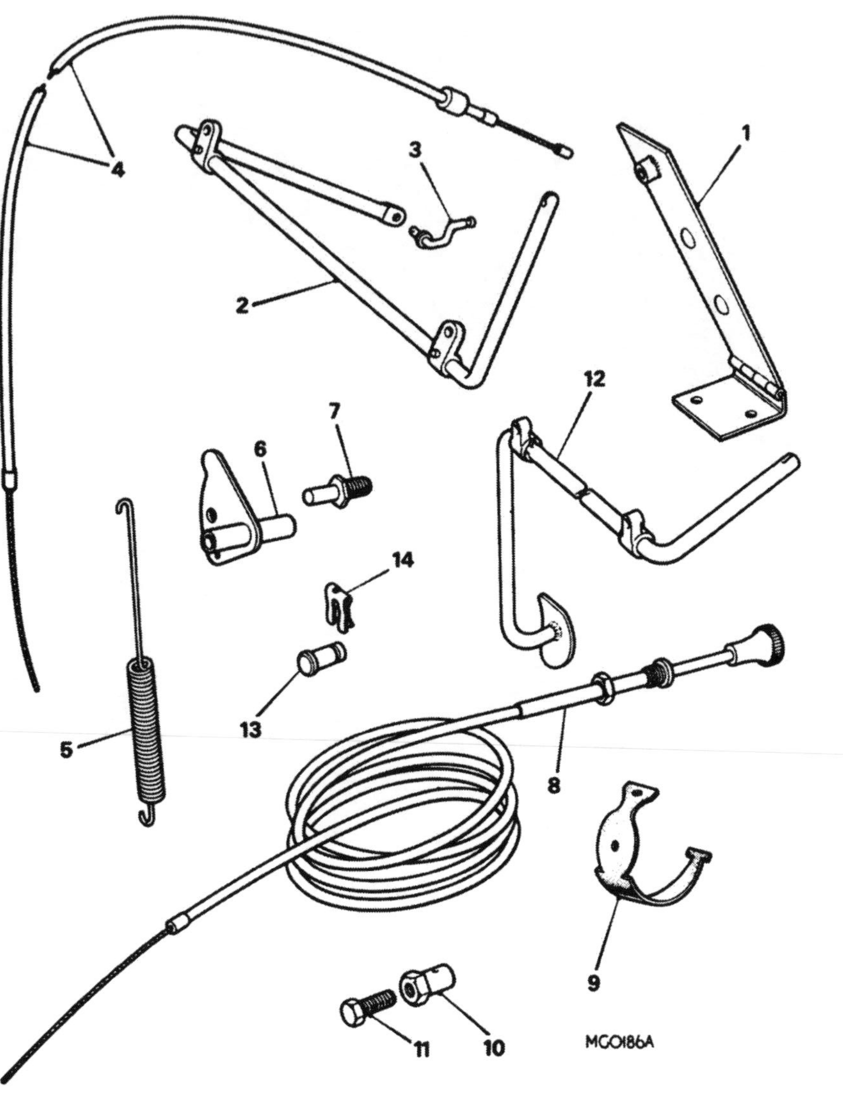

AUSTIN-HEALEY SPRITE MK. 3 AND MK. 4 & MG MIDGET MK. 2 AND MK. 3

NO.	PART NO.	DESCRIPTION	QTY	CHANGE POINT	REMARKS
		ENGINE CONTROLS.			
1	AHA 6256	Pedal-accelerator $	1	Use prior to CHA 494-RHD CHA 496-LHD	
12	CHA 494	Pedal-accelerator(with lever)-RHD	1	(C)G-AN6-154101 ON	
	CHA 496	Pedal-accelerator(with lever)-lhd	1		
	HZS 404	Screw	2		
	LWZ 204	Washer-spring	2		
2	2A 2077	Lever-pedal	1		
2	AHA 8514	Lever-pedal $	1		USA,Canada, Sweden and Germany
	HZS 407	Screw	2		
	LWZ 204	Washer-spring	2		
	HZS 407	Screw	1		
	FNZ 204	Locknut	1		
3	AHA 6255	Link-pedal to lever	1	Finished at (C)G-AN5-154100	
	PWZ 104	Washer-plain	1		
4	AHA 5746	Cable-accelerator control $	1		
4	CHA 475	Cable-accelerator control-RHD $	1	(C)G-AN6-154101 ON	
	CHA 405	Cable-accelerator control-LHD $	1		Not California
	CHA 485	Cable-accelerator control-LHD	1	(C)G-AN6-160160 ON	California only
5	AEA 602	Spring-throttle return	3		
6	AEA 597	Lever-throttle	1		
7	ACC 5062	Pin-cable to lever	1		
	PWZ 203	Washer-plain	1		
	PWZ 104	Washer-plain	1		
	NH 604041	Nut	1		
13	BHA 5357	Pin-cable to lever-RHD	1	(C)G-AN6-154101 ON	
14	BHA 5358	Clip-pin-RHD	1		
	PWZ 203	Washer-plain-RHD	2		
8	AHA 7748	Cable-mixture control	NLA	Use prior to CHA 288	Use CHA 288
8	AHA 8713	Cable-mixture control $	1		USA,Canada, Sweden and Germany
8	CHA 288	Cable-mixture control	1	(C)G-AN5-147531 TO 154100 (C)G-AN6-154101 ON (Except USA and Canada)	
8	CHA 446	Cable-mixture control	1	(C)G-AN6-154101 ON (USA and CANADA)	Not required with Automatic choke
	WA 110061	Washer-plain	1		
9	13H 6107	Strap-cable to heater clip	1		
10	AHA 6367	Pin-cable to carburetter	1		
11	53K 3503	Screw-pin	1		

$ This item is subject to safety regulations.

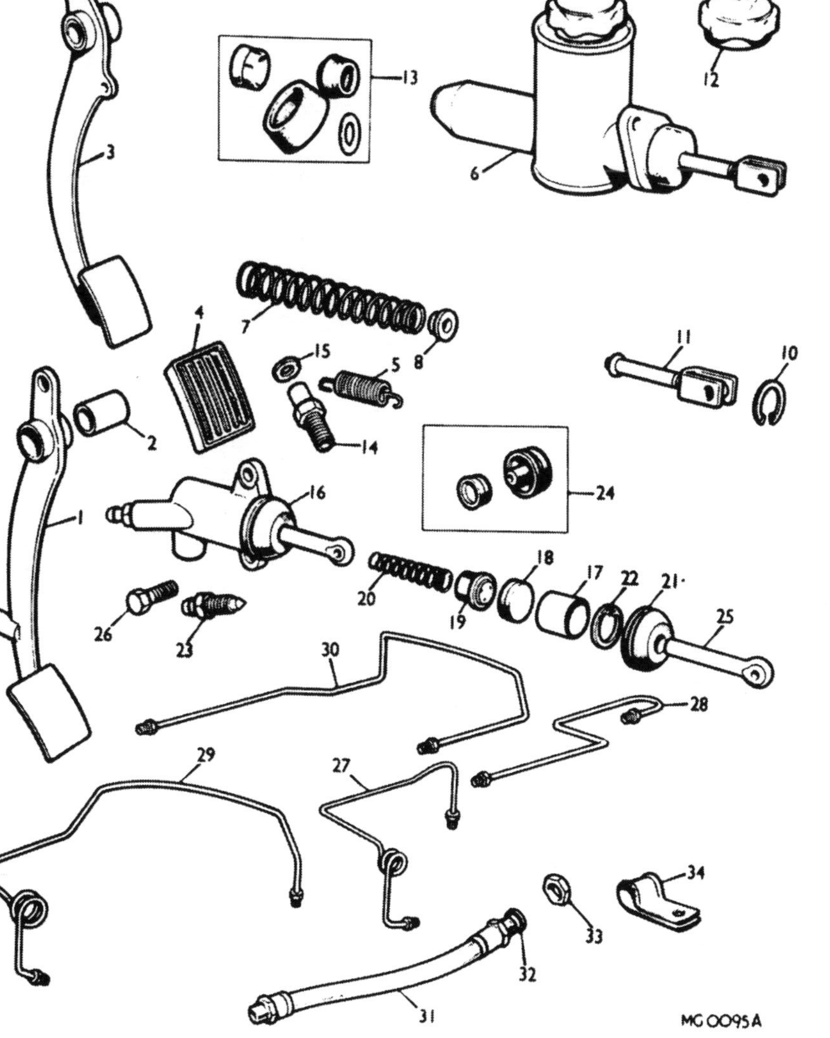

AUSTIN-HEALEY SPRITE MK. 3 AND MK. 4 & MG MIDGET MK. 2 AND MK. 3

NO.	PART NO.	DESCRIPTION	QTY	CHANGE POINT	REMARKS
		CLUTCH PEDAL AND LINKAGE			
3	AHA 8071	PEDAL ASSEMBLY-CLUTCH $	1	(C)H-AN9-64735 TO 85286 (C)H-AN10-85287 TO 86803 (C)A-AN10-86804 TO 87824 (C)G-AN4-52390 TO 74885 (C)G-AN5-74886 ON	
2	LBS 810	Bush	1		
4	AHA 5326	Pad-pedal rubber	1		
	HZS 408	Screw-pedal adjustment	1	(C)H-AN8-38329 TO 64734 (C)G-AN3-25788 TO 52389	
	FNZ 204	Locknut	2		
5	2A 5574	Spring-pedal return	NLA		
5	AAA 1628	Spring-pedal return	1	(C)H-AN9-64735 TO 85286 (C)H-AN10-85287 TO 86803 (C)A-AN10-86804 TO 87824 (C)G-AN4-52390 TO 74885 (C)G-AN5-74886 ON	

$ This item is subject to safety regulations.

AUSTIN-HEALEY SPRITE MK. 3 AND MK. 4 & MG MIDGET MK. 2 AND MK. 3

MG0095A

NO.	PART NO.	DESCRIPTION	QTY	CHANGE POINT	REMARKS
		CLUTCH MASTER AND OPERATING CYLINDERS			
6	BHA 4615	CYLINDER AND SUPPLY TANK ASSEMBLY-CLUTCH MASTER	1	Use prior to AAU 2298	
6	AAU 2298	CYLINDER AND SUPPLY TANK ASSEMBLY-CLUTCH MASTER	1	(C)G-AN6-167343 ON (N.America) (C)G-AN6-169644 ON (Except N.America)	
7	27H 7751	Spring-piston return	1		
8	17H 7554	Retainer-spring	1		
10	17H 7560	Circlip	1		Prior to (C)H-AN8-64735 AND G-AN3-52390.Refer to Brake master CYLINDER
11	27H 8459	Push-rod	1	Use prior to AAU 3469	
11	AAU 3469	Push-rod	1	(C)G-AN6-167343 ON (N.America) (C)G-AN6-169644 ON (Except N.America)	
12	17H 6861	Cap-filler	1		
13	8G 8730	KIT-REPAIR-MASTER CYLINDER	1	(C)H-AN9-64735 ON (C)G-AN4-52390 ON	
	CLZ 513	Pin-clevis	1		
	PWZ 105	Washer-plain	1		
14	21K 8564	Adaptor-master cylinder	1	Use prior to ACB 9641	
14	ACB 9641	Adaptor-master cylinder	NLA	(C)G-AN6-154101 ON	
15	3H 2287	Gasket	1	(C)H-AN9-64735 ON (C)G-AN4-52390 ON	
	HZS 507	Screw	2		
	PWZ 105	Washer-plain	2		
	WL 600051	Washer-spring	2		
	FNZ 505	Nut	2		
		CLUTCH OPERATING CYLINDER 1098cc(10CC)			
16	22A 233	CYLINDER ASSEMBLY-CLUTCH OPERATING	1		
17	17H 7841	Piston	1		
18	17H 7868	Cup-piston	1		
19	17H 7540	Filler-cup	1		
20	17H 7580	Spring-filler	1		
21	17H 7268	Boot	1		
22	AAA 81	Circlip	1		
23	3H 2428	Screw-bleeder	1		
24	8G 8446	KIT-OPERATING-CYLINDER REPAIR	1		
25	13H 21	Push-rod	1		
	CLZ 517	Pin-clevis	1		
	PWZ 105	Washer-plain	1		
26	53K 152	Bolt-cylinder to gearbox	2		
	LWZ 305	Washer-spring	2		

AUSTIN-HEALEY SPRITE MK. 3 AND MK. 4 & MG MIDGET MK. 2 AND MK. 3

NO.	PART NO.	DESCRIPTION	QTY	CHANGE POINT	REMARKS
		CLUTCH MASTER AND OPERATING CYLINDERS-continued.			
		CLUTCH OPERATING CYLINDER-1275cc(12CC,12CD,12CE,12CJ, 12V)			
16	13H 3654	CYLINDER ASSEMBLY-CLUTCH OPERATING	1		
17	17H 7417	Piston	1		
18	7H 7913	Filler-cup	1		
20	17H 7580	Spring-filler	1		
22	17H 7819	Circlip	1		] Alternatives
	CCN 216	Circlip	1		
23	3H 2428	Screw-bleeder	1		
24	18G 8207	KIT-CYLINDER-REPAIR	NLA		Use BHM 7061
24	BHM 7061	Kit cylinder repair	1		
25	13H 3655	Push-rod	1		
	CLZ 517	Pin-clevis	1		
	PWZ 105	Washer-plain	1		
26	53K 152	Bolt-cylinder to gearbox	NLA		
	LWZ 305	Washer-spring	2		

MG 0095A

AUSTIN-HEALEY SPRITE MK. 3 AND MK. 4 & MG MIDGET MK. 2 AND MK. 3

NO.	PART NO.	DESCRIPTION	QTY	CHANGE POINT	REMARKS
		CLUTCH PIPES			
		PIPE			
	2A 5615	Master cylinder to operating cylinder-RHD-142.2cm(56")	NLA	(C)H-AN8-38829 TO 64734 (C)G-AN3-25788 TO 52389	Make frompipe 37H 7147 M with 2 off tube nut 3H 2249
	AAK 806	Master cylinder to operating cylinder-RHD-88.9cm(35")	NLA	(C)H-AN9-64735 TO 85286 (C)H-AN10-85286 TO 86803 (C)A-AN10-86804 TO 87824 (C)G-AN4-52390 TO 74885 (C)G-AN5-74886 TO 154100	Make from pipe 37H 7148 M with 2 off tube nut BCA 4370
	BHA 5376	Master cylinder to operating cylinder-RHD	1	(C)G-AN6-154101 ON	
	AHA 5508	Master cylinder to operating cylinder-LHD-233.7cm(92")	NLA	(C)H-AN8-38829 TO 39634 (C)G-AN3-25788 TO 26641	Make from pipe 37H 7147 M with 2 off tube nut 3H 2249
	7H 7991	Master cylinder to operating cylinder-LHD-18.03cm(71")	NLA	(C)H-AN8-39635 TO 64734 (C)G-AN3-26642 TO 52389	
	AAK 769	Master cylinder to operating cylinder-LHD-139.7cm(55")	NLA	(C)H-AN9-64735 TO 85286 (C)H-AN10-85287 TO 86803 (C)A-AN10-86804 TO 87824 (C)G-AN4-52390 TO 74886 (C)G-AN5-74886 TO 154100	make from pipe 37H 7148 M with 2 off tube nut BCA 4370
	BHA 5375	Master cylinder to operating cylinder-LHD	1	(C)G-AN6-154101 ON	

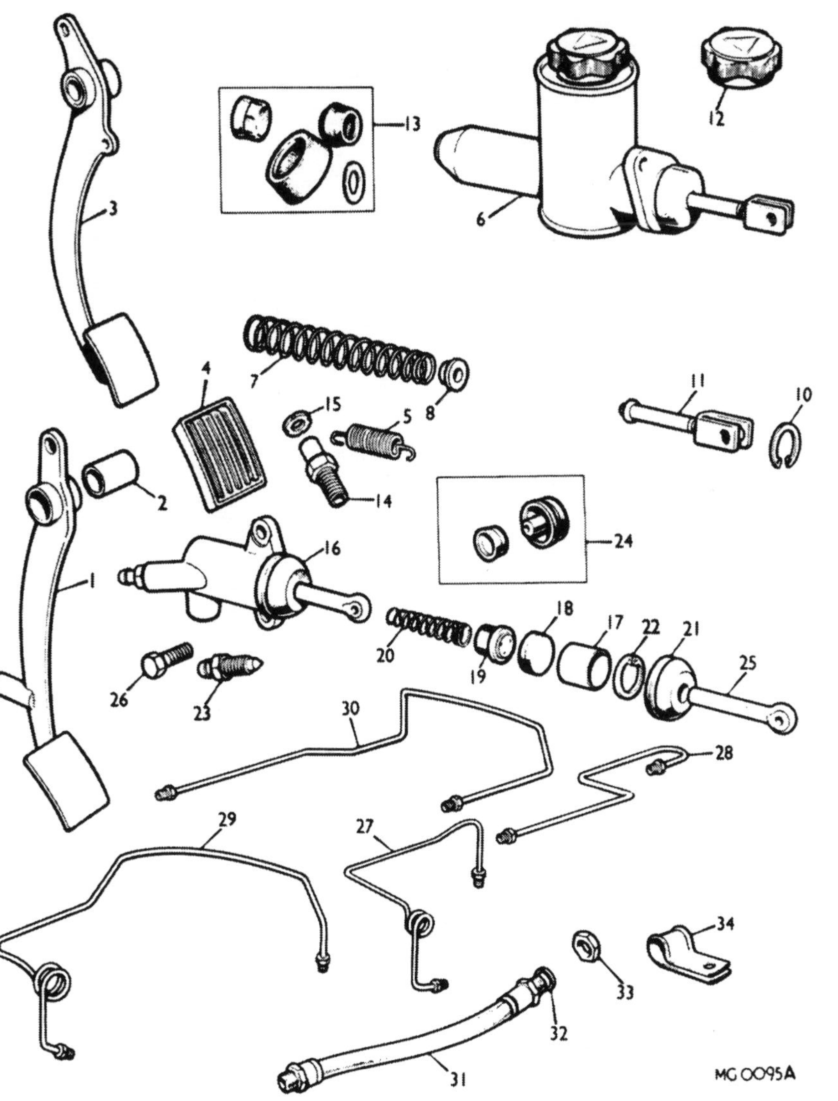

AUSTIN-HEALEY SPRITE MK. 3 AND MK. 4 & MG MIDGET MK. 2 AND MK. 3

CLUTCH PIPES-continued

NO.	PART NO.	DESCRIPTION	QTY	CHANGE POINT	REMARKS
31	ACC 5509	Hose-operating cylinder	1	(C)H-AN9-64735 TO 85286 (C)H-AN10-85287 TO 86803 (C)A-AN10-86804 TO 87824 (C)G-AN4-52390 TO 74885 (C)G-AN5-74886 TO 154100	
32	3H 550	Gasket-hose	1		
33	2K 8686	Nut-hose	1		
	LWZ 510	Washer-lock	1		
	PCR 409	Clip-pipe to pedal box	1		
	PCR 409	Clip-pipe to heater platform and foot well	3	(C)H-AN8-39635 TO 64734 (C)G-AN3-26642 TO 52389	
34	AHA 8161	Clip-pipe to heater platform	1	(C)H-AN9-64735 TO 85286 (C)H-AN10-85287 TO 86803 (C)A-AN10-86804 TO 87924 (C)G-AN4-52390 TO 74885 (C)G-AN5-74886 ON	
	37H 7147 M	Pipe-clutch-4.762mm(.1875")O/D	A/R		Supplied in 7 metre(22'9") rolls
	37H 7148 M	Pipe-clutch-6.35mm(.25")O/D	A/R		
	3H 2249	Nut-tube-internal	A/R		
	BCA 4370	Nut-tube-internal	A/R		

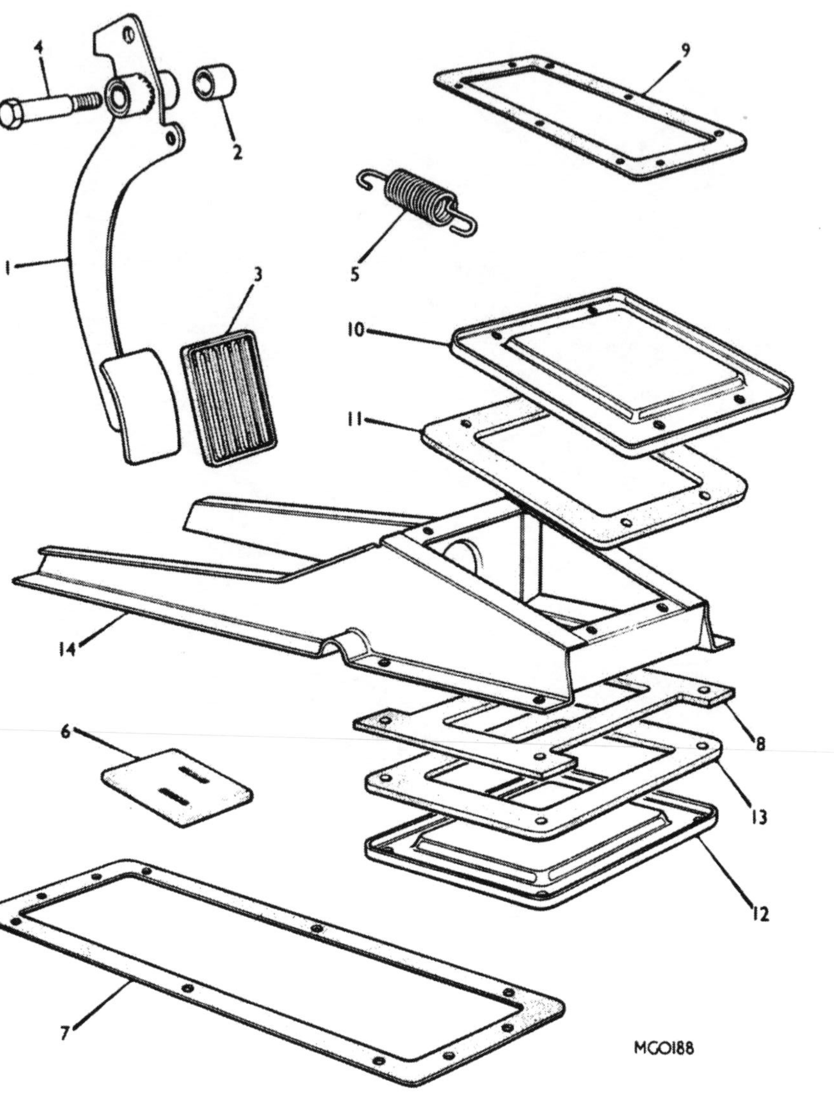

AUSTIN-HEALEY SPRITE MK. 3 AND MK. 4 & MG MIDGET MK. 2 AND MK. 3

BRAKE PEDAL-SINGLE LINE SYSTEM

NO.	PART NO.	DESCRIPTION	QTY	CHANGE POINT	REMARKS
3	AHA 5326	Pad-pedal(rubber)	1	(C)H-AN8-38829 TO 64734	
5	2A 5574	Spring-pedal return	NLA		
7	AHA 6366	Washer-joint	1		
	HZS 405	Screw	9		
	HZS 408	Screw	1		
	LWZ 304	Washer-spring	10		
9	AHA 6366	Washer-joint	1		
	HZS 405	Screw	8		
	LWZ 304	Washer-spring	8		
1	AHA 9723	PEDAL ASSEMBLY-BRAKE	1	(C)H-AN9-64735 TO 85286 (C)H-AN10-85287 TO 86803 (C)A-AN10-86804 TO 87824 (C)G-AN4-52390 TO 74885 (C)G-AN5-74886 ON	
2	LBS 810	Bush	2		
3	AHA 5326	Pad-pedal(rubber)	1	(C)H-AN9-64735 TO 85286 (C)H-AN10-85287 TO 86803 (C)A-AN10-86804 TO 87824 (C)G-AN4-52390 TO 74885 (C)G-AN5-74886 ON	
4	AHA 8075	Bolt-brake and clutch pedal $	1		
	LWZ 206	Washer-spring	1		
	PWZ 108	Washer-plain	1		
	FNZ 506	Nut	1		
5	AAA 1628	Spring-pedal return $	1		
14	AHA 8408	Box-pedal $	1		
11	AHA 8073	Seal	1		
8	AHA 8072	Washer-joint	1		
	HZS 405	Screw	6		
	PMZ 410	Screw	NLA		Use SE 604051
	SE 604051	Screw	2		
	WL 600051	Washer-spring	8		
12	AHA 8145	Plate-blanking	1		
13	AHA 8146	Seal	1		
	HZS 405	Screw	4		
	WL 600051	Washer-spring	4		

$ This item is subject to safety regulations.

AUSTIN-HEALEY SPRITE MK. 3 AND MK. 4 & MG MIDGET MK. 2 AND MK. 3

BRAKE MASTER CYLINDER-SINGLE LINE SYSTEM

NO.	PART NO.	DESCRIPTION	QTY	CHANGE POINT	REMARKS
1	GMC 112	CYLINDER AND SUPPLY TANK BRAKE AND CLUTCH-MASTER	1	(C)H-AN8-38829 TO 64734 (C)G-AN3-25788 TO 52389	
2	37H 2496	Gasket-cover	NLA		
3	AAA 4758	Screw-cover to body	5		
	LWZ 404	Washer-shakeproof	5		
4	27H 7751	Spring-piston return	2		
5	17H 7554	Retainer-return spring	2		
7	AAA 4757	Gasket-boot fixing plate	1		
8	AAA 4756	Plate-boot fixing	1		
	LWZ 404	Washer-shakeproof	2		
9	17H 6861	Cap-filler	1		
10	8G 8766	KIT-REPAIR-BRAKE MASTER CYLINDER	1		
	FNZ 205	Locknut	2		
12	2A 5576	Fork end-push-rod	2		
13	1B 3498	Circlip-pin	2		
	HBZ 624	Bolt	1		
	LWZ 206	Washer-spring	2		
	FNZ 106	Nut	2		
14	GMC 113	CYLINDER AND SUPPLY TANK-BRAKE MASTER	1	(C)H-AN9-64735 TO 85286 (C)H-AN10-85287 TO 86803 (C)A-AN10-86804 TO 87824 (C)G-AN4-52390 TO 74885 (C)G-AN5-74886 TO 154100 (C)G-AN6-154101 TO (+)	
15	27H 7751	Spring-piston return	1		
5	17H 7554	Retainer-spring	1		
16	17H 7560	Circlip	1		
17	27H 8459	Push-rod	1		
9	17H 6861	Cap-filler	1		
18	8G 8258	KIT-REPAIR-BRAKE MASTER CYLINDER	1		
14	GMC 151	CYLINDER AND SUPPLY TANK BRAKE MASTER	1	(C)G-AN6(+)ON	Identify by Two concentric Circles
15	27H 7751	Spring-piston return	1		
5	17H 7554	Retainer-spring	1		
16	17H 7560	Circlip	1		
17	AAU 3469	Push rod	1		
	513123	Cap-filler	1		
18	BHM 7125	Kit-cylinder repair	1		
19	CLZ 513	Pin-clevis	1	(C)H-AN9-64735 TO 85286 (C)H-AN10-85287 TO 86803 (C)A-AN10-86804 TO 87824 (C)G-AN4-52390 TO 74885 (C)G-AN5-74886 TO 154100 (C)G-AN6-154101 ON	
	PWZ 105	Washer-plain	1		
	HZS 507	Screw	1		
	PWZ 105	Washer-plain	1		
	WL 600051	Washer-spring	1		
	FNZ 505	Nut	1		
20	BHA 4661	Tank-fluid(plastic)	1		
21	BHA 4660	Clip-locking	1		
22	BCA 4964	Seal	1		

(+) Change point not known.

161

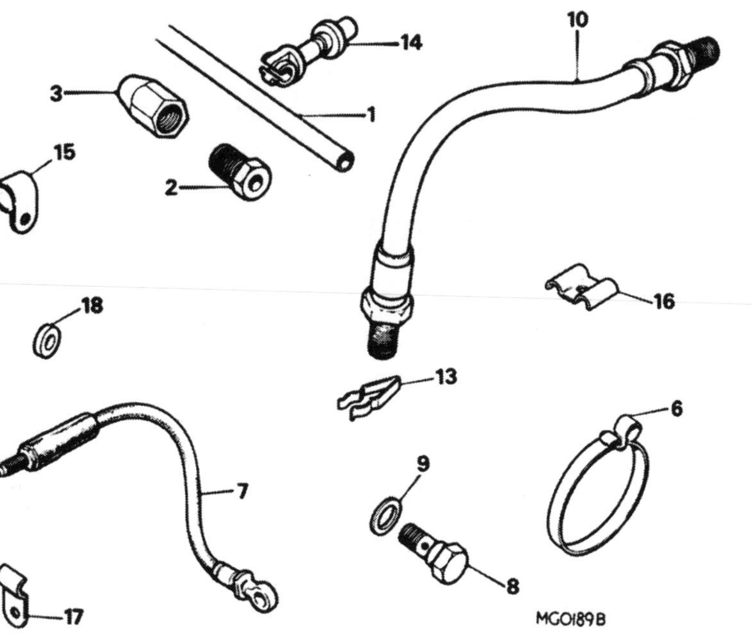

AUSTIN-HEALEY SPRITE MK. 3 AND MK. 4 & MG MIDGET MK. 2 AND MK. 3

BRAKE PIPES AND FITTINGS-SINGLE LINE BRAKING SYSTEM

NO.	PART NO.	DESCRIPTION	QTY	CHANGE POINT	REMARKS
		PIPE			
	2A 2183	Master cylinder to 4-way RHD 28"(72cm)	NLA	Finished at (C)G-AN5-154100	Use 37H 7147 M with 2 off nut 3H 2249
	2A 5619	Master cylinder to 4-way LHD 64"(163cm) $	NLA		
	2A 5606	4-way connection to RH front hose 14"(36cm) $	NLA		Use 37H 7147 M with 1 Off Nut 3H 2249 and 1 off nut 11D 5050
	2A 5609	4-way connection to LH front hose 47"(100cm) $	NLA		
	2A 5611	4-way connection to rear brake hose 74"(188cm) $	1		
1	37H 7147 M	Master cylinder to RH front hose-33"(83.8cm)	1	(C)G-AN6-154101 ON	With 1 off nut 3H 2249 and 11D 5050
1	37H 7147 M	Master cylinder to 3-way 60"(152.4cm)	1		With 2 off nut 3H 2249
1	37H 7147 M	3-way to LH front hose-11.5"(29.2cm)	1		With 1 off nut 3H 2249 and 11D 5050
1	37H 7147 M	3-way to rear hose-81"(205.7cm)	1		With 1 off nut 3H 2249 and 11D 5050
	AHA 6482	3-way connection to RH rear brake 22"(56cm) $	NLA		Use 37H 7147 M with 2 off nut 3H 2249
	ACB 9162	3-way connection to LH rear brake 30"(77cm) $	NLA		
1	37H 7147 M	Pipe-brake .187"(4.762mm)O/D	A/R		Supplied in 7 metre(22'9")rolls
2	3H 2249	Nut-tube-internal	A/R		
3	11D 5050	Nut-tube-external	A/R		

$ This item is subject to safety regulations

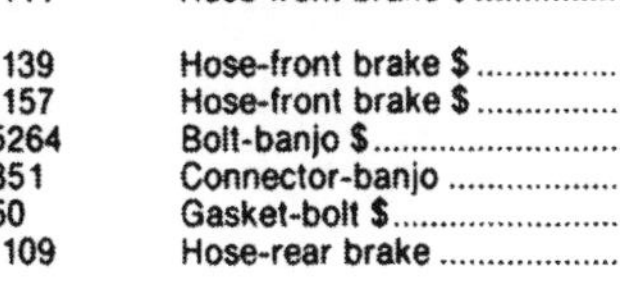
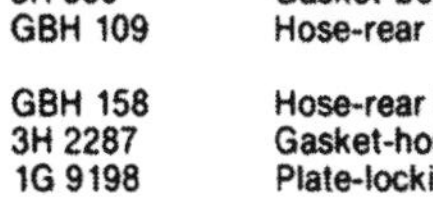
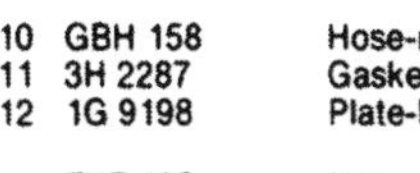
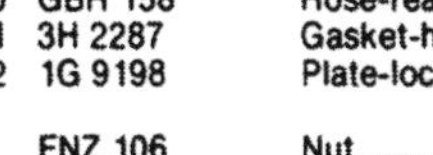
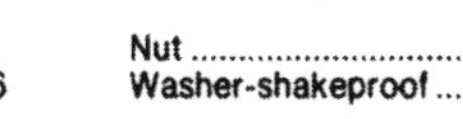
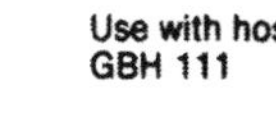
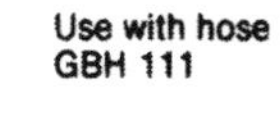

AUSTIN-HEALEY SPRITE MK. 3 AND MK. 4 & MG MIDGET MK. 2 AND MK. 3

BRAKE PIPES AND FITTINGS-SINGLE LINE BRAKING SYSTEM-continued

NO.	PART NO.	DESCRIPTION	QTY	CHANGE POINT	REMARKS
4	17H 7108	Connection-4-way $	1	Use prior to 3H 2424-3 Way	
5	3H 2424	Connection-3-way-front	1	(C)G-AN6-154101 ON	
	HBZ 408	Bolt	1		
	LWZ 204	Washer-spring	1		
5	3H 2424	Connection-3-way-rear	1		
	HBZ 410	Bolt	1		
	LWZ 204	Washer-spring	1		
	NH 604041	Nut	1		
6	ACA 5375	Strap-pipe to rear axle	NLA		
7	GBH 111	Hose-front brake $	2	Use prior to GBH 139	
7	GBH 139	Hose-front brake $	NLA	See(1)foot of page	Use GBH 157
7	GBH 157	Hose-front brake $	2	(C)G-AN6-162565 ON	
8	11D 5264	Bolt-banjo $	2		
	7H 7851	Connector-banjo	1		
9	3H 550	Gasket-bolt $	2		
10	GBH 109	Hose-rear brake	NLA	Use prior to GBH 158	Use GBH 158
10	GBH 158	Hose-rear brake $	1	(C)G-AN6-162565 ON	
11	3H 2287	Gasket-hose $	3		
12	1G 9198	Plate-locking hose	3		Use with hose GBH 111
	FNZ 106	Nut	3		
	LWN 406	Washer-shakeproof	3		

$This item is subject to safety regulations

CHANGE POINTS
(1)G-AN5-114643 TO G-AN5-154100(PLUS 114352, 114473, 114475 TO 114480, 114526 TO 114541,114543 AND 114580 TO 114588)
G-AN6-154101 TO 162564.

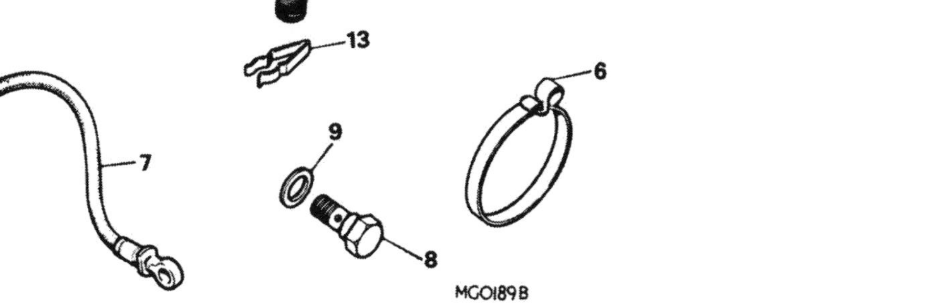

AUSTIN-HEALEY SPRITE MK. 3 AND MK. 4 & MG MIDGET MK. 2 AND MK. 3

BRAKE PIPES AND FITTINGS-SINGLE LINE SYSTEM-continued

NO.	PART NO.	DESCRIPTION	QTY	CHANGE POINT	REMARKS
13	6K 35	Clip-brake pipe to frame	A/R	Use prior to 88 623312	
14	623312	Clip-brake pipe to frame	2	See(1)foot of page	
15	PCR 307	Clip-brake pipe to tunnel	2		
15	PCR 307	Clip-brake pipe to foot well	1		
16	2H 400	Clip-brake and clutch pipe to foot well-RHD	1		
17	CHR 307	Clip-brake and clutch pipe to dash-LHD	A/R		
15	PCR 309	Clip-brake pipe to cover-plate bolt-LHD	1		
18	AHH 6247	Spacer-pipe to cover-plate bolt-LHD	NLA		
	LNZ 102	Stiffnut	1		
	NH 604041	Nut	1		
	PWZ 104	Washer-plain	1		
	LWZ 204	Washer-spring	1		
	PMZ 307	Screw	3		
	PWZ 103	Washer-plain	3		
	LNZ 203	Locknut	3		
	PMZ 305	Screw-RHD	1		
	LWZ 203	Washer-spring-RHD	1		
	PMZ 305	Screw-LHD	A/R		
	LWZ 203	Washer-spring-LHD	A/R		
	FNZ 103	Nut-LHD	A/R		
19	C 16062	Switch-stop light	1	Use prior to BHA 4675	
20	BHA 4675	Switch-stop light	1	] (C)G-AN6-154101 ON	
	FNZ 206	Nut-switch	1	]	

CHANGE POINTS
(1) (C)G-AN5-114643 ON(PLUS 114352, 114473, 114475 TO 114480, 114526 TO 114541, 114543 AND 114580 TO 114588)

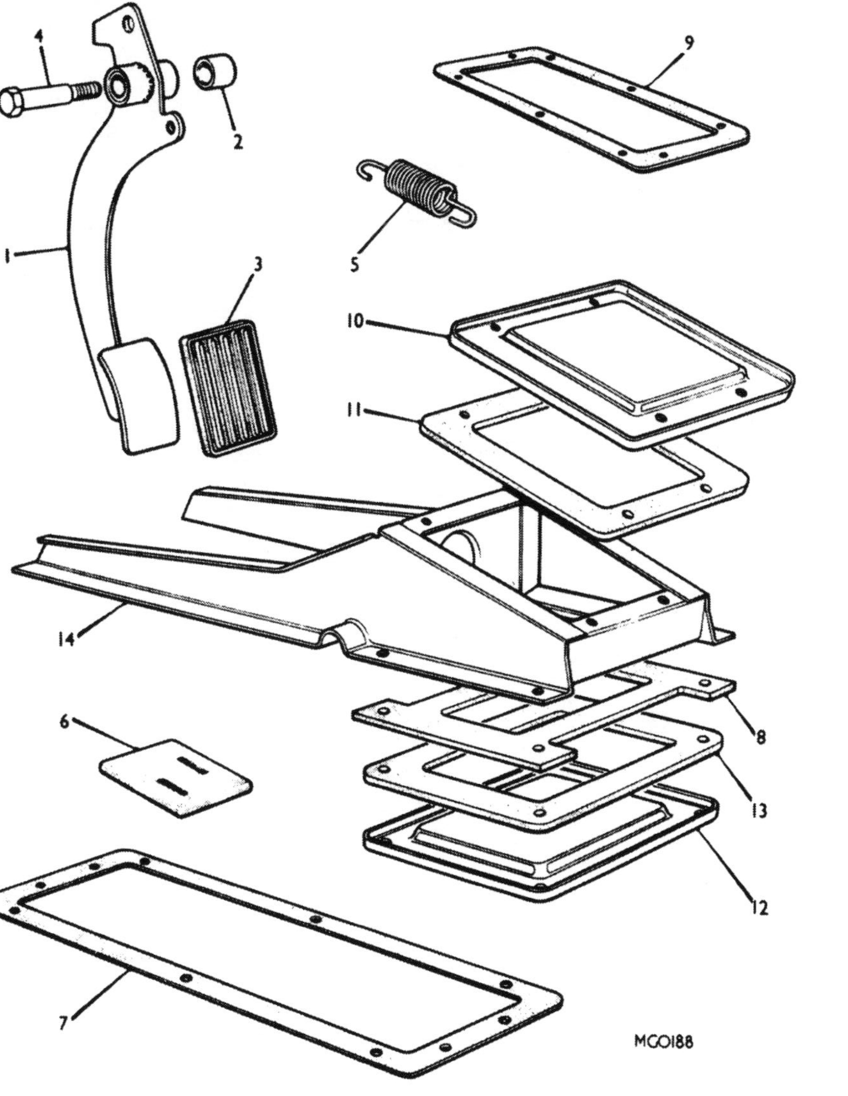

AUSTIN-HEALEY SPRITE MK. 3 AND MK. 4 & MG MIDGET MK. 2 AND MK. 3

NO.	PART NO.	DESCRIPTION	QTY	CHANGE POINT	REMARKS
		BRAKE PEDAL-DUAL LINE SYSTEM			
1	AHA 8069	PEDAL ASSEMBLY-BRAKE	1	Use prior to AHA 9723	
1	AHA 9723	PEDAL ASSEMBLY-BRAKE	1	(C)G-AN5-100179 ON	
2	LBS 810	Bush	1		
3	AHA 5326	Pad-pedal(rubber)	1		
4	AHA 8075	Bolt-brake and clutch pedal $	1		
	LWZ 206	Washer-spring	1		
	PWZ 108	Washer-plain	1		
	FNZ 506	Nut	1		
5	AAA 1628	Spring-pedal return $	1		
14	AHA 8408	Box-pedal	1	Use prior to CHA 375	
14	CHA 375	Box-pedal	1	] (C)G-AN6-154101 ON	
10	CHA 333	Cover-top-pedal box	1		
11	AHA 8073	Seal	1		
8	AHA 8072	Gasket	1		
	HZS 405	Screw	6		
	PMZ 410	Screw	NLA		Use SE 604051
	SE 604051	Screw	2		
	WL 600051	Washer-spring	8		
12	AHA 8145	Plate-blanking	1		
13	AHA 8146	Seal	1		
	HZS 405	Screw	4		
	WL 600051	Washer-spring	4		

$ This item is subject to safety regulations

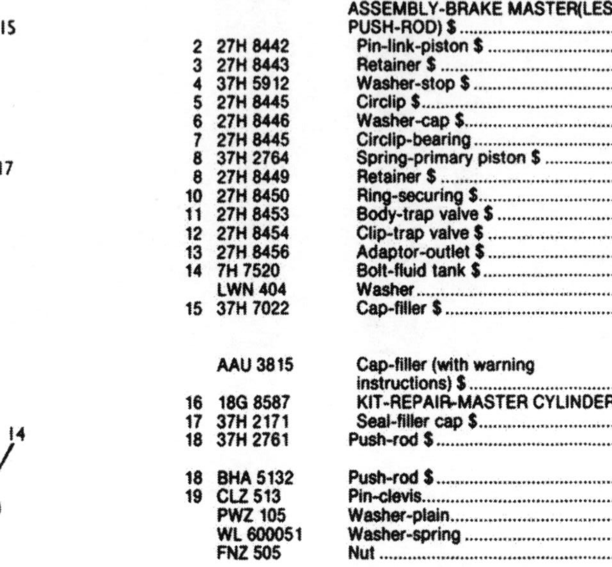
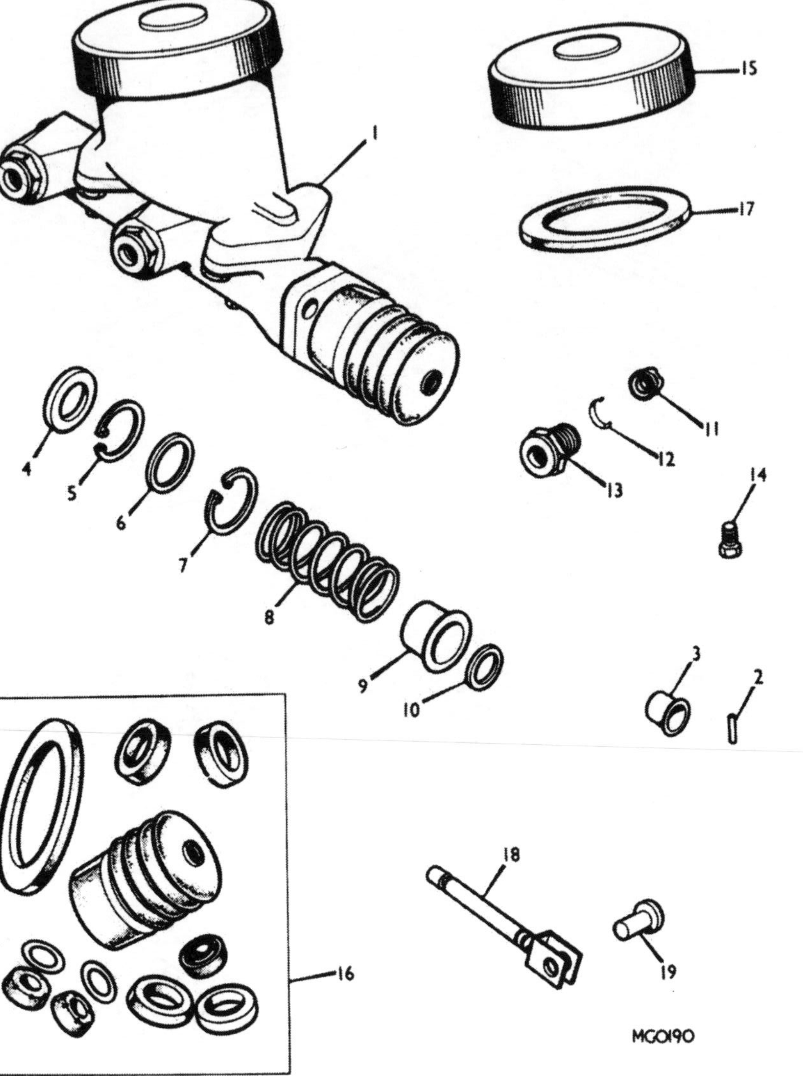

AUSTIN-HEALEY SPRITE MK. 3 AND MK. 4 & MG MIDGET MK. 2 AND MK. 3

NO.	PART NO.	DESCRIPTION	QTY	CHANGE POINT	REMARKS
		BRAKE MASTER CYLINDER-DUAL LINE SYSTEM			
1	37H 2760	CYLINDER AND SUPPLY TANK ASSEMBLY-BRAKE MASTER(LESS PUSH-ROD) $	1		
2	27H 8442	Pin-link-piston $	1		
3	27H 8443	Retainer $	1		
4	37H 5912	Washer-stop $	1		
5	27H 8445	Circlip $	1		
6	27H 8446	Washer-cap $	1		
7	27H 8445	Circlip-bearing	1		
8	37H 2764	Spring-primary piston $	1		
8	27H 8449	Retainer $	1		
10	27H 8450	Ring-securing $	1		
11	27H 8453	Body-trap valve $	2		
12	27H 8454	Clip-trap valve $	2		
13	27H 8456	Adaptor-outlet $	2		
14	7H 7520	Bolt-fluid tank $	4		
	LWN 404	Washer	4		
15	37H 7022	Cap-filler $	1		Use AAU 3815 for this application.
	AAU 3815	Cap-filler (with warning instructions) $	1		
16	18G 8587	KIT-REPAIR-MASTER CYLINDER $	1		
17	37H 2171	Seal-filler cap $	1		
18	37H 2761	Push-rod $	1	Use prior to BHA 5132	
18	BHA 5132	Push-rod $	1	(C)G-AN5-100745 ON	
19	CLZ 513	Pin-clevis	1		
	PWZ 105	Washer-plain	1		
	WL 600051	Washer-spring	1		
	FNZ 505	Nut	1		

$ This item is subject to safety regulations

AUSTIN-HEALEY SPRITE MK. 3 AND MK. 4 & MG MIDGET MK. 2 AND MK. 3

MGO185A

BRAKE PIPES AND FITTINGS-DUAL LINE BRAKING SYSTEM

NO.	PART NO.	DESCRIPTION	QTY	CHANGE POINT	REMARKS
		PIPE			
	AHA 8552	Master cylinder to pressure switch-front-66"(168cm) $	NLA		Use pipe 37H 7147M and 1 off nut 3H 2249, 1 off nut BHA 4706
	13H 1265	Master cylinder to pressure switch rear-69"(176cm) $	NLA		Use pipe 37H 7147M and 2 off nut 3H 2249
	AHA 8510	Pressure switch to front brake hose-RH-17" (44cm) $	NLA	Finished at (C)G-AN5-154100	Use 37H 7147 M with 1 off nut BHA 4706 and 1 OFF NUT 11D 5050
	AHA 8551	Pressure switch to front brake hose-LH-49" (125cm) $	NLA		
	13H 5905	Pressure switch to rear brake hose 76"(193cm) $	NLA		Use pipe 37H 7147 M and 1 off nut 3H 2249, 1 off nut 11D 5050
	AHA 6482	3-way connection to RH rear brake-22"(56cm) $	NLA		Use 37H 7147 M with 2 off nut 3H 2249
	ACB 9162	3-way connection to LH rear brake-30"(77cm) $	NLA		
1	37H 7147 M	Pipe-brake-.187"(4.762mm) O/D	A/R		Supplied in 7 metre(22'9")rolls
2	3H 2249	Nut-tube-internal	A/R		
3	BHA 4706	Nut-tube-internal	A/R		
4	11D 5050	Nut-tube-external	A/R		

$ This item is subject to safety regulations

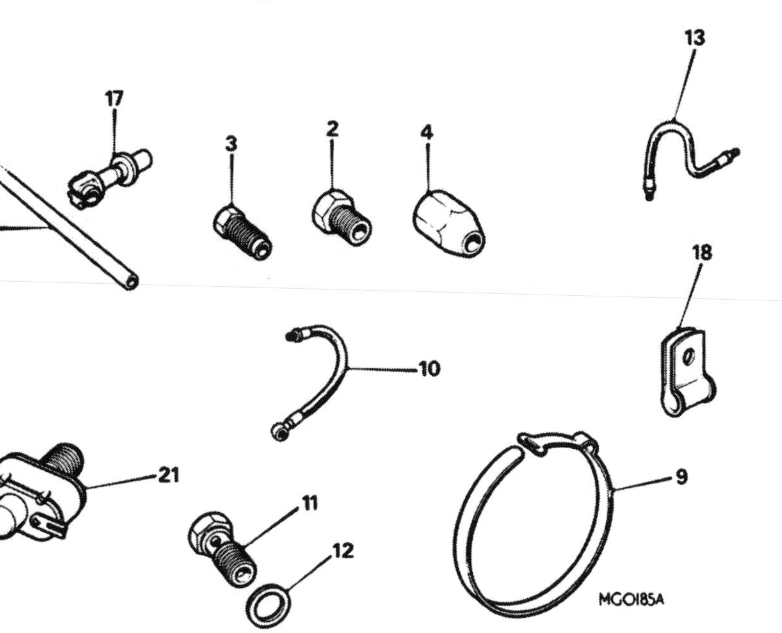

AUSTIN-HEALEY SPRITE MK. 3 AND MK. 4 & MG MIDGET MK. 2 AND MK. 3

BRAKE PIPES AND FITTINGS-DUAL LINE BRAKING SYSTEM-continued.

NO.	PART NO.	DESCRIPTION	QTY	CHANGE POINT	REMARKS
	37H 7147 M	Pipe-master cylinder to pressure switch-front 15.5"(39.4cm)long $	1	(C)G-AN6-154101 ON	With 1 off nut BHA 4706 and 3H 2249.
	37H 7147 M	Pipe-master cylinder to pressure switch-rear 17.5"(44.5cm)long $	1		With 2 off nut 3H 2249.
	37H 7147 M	Pipe-pressure switch to front brake hose-RH-41" (104.1cm)long $	1		With 1 off nut 11D 5050 and BHA 4706.
	37H 7147 M	Pipe-pressure switch to front brake hose-LH-10"(25.4cm)long $	1		
	37H 7147 M	Pipe-pressure switch to rear brake hose-81"(205.7cm)long $	1		With 1 off nut 1D 5050 and 3H 2249.
	37H 7147 M	Pipe-3-way connection to RH rear brake-22"(56cm)long $	1		With 2 off nut 3H 2249.
	37H 7147 M	Pipe-3-way connection to LH rear brake-30"(77cm)long $	1		
1	37H 7147 M	Pipe-brake-.187"(4.762mm) O/D	A/R		Supplied in 7 metre(22'9") rolls.
2	3H 2249	Nut-tube-internal	A/R		
3	BHA 4706	Nut-tube-internal	A/R		
4	11D 5050	Nut-tube-external	A/R		

$ This item is subject to safety regulations.

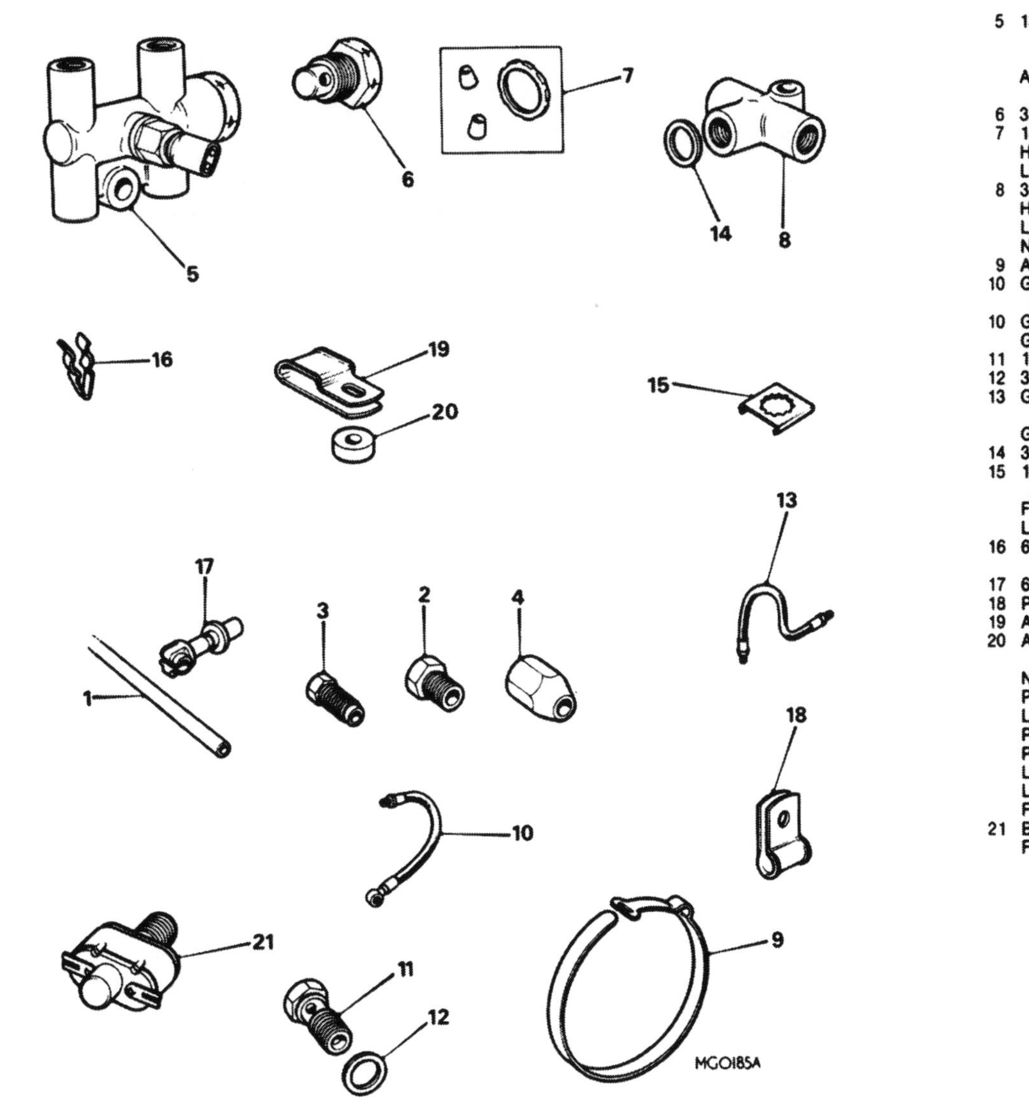

AUSTIN-HEALEY SPRITE MK. 3 AND MK. 4 & MG MIDGET MK. 2 AND MK. 3

BRAKE PIPES AND FITTINGS-DUAL LINE BRAKING SYSTEM-continued

NO.	PART NO.	DESCRIPTION	QTY	CHANGE POINT	REMARKS
5	13H 5905	SWITCH ASSEMBLY-PRESSURE FAILURE $	1	Use prior to AAU 2583	
	AAU 2583	SWITCH ASSEMBLY-PRESSURE FAILURE $	1	(C)G-AN6-166304 ON	
6	37H 4652	Cap-end	1		
7	18G 8353	KIT-REPAIR $	1		
	HBZ 408	Bolt	1		
	LWZ 204	Washer-spring	1		
8	3H 2424	Connection-3-way-rear $	1		
	HBZ 410	Bolt	1		
	LWZ 204	Washer-spring	NLA		
	NH 604041	Nut	1		
9	ACA 5375	Strap-pipe to rear axle	2		
10	GBH 111	Hose-front brake	2	Use prior to GBH 139	
10	GBH 139	Hose-front brake	NLA	See(1)foot of page	Use GBH 157
	GBH 157	Hose-front brake $	2	(C)G-AN6-162565 ON	
11	11D 5264	Bolt-banjo $	2		
12	3H 550	Gasket-bolt $	2		
13	GBH 109	Hose-rear brake	NLA	Use prior to GBH 158	Use GBH 158
	GBH 158	Hose-rear brake $	1	(C)G-AN6-162565 ON	
14	3H 2287	Gasket-hose $	3		
15	1G 9198	Plate-locking-hose	3		Use with hose GBH 111
	FNZ 106	Nut	3		
	LWN 406	Washer-shakeproof	3		
16	6K 35	Clip-brake pipe to frame	2		Use with hose GBH 111
17	623312	Clip-brake pipe to frame	2		
18	PCR 307	Clip-brake pipe to tunnel	2		
19	AHA 8683	Clip-pipe	NLA		
20	AHH 6247	Spacer-pipe to cover plate bolt	NLA		
	NH 604041	Nut	1		
	PWZ 104	Washer-plain	1		
	LWZ 204	Washer-spring	1		
	PMZ 307	Screw	2		
	PMZ 103	Washer-plain	2		
	LNZ 203	Locknut	2		
	LWZ 203	Washer-spring	2		
	FNZ 103	Nut	2		
21	BHA 4675	Switch-stoplight $	1		
	FNZ 206	Nut	1		

$ This item is subject to safety regulations

CHANGE POINTS
(1).(C)G-AN5-11487 TO 154100(PLUS 114244,114332,114333,114361 TO 114365, 114377,114385,114398 TO 114406,114416 TO 114419,114446 TO 114472 AND AND 114483 TO 114486)
(C)G-AN6-154101 TO 162564.

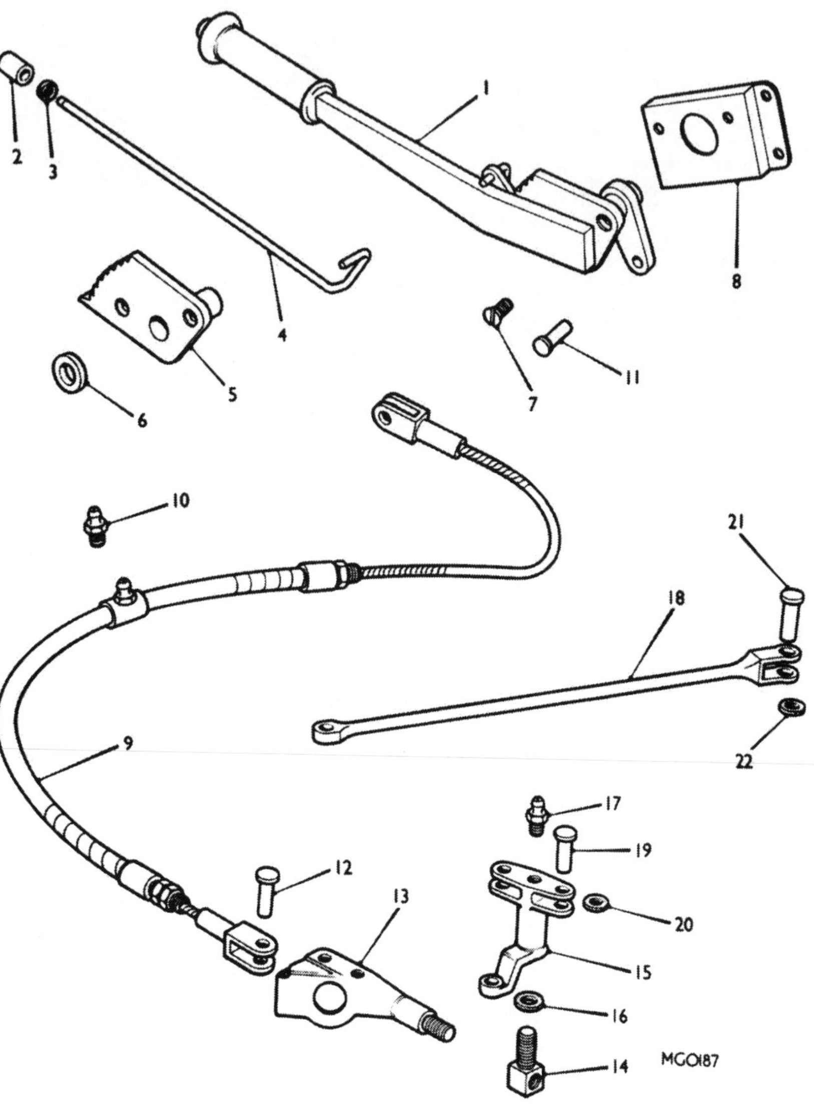

AUSTIN-HEALEY SPRITE MK. 3 AND MK. 4 & MG MIDGET MK. 2 AND MK. 3

NO.	PART NO.	DESCRIPTION	QTY	CHANGE POINT	REMARKS
		HAND BRAKE LEVER AND LINKAGE			
1	AHA 6406	HAND BRAKE ASSEMBLY $	1	Use prior to CHA 567	
	CHA 567	HAND BRAKE ASSEMBLY $	1	(C)G-AN6-166304 ON (USA and Canada)	
2	17H 7890	Plunger-thumb $	1		
3	7H 5951	Washer-plunger(rubber) $	1		
4	17H 2093	Rod-pawl $	NLA		
	AWZ 104	Washer-anti-rattle	1		
5	7H 5947	Ratchet and tube $	1		
	FNZ 106	Nut-main spindle	1		
6	17H 2091	Washer-anti-rattle-main spindle $	1		
	LWZ 406	Washer-shakeproof-main spindle	1		
	AAU 2492	Switch and leads-handbrake-LHD	1	(C)G-AN6-166304 ON	
7	88G 295	Screw-handbrake to bracket $	2		
8	2A 7291	Bracket-handbrake mounting $	1		
	HZS 505	Screw	3		
	WL 600051	Washer-spring	3		
9	2A 7308	CABLE ASSEMBLY-HANDBRAKE S	1		
10	UHN 105	Lubricator-cable	1		
	FNZ 207	Locknut	2		
11	CLZ 515	Pin-clevis	1		
	PWZ 105	Washer-plain	1		
12	CLZ 414	Pin-clevis	1		
	PWZ 104	Washer-plain	1		
13	ATA 7320	Support-balance lever $	1		
	HZS 506	Screw-support to axle	2		
	PMZ 105	Washer-plain	2	Use prior to CHA 634 And CHA 638	
	LWZ 305	Washer-spring	2		
	NH 605041	Nut	2		
14	2A 7058	Carrier-balance lever $	1		
15	2A 7057	Lever-balance $	1		
16	2K 5820	Washer-balance lever(felt)	1		
17	UHN 490	Lubricator-balance lever	1		
18	BTA 498	Cross-rod-RH $	1		Disc wheels
	BTA 497	Cross-rod-LH $	1		Disc wheels
18	BTA 495	Cross-rod-RH $	1		Wire wheels
	BTA 494	Cross-rod-LH $	1		Wire wheels
19	CLZ 314	Pin-cross-rod to balance lever	2		
20	6K 690	Washer-pin(felt)	4		
21	2K 6930	Pin-cross-rod to brake $	2		
22	2K 5291	Washer-pin(felt)	4		
	CHA 638	Cable-handbrake	1		Disc wheels
	CHA 634	Cable-handbrake	1		Wire wheels
	CLZ 514	Pin-clevis	1		
	WA 108051	Washer-plain	1		
	SH 604041	Screw-cable clip	1		
	WA 106041	Washer-plain	2		
	WL 600041	Washer-spring	1	(C)G-AN6-182001 ON	
	NH 604041	Nut	1		
	SH 604061	Screw-strap	2		
	WL 600041	Washer-spring	2		
	SH 605061	Screw-clamp	1		
	WL 600051	Washer-spring	1		
	WA 106041	Washer-plain	2		
	CLZ 411	Pin-clevis	2		

$ This item is subject to safety regulations

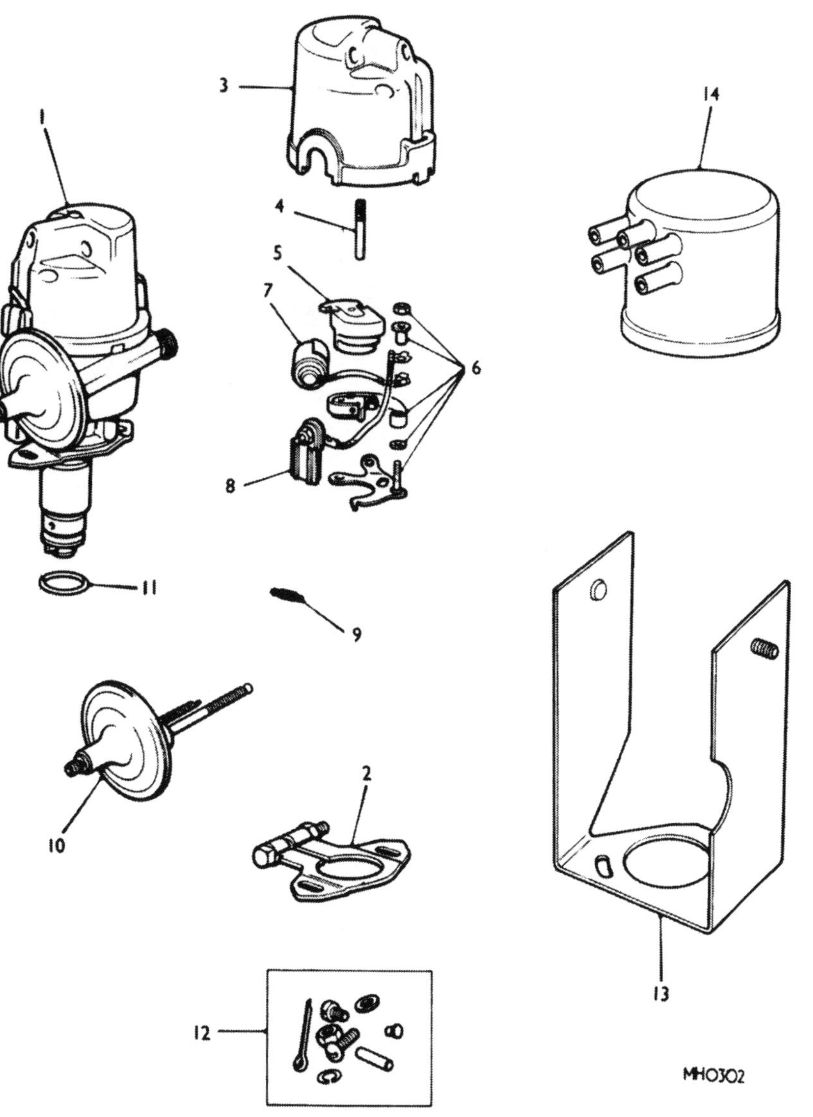

AUSTIN-HEALEY SPRITE MK. 3 AND MK. 4 & MG MIDGET MK. 2 AND MK. 3

DISTRIBUTOR-10CC-1098cc.

NO.	PART NO.	DESCRIPTION	QTY	CHANGE POINT	REMARKS
1	12G 811	DISTRIBUTOR ASSEMBLY	NLA		
2	3H 2138	Plate-clamping	1		
3	GDC 102	COVER ASSEMBLY	1		
4	17H 5065	Brush and spring	1		
5	GRA 101	Arm-rotor	1		
6	GCS 101	Contacts	1SET		
7	GSC 101	Condenser	1		
8	37H 2981	Terminal-bush and lead	1		
9	17H 6657	Spring-automatic advance	1SET		
10	17H 8622	Vacuum unit	1		
11	27H 6547	'O'ring-oil seal	1		
12	17H 5106	Sundry parts	1SET		
	HZS 404	Screw-distributor to housing	2		
	LWZ 404	Washer-shakeproof-screw	2		
13	12G 395	Body-suppression screen	1		]
	LNZ 203	Nut	2		] France.
	PWZ 203	Washer	2		]
14	8G 726	Cover-waterproof	1		Canada.

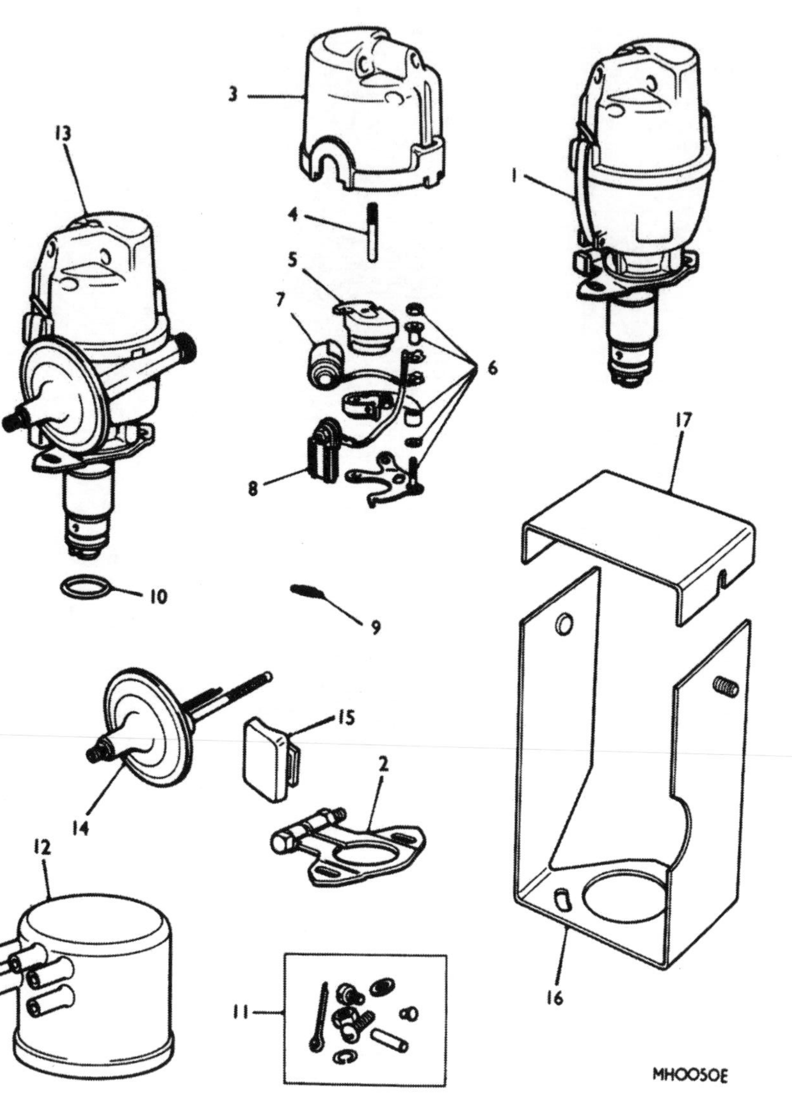

AUSTIN-HEALEY SPRITE MK. 3 AND MK. 4 & MG MIDGET MK. 2 AND MK. 3

NO.	PART NO.	DESCRIPTION	QTY	CHANGE POINT	REMARKS
		DISTRIBUTOR-1275cc,12CC,12CD,12CE,12CJ AND 12V.			
1	12G 815	DISTRIBUTOR ASSEMBLY	1	Use prior to 12G 2055/7	
2	3H 2138	Plate-clamping	1		
3	GDC 102	COVER ASSEMBLY-MOULDED	1		
4	17H 5065	Brush and spring	1		
5	GRA 101	Arm-rotor	1		
6	GCS 111	Contacts	1SET		
7	GSC 101	Condenser	1		
8	37H 2981	Terminal-bush and lead	1		
9	7H 6950	Spring-automatic advance	1SET		
10	27H 6547	'O'ring-oil seal	1		
11	57H 5135	Sundry parts	1SET		
	HZS 404	Screw-distributor to housing	2		
	LWZ 404	Washer-shakeproof-screw	2		
12	8G 726	Cover-waterproof	1		
13	12G 2055	DISTRIBUTOR ASSEMBLY	1	(E)12CC/Da/H11639 TO 16300 (E)12CE/Da/101 TO(+) (E)12V/586F/101 TO(+) (E)12V/588F/101 TO(+) (E)12V/778F/101 ON	
13	12G 2057	DISTRIBUTOR ASSEMBLY	1	(E)12CD/Da/101 TO (+) (E)12CJ/Da/H21201 TO(+)	
2	3H 2138	Plate-clamping	1	(E)12CC/Da/H11639 TO 16300 (E)12CE/Da/101 TO (+) (E)12V/586F/101 ON (E)12V/588F/101 ON (E)12V/778F/101 ON (E)12CD/DA/101 TO(+) (E)12CJ/DA/H21201 TO(+)	
10	27H 6547	'O'ring-oil seal	1		
14	27H 7645	Unit-vacuum	1		
9	37H 2260	Spring-automatic advance	1SET		
7	GSC 101	Condenser	1		
6	GCS 101	Contact set	1		
8	37H 2981	Terminal-bush and lead	1		
5	GRA 101	Arm-rotor	1		
3	GDC 102	COVER ASSEMBLY	1		
4	17H 5065	Brush and spring	1		
11	17H 5106	Sundry parts	1SET		

(+) Change point not available.

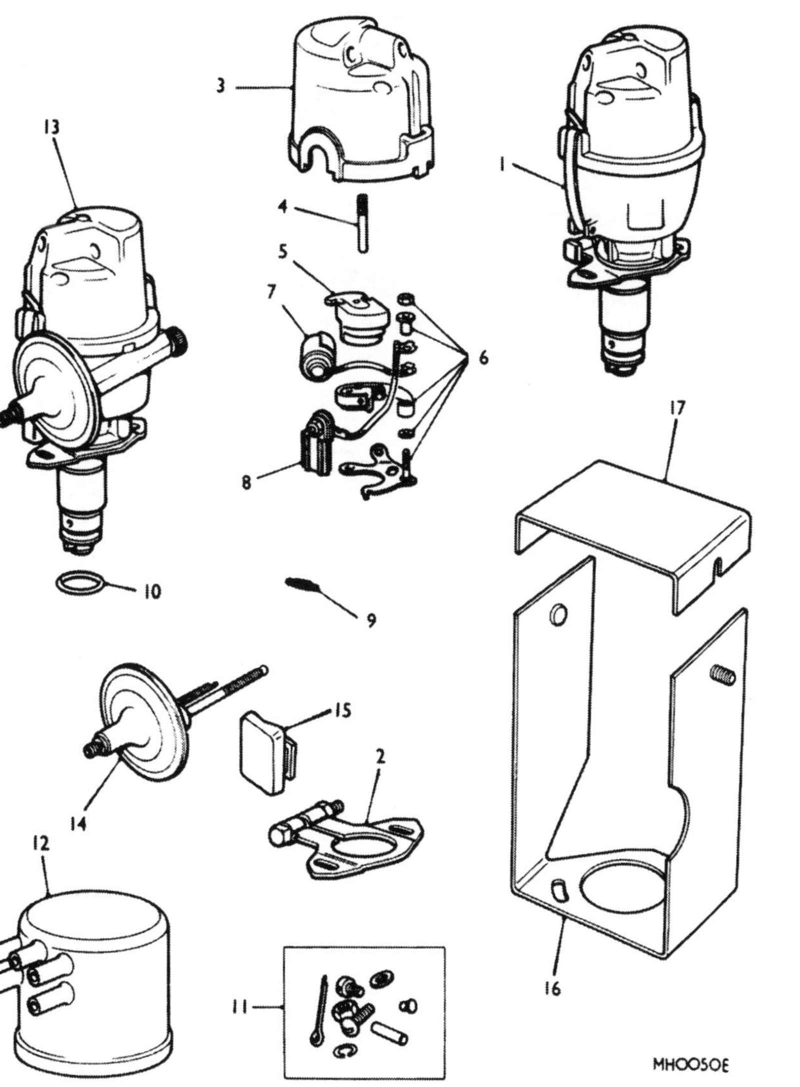

AUSTIN-HEALEY SPRITE MK. 3 AND MK. 4 & MG MIDGET MK. 2 AND MK. 3

DISTRIBUTOR-1275cc 12CC,12CD,12CE,12CJ AND 12V-continued.

NO.	PART NO.	DESCRIPTION	QTY	CHANGE POINT	REMARKS
13	12G 3159	DISTRIBUTOR ASSEMBLY-LC	1	(E)12V/587Z/101 TO (+)	
2	3H 2138	Plate-clamping	1		
10	27H 6547	'O'ring-oil seal	1		
14	37H 7110	Unit-vacuum	1		
9	37H 7109	Spring-automatic advance	1		
7	GSC 101	Condenser	1		
6	GCS 101	Contact set	1SET		
8	37H 2981	Terminal-bush and lead	1		
5	GRA 101	Arm-rotor	1		
3	GDC 102	COVER ASSEMBLY	1		
4	17H 5065	Brush and spring	1		
11	17H 5106	Sundry parts	1SET		
13	13H 8433	DISTRIBUTOR ASSEMBLY-LC	1	(E)12V/671Z/101 ON	
2	3H 2138	Plate-clamping	1		
3	GDC 102	COVER ASSEMBLY	1		
4	17H 5065	Brush and spring	1		
5	GRA 101	Arm-rotor	1		
6	GCS 101	Set-contact	1SET		
7	GSC 101	Condenser	1		
8	37H 2981	Terminal-bush and lead	1		
14	37H 7837	Unit-vacuum	1		
10	27H 65 .7	Ring-'O'-oil seal	1		
15	BMK 1989	Seal(rubber)-distributor	2		France.
16	12G 335	Body-suppression screen	1		
17	12G 337	Cover-suppression screen	1		
	WNZ 103	Nut-wing	1		

(+) Change point not available.

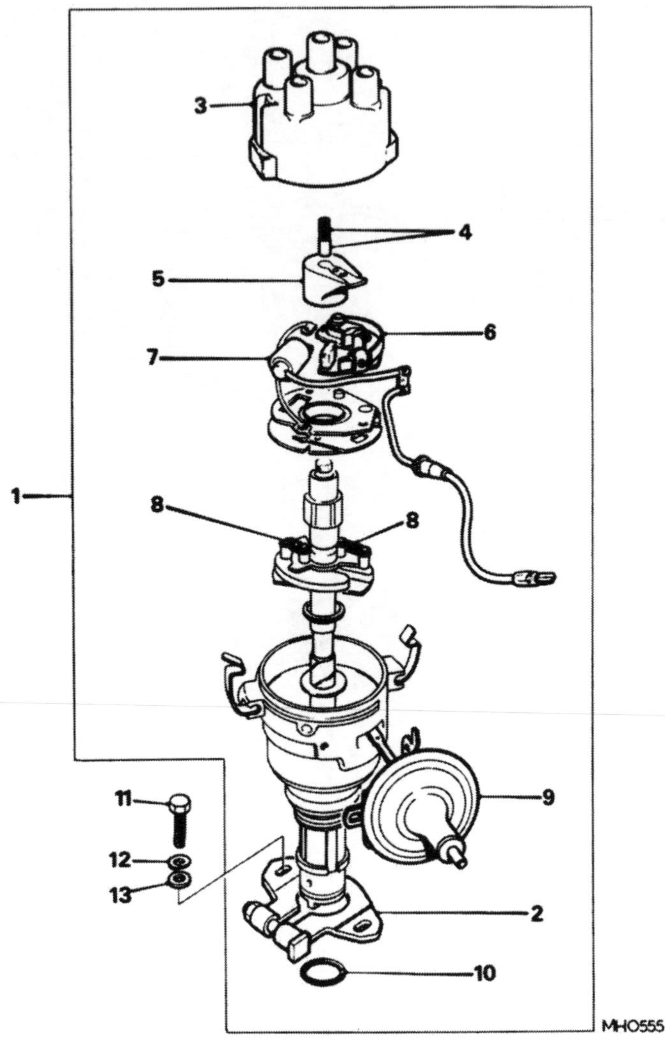

AUSTIN-HEALEY SPRITE MK. 3 AND MK. 4 & MG MIDGET MK. 2 AND MK. 3

NO.	PART NO.	DESCRIPTION	QTY	CHANGE POINT	REMARKS
		DISTRIBUTOR-MIDGET 1500-NOT USA.			
1	RKC 638	DISTRIBUTOR ASSEMBLY	1		
2	RTC 1773	Plate-clamping	NLA		
3	GDC 132	Cover moulded	1		
4	37H 8230	Brush and spring	1		
5	GRA 114	Arm-rotor	1		
6	GCS 118	Contact set	1		
7	GSC 110	Condenser(with lead)	1		
8	RTC 1776	Spring-Automatic advance	1SET		
9	RTC 1775	Vacuum unit	1		
10	27H 6547	'O'ring	1		

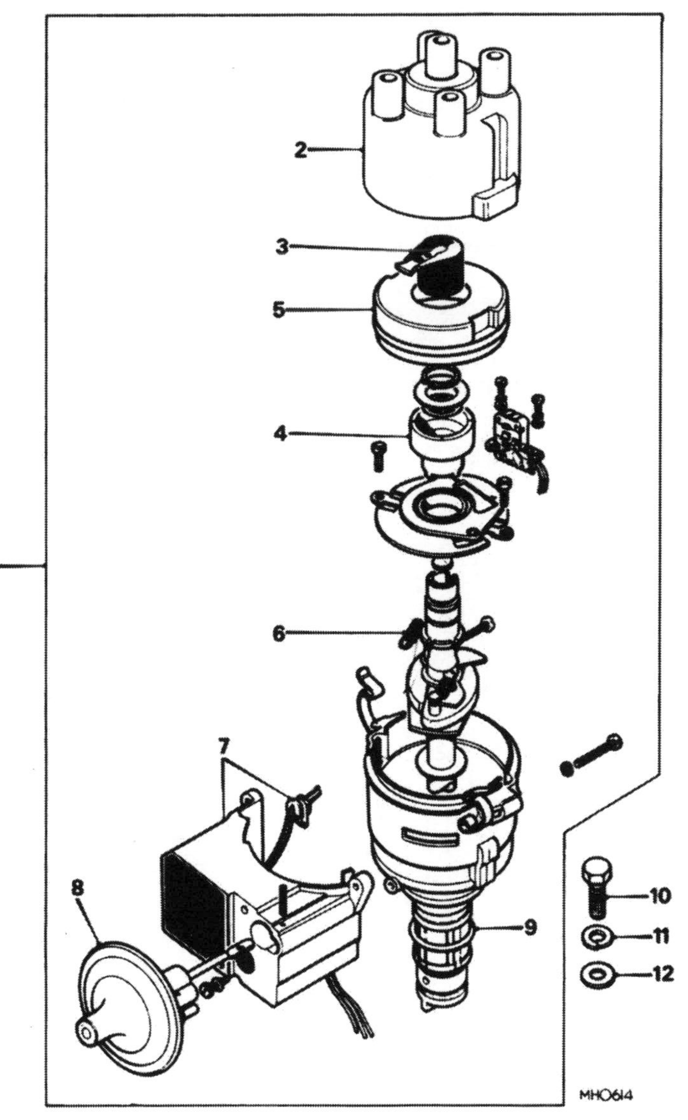

AUSTIN-HEALEY SPRITE MK. 3 AND MK. 4 & MG MIDGET MK. 2 AND MK. 3

DISTRIBUTOR-MIDGET 1500-USA AND CANADA

NO.	PART NO.	DESCRIPTION	QTY	CHANGE POINT	REMARKS
1	TKC 1224	DISTRIBUTOR ASSEMBLY	1		USA and Canada TO 1976 California 1976 TO 1977
	RTC 1773	Plate-clamping	NLA		
2	GDC 132	Cover-moulded	1		
	37H 8230	Brush and spring	1		
3	GRA 114	Arm-rotor	1		
4	RTC 1739	ROTOR ASSEMBLY TIMING	1		
5	RTC 1738	Cover-anti-flash	1		
6	RTC 1780	Spring-automatic advance	1SET		
7	RTC 1781	Module-electronic	1		
8	RTC 1782	Vacuum unit(with roll pin)	1		
9	27H 6547	'O'ring oil seal	1		
1	TKC 2755	DISTRIBUTOR ASSEMBLY	1		Federal 1976 TO 1977.
	RTC 1773	Plate-clamping	NLA		
2	GDC 136	Cover-moulded	1		
	37H 8230	Brush and spring	1		
3	GRA 114	Arm-rotor	1		
4	RTC 1739	Rotor-timing	1		
5	RTC 1738	Cover-anti-flash	1		
7	37H 8829	Module-electronic	1		
8	RTC 1733	Vacuum unit	1		
9	27H 6547	'O'ring	1		
1	TKC 3289	DISTRIBUTOR ASSEMBLY	1		Federal 1977 ON
7	AAU 6313	AMPLIFIER AND VACUUM UNIT ASSEMBLY	1		
8	AAU 6312	Vacuum unit	1		
1	TKC 3287	DISTRIBUTOR ASSEMBLY	1		California 1977 ON.
7	AAU 4365	AMPLIFIER AND VACUUM UNIT ASSEMBLY	1		
8	AAU 6311	Vacuum unit	1		

AUSTIN-HEALEY SPRITE MK. 3 AND MK. 4 & MG MIDGET MK. 2 AND MK. 3

NO.	PART NO.	DESCRIPTION	QTY	CHANGE POINT	REMARKS
		IGNITION COIL LEAD KIT AND VACUUM PIPE-MIDGET 1500			
1	151103	Pipe-suction-distributor to carburetter	1		
4	128262	Connection-pipe to distributor	1		
2	131211	Connection-pipe to carburetter	1		
5	GHT 152	Kit-ignition lead	1		
3	GCL 111	Coil-ignition	1		
7	WL 600051	Washer-spring	2		
	NT 605041	Nut	2		

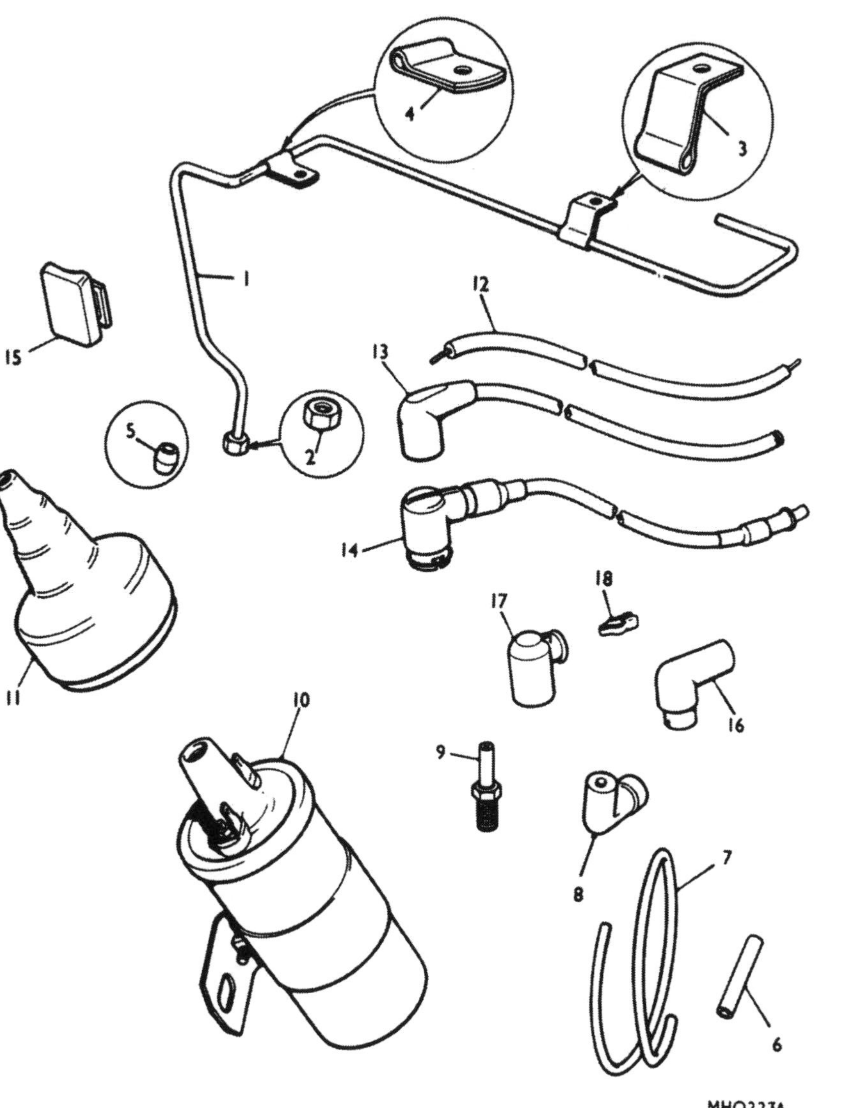

AUSTIN-HEALEY SPRITE MK. 3 AND MK. 4 & MG MIDGET MK. 2 AND MK. 3

VACUUM CONTROL PIPE-IGNITION COIL-NOT 1500

NO.	PART NO.	DESCRIPTION	QTY	CHANGE POINT	REMARKS
1	AEA 579	PIPE ASSEMBLY-VACUUM CONTROL	1		10CC,12CC,12CE, 12V/586,12V/588.
2	6K 650	Nut-distributor end	1		
4	ACH 9009	Clip-pipe to cylinder head	1		
1	12G 1652	PIPE ASSEMBLY-VACUUM CONTROL	1		12CD,12CJ,12V/ 587.
2	6K 650	Nut-distributor end	1		
5	6K 649	Olive	1		
3	PCR 209	Clip-pipe to gulp valve	1		
4	PCR 211	Clip-pipe to water outlet elbow	1		
6	ACH 9041	Connection-pipe to carburetter (rubber)	1		
7	37H 4229 M	Pipe-vacuum control(plastic)- 20"(51cm)long	A/R		Supplied in 30 metre(100')rolls.
8	12B 2062	Connection-pipe	2		
9	12H 2461	Adaptor-vacuum ignition	1	(E)12V/587Z/101 TO(+) (E)12V/671Z/101 ON	
	PWZ 105	Washer-plain	2		
	LWZ 305	Washer-spring	2		
	NH 605041	Nut	2		
8	12B 2062	Connection-pipe	2		
10	GCL 110	Coil-ignition	1	Use prior to GCL 111	
10	GCL 111	Coil-ignition(ballast)	1		Midget 1500
	13H 9440	Resistor-electronic ignition driver-Ballast $	1		Midget 1500 USA and Canada
	HZS 405	Screw-coil to bracket on body	2		
	PWZ 204	Washer-plain	2		
	LWZ 204	Washer-spring	2		
	NH 604041	Nut	2		
11	8G 727	Cover-waterproof	1		Canada and Denmark.

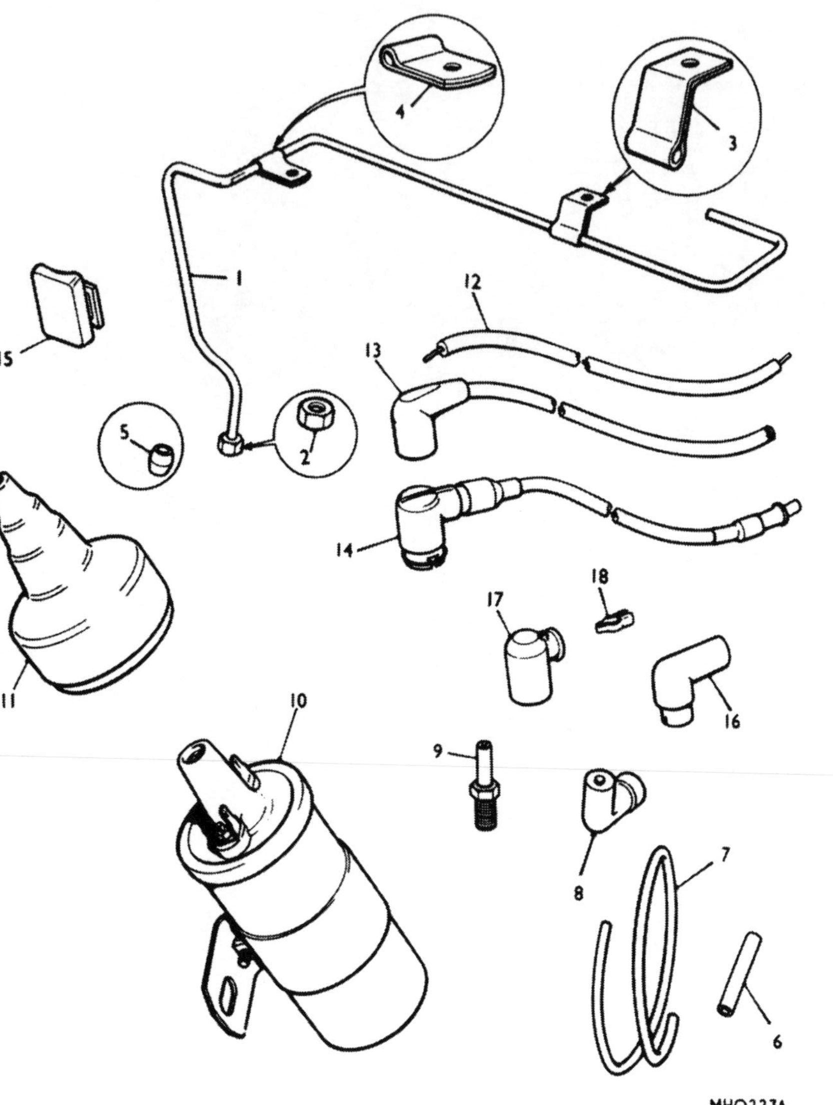

AUSTIN-HEALEY SPRITE MK. 3 AND MK. 4 & MG MIDGET MK. 2 AND MK. 3

NO.	PART NO.	DESCRIPTION	QTY	CHANGE POINT	REMARKS
		IGNITION CABLES-1098cc			
12	AAA 5981	CABLE-IGNITION	A/R		Supplied only in 110'(30 METRES) ROLLS
	AAA 5981	No.1 plug lead-12"(305mm)	1		
	AAA 5981	No.2 plug lead-11"(279mm)	1		
	AAA 5981	No.3 plug lead-8.5"(216mm)	1		
	AAA 5981	No.4 plug lead-9"(229mm)	1		
12	AAA 5981	Cable-coil to distributor-9"(229mm)	A/R		
		CABLE-IGNITION COMPLETE			
13	8G 2630	No.1 plug lead-14"(356mm)	1		Use with side ENTRY Distributor cap
13	8G 2630	No.2 plug lead-14"(356mm)	1		
13	8G 2629	No.3 plug lead-8.5"(216mm)	1		
13	8G 2629	No.4 plug lead-11"(279mm)	1		
		CABLE-IGNITION(WITH CONNECTORS)			
14	12G 346	No.1 plug lead-12"(305mm)	1		France
	12G 347	No.2 plug lead-12"(305mm)	1		
	12G 348	No.3 plug lead-9.5"(241mm)	1		
	12G 349	No.4 plug lead-9.5"(241mm)	1		
14	12G 350	Cable-coil to distributor (with connectors)-10.5"(267mm)	1		
15	BMK 1989	Seal(rubber)-distributor	2		
	2H 4245	Sleeve-identification-No.3 plug lead	1		
16	3H 1422	Suppressor-sparking plug	4		
17	8G 576	CONNECTOR ASSEMBLY-SPARKING PLUG	4		
18	7H 6894	Clip-cable end	4		

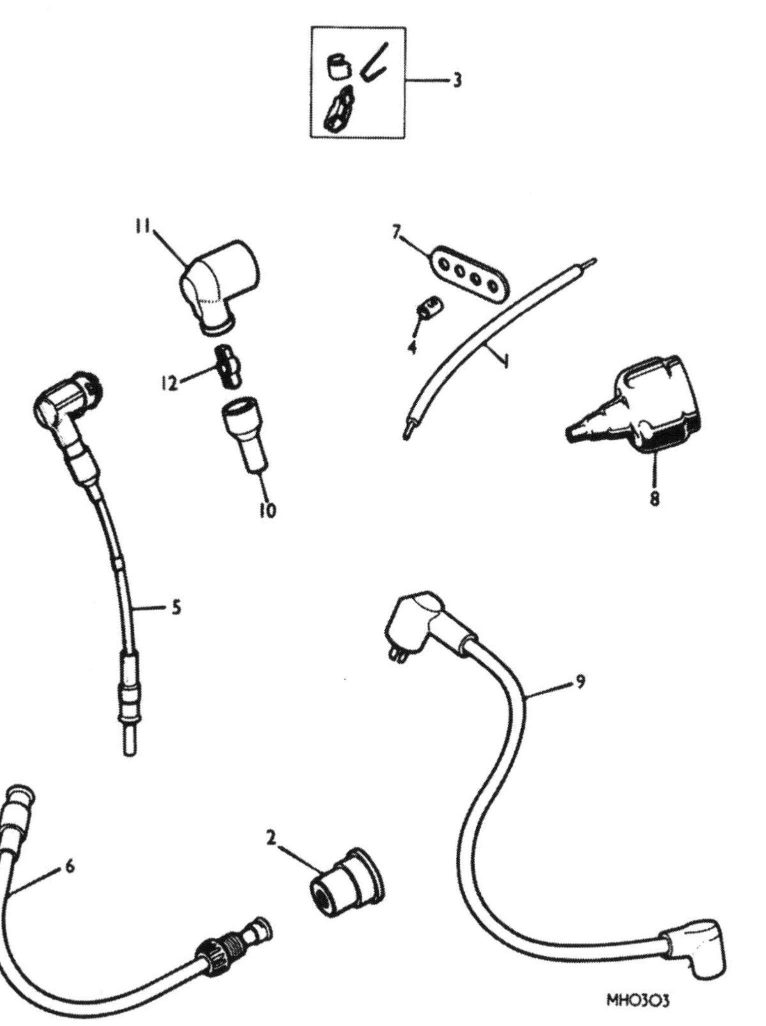

AUSTIN-HEALEY SPRITE MK. 3 AND MK. 4 & MG MIDGET MK. 2 AND MK. 3

IGNITION CABLES-1275cc-POSITIVE EARTH ELECTRICAL SYSTEM

NO.	PART NO.	DESCRIPTION	QTY	CHANGE POINT	REMARKS
1	AAA 5981 M	CABLE IGNITION-12CC	A/R		Supplied in 30 METRE(100')ROLLS
	AAA 5981 M	No.1 plug-311mm(12.25")	1		
	AAA 5981 M	No.2 plug-298mm(11.75")	1		
	AAA 5981 M	No.3 plug-254mm(10")	1		
	AAA 5981 M	No.4 plug-298mm(11.75")	1		
1	AAA 5981 M	Cable-coil to distributor-298mm(11.75")12CC	1		
		CABLE-IGNITION-COMPLETE			
9	8G 2630	No.1 and 2 plug-356mm(14")	2		Use with side ENTRY DISTRIBUTOR
	8G 2628	No.3 plug-216mm(8.5")	1		
	8G 2629	No.4 plug-279mm(11")	1		
1	AAA 5981	Cable-coil to distributor-298mm(11.75")	1		Supplied in 30 metre(100')rolls
10	8G 728	Sleeve-sealing	4		12CC-Denmark Canada only
11	WC 200	CAP-SPARKING PLUG	4		
12	7H 6894	Clip-cable end	4		
4	2H 4245	Sleeve-identification-plug lead-No.3	1		12CC French MARKET
		CABLE IGNITION(WITH CONNECTORS)			
5	12G 346	No.1 plug	1		
	12G 347	No.2 plug	1		
	12G 348	No.3 plug	1		
	12G 349	No.4 plug	1		
6	12G 350	Cable-coil to distributor	1		
		CABLE-IGNITION(WITH CONNECTORS)-12CC			French market Use with DISTRIBUTOR 12G 2057
5	12G 2145	No.1 plug-305mm(12")	1		
	12G 2146	No.2 plug-305mm(12")	1		
	12G 2147	No.3 plug-241mm(9.5")	1		
	12G 2148	No.4 plug-241mm(9.5")	1		
6	12G 2149	Cable-coil to distributor-267mm(10.5")	1		
7	1G 2673	Spacer-ignition cable	NLA		

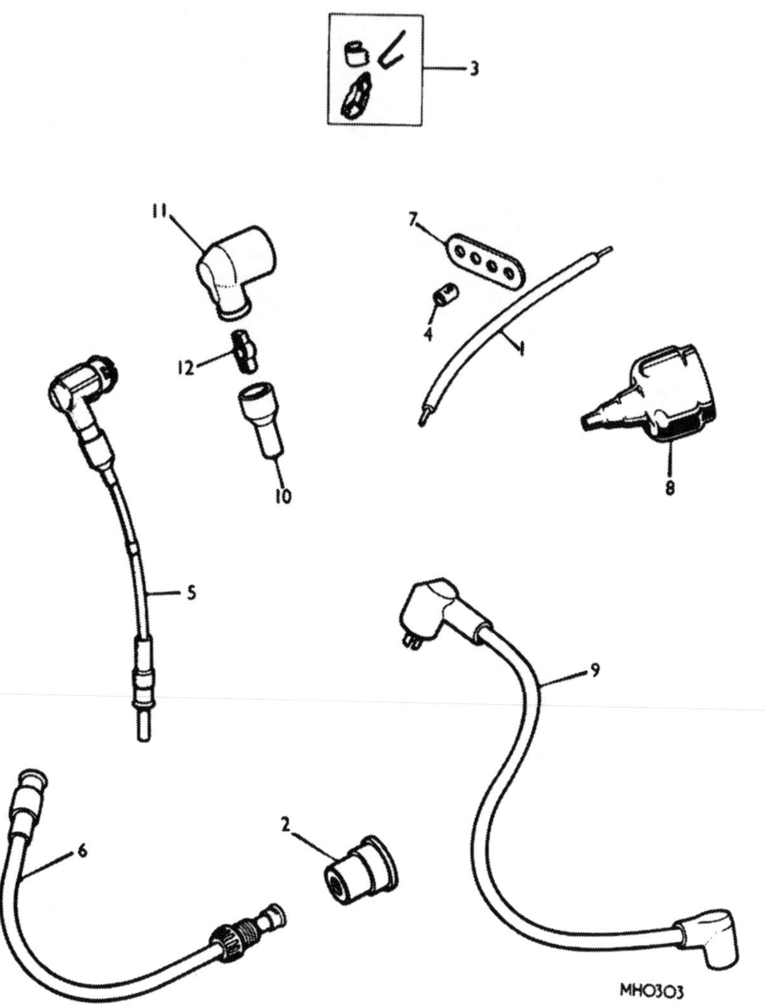

AUSTIN-HEALEY SPRITE MK. 3 AND MK. 4 & MG MIDGET MK. 2 AND MK. 3

NO.	PART NO.	DESCRIPTION	QTY	CHANGE POINT	REMARKS
		IGNITION CABLES-1275cc-NEGATIVE EARTH ELECTRICAL SYSTEM-12CD,12CE,12CJ AND 12V			
1	AAA 5981 M	CABLE-IGNITION	A/R		Supplied in 30 METRE(100')ROLLS
	AAA 5981 M	No.1 plug-12.25"(311mm)	1		
	AAA 5981 M	No.2 plug-11.75"(298mm)	1		
	AAA 5981 M	No.3 plug-10"(254mm)	1		
	AAA 5981 M	No.4 plug-11.75"(298mm)	1		
	AAA 5981 M	Cable-coil to distributor-9"(229mm)	A/R		
		CABLE-IGNITION-COMPLETE			
	12H 3348	No.1 and 2 plug-11.5"(292mm)	2		Use with vertical ENTRY DISTRIBUTOR
	32H 352	Cable-coil to distributor-11.5"(292mm)	1		
	12G 2514	Cover-coil-vented	1		
4	2H 4245	Sleeve-identification-plug lead-No.3	1		French market
		CABLE-IGNITION(WITH CONNECTORS)			
5	12G 346	No.1 plug	1		
	12G 347	No.2 plug	1		
	12G 348	No.3 plug	1		
	12G 349	No.4 plug	1		
		CABLE-IGNITION(WITH CONNECTORS)12CD,12CE,12V			
5	12G 2145	No.1 plug-12"(305mm)	1		French market. Use with DISTRIBUTOR 12G 2057
	12G 2146	No.2 plug-12"(305mm)	1		
	12G 2147	No.3 plug-9.5"(241mm)	1		
	12G 2148	No.4 plug-9.5"(241mm)	1		
6	12G 2149	Coil to distributor-10.5"(267mm)	1		
7	12G 2673	Spacer-ignition cable	1		
8	12G 1980	Cover-ignition coil	1		

AUSTIN-HEALEY SPRITE MK. 3 AND MK. 4 & MG MIDGET MK. 2 AND MK. 3

DYNAMO-POSITIVE EARTH ELECTRICAL SYSTEM

NO.	PART NO.	DESCRIPTION	QTY	CHANGE POINT	REMARKS
	13H 826	DYNAMO ASSEMBLY(22742)	NLA		Use BMK 1241
1	GGB 102	Brush	1SET		
2	17H 6821	BRACKET ASSEMBLY-COMMUTATOR END	1		
3	7H 5390	Bush	1		
4	47H 5394	Oiler	1		
5	47H 5389	Spring-brush tension	1SET		
6	97H 626	Bearing-drive end	1		
7	17H 6822	Bracket-drive end	1		
	FNN 207	Nut-shaft	1		
	LWZ 207	Washer-spring	1		
8	37H 4310	Armature	1		
9	WKN 404	Key-armature	1		
10	37H 6787	COIL ASSEMBLY-FIELD	1SET		
11	37H 3752	Terminal-coil	1		
12	17H 5217	Bolt-bracket fixing	2		
13	57H 5085	Sundry parts	1SET		
	13H 219	DYNAMO ASSEMBLY(22700 A to M)	NLA		Use BMK 1241
1	GGB 102	Brushes	1SET		
15	47H 5395	BRACKET ASSEMBLY-COMMUTATOR END	1		
4	47H 5394	Oiler	1		
3	7H 5390	Bushing	1		
5	47H 5389	Spring-brush tension	1		
6	97H 626	Bearing-drive end	1		
16	27H 3548	Collar-bearing	1		
17	27H 3798	Retainer	1		
18	27H 7647	BRACKET ASSEMBLY-DRIVE END	1		
19	27H 3831	Plate-retaining	1		
20	37H 1878	Circlip	1		
21	27H 3832	'O'ring	1		
	FNZ 207	Nut	1		
	LWN 207	Washer-shakeproof	1		
8	37H 4310	Armature	1		
9	WKN 404	Key	1		
10	37H 6787	COIL ASSEMBLY-FIELD	1		
11	37H 3752	Terminal	1		
12	17H 5217	Bolt-fixing	2		
13	37H 6836	Sundry parts	1		

AUSTIN-HEALEY SPRITE MK. 3 AND MK. 4 & MG MIDGET MK. 2 AND MK. 3

DYNAMO-POSITIVE EARTH ELECTRICAL SYSTEM-continued

NO.	PART NO.	DESCRIPTION	QTY	CHANGE POINT	REMARKS
	13H 4813	DYNAMO ASSEMBLY(22775)-12CD, 12CE	NLA		Use BMK 1241 See TIB 1B 90 for repolarisation instructions.
1	GGB 102	Brush	1SET		
2	17H 6821	BRACKET ASSEMBLY-COMMUTATOR END	1		
3	7H 5390	Bush	1		
4	47H 5394	Oiler	1		
5	47H 5389	Spring-brush tension	1SET		
6	97H 626	Bearing-drive end	1		
22	37H 3348	BRACKET ASSEMBLY-DRIVE END	1		
19	27H 3831	Plate-bearing retainer	1		
20	37H 1878	Circlip	1		
21	27H 3832	'O'ring-oil seal(rubber)	1		
16	27H 3548	Collar-drive end bearing	1		
17	27H 3798	Retainer-bearing ring	1		
8	37H 4310	Armature	1		
9	WKN 404	Key	1		
	FNN 207	Nut-shaft	1		
	LWN 207	Washer-spring	1		
10	37H 6787	COIL ASSEMBLY-FIELD	1SET		
11	37H 3752	Terminal	1		
12	17H 5217	Bolt-through-fixing	2		
13	57H 5085	Sundry parts	1SET		
	BMK 1241	DYNAMO ASSEMBLY(22715)	1		
18	27H 7647	Bracket-drive end	1		
	37H 6834	Kit-bearing retention	1		
	97H 626	Bearing-drive end	1		
8	37H 4310	Armature	1		
	37H 6787	Kit-field coil	1		
	37H 3752	Kit-terminal	1		
15	47H 5395	BRACKET ASSEMBLY-COMMUTATOR END	1		
4	47H 5394	Oiler	1		
3	7H 5390	Bearing-bush	1		
5	47H 5389	Spring-bush	1		
1	GGB 102	Brush set	1SET		
12	17H 5217	Bolt-through-fixing	2		
13	37H 6836	Kit-sundry parts	1SET		

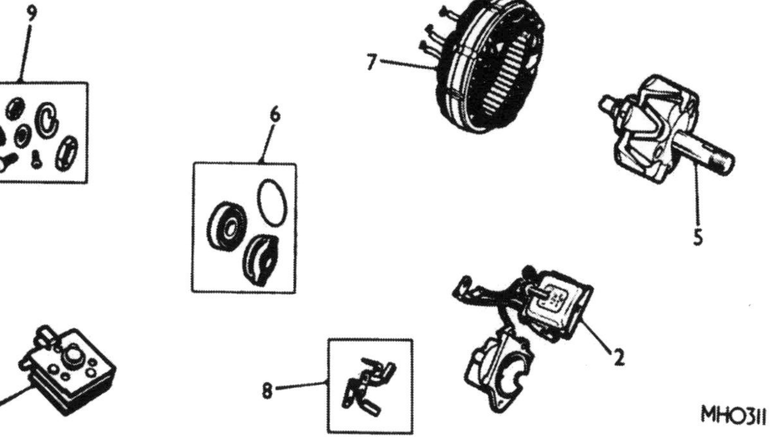

AUSTIN-HEALEY SPRITE MK. 3 AND MK. 4 & MG MIDGET MK. 2 AND MK. 3

ALTERNATOR AND FITTINGS-1275cc-12V-OPTIONAL EXTRA

NO.	PART NO.	DESCRIPTION	QTY	CHANGE POINT	REMARKS
1	37H 7331	ALTERNATOR ASSEMBLY-16ACR (23606,23685A)	NLA	Use prior to 37H 8208	Use 37H 8314
1	37H 8314	ALTERNATOR ASSEMBLY-16ACR	1		
	37H 8208	ALTERNATOR ASSEMBLY-(17ACR)	1	(E)12V/588F/2551 ON (E)12V/671Z/9570 ON (E)12V/778F/101 ON	
2	37H 6911	Regulator	1		Use with 37H 7331.
3	37H 6913	Rectifier	1		
2	37H 7964	Regulator	1		Use with 37H 8314 and 37H 8208.
3	37H 7965	Rectifier	1		
4	18G 8619	Kit-drive end bracket	1		
5	37H 4196	Rotor	1		Use with 37H 7331 and 37H 8314.
5	37H 6024	Rotor	1		Use with 37H 8208.
6	18G 8620	Kit-bearing-slip ring end	1		
7	37H 2257	Stator	1		Use with 37H 7331 and 37H 8314.
7	37H 6023	Stator	1		Use with 37H 8208.
	37H 6915	Brush box	1		
8	37H 4199	Brush	1SET		
9	37H 2258	Kit-sundry parts	1		
	37H 7517	Device-surge protection	1		Use with 37H 8314 and 37H 8208.
	37H 7963	Capacitor-suppression	1		

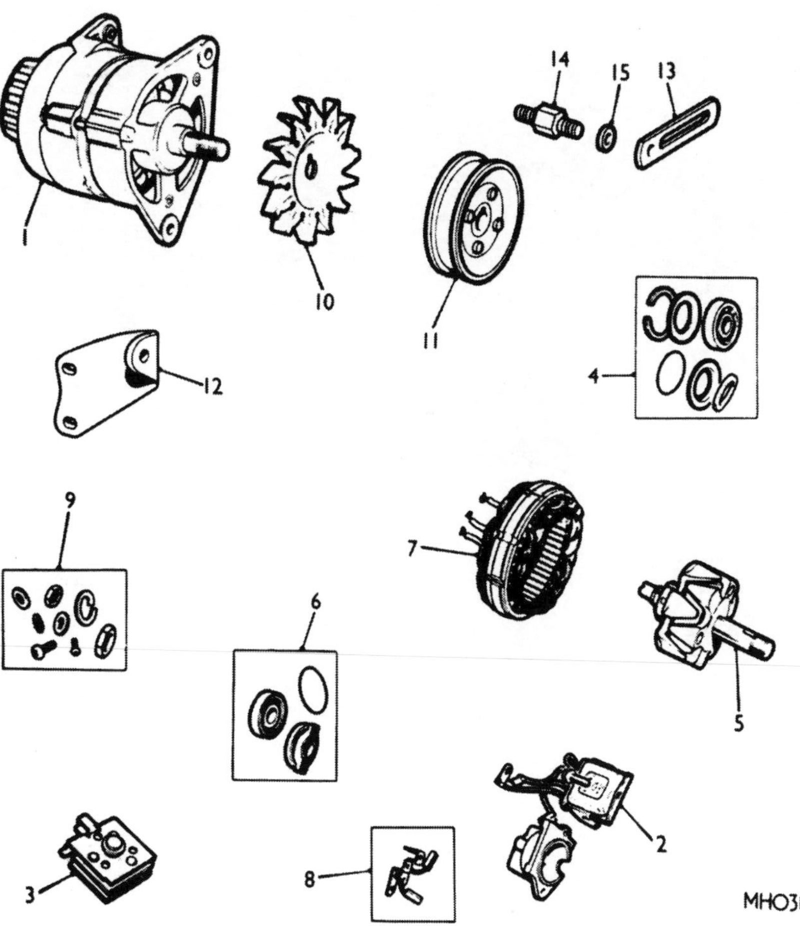

AUSTIN-HEALEY SPRITE MK. 3 AND MK. 4 & MG MIDGET MK. 2 AND MK. 3

NO.	PART NO.	DESCRIPTION	QTY	CHANGE POINT	REMARKS
		ALTERNATOR AND FITTINGS-1275CC-12V-OPTIONAL EXTRA-Continued.			
10	12H 2515	Fan	NLA		Use 13H 9551.
10	13H 9551	Fan	1		
11	12G 1054	Pulley	1	Use prior to 37H 7061.	
11	13H 7061	Pulley	1	(E)12V/588F/3193 ON. (E)12V/671Z/12846 ON. (E)12V/776F/101 ON.	
12	12G 1053	Bracket-rear	1		
13	2A 497	Link-adjusting	1		
14	12G 3037	Pillar-adjusting link	1		
	LNZ 206	Nut-link to pillar	1		
15	1B 8806	Washer	1		
	SH 605131	Bolt-alternator to bracket	1		
	LWN 305	Washer-spring	1		
	WC 108051	Washer-plain	1		
	LNZ 205	Nut	1		
	BH 605151	Bolt-alternator to water pump	1		
	LWZ 305	Washer-spring	1		
	GHF 301	Washer-plain	1		
	LNZ 205	Nut	1		
	SH 605071	Screw-alternator to crankcase	2		
	LWZ 305	Washer-spring	2		
	SH 505051	Screw-link to alternator	1		
	LWZ 305	Washer-spring	1		
	NT 606041	Nut-alternator adjusting link	1		
	WL 600061	Washer-spring			

ILLUSTRATION NOT USED

AUSTIN-HEALEY SPRITE MK. 3 AND MK. 4 & MG MIDGET MK. 2 AND MK. 3

ALTERNATOR AND FIXINGS-MIDGET 1500.

NO.	PART NO.	DESCRIPTION	QTY	CHANGE POINT	REMARKS
	37H 8314	ALTERNATOR ASSEMBLY-BATTERY SENSED-16ACR	1		
	37H 7964	Regulator	1		
	37H 7965	Rectifier	1		
	18G 8619	Kit-bearing-drive end	1		
	37H 4196	Rotor	1		
	18G 8620	Kit-bearing-slip ring end	1		
	37H 2257	Stator	1		
	37H 4199	Brush-set	1		
	37H 2258	Sundry parts-set	1		
	37H 7517	Device-surge protection	1		
	37H 7963	Capacitor-suppression	1		
	147990	Fan-alternator	1		
	154334	Pulley-alternator	1		
	147899	Bracket-mounting	1		
	CHA 304	Bracket-mounting	1		USA and Canada.
	WL 600051	Washer-lock	2		
	GHF 103	Setscrew	2		
	HB 839	Bolt-pivot	1		Not USA and Canada.
	147483	Spacer-pivot bolt	1		Not USA and Canada.
	WP 139	Washer-plain	1		Not USA and Canada.
	143802	Nut	1		Not USA and Canada.
	UKC 3128	Tube-distance	1		USA and Canada.
	HB 841	Bolt	1		USA and Canada.
	156464	Link-adjusting and lifting eye-front	1		
	HU 858	Screw-link to alternator	1		
	WP 17	Washer	2		
	JN 2158	Nut	1		
	GFB 105	Belt-fan	1		
	CHA 328	Belt-fan	1		USA and Canada.

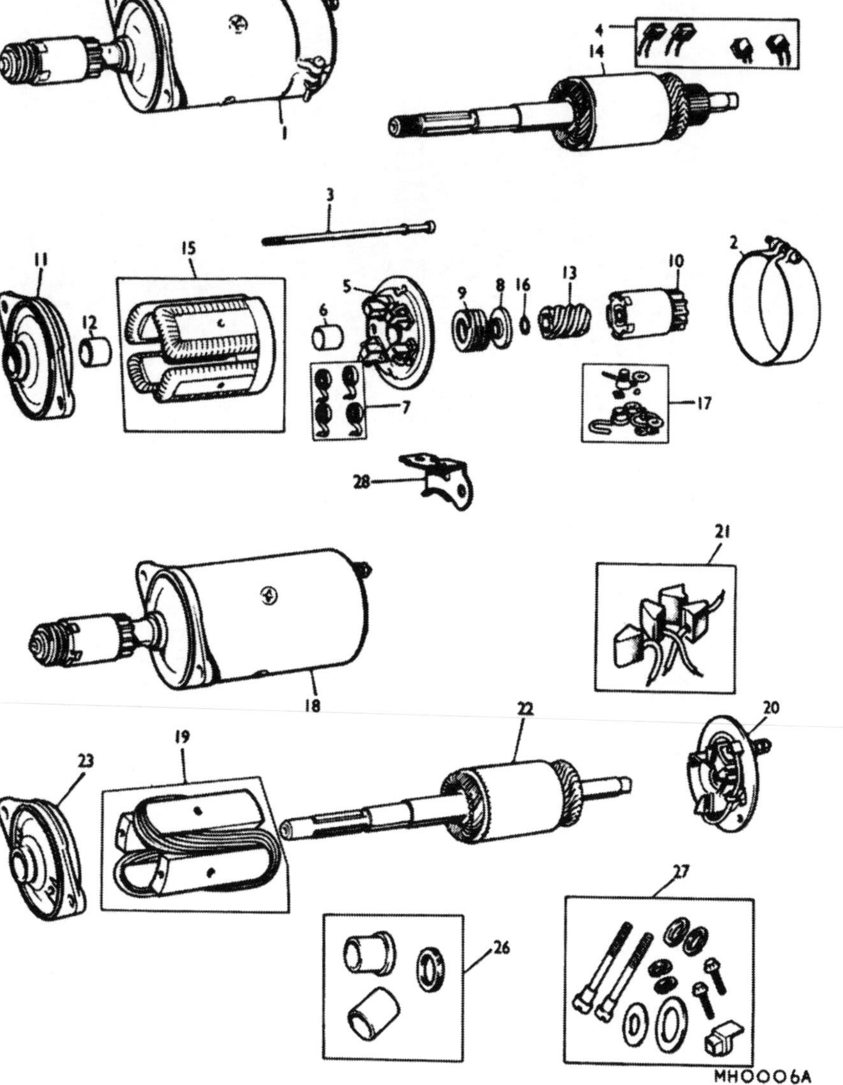

AUSTIN-HEALEY SPRITE MK. 3 AND MK. 4 & MG MIDGET MK. 2 AND MK. 3

NO.	PART NO.	DESCRIPTION	QTY	CHANGE POINT	REMARKS
		STARTER-EXCEPT MIDGET 1500.			
	13H 559	STARTER ASSEMBLY (25079 A to H)	NLA		Use 13H 5798.
2	7H 5038	Band-cover	1		
3	7H 5040	Brush	1SET		
4	27H 6768	BRACKET ASSEMBLY-COMMUTATOR END	1		
5	47H 5340	Bush	1		
6	47H 5341	Spring-brush tension	1SET		
7	27H 3755	Cap-shaft	1		
8	67H 5014	BRACKET ASSEMBLY-DRIVE END	1		
9	47H 5346	Bush	1		
10	67H 5012	Armature	1		
11	7H 5051	Coil-field	1SET		
12	7H 5045	Spring-main	1		
13	67H 5010	Pinion and barrel	1		
14	7H 6887	Ring-spring and pinion retaining	1		
15	67H 5013	Sleeve-screwed	1		
16	17H 5444	Bolt-bracket fixing	2		
17	7H 5156	Sundry parts	1SET		
18	13H 5798	STARTER ASSEMBLY-TYPE M35J (25149)	1		
19	37H 4670	Coil-field	1SET		
20	37H 4672	Bracket-commutator end	1		
21	37H 4673	Brushes	NLA		Use GSB 105.
21	GSB 105	Brushes	1SET		
22	37H 4674	Armature	1		
23	37H 4675	Bracket-drive end	1		
14	7H 6887	Ring-jump	1		
7	27H 3755	Cup-shaft	1		
12	7H 5045	Spring-main	1		
13	67H 5010	Pinion and barrel	1		
15	67H 5013	Sleeve-screwed	1		
25	37H 4678	Kit-bush	1		
	BH 606141	Bolt-starter to rear mounting plate	2		
	WL 600061	Washer-spring	2		
	NH 606041	Nut	2		
	13H 4044	Relay-starter motor solenoid	1	(C)G-AN5-138801 ON	N.America

ILLUSTRATION NOT USED

NO.	PART NO.	DESCRIPTION	QTY	CHANGE POINT	REMARKS
		STARTER AND FIXINGS-MIDGET 1500.			
	13H 5798	STARTER ASSEMBLY-TYPE M35J	1		
	37H 4670	Coil-field-set	1		
	37H 4672	Bracket-commutator end	1		
	GSB 105	Brush-set	1		
	37H 4674	Armature	1		
	37H 4675	Bracket-drive end	1		
	7H 6887	Ring-jump	1		
	27H 3755	Cup-shaft	1		
	7H 5045	Spring-main	1		
	67H 5010	Pinion and barrel	1		
	67H 5013	Sleeve-screwed	1		
	37H 4678	Kit-bush	1		
	131570	Piece-packing	1		
	104549	Shim	1		
	BH 606071	Bolt	2		
	WE 600061	Washer	2		
	WL 600061	Washer-lock	2		
	NH 606041	Nut	2		

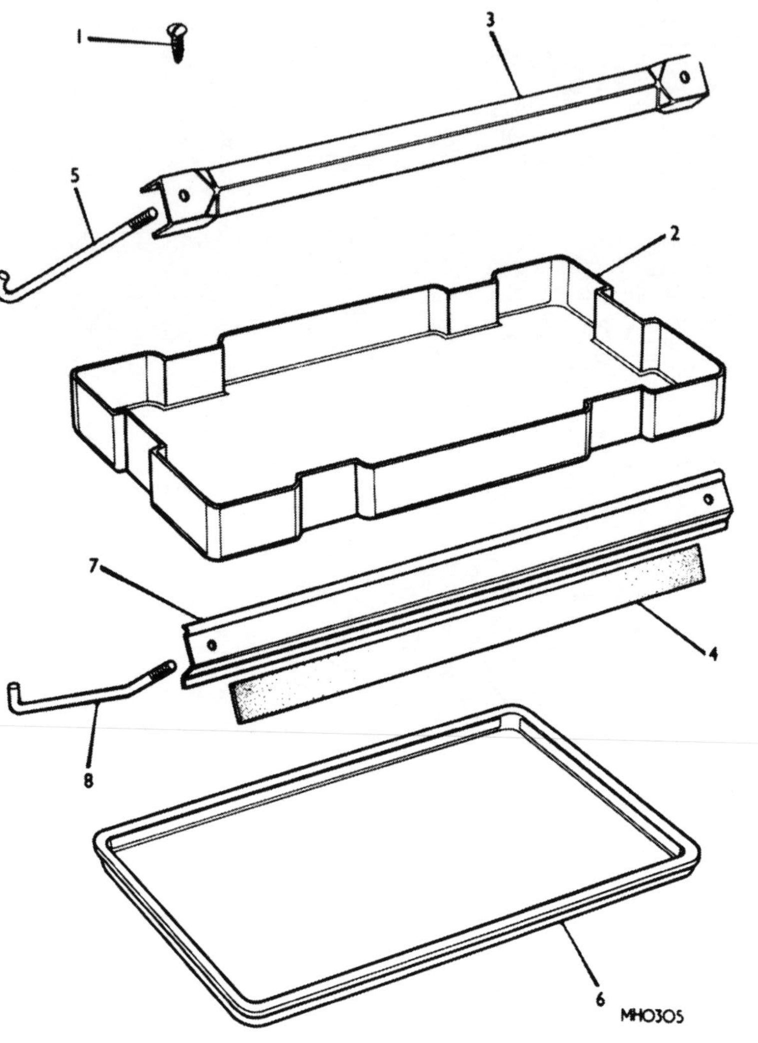

AUSTIN-HEALEY SPRITE MK. 3 AND MK. 4 & MG MIDGET MK. 2 AND MK. 3

NO.	PART NO.	DESCRIPTION	QTY	CHANGE POINT	REMARKS
		BATTERY AND FIXINGS.			
	NSP	Battery	1		
1	2K 8645	Screw-terminal	2		
2	AHA 6305	Tray-battery	1	(C)H-AN8-38829 TO 64734 (C)H-AN9-64735 TO 72040 (C)G-AN3-25788 TO 52389 (C)G-AN4-52390 TO 60459	
3	AHA 6934	Bar-battery fixing	1		
4	37H 3743	Packing-bar to battery	A/R		Supplied in multiples of feet.
5	AHA 7769	Rod-battery fixing	2		
6	ACA 9673	Tray-battery	1	(C)H-AN9-72041 TO 85286 (C)H-AN10-85287 TO 86803 (C)A-AN10-86804 TO 87824 (C)G-AN4-60460 TO 74885 (C)G-AN5-74886 ON	
7	34G 2065	Bar-battery	1		
4	37H 3743	Packing-bar to battery	A/R		Supplied in multiples of feet
8	AHA 8674	Rod-battery	1		
	LWZ 204	Washer-spring	2		
	NH 604041	Nut	2		

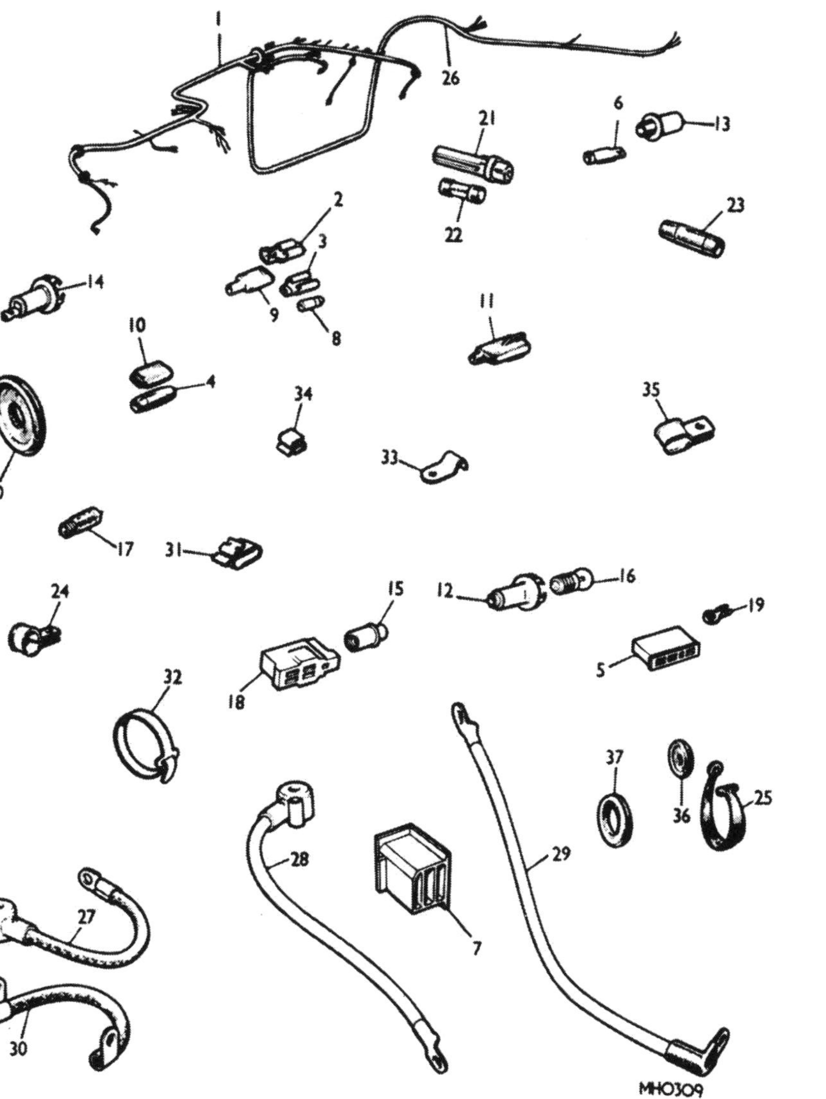

AUSTIN-HEALEY SPRITE MK. 3 AND MK. 4 & MG MIDGET MK. 2 AND MK. 3

NO.	PART NO.	DESCRIPTION	QTY	CHANGE POINT	REMARKS
		WIRING CABLES AND FITTINGS CONNECTORS,AND BULB HOLDERS			
1	AHA 7780	CABLE ASSEMBLY-MAIN HARNESS	NLA	(C)H-AN8-38829 TO 64734 (C)G-AN3-25788 TO 52389	
1	AHA 8694	CABLE ASSEMBLY-MAIN HARNESS-EXCEPT N.AMERICA	NLA	Use prior to AHA 9612	
1	AHA 9612	CABLE ASSEMBLY-MAIN HARNESS	1	(C)H-AN10-85287 TO 86302 (C)G-AN5-74886 TO 89514	Except USA, Canada and Sweden.
1	AHA 9763	CABLE ASSEMBLY-MAIN HARNESS	NLA	(C)H-AN10-86303 TO 86803 (C)A-AN10-86804 TO 87824 (C)G-AN5-89515 TO 105500	Except USA and Canada.
1	AHA 9923	CABLE ASSEMBLY-MAIN HARNESS	1	(C)G-AN5-105501 TO 128262	
1	CHA 46	CABLE ASSEMBLY-MAIN HARNESS	1	(C)G-AN5-128263 TO 138800	
1	CHA 214	CABLE ASSEMBLY-MAIN HARNESS	1	(C)G-AN5-138801 TO 154100	
1	CHA 455	CABLE ASSEMBLY-MAIN HARNESS	1	(C)G-AN6-154101 ON	

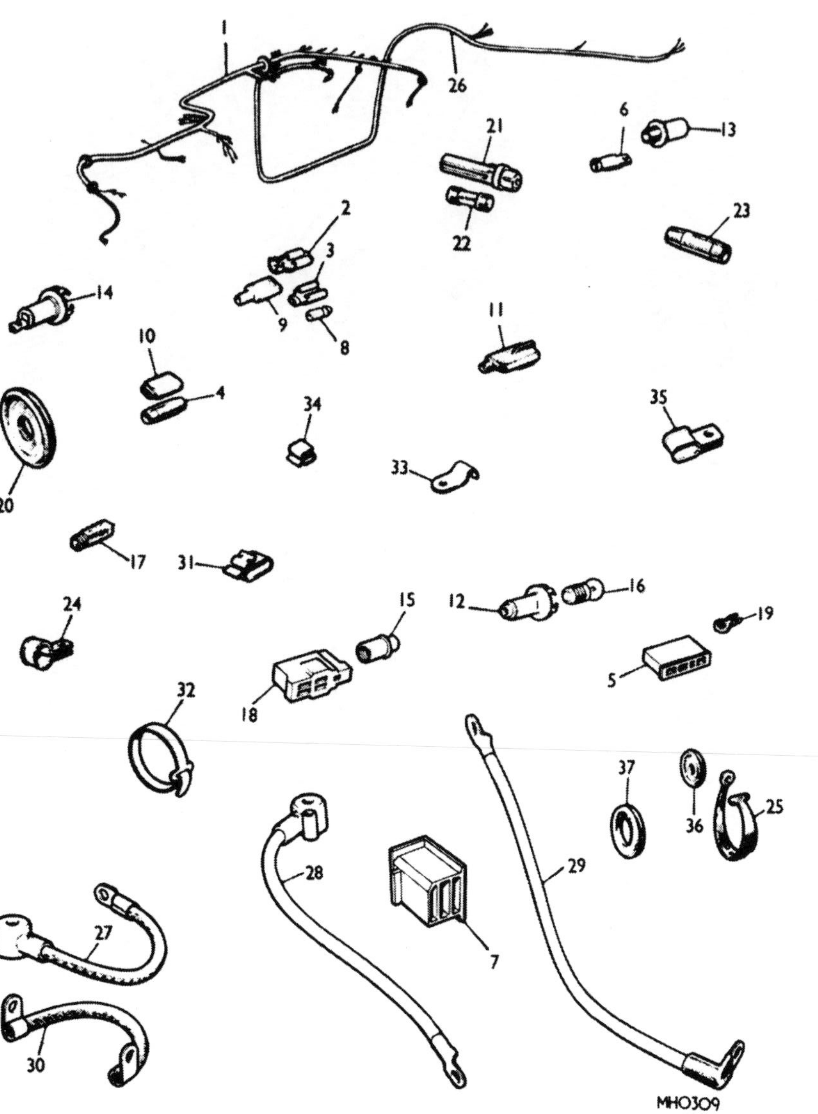

AUSTIN-HEALEY SPRITE MK. 3 AND MK. 4 & MG MIDGET MK. 2 AND MK. 3

NO.	PART NO.	DESCRIPTION	QTY	CHANGE POINT	REMARKS
		WIRING CABLES AND FITTINGS CONNECTORS,AND BULB HOLDERS-continued			
1	AHA 8692	CABLE ASSEMBLY-MAIN HARNESS-N.AMERICA	1		Used with rocker type switches with two blade wiper system.
1	AHA 8953	CABLE ASSEMBLY-MAIN HARNESS-N.AMERICA	1	Use prior to AHA 9611	Used with rocker type switches with three blade wiper system. USA,Canada and Sweden.
1	AHA 9611	CABLE ASSEMBLY-MAIN HARNESS	1	(C)H-AN10-85287 TO 86302 (C)G-AN5-74886 TO 89514	
1	AHA 9730	CABLE ASSEMBLY-MAIN HARNESS	1	(C)H-AN10-86303 TO 86803 (C)A-AN10-86804 TO 87824 (C)G-AN5-89515 TO 105500	USA and Canada
1	AHA 9922	CABLE ASSEMBLY-MAIN HARNESS	1	(C)G-AN5-105501 TO 112275	USA and Canada
1	AHA 9962	CABLE ASSEMBLY-MAIN HARNESS	1	(C)G-AN5-112276 TO 123730	USA and Canada
1	CHA 142	CABLE ASSEMBLY-MAIN HARNESS	1	(C)G-AN5-123731 TO 138000	USA and Canada
1	CHA 213	CABLE ASSEMBLY-MAIN HARNESS	1	(C)G-AN5-138801 TO 154100	USA and Canada
1	CHA 454	CABLE ASSEMBLY-MAIN HARNESS $	1	(C)G-AN6-154101 TO 159053	USA and Canada
1	CHA 524	CABLE ASSEMBLY-MAIN HARNESS $	1	(C)G-AN6-159054 TO 166300	USA and Canada
1	CHA 569	CABLE ASSEMBLY-MAIN HARNESS $	1	(C)G-AN6-166304 ON	USA and Canada

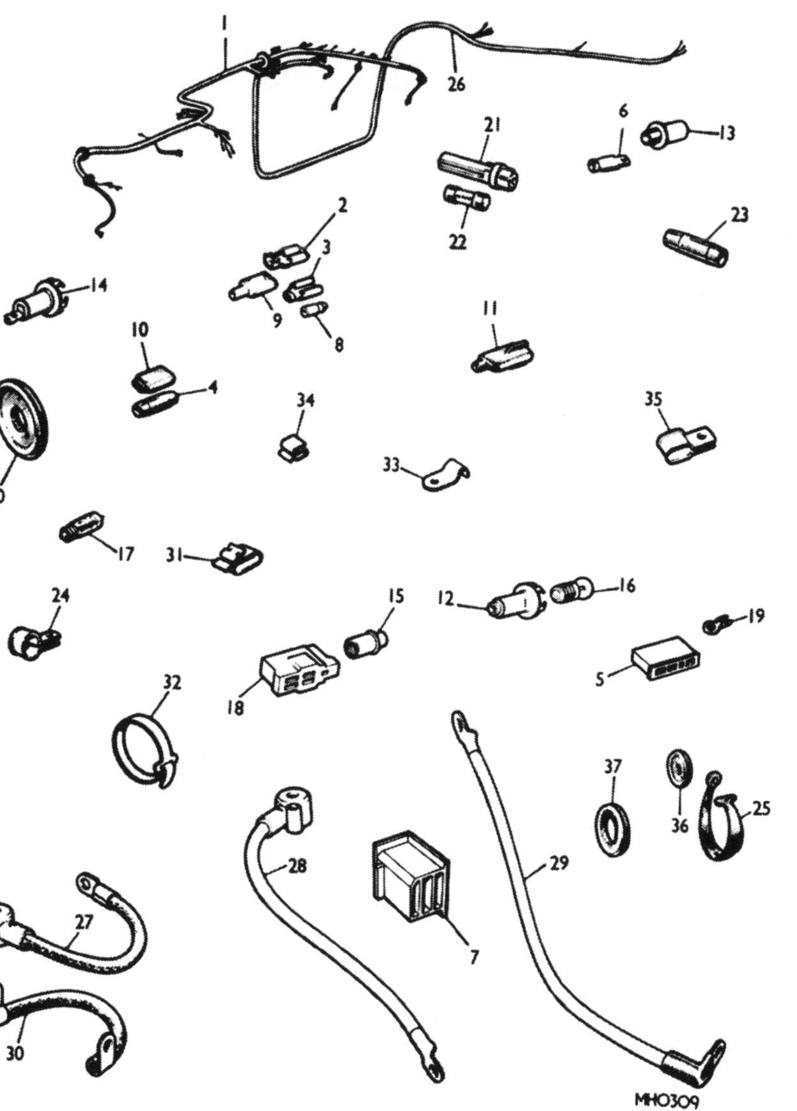

AUSTIN-HEALEY SPRITE MK. 3 AND MK. 4 & MG MIDGET MK. 2 AND MK. 3

WIRING CABLES AND FITTINGS CONNECTORS,AND BULB HOLDERS-continued

NO.	PART NO.	DESCRIPTION	QTY	CHANGE POINT	REMARKS
		CONNECTOR			
2	47H 5419	Socket-single(35amp)	A/R		
2	47H 5496	Socket-single(17.5amp)	A/R		
3	RTC 220	Socket-double(17.5amp)	A/R		
4	104618	Snap-single-2-way	A/R		
	RTC 603	Snap-single-4-way	A/R		
	BHA 4460	Snap-single-6-way	A/R		
5	BMK 1398	Blade	A/R		
6	BHA 4552	Blade(6amp)	A/R		Use with main harness AHA 8692
2	13H 2055	Socket	A/R		Use with main harnesses AHA 9730 and AHA 9763
2	13H 2050	Socket-single	A/R		
8	3632	Plug-snap connector	A/R		
		SLEEVE-INSULATOR			
9	515399	35amp connector	A/R		
9	511269	17.5amp connector	A/R		
10	5L 287	17.5 amp double connector	A/R		
11	27H 8849	Main harness	A/R		Use with main harness AHA 8692
11	BMK 449	(14amp)	NLA		
12	13H 1923	Bulb holder(screw type)-instrument illumination	A/R		
13	13H 1926	Bulb holder(screw type)-instrument illumination and warning lamp	A/R		
14	13H 1925	Bulb holder(bayonet type)-ignition,main beam and oil filter warning light	A/R		
16	GLB 987	Bulb(screw type)	A/R		
17	GLB 281	Bulb(bayonet type)	A/R		
18	BMK 1409	Socket-moulded-5-way	A/R		Use with main harness AHA 8694
19	17H 5287	Eyelet-.75"	NLA		
19	2H 4528	Eyelet-.25" earthing	A/R		
20	2H 2065	Grommet	A/R		

AUSTIN-HEALEY SPRITE MK. 3 AND MK. 4 & MG MIDGET MK. 2 AND MK. 3

WIRING CABLES AND FITTINGS CONNECTORS,AND BULB HOLDERS-continued

NO.	PART NO.	DESCRIPTION	QTY	CHANGE POINT	REMARKS
21	7H 6978	Holder-fuse	2		
22	27H 5903	Fuse-10amp	NLA		Use GFS 410
22	GFS 410	Fuse-10amp	A/R		
23	104618	Connector-snap	2		
8	3632	Plug	4		USA and Canada
24	PCR 709	Clip	NLA		
	LWZ 204	Washer-spring	1		
	NH 604041	Nut	1		
25	13H 6107	Strap-cable	1/2		Quantity increased when optional extra indicator switch is fitted.
26	AHA 8421	CABLE ASSEMBLY-BODY HARNESS	NLA	Use prior to AHA 9614	
26	AHA 9614	CABLE ASSEMBLY-BODY HARNESS	1	(C)H-AN10-85287 TO 86302	Except USA and Canada
26	AHA 9613	CABLE ASSEMBLY-BODY HARNESS	1	(C)G-AN5-74886 TO 89514	USA and Canada
26	AHA 9765	CABLE ASSEMBLY-BODY HARNESS	1	Use prior to CHA 432	Except USA and Canada
26	CHA 432	CABLE ASSEMBLY-BODY HARNESS	1	(C)G-AN6-154101 ON	
26	AHA 9764	CABLE ASSEMBLY-BODY HARNESS	1	(C)H-AN10-86303 TO 86803 (C)A-AN10-86804 TO 87824 (C)G-AN5-89515 TO 105500	USA and Canada
26	AHA 9952	CABLE ASSEMBLY-BODY HARNESS	1	(C)G-AN5-105501 TO 112275	
26	AHA 9963	CABLE ASSEMBLY-BODY HARNESS	1	(C)G-AN5-112276 TO 138800	
26	CHA 215	CABLE ASSEMBLY-BODY HARNESS	1	(C)G-AN5-138801 TO 154100	
26	CHA 407	CABLE ASSEMBLY-BODY HARNESS	1	(C)G-AN6-154101 TO 159053	
26	CHA 525	CABLE ASSEMBLY-BODY HARNESS	1	(C)G-AN6-159054 ON	
2	BMK 1398	Connector-socket-single	A/R		Use with body harnesses AHA 9765 and AHA 9764
4	104618	Connector-snap-single	A/R		
	RTC 603	Connector-snap-double	A/R		
2	47H 5496	Connector-socket-single(14amp)	2		
8	3632	Nipple-snap connector	A/R		
9	511269	Insulator-socket connector	2		
	CHA 429	CABLE ASSEMBLY-FASCIA HARNESS-RHD	1	(C)G-AN6-154101 ON	

AUSTIN-HEALEY SPRITE MK. 3 AND MK. 4 & MG MIDGET MK. 2 AND MK. 3

WIRING CABLES AND FITTINGS CONNECTORS,AND BULB HOLDERS-continued

NO.	PART NO.	DESCRIPTION	QTY	CHANGE POINT	REMARKS
		CABLE-BATTERY			
27	1B 2802	Positive to earth	1	(C)H-AN8-38829 TO 64734	
28	BHA 4257	Negative to starter switch	1	(C)H-AN9-64735 TO 72040 (C)G-AN3-25788 TO 52389 (C)G-AN4-52390 TO 60459	
28	BHA 5062	Positive to solenoid	1	(C)H-AN9-72041 TO 85286 (C)H-AN10-85287 TO 86803 (C)A-AN10-86804 TO 87824 (C)G-AN4-60460 TO 74885 (C)G-AN5-74886 ON	
27	AHA 8697	Negative to earth	1		
29	AHA 7776	Cable-starter switch to starter	1	Use prior to CHA 390	
29	CHA 390	Cable-starter switch to starter	1	(C)G-AN6-154101 ON	
30	2K 6167	Cable-engine to earth	1	Use prior to AHH 5452.	
	AHH 5452	Cable-engine to earth	1	(C)G-AN6-154101 ON	
	HZS 504	Screw	1		
	LWZ 305	Washer-spring	1		
	LWZ 306	Washer-spring	1		
24	PCR 607	Clip-harness to wheelarch	1		
31	BHA 4473	Clip-harness to bonnet locking platform	1		
31	BHA 4473	Clip-harness to bonnet locking platform	2		
24	PCR 607	Clip-headlamp and sidelamp harness	2		
32	AHH 7108	Clip-cables to column	A/R		
33	CHR 405	Clip-harness to sill	2		
24	PCR 507	Clip-harness to tail lamp fixing stud	2		
34	BMK 385	Clip-fuel pump and tank unit cables to tank	4		
24	PCR 807	Clip-negative cable to foot-well	1		
	PTZ 603	Screw	2		
	FNZ 103	Nut	2		
	LWZ 203	Washer-spring	2		
	PMZ 308	Screw	1		
	LWZ 203	Washer-spring	1		
	PMZ 412	Screw-harness-earth to dash	1		
	LWZ 204	Washer-spring	1		
36	RFR 305	Grommet-harness	2		
37	RFR 110	Grommet-harness	NLA		
36	RFR 305	Grommet-wiper motor cable through dash	1		

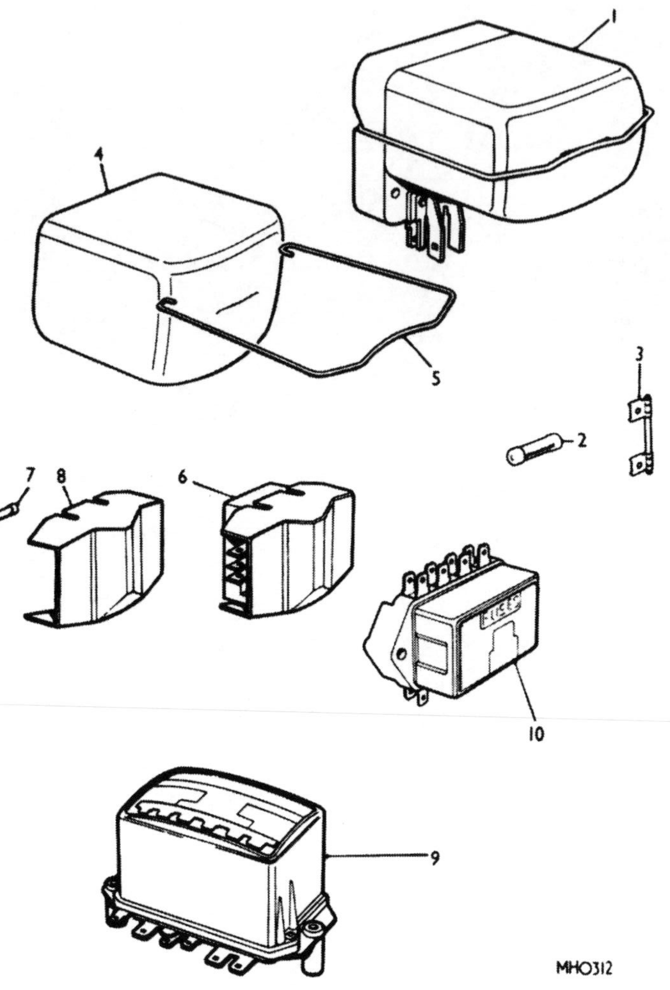

AUSTIN-HEALEY SPRITE MK. 3 AND MK. 4 & MG MIDGET MK. 2 AND MK. 3

NO.	PART NO.	DESCRIPTION	QTY	CHANGE POINT	REMARKS
		CONTROL BOX AND FUSE BOX			
1	BCA 4308	CONTROL BOX ASSEMBLY	1	Use prior to 37H 6902 and 37H 4727	
2	7H 5066	Resistance(63 ohms)-carbon type	NLA		
3	47H 5589	Resistance(60 ohms)-wire wound	1		
4	7H 5522	Cover	1		
	PMZ 320	Screw	2		
	LWZ 203	Washer-spring	2		
6	37H 3373	FUSEBOX ASSEMBLY	1		
7	GFS 35	Fuse(35-amp)	1 PK		Pack consists of ten fuses
8	505158	Cover	1		
	PMZ 310	Screw	1		
	LWZ 203	Washer-spring	1		
9	37H 6902	Control box	NLA	(C)H-AN10-85287 TO 86803 (C)A-AN10-86804 TO 87824 (C)G-AN5-74886 TO 105500 USA and Canada, 128262-except USA and Canada	Use GEU 605
	PMZ 318	Screw	3		
	LWZ 203	Washer-spring	3		
10	37H 4727	BOX ASSEMBLY-FUSE	1	(C)H-AN10-85287 TO 86803 (C)A-AN10-86804 TO 87824 (C)G-AN5-74886 ON	
7	GFS 35	Fuse(35-amp)	1 PK		Pack consists of ten fuses
	PMZ 316	Screw	2		
	LWZ 203	Washer-spring	2		
	563417	Relay-starter motor solenoid	1	(C)G-AN5-138801 TO 154100 (C)G-AN6-154101 TO 159053	N.America
	13H 9475	Relay-battery cut-off	1	(C)G-AN6-166304 ON	N.America

AUSTIN-HEALEY SPRITE MK. 3 AND MK. 4 & MG MIDGET MK. 2 AND MK. 3

NO.	PART NO.	DESCRIPTION	QTY	CHANGE POINT	REMARKS
		SWITCHES-TOGGLE/ROCKER TYPE SYSTEM			
		SWITCH			
1	BCA 4294	Lighting and fog lamp	2	Use prior to BHA 5109,BHA 5111 AND BHA 5112	
2	149011	Panel light and windscreen wiper	2		
3	BHA 5111	Lighting	1	(C)G-AN5-105501 ON	Rocker type SWITCH.Not N.America
4	BHA 5109	Windscreen wiper	1		
5	BHA 5112	Panel light	1		
	BHA 5267	Hazard warning	1	(C)G-AN5-138801 ON	
6	RTC 432	Headlamp dipper	1		
7	13H 337	SWITCH ASSEMBLY-IGNITION	1	Use prior to 13H 926	
8	47H 5481	Nut-locking	NLA		
7	13H 926	SWITCH ASSEMBLY-IGNITION	1	(C)H-AN10-86303 TO 86803 (C)A-AN10-86804 TO 87824 (C)G-AN5-89515 ON	
8	47H 5481	Nut-locking	NLA		
	BCA 4501	SWITCH ASSEMBLY-STARTER SOLENOID	NLA	Use prior to BMK 1727	Use BMK 1727
	AJD 8019 Z	Nut	2		
	LWZ 203	Washer-spring	2		
9	27H 5576	Cap(rubber)	1		
10	13H 4485	Nut-contact screw	NLA		
	WL 600051	Washer-spring	4		
11	47H 5160	Connector-Lucar-starter push	NLA		
12	47H 5158	Connector-Lucar-fuse box	1		
13	21K 9068	Connector-Lucar-control box	1		
	PMZ 306	Screw	2		
	LWZ 203	Washer-spring	2		

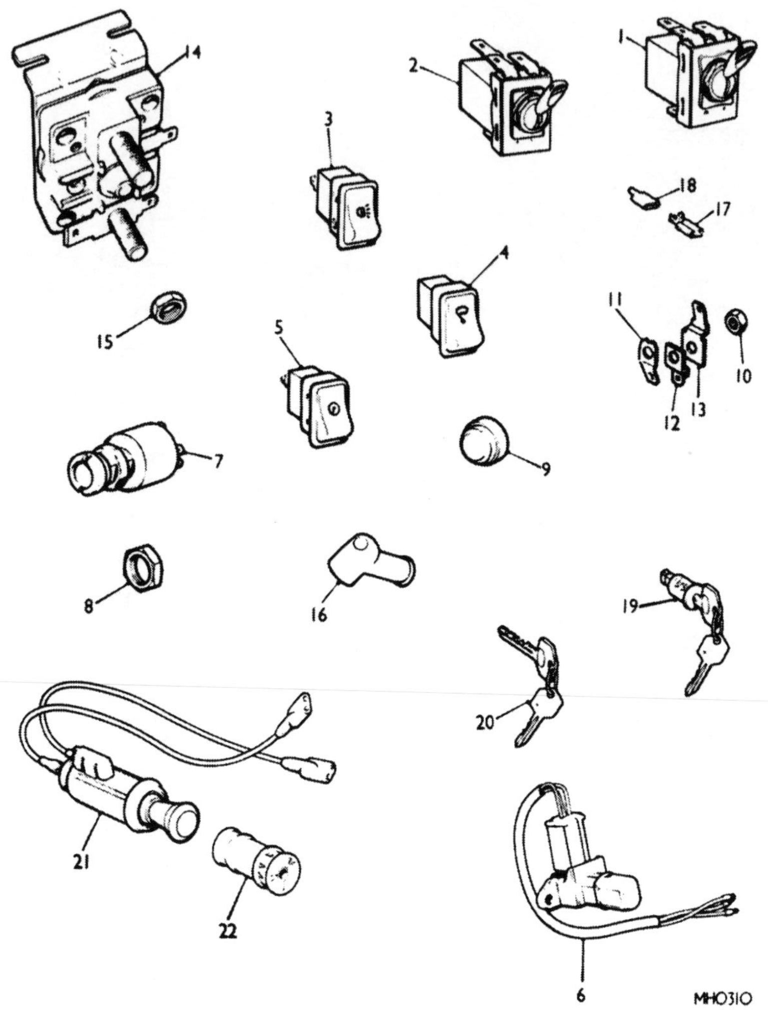

AUSTIN-HEALEY SPRITE MK. 3 AND MK. 4 & MG MIDGET MK. 2 AND MK. 3

NO.	PART NO.	DESCRIPTION	QTY	CHANGE POINT	REMARKS
		SWITCHES-TOGGLE/ROCKER TYPE SYSTEM-continued			
14	BMK 1727	Switch-starter solenoid	1	(C)H-AN9-71624 TO 85286 (C)H-AN10-85287 TO 86803 (C)A-AN10-86804 TO 87824 (C)G-AN4-59608 TO 74885 (C)G-AN5-74886 TO 154100	
15	13H 4485	Nut	NLA		
	PMZ 308	Screw	2		
	PWZ 103	Washer-plain	2		
	13H 5952	Switch-starter solenoid	1	(C)G-AN6-154101 ON	
	PJZ 1005	Screw	2		
	PWZ 103	Washer-plain	2		
16	8G 548	Bootee-terminal insulating-starter switch	2		
	PMZ 308	Screw	2		
	LWZ 203	Washer-spring	2		
	FNZ 103	Nut	2		
17	47H 5496	Connector-socket-panel light switch	1		Use when cigar-LIGHTER IS NOT FITTED
18	511269	Insulator-connector	1		
	PMZ 310	Screw	2		
	LWZ 203	Washer-spring	2		
	PMZ 416	Screw-RHD	NLA		
	PMZ 408	Screw-LHD	2		
	LWZ 204	Washer-spring	2		
19	24G 1345	Barrel-lock-ignition switch	1		Use when steering lock is not fitted.
21	AHH 7010	CIGAR-LIGHTER ASSEMBLY	NLA		Optional extra
22	27H 9735	Heating unit	1		

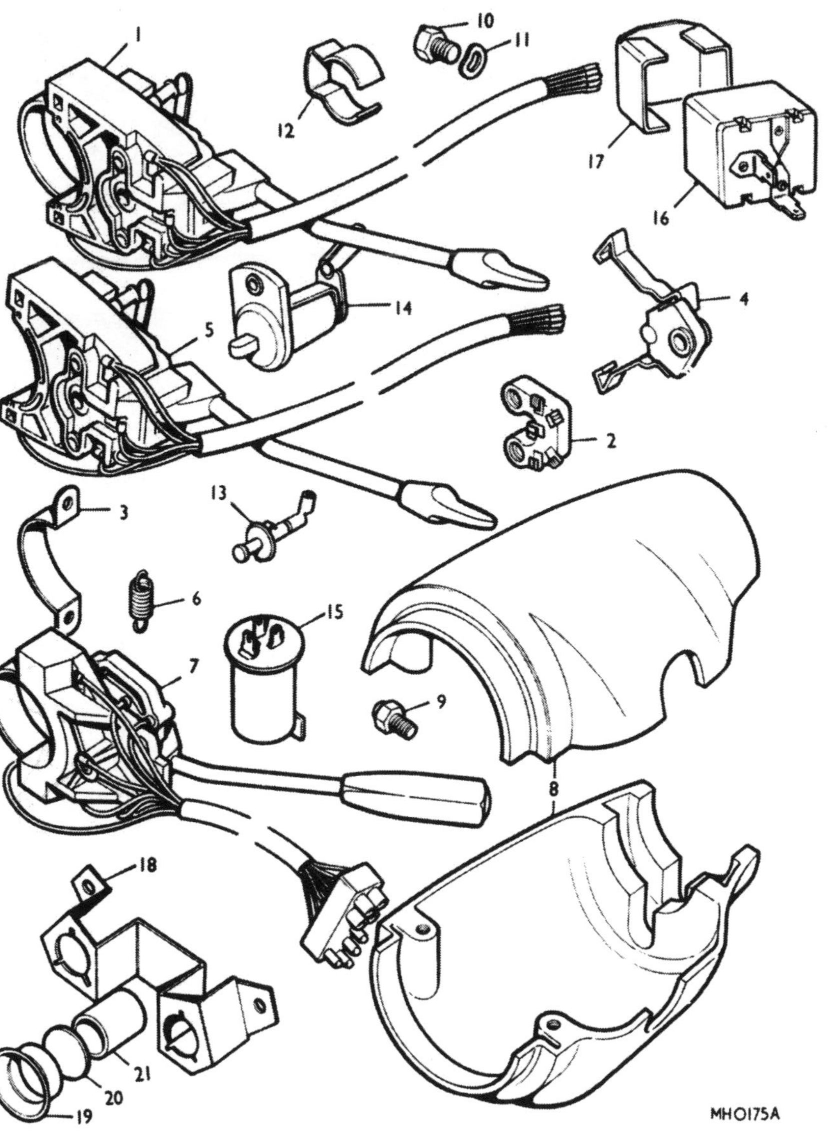

AUSTIN-HEALEY SPRITE MK. 3 AND MK. 4 & MG MIDGET MK. 2 AND MK. 3

NO.	PART NO.	DESCRIPTION	QTY	CHANGE POINT	REMARKS
		SWITCHES-TOGGLE/ROCKER TYPE SYSTEM-continued.			
1	BHA 4627	SWITCH ASSEMBLY-DIRECTION INDICATOR	1	Use prior to BHA 4895	
1	BHA 4895	SWITCH ASSEMBLY-DIRECTION INDICATOR	1	(C)H-AN9-84674 TO 85286 (C)G-AN4-73974 TO 74885	
1	BHA 4628	SWITCH ASSEMBLY-DIRECTION INDICATOR AND HEADLAMP FLASHER	1	Use prior to BHA 4896	optional extra
	BHA 4896	SWITCH ASSEMBLY-DIRECTION INDICATOR AND HEADLAMP FLASHER	NLA	(C)H-AN9-84674 TO 85286 (C)H-AN10-85287 TO 86803 (C)A-AN10-86803 TO 87824 (C)G-AN4-73974 TO 74885 (C)G-AN5-74886 ON	optional extra
2	67H 5021	Contact	1	(C)H-AN8-38829 TO 56902 (C)G-AN3-25788 TO 44164	
4	18G 8786	Kit-spring and bush	1	(C)H-AN8-56903 TO 64734 (C)H-AN9-64735 TO 85856 (C)A-AN10-86804 TO 87824 (C)G-AN3-44165 TO 52389 (C)G-AN4-52390 TO 74885 (C)G-AN5-74886 ON	See TIB.1B 16.
5	27H 6787	Lever	1		
6	27H 5386	Spring-pawl	2		

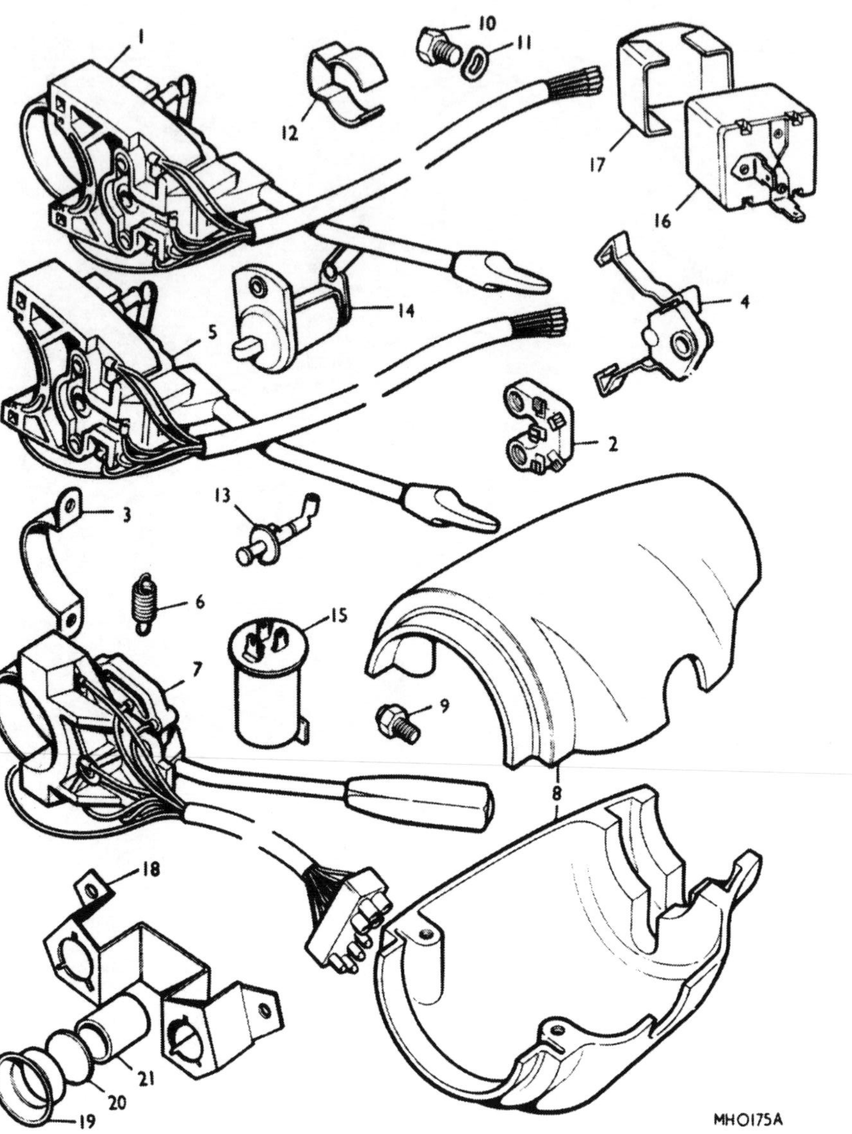

AUSTIN-HEALEY SPRITE MK. 3 AND MK. 4 & MG MIDGET MK. 2 AND MK. 3

SWITCHES-TOGGLE/ROCKER TYPE SYSTEM-continued.

NO.	PART NO.	DESCRIPTION	QTY	CHANGE POINT	REMARKS
1	BHA 4948	Switch-direction indicator/ horn/headlamp flasher	1	(C)H-AN10-85287 TO 86302 (C)G-AN5-74886 TO 89514	
7	37H 8050	Switch-direction indicator/ headlamp flasher	1	(C)H-AN10-86303 TO 86803 (C)A-AN10-86804 TO 87824 (C)G-AN5-89515 ON	
	37H 8051	Clip-direction indicator switch(with horn contact)	1		
8	18G 8387	Cowling-indicator switch-to top and bottom-RHD	1PR	Use prior to 18G 8713 and 18G 8714	
8	18G 8388	Cowling-indicator switch-to top and bottom-LHD	1PR		
8	18G 8713	Cowling-indicator switch-RHD	1PR	(C)H-AN10-85287 TO 86803 (C)A-AN10-86804 TO 87824 (C)G-AN5-74886 ON	
	18G 8714	Cowling-indicator switch-LHD	1PR		
10	AHA 8752	Stud-trip flasher	1	(C)H-AN8-56903 TO 64734 (C)H-AN9-64735 TO 72528 (C)G-AN3-44165 TO 52389 (C)G-AN4-52390 TO 61165	
12	AHA 8752	Striker-direction indicator trip	1	(C)H-AN9-72529 TO 85286 (C)G-AN4-61166 TO 74885	
12	BHH 254	Striker-direction indicator trip	1	(C)H-AN10-85287 TO 86803 (C)A-AN10-86804 TO 87824 (C)G-AN5-74886 TO 134124	
12	BHH 1301	Striker-direction indicator trip	1	(C)G-AN5-134125 ON	
13	13H 391	Switch-courtesy light-trunk	1	(C)H-AN10-86303 TO 86803 (C)A-AN10-86804 TO 87824 (C)G-AN5-89515 ON	
14	BHA 5058	Switch-courtesy light-interior	2		
	PTZ 604	Screw	2		

MHO175A

SWITCHES-TOGGLE/ROCKER TYPE SYSTEM-continued.

NO.	PART NO.	DESCRIPTION	QTY	CHANGE POINT	REMARKS
15	GFU 103	Unit-flasher	1	Use prior to GFU 107	
16	GFU 107	Unit-flasher $	1	(C)H-AN9-72041 TO 85286 (C)H-AN10-85287 TO 86803 (C)A-AN10-86804 TO 87824 (C)G-AN4-60460 TO 74885 (C)G-AN5-74886 ON	
	PMZ 408	Screw-flasher unit	1	Use prior to BHA 4780	
	LWZ 204	Washer	1		
17	BHA 4780	Clip-flasher unit	1	(C)H-AN9-72041 TO 85286 (C)G-AN10-85287 TO 86803 (C)A-AN10-86804 TO 87824 (C)G-AN4-60460 TO 74885 (C)G-AN5-74886 ON	
	PTZ 1004	Screw	1		
	LWZ 203	Washer-spring	2		
	FNZ 103	Nut	2		
20	AHH 6334	Window-flasher warning light	NLA		
16	ATJ 8880	Unit-flasher-hazard warning $	1	(C)G-AN5-138801 ON	
17	BHA 4780	Clip-unit	1		

$ This item is subject to safety regulations.

AUSTIN-HEALEY SPRITE MK. 3 AND MK. 4 & MG MIDGET MK. 2 AND MK. 3

NO.	PART NO.	DESCRIPTION	QTY	CHANGE POINT	REMARKS
		SWITCHES-(USA TYPES).			
1	18G 8548	Cowl-switch $	1PR	Use prior to 18G 9012	Use with alternative steering lock kit 18G 8901.
1	18G 8841	Cowl-switch $	1PR		
	18G 9012	Cowl-switch	1PR	(C)G-AN5-123731 TO 154150 (C)G-AN6-154101 TO 183082	
	BHM 7090	Cowl-switch	1	(C)G-AN6-183083 ON	
	AAM 222	Plug-blanking	2		
	PMZ 316	Screw	2		
	ZPT 1003	Screw	2		
2	BHA 4696	Switch-direction indicator, horn,headlamp dipper and flasher	1	Use prior to 37H 6022	USA and CANADA.
2	37H 6022	Switch-direction indicator, headlamp dipper and flasher	1	(C)G-AN5-89515 TO 112999	USA.
2	37H 7424	Switch-direction indicator, headlamp dipper and flasher	1	(C)G-AN5-113000 TO 138800	USA.
2	37H 8521	Switch-direction indicator, headlamp dipper and flasher $	1	(C)G-AN5-138801 ON	USA.
2	37H 6022	Switch-direction indicator, headlamp dipper and flasher	1	(C)G-AN5-89515 TO 138800	Canada,Sweden and Germany.
2	37H 8523	Switch-direction indicator, headlamp dipper and flasher $	1	(C)G-AN5-138801 ON	Canada,Sweden and Germany.
	37H 8566	Clip-direction indicator switch(with horn contact) $	1	(C)G-AN5-138801 ON	USA,Canada, Sweden and Germany.
3	37H 2678	Switch-windscreen wiper washer,overdrive $	1	Use prior to 37H 7425	USA.
3	37H 7425	Switch-windscreen wiper washer,overdrive $	1	(C)G-AN5-113000 TO 138800	USA.
3	37H 8522	Switch-windscreen wiper, washer,overdrive $	1	(C)G-AN5-138801 ON	USA.
3	37H 2678	Switch-windscreen wiper washer,overdrive $	1	(C)G-AN4-60441 TO 74885 (C)G-AN5-74886 TO 138800	Canada,Sweden and Germany.
3	37H 8524	Switch-windscreen wiper, washer,overdrive $	1	(C)G-AN5-138801 ON	Canada,Sweden and Germany.

$ This item is subject to safety regulations.

AUSTIN-HEALEY SPRITE MK. 3 AND MK. 4 & MG MIDGET MK. 2 AND MK. 3

SWITCHES-USA TYPE-continued.

NO.	PART NO.	DESCRIPTION	QTY	CHANGE POINT	REMARKS
4	BHA 4831	Switch-heater $	1	(C)G-AN4-60441 TO 74885 (C)G-AN5-74886 ON	Sweden and Germany.
4	BHA 4831	Switch-heater $	1	Use prior to BHA 5150 and 13H 6952	USA and CANADA.
4	BHA 5150	Switch-heater $	1	(C)G-AN5-113000 TO 123750	USA.
4	13H 6952	Switch-heater $	1		Canada.
5	BHA 5184	Switch-heater(illuminated)	1	(C)G-AN5-123751 ON	USA.
6	BHA 5192	Switch-heater(illuminated)	1		Canada.
7	BHA 4805	Switch-panel light $	NLA	Use prior to 37H 7970	USA,Canada, Sweden and Germany.
8	37H 7970	Switch-rheostat(illuminated)	1	(C)G-AN5-123751 ON	
9	37H 7971	Knob-rheostat switch	1		
10	37H 2679	Switch-hazard warning $	1	Use prior to 37H 7422	USA and Canada.
10	37H 7422	Switch-hazard warning $	1	(C)G-AN5-112276 TO 123750	
11	BHA 5185	Switch-hazard warning (illuminated)	1	(C)G-AN5-123751 ON	USA.
12	BHA 5193	Switch-hazard warning (illuminated)	1		Canada.
10	37H 2679	Switch-hazard warning	1		Sweden and Germany.
13	13H 6322	Switch-lighting $	1	Use prior to BHA 5149	USA.
13	BHA 5149	Switch-lighting $	1	(C)G-AN5-113000 TO 123750	
14	BHA 5183	Switch-lighting(illuminated)	1	(C)G-AN5-123751 ON	
13	13H 6322	Switch-lighting $	1	Use prior to BHA 5191	Canada.
15	BHA 5191	Switch-lighting(illuminated)	1	(C)G-AN5-123751 ON	
13	13H 6322	Switch-lighting $	1	(C)G-AN4-60441 TO 74885 (C)G-AN5-74886 ON	Sweden and Germany.
16	BHA 4742	Switch-brake check light (3 terminal) $	1		USA and Canada.
17	BHA 4933	Switch-brake check light (4 terminal) $	1	Use prior to BHA 4990.	
17	BHA 4990	Switch-brake check light (4 terminal)	1	(C)G-AN5-74886 TO 154100 (C)G-AN6-154101 TO 166300	USA,Canada and Sweden.
18	BHA 4732	Switch-ignition	1		USA,Canada, Sweden and Germany.

$ This item is subject to safety regulations.

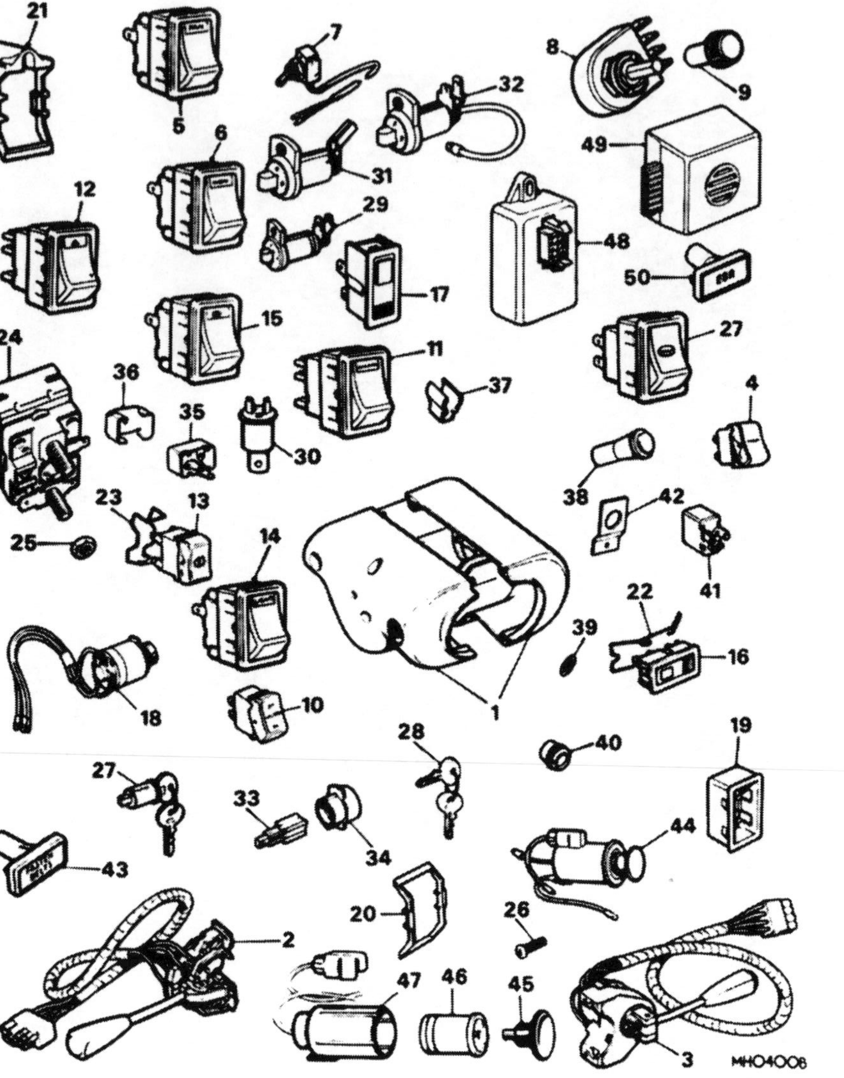

AUSTIN-HEALEY SPRITE MK. 3 AND MK. 4 & MG MIDGET MK. 2 AND MK. 3

SWITCHES-USA TYPE-continued.

NO.	PART NO.	DESCRIPTION	QTY	CHANGE POINT	REMARKS
19	BHA 4832	Bezel-switch(heater and Hazard warning)	2	Use prior to BHA 4993 and 37H 4495.	USA.
19	37H 4495	Bezel-switch(lighting)	1		
19	BHA 4993	Bezel-awitch(heater and lighting)	2	(C)G-AN5-74886 TO 112999	
19	37H 4495	Bezel-switch(hazard warning)	1	(C)G-AN5-74886 TO 99454.	
19	37H 4497	Bezel-switch(hazard warning)	1	(C)G-AN5-99455 TO 112275.	
20	BHA 5153	Clip-switch(heater and lighting)	2	(C)G-AN5-113000 TO 123750.	
21	BHH 1085	Clip-illuminated switch	6	(C)G-AN5-123751 ON.	
19	BHA 4832	Bezel-switch(heater and hazard warning)	2	Use prior to BHA 4993 and 37H 4495	Canada.
19	37H 4495	Bezel-switch(lighting)	1		
19	BHA 4993	Bezel-switch(heater)	1	(C)G-AN5-74886 TO 123750	
19	BHA 4993	Bezel-switch(lighting)	1	(C)G-AN5-74886 TO 112999	
20	BHA 5153	Clip-switch(lighting)	1	(C)G-AN5-113000 TO 123750	
19	37H 4495	Bezel-switch(Hazard warning)	1	(C)G-AN5-74886 TO 99454	
19	37H 4497	Bezel-switch(hazard warning)	1	(C)G-AN5-99455 TO 112275	
21	BHH 1085	Clip-illuminated switch	6	(C)G-AN5-123751 ON	
19	BHA 4832	Bezel-switch(heater and hazard warning)	2	Use prior to BHA 4993 and 37H 4495	Sweden.
19	37H 4495	Bezel-switch(lighting)	1		
19	BHA 4993	Bezel-switch(heater and lighting)	2	(C)G-AN5-74886 ON	Sweden and Germany.
19	37H 4495	Bezel-switch(hazard warning)	1	(C)G-AN5-74886 TO 99454	
19	37H 4497	Bezel-switch(hazard warning)	1	(C)G-AN5-99455 ON	
22	AHH 8920	Clip-spring-brake check light switch	1		USA,Canada, Sweden and Germany.
23	AHH 8921	Clip-spring-brake check light switch	NLA		
24	BMK 1727	Switch-starter solenoid	1	Use prior to 13H 5952	
25	13H 4485	Nut	NLA		
	PMZ 308	Screw	2		
	PWZ 103	Washer-plain	2		
	13H 5952	Switch-starter solenoid	1	(C)G-AN6-154101 ON	
	PJZ 1005	Screw	2		
	PWZ 103	Washer-plain	2		
	PMZ 406	Screw-dip switch blanking hole	2		
26	AHH 8895	Screw-clamp to column-wiper switch	2		
	RMZ 204	Screw-panel light switch to cowl	2		

AUSTIN-HEALEY SPRITE MK. 3 AND MK. 4 & MG MIDGET MK. 2 AND MK. 3

NO.	PART NO.	DESCRIPTION	QTY	CHANGE POINT	REMARKS
		SWITCHES-USA TYPE-continued.			
27	24G 1345	Barrel-lock-ignition switch	1		Use when steering LOCK IS Not FITTED Sweden and Germany.
29	BHA 4992	Switch-ignition	1		
	PTZ 604	Screw-switch	1		
27	24G 1345	Barrel-lock-ignition switch	1	Use prior to BHA 4974	Use when steering lock is not fitted USA and Canada.
30	BHA 4974	Buzzer-ignition key warning	1	(C)G-AN5-74886 TO 138800	USA and CANADA.
	13H 8600	Buzzer-ignition key warning $	1	(C)G-AN5-138801 TO 159053	
29	BHA 4992	Switch-ignition	1	Use prior to BHA 5063	
31	BHA 5063	Switch-ignition key audible warning and courtesy light	1	(C)G-AN5-89515 TO 143302	
31	BHA 5310	Switch-ignition key audible warning and courtesy light $	1	(C)G-AN5-143303 ON	
	PTZ 6034	Screw-switch	1		
32	BHA 5058	Switch-courtesy light-interior	2/1		Quantity reduced for USA and Canada when ignition switch BHA 5063 is fitted.
33	BHA 4803	Extension-spindle	NLA		USA,Canada, Sweden and Germany.
34	BHA 4802	Housing-lock	1		
35	GFU 107	Unit-flasher $	1		
36	BHA 4780	Clip	1		
	PTZ 1004	Screw	1		
37	BHH 402	Striker-trafficator	1	(C)G-AN5-89515 ON	
	LWZ 204	Washer-spring	2		
38	BHA 5124	Light-direction indicator warning	2	(C)G-AN5-105501 ON	
39	BHA 5125	Washer-retaining	2		

$ This item is subject to safety regulations.

MHO4OO8

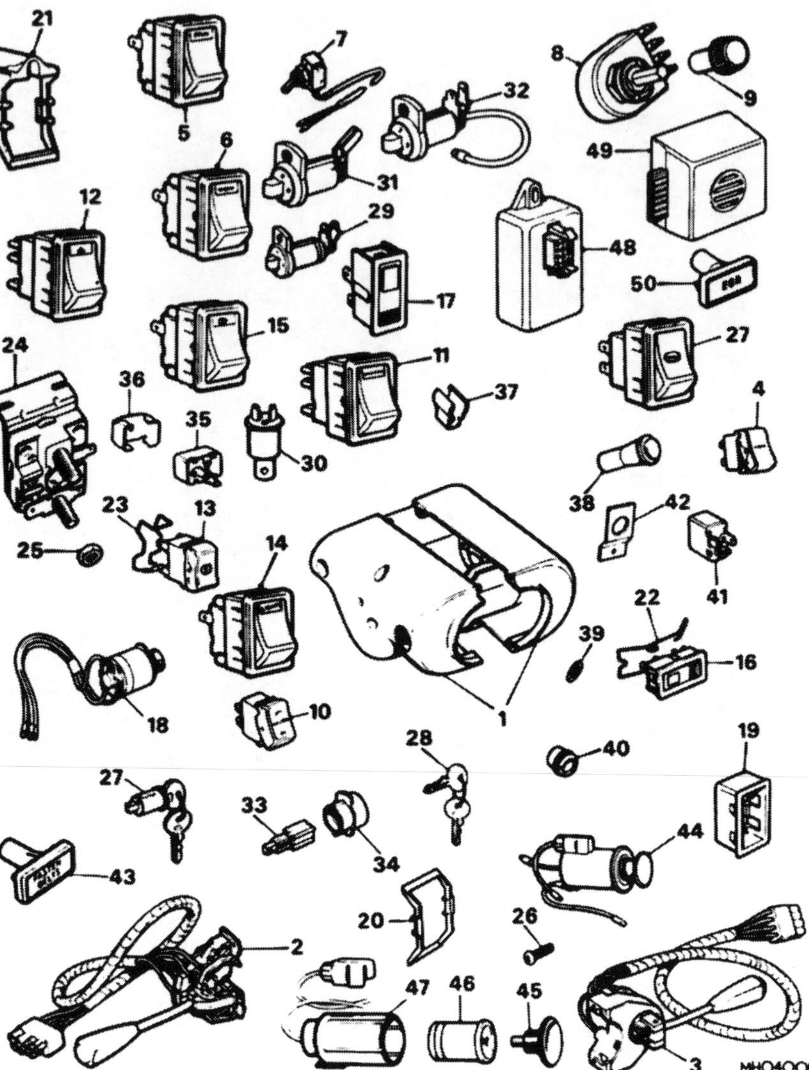

AUSTIN-HEALEY SPRITE MK. 3 AND MK. 4 & MG MIDGET MK. 2 AND MK. 3

SWITCHES-USA TYPE-continued

NO.	PART NO.	DESCRIPTION	QTY	CHANGE POINT	REMARKS
40	BHA 4804	Lamp-hazard warning $	1	Use prior to 13H 4665	USA and CANADA
40	13H 4665	Lamp-hazard warning	1	(C)G-AN5-74886 ON	USA,Canada Sweden and Germany
41	13H 4666	Unit-hazard warning	1	Use prior to ATJ 8880	
41	ATJ 8880	Unit-hazard warning $	1	(C)G-AN5-99455 ON	
42	AHH 8889	Bracket-hazard warning lamp	1		USA,Canada Sweden and Germany
	PTZ 603	Screw	1		
	PWZ 102	Washer-plain	1	Use prior to BHA 4780 and LNZ 102	
	LWZ 202	Washer-spring	1		
	CNZ 102	Nut	1		
36	BHA 4780	Clip-hazard warning unit	1	(C)G-AN5-123731 ON	
	LNZ 102	Nut	1		
43	13H 7986	Light-warning'Fasten belts'	1	(C)G-AN5-112276 ON	
48	13H 9801	Unit-control-sequential seat system $	1	(C)G-AN5-138801 TO 154100 (C)G-AN6-154101 TO 159053	USA and Canada.
49	AAU 1110	Unit-buzzer-time delay $	1	(C)G-AN6-159054 ON	
50	13H 9408	Light-warning-EGR	1	(C)G-AN6-154101 ON	USA and Canada (Finished Canada At (C)175273) California only
	13H 9571	Light-warning-Catalyst	1	(C)G-AN6-160160 ON	
44	BHA 4765	CIGAR LIGHTER ASSEMBLY	1	Use prior to BHA 5137	
44	BHA 5137	CIGAR LIGHTER ASSEMBLY	1	(C)G-AN5-105501 TO 182000	USA,Canada, Sweden and Germany
45	37H 2503	Knob	1		
46	27H 9735	Unit-heating	1		
47	37H 2505	Clamp-shell	1		
	AAU 5101	LIGHTER-CIGAR	1		
	AAU 5944	Unit-'pop out'	1	(C)G-AN6-182001 ON	
	AAU 6008	Knob	1		
	AAU 2092	Light-warning-brake $	1	(C)G-AN6-166304 ON	USA and Canada

$ This item is subject to safety regulations.

MH O174A

AUSTIN-HEALEY SPRITE MK. 3 AND MK. 4 & MG MIDGET MK. 2 AND MK. 3

NO.	PART NO.	DESCRIPTION	QTY	CHANGE POINT	REMARKS
		HORN AND CONTROLS			
1	BHA 4515	HORN ASSEMBLY-HIGH NOTE	NLA	Use prior to BHA 5367/8	Use 37H 7542
1	BHA 4514	HORN ASSEMBLY-LOW NOTE	NLA		Use 37H 7543
	37H 7542	HORN-HIGH NOTE(LESS BRACKET)	1		Except Sweden And Germany.
	37H 7543	HORN-LOW NOTE(LESS BRACKET)	1		
2	57H 5309	Bracket	1/2		Quantities increased with Twin horns
	PMZ 410	Screw	2/4		
	LWZ 204	Washer-spring	2/4		
	NH 604041	Nut	2/4		
	AHA 6657	Bracket-horn mounting-RH	1		Use when twin horns are fitted
	AHA 6658	Bracket-horn mounting-LH	1		
1	BHA 5367	HORN ASSEMBLY-HIGH NOTE	1	(C)G-AN6-154101 ON	
1	BHA 5368	HORN ASSEMBLY-LOW NOTE	1		
5	BHA 4441	HORN-PUSH ASSEMBLY-SPRITE	1	Use prior to BHA 4679 and BHA 5010	Except USA and Canada
6	BHA 4442	HORN-PUSH ASSEMBLY-MIDGET	1		
7	27H 3387	ROTOR ASSEMBLY-TOP AND CABLE	1		
8	7H 6902	Spring	1		
9	27H 5401	Slip-ring	1		
10	AHA 8525	Housing-motif-'Sprite'	1		USA,Canada and Sweden
11	AHH 8682	Housing-motif-'Midget'	1		
12	57H 5423	Clip-motif housing	3		
13	BHA 5010	Bezel and motif-'Sprite'	1	(C)H-AN10-85287 TO 86302 (C)G-AN5-74886 TO 89514	
14	BHA 4979	Bezel and motif-'Midget'	1		
15	BHA 5053	Horn push-'Sprite'	1	(C)H-AN10-86303 TO 86803 (C)A-AN10-86804 TO 87824	
16	BHA 5043	Horn push-'Midget'	1	(C)G-AN5-89515 TO 105500	
16	BHA 5135	Horn push-'Midget'	1	(C)G-AN5-105501 TO 154100 (C)G-AN6-154101 TO 157172	
16	AAU 1161	Horn push	1	(C)G-AN6-157173 ON	
	BHA 5041	Brush	1	(C)H-AN10-86303 TO 86803 (C)A-AN10-86804 TO 87824 (C)G-AN5-89515 ON	
	BHA 5042	Slip ring	1		

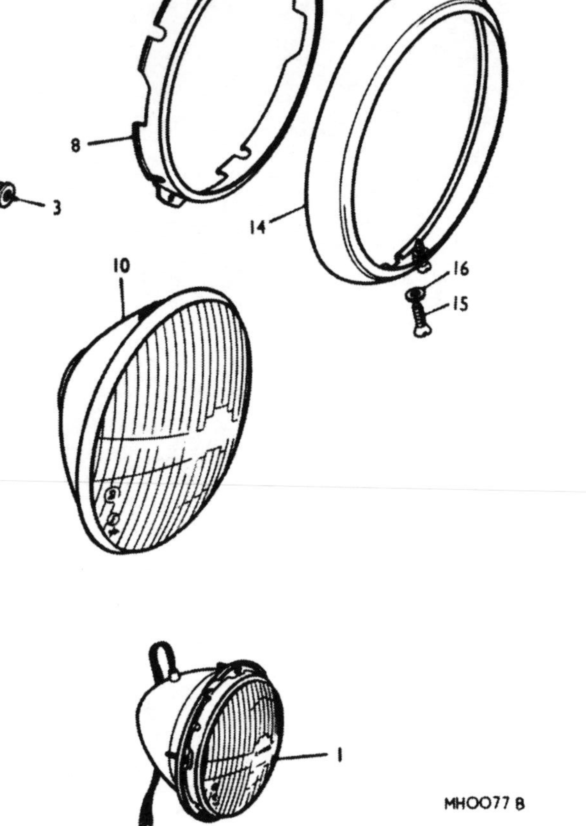

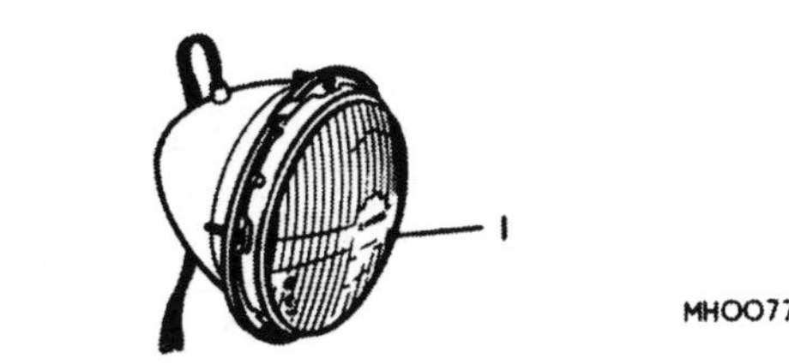

AUSTIN-HEALEY SPRITE MK. 3 AND MK. 4 & MG MIDGET MK. 2 AND MK. 3

HEADLAMPS-RHD AND LHD FOR USA AND CANADA.

NO.	PART NO.	DESCRIPTION	QTY	CHANGE POINT	REMARKS
1	27H 8499	HEADLAMP ASSEMBLY	2		
2	67H 5025	Screw-trimmer	NLA		Use BHM 7058
3	27H 7824	Nut-trimmer screw	NLA		Use BMK 2435
3	BMK 2435	Nut-trimmer screw	NLA		Use BHM 7058
4	600226	ADAPTOR ASSEMBLY	2		
5	27H 6713	Sleeve-terminal	NLA		
6	27H 5354	Nut-rim fixing screw	2		
7	37H 5190	Bracket-rim fixing screw	2		
8	515218	Plate-light unit retaining	2		RHD
	PJZ 602	Screw	6		
9	67H 5026	Spring-unit seating rim	2		
10	GLU 101	Unit-light	2		
14	47H 5554	RIM ASSEMBLY	2		
15	RTC 465	Screw	2		
16	21G 9057	Washer(rubber)	2	Finished at (C)G-AN5-154100	
17	9403	Gasket(rubber)	2		
1	27H 8207	HEADLAMP ASSEMBLY $	2		
2	67H 5025	Screw-trimmer	NLA		Use BHM 7058
3	27H 7824	Nut-trimmer screw	NLA		Use BMK 2435
3	BMK 2435	Nut-trimmer screw	NLA		Use BHM 7058
4	600226	ADAPTOR ASSEMBLY	2		USA and Canada
5	27H 6713	Sleeve-terminal	NLA		
6	27H 5354	Nut-rim fixing screw	2		
7	37H 5190	Bracket-rim fixing screw	2		
8	515218	Plate-light unit retaining	2		
	PJZ 602	Screw	6		
9	67H 5026	Spring-unit seating rim	2		
10	GLU 112	Unit-light	2		
14	47H 5554	RIM ASSEMBLY	2		
15	RTC 465	Screw	2		
16	21G 9057	Washer(rubber)	2		
17	9403	Gasket(rubber)	2		
	BHM 7058	Kit-trimmer screw	2		

$ This item is subject to safety regulations

AUSTIN-HEALEY SPRITE MK. 3 AND MK. 4 & MG MIDGET MK. 2 AND MK. 3

HEADLAMPS-RHD AND LHD FOR USA AND CANADA-1500.

NO.	PART NO.	DESCRIPTION	QTY	CHANGE POINT	REMARKS
1	37H 8813	HEADLAMP ASSEMBLY	2		
2	67H 5025	Screw-trimmer	4		
3	BMK 2435	Retainer	NLA		Use BHM 7058.
4	37H 8814	Adaptor and cable	2		
5	515218	Plate-light unit retaining	2		
15	PJZ 602	Screw-fixing-unit rim	6		RHD.
6	67H 5026	Spring-fixing-unit rim	2		
7	GLU 104	Unit-light	2		
8	GLB 501	Bulb-pilot	2		
9	27H 5354	Nut-fixing screw	2		
	47H 5554	Rim and screw	2	(C)G-AN6-154101 ON	
11	9403	Gasket-body	2		
12	27H 8266	HEADLAMP ASSEMBLY $	2		
2	67H 5025	Screw-trimmer	4		
3	BMK 2435	Retainer	NLA		Use BHM 7058.
13	27H 6713	Adaptor and cable	NLA		USA and Canada.
5	515218	Plate-light unit retaining	2		
15	PJZ 602	Screw-fixing unit rim	6		
6	67H 5026	Spring-fixing unit rim	2		
14	BHA 5315	Unit-light $	2		
10	57H 5296	Rim and screw	2		
11	9403	Gasket-body	2		
	BHM 7058	Kit-screw-trimmer	2		

$ This item is subject to safety regulations.

MHO547

AUSTIN-HEALEY SPRITE MK. 3 AND MK. 4 & MG MIDGET MK. 2 AND MK. 3

NO.	PART NO.	DESCRIPTION	QTY	CHANGE POINT	REMARKS
		HEADLAMPS-LHD EXCEPT EUROPE,USA,CANADA AND MIDGET 1500			
	NSP	HEADLAMP ASSEMBLY-RIGHT DIP MK.6	2		Use 27H 8206 with rim and gasket
1	17H 5394	Screw-trimmer	6		
2	17H 5231	Spring-trimmer screw	6		
3	27H 5253	Sleeve-sealing	6		
4	17H 5306	ADAPTOR ASSEMBLY	2		
5	27H 6713	Sleeve-terminal	NLA		
6	27H 5354	Nut-rim fixing screw	2		
7	37H 5190	Bracket-rim fixing screw	2		
9	17H 5205	PLATE ASSEMBLY-LIGHT UNIT RETAINING	2		
	PJZ 602	Screw	6		
10	262342	Unit-light	2		
11	BFS 355	Bulb	2		
12	47H 5554	RIM ASSEMBLY	2		
13	RTC 465	Screw	2		
14	21G 9057	Washer(rubber)	2		
15	57H 5457	Gasket(rubber)	2		
16	27H 8206	HEADLAMP ASSEMBLY-RIGHT DIP MK.10	2	Use prior to 27H 8204	
16	27H 8204	HEADLAMP ASSEMBLY-RIGHT DIP MK.10	2	(C)H-AN10-85287 TO 86803 (C)A-AN10-86804 TO 87824 (C)G-AN5-74886 TO 154100	
17	67H 5025	Screw-trimmer	4		
18	27H 7824	Nut-trimmer screw	4		
4	17H 5306	ADAPTOR ASSEMBLY	2		Use with head-lamp assembly 27H 8206
5	27H 6713	Sleeve-terminal	NLA		
6	27H 5354	Nut-rim fixing screw	2		
7	37H 5190	Bracket-rim fixing screw	2		
19	515218	Plate-light unit retaining	2		
	PJZ 602	Screw	6		
20	67H 5026	Spring-unit seating rim	2		
10	262342	Unit-light	2		Use with head-LAMP ASSEMBLY 27H 8206
21	BFS 415	Bulb	2		
23	27H 4146	UNIT ASSEMBLY-LIGHT	NLA		Use GLU 513. Use with head-Lamp assembly 27H 8206.
24	47H 5125	Spring-bulb-retaining	2		
25	GLB 410	Bulb	2		
12	47H 5554	RIM ASSEMBLY	2		
13	RTC 465	Screw	2		
14	21G 9057	Washer(rubber)	2		
22	9405	Gasket(rubber)	2		
	PMZ 310	Screw-headlamp to wing	8		
	LWZ 203	Washer-spring	8		
	FNZ 103	Nut	8		

NOTE:
See TIB 1B45 F18 for identification of Mk.6 and Mk.10 headlamps

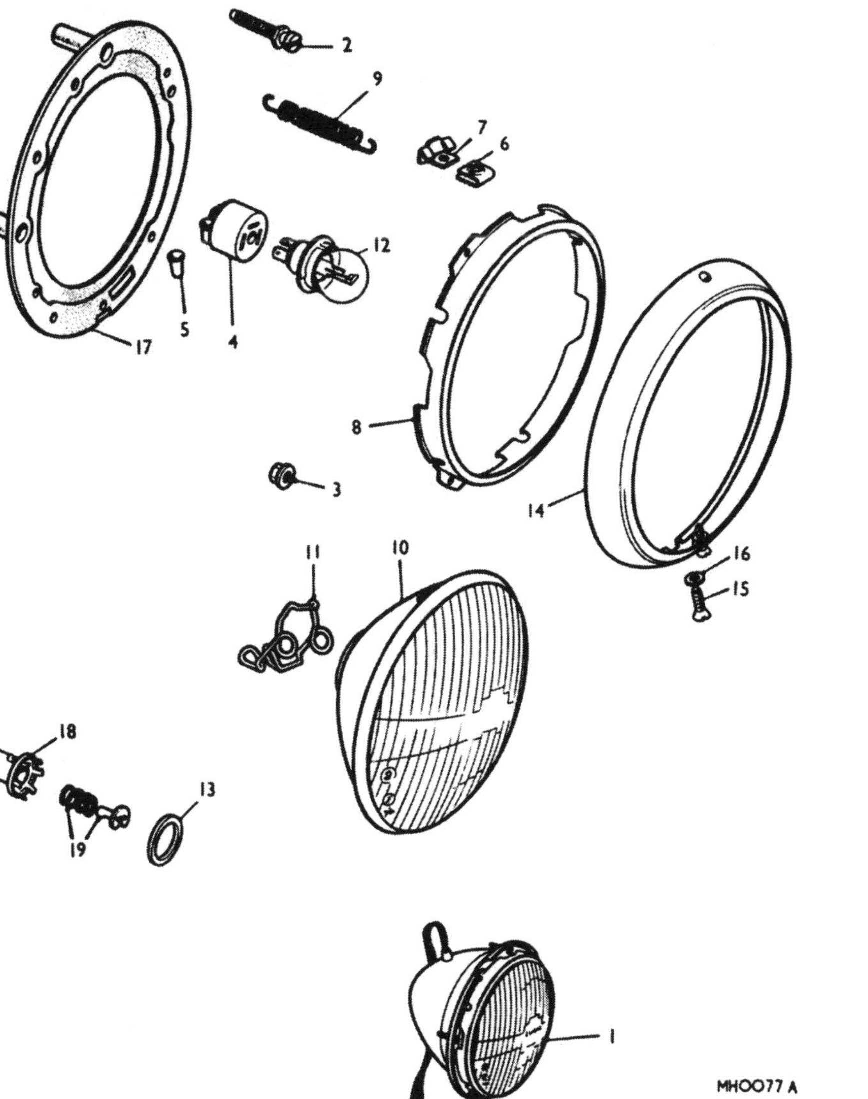

AUSTIN-HEALEY SPRITE MK. 3 AND MK. 4 & MG MIDGET MK. 2 AND MK. 3

HEADLAMPS-EUROPE EXCEPT FRANCE AND MIDGET 1500

NO.	PART NO.	DESCRIPTION	QTY	CHANGE POINT	REMARKS
	NSP	HEADLAMP ASSEMBLY-VERTICAL DIP MK.6	2		Use 27H 8204 with rim and gasket.
2	17H 5394	Screw-trimmer	6	(C)H-AN8-38829 TO 50191 EXCEPT Germany (C)G-AN3-25788 TO 28969 Germany,52389 except Germany	
18	17H 5231	Spring-trimmer screw	6		
19	27H 5253	Sleeve-sealing	6		
4	600226	ADAPTOR ASSEMBLY	2		
5	27H 6713	Sleeve-terminal	NLA		
6	27H 5354	Nut-rim fixing screw	2		
7	37H 5190	Bracket-rim fixing screw	2		
20	17H 5205	PLATE ASSEMBLY-LIGHT UNIT RETAINING	2		
	PJZ 602	Screw	6		
10	27H 4146	UNIT ASSEMBLY-LIGHT	NLA		Use GLU 513 (Except Germany) Use GLU 515 (Germany)
11	47H 5125	Spring-bulb retaining	2		
12	GLB 410	Bulb	2		
14	47H 5554	RIM ASSEMBLY	2		
15	RTC 465	Screw	2		
	GLU 513	Unit-light	2		
16	21G 9057	Washer(rubber)	2		
21	57H 5457	Gasket(rubber)	2		
1	27H 8204	HEADLAMP ASSEMBLY-VERTICAL DIP MK.10	2	(C)H-AN9-64735 TO 85286 (C)G-AN4-52390 TO 74885	
2	67H 5025	Screw-trimmer	NLA		Use BHM 7058
3	27H 7824	Nut-trimmer screw	NLA		Use BMK 2435
3	BMK 2435	Nut-trimmer screw	NLA		Use BHM 7058
4	600226	ADAPTOR ASSEMBLY	2		
5	27H 6713	Sleeve-terminal	NLA		
6	27H 5354	Nut-rim fixing screw	2		
7	37H 5190	Bracket-rim fixing screw	2		
8	515218	Plate-light unit retaining	2		
	PJZ 602	Screw	6		
9	67H 5026	Spring-unit seating rim	2		
10	27H 4146	UNIT ASSEMBLY-LIGHT	NLA		Use GLU 513 (Except Germany) Use GLU 515 (Germany)
11	47H 5125	Spring-bulb retaining	2		
12	GLB 410	Bulb	2		
14	47H 5554	RIM ASSEMBLY	2		
15	RTC 465	Screw	2		
	GLU 513	Unit-light	2		
16	21G 9057	Washer(rubber)	2		
17	9403	Gasket(rubber)	2		
	BHM 7058	Kit-trimmer screw	2		

NOTE:
See TIB 1B45 F18 for identification of Mk.6 and Mk.10 headlamps

AUSTIN-HEALEY SPRITE MK. 3 AND MK. 4 & MG MIDGET MK. 2 AND MK. 3

HEADLAMPS-FRANCE EXCEPT MIDGET 1500

NO.	PART NO.	DESCRIPTION	QTY	CHANGE POINT	REMARKS
	NSP	HEADLAMP ASSEMBLY-VERTICAL DIP-MK 6	2		Use 37H 1368 with rim and gasket.
2	17H 5394	Screw-trimmer	2		
18	17H 5231	Spring-trimmer screw	6		
19	27H 5253	Sleeve-sealing	6		
4	600226	ADAPTOR ASSEMBLY	2		
5	27H 6713	Sleeve-terminal	NLA		
6	27H 5354	Nut-rim fixing screw	2		
7	37H 5190	Bracket-rim fixing screw	2		
20	17H 5205	PLATE ASSEMBLY-LIGHT UNIT RETAINING	2	(C)H-AN8-38829	
	PJZ 602	Screw	2	TO(+)	
10	27H 4146	UNIT ASSEMBLY-LIGHT	NLA	(C)G-AN3-25788	Use GLU 513
	GLU 513	Unit-light	2		
11	47H 5125	Spring-bulb retaining	2	TO(+)	
12	GLB 411	Bulb	2		
14	47H 5554	RIM ASSEMBLY	2		
15	RTC 465	Screw	2		
16	21G 9057	Washer(rubber)	2		
1	37H 1368	HEADLAMP ASSEMBLY-VERTICAL DIP MK 10	2		
2	67H 5025	Screw-trimmer	NLA	(C)H-AN8-(+)TO	Use BHM 7058
3	27H 7824	Nut-trimmer screw	NLA	64734	Use BMK 2435
3	BMK 2435	Nut-trimmer screw	NLA	(C)H-AN9-64735	Use BHM 7058
4	600226	ADAPTOR ASSEMBLY	2	TO 85286	
5	27H 5713	Sleeve-terminal	6	(C)H-AN10-85287	
6	27H 5354	Nut-rim fixing screw	2	TO 86803	
7	37H 5190	Bracket-rim fixing screw	2	(C)A-AN10-86804	
8	515218	Plate-light unit retaining	2	TO 87824	
	PJZ 602	Screw	6	(C)G-AN3-(+)TO	
9	67H 5026	Spring-unit seating	2	52389	
10	27H 4146	UNIT ASSEMBLY-LIGHT	NLA	(C)G-AN4-52390	Use GLU 513
	GLU 513	Unit-light	2	TO 748985	
11	47H 5125	Spring-bulb retaining	2	(C)G-AN5-74886 TO	
12	GLB 411	Bulb	2	154100	
14	17H 5143	RIM ASSEMBLY	NLA		Use 47H 5554.
14	47H 5554	RIM ASSEMBLY	2		
15	RTC 465	Screw	2		
17	9403	Gasket(rubber)	2		
	BHM 7058	Kit-trimmer screw	2		

(+) Change point not available

(1) See TIB 1B45 F18 for identification of Mk6 and Mk10 headlamps

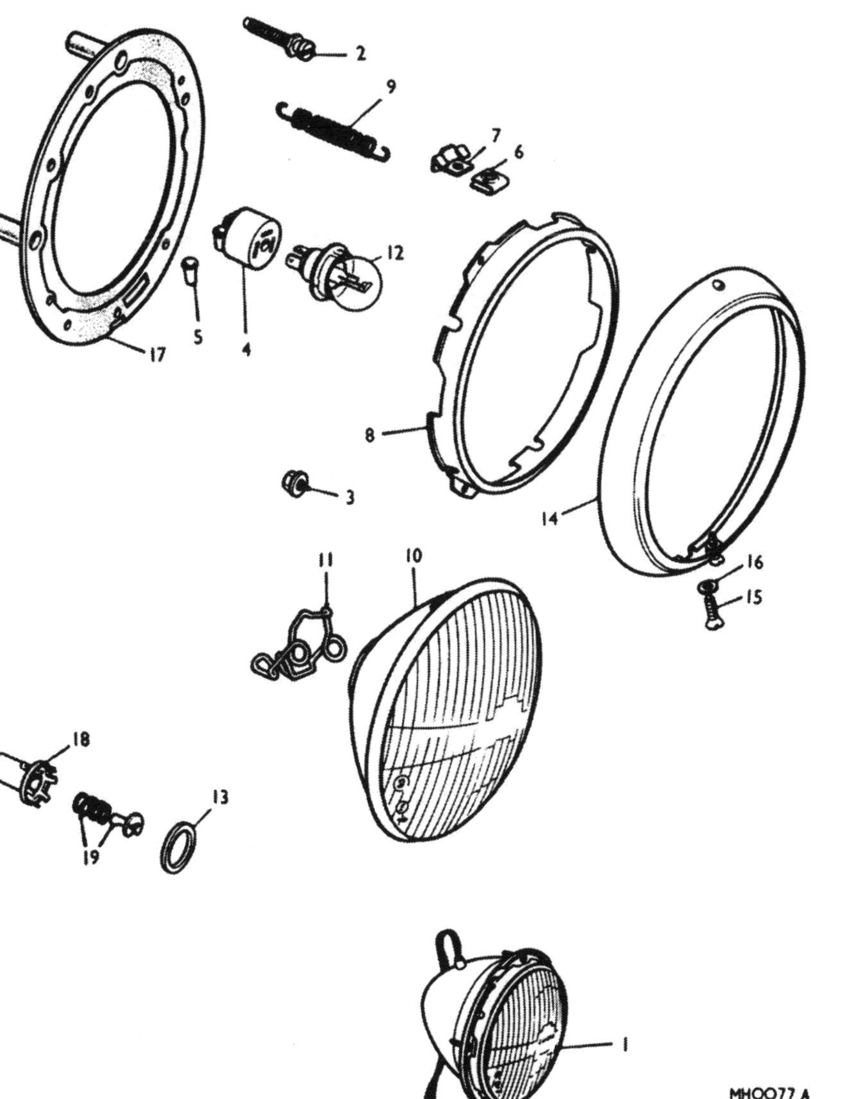

AUSTIN-HEALEY SPRITE MK. 3 AND MK. 4 & MG MIDGET MK. 2 AND MK. 3

NO.	PART NO.	DESCRIPTION	QTY	CHANGE POINT	REMARKS
		HEADLAMPS-WEST GERMANY EXCEPT MIDGET 1500			
1	27H 8210	HEADLAMP ASSEMBLY-VERTICAL DIP MK 10	2	Use prior to 27H 8204	
1	27H 8204	HEADLAMP ASSEMBLY	2	(C)H-AN10-83287 TO 86803 (C)A-AN10-86804 TO 87824 (C)G-AN5-74886 TO 154100	
2	67H 5025	Screw-trimmer	NLA		Use BHM 7058
3	27H 7824	Nut-trimmer screw	NLA		Use BMK 2435
3	BMK 2435	Nut-trimmer screw	NLA		Use BHM 7058
4	600226	ADAPTOR ASSEMBLY	2		
5	27H 6713	Sleeve-terminal	NLA		
18	27H 5977	Holder-pilot bulb	2	(C)H-AN8-50192 TO 64734 (C)H-AN9-64735 TO 85286 (C)H-AN10-85287 TO 86803 (C)A-AN10-86804 TO 87824 (C)G-AN3-38970 TO 52389 (C)G-AN4-52390 TO 74885 (C)G-AN5-74886 TO 154100	
19	244700	Interior-holder	2		Part of headlamp 27H 8210
6	27H 5354	Nut-rim fixing screw	2		
7	37H 5190	Bracket-rim fixing screw	2		
8	515218	Plate-light unit retaining	2		
	PJZ 602	Screw	6		
9	67H 5026	Spring-unit seating rim	2		
10	27H 5978	UNIT ASSEMBLY-LIGHT	2		Part of headlamp 27H 8210
10	27H 4146	UNIT ASSEMBLY-LIGHT	NLA		Use GLU 515
	GLU 515	Unit-light	2		
11	47H 5125	Spring-bulb retaining	2		
12	GLB 410	Bulb-main	2		
13	47H 5353	Ring-sealing-pilot bulb holder	2		Part of headlamp 27H 8210
14	47H 5554	RIM ASSEMBLY	2		
15	RTC 465	Screw	2		
16	21G 9057	Washer(rubber)	2		
17	9403	Gasket(rubber)	2		
	BHM 7058	Kit-trimmer screw	2		

MHO113A

AUSTIN-HEALEY SPRITE MK. 3 AND MK. 4 & MG MIDGET MK. 2 AND MK. 3

NO.	PART NO.	DESCRIPTION	QTY	CHANGE POINT	REMARKS
		LAMP-SIDE AND FLASHER			
1	13H 429	LAMP ASSEMBLY-SIDE AND FLASHER-AMBER-RH	1	(C)H-AN8-38829 TO 50191 Germany. (C)H-AN8-38829 TO 64734.Except Germany (C)H-AN9-64735 TO 85286.Except Germany (C)H-AN10-85287 TO 86803 (C)A-AN10-86804 TO 87824 (C)G-AN3-25788 TO 38969.Germany (C)G-AN3-25788 TO 52389.Except Germany (C)G-AN4-52390 TO 74885.Except Germany (C)G-AN5-74886 TO 154100	UK and W.Germany
	13H 428	LAMP ASSEMBLY-SIDE AND FLASHER-AMBER-LH	1		
3	57H 5155	Rim	2		
4	57H 5158	Lens-RH	1		
	57H 5159	Lens-LH	1		
6	57H 5157	Gasket-lens seating	2		
7	57H 5156	Shield-flasher bulb-Amber	2		
8	244700	Interior-bulb holder-sidelamp	2		
9	GLB 989	Bulb-sidelamp	2		
10	17H 5400	Screw	4		
8	37H 5452	Interior-bulb holder-flasher lamp	2		
9	GLB 382	Bulb-flasher	2		
13	37H 1894	Grommet-sidelamp cable	2		
14	17H 5216	Grommet-flasher lamp cable	2		
15	BHA 4487	LAMP ASSEMBLY FLASHER-AMBER	NLA	(C)H-AN8-50192 TO 64734 (C)H-AN9-64735 TO 85286 (C)G-AN3-38970 TO 52389 (C)G-AN4-52390 TO 74885	W.Germany
3	57H 5308	RIM ASSEMBLY	2		
3	57H 5155	Rim	2		
10	17H 5400	Screw	4		
17	21G 9057	Washer	4		
18	27H 6243	Lens	2		
6	57H 5157	Gasket-lens seating	2		
	BHA 5318	LAMP ASSEMBLY-DIRECTION INDICATOR-FRONT	2	(C)G-AN6-154101 ON	UK only
	37H 8759	Lens(with screws,washers and seating gasket)	2		
	37H 5452	Bulbholder	2		
	GLB 382	Bulb-21w	2		
	27H 6713	Sleeve-terminal	NLA		

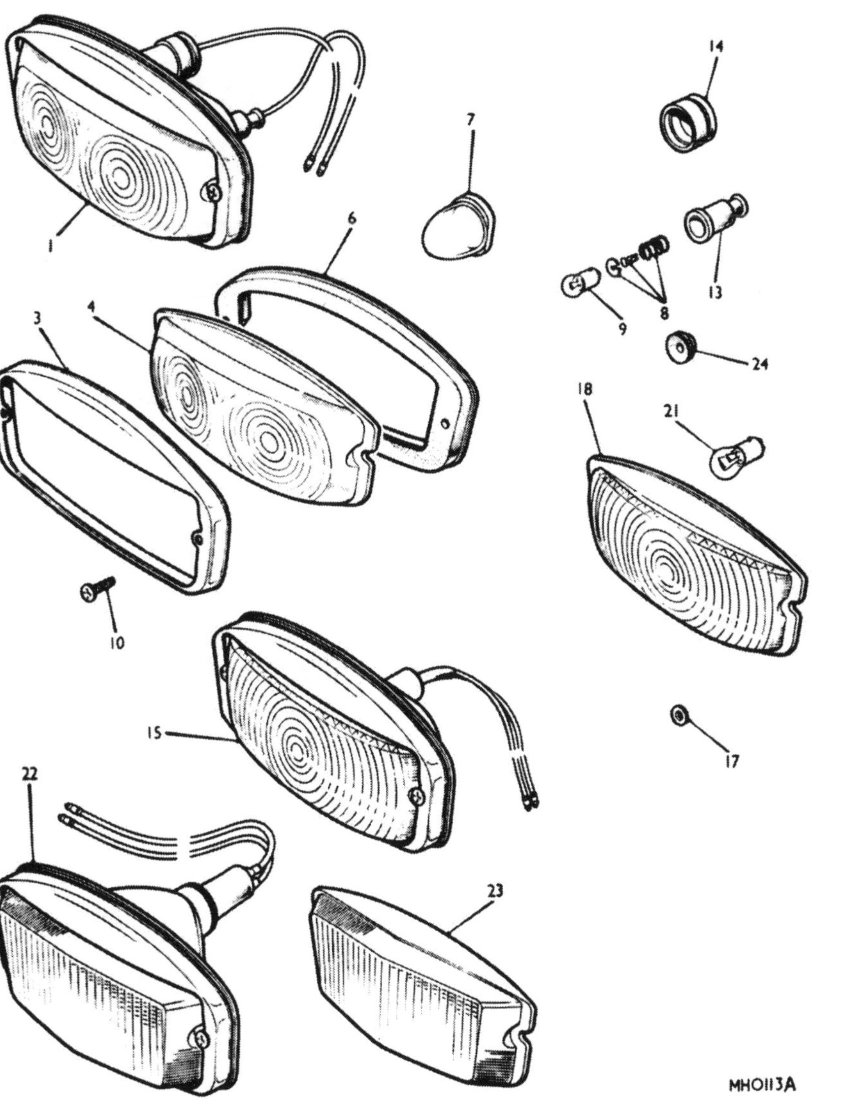

AUSTIN-HEALEY SPRITE MK. 3 AND MK. 4 & MG MIDGET MK. 2 AND MK. 3

LAMP-SIDE AND FLASHER-continued

NO.	PART NO.	DESCRIPTION	QTY	CHANGE POINT	REMARKS
15	BHA 4204	LAMP ASSEMBLY-SIDE AND FLASHER-WHITE	2		Not UK
3	57H 5308	RIM ASSEMBLY	2		
17	21G 9057	Washer	4		
18	57H 5307	Lens	2		
6	57H 5157	Gasket-lens seating	2		
21	GLB 380	Bulb	2		
15	BHA 4748	LAMP ASSEMBLY-SIDE AND FLASHER-AMBER $	2	Use prior to BHA 4905	USA and Canada
3	57H 5308	RIM ASSEMBLY	2		
3	57H 5155	Rim	2		
10	17H 5400	Screw	4		
17	21G 9057	Washer	4		
18	27H 6243	Lens $	2		
6	57H 5157	Gasket-lens seating	2		
21	GLB 380	Bulb	2		
22	BHA 4905	LAMP ASSEMBLY-SIDE AND FLASHER-AMBER	2	(C)G-AN5-74886 TO 154100	
3	57H 5155	Rim	2		
23	37H 4738	Lens	2		
6	57H 5157	Gasket-lens seating	2		
21	GLB 380	Bulb	2		
24	2A 9156	Nut-earthing	NLA		
	BHA 5320	LAMP ASSEMBLY-SIDE AND FLASHER-AMBER	2	(C)G-AN6-154101 ON	
	37H 8759	Lens(with screws,washers and gaskets)	2		
	GLB 380	Bulb-6/21w	2		
	27H 6679	Grommet	2		
	27H 6713	Sleeve-terminal	NLA		

$ This item is subject to safety regulations

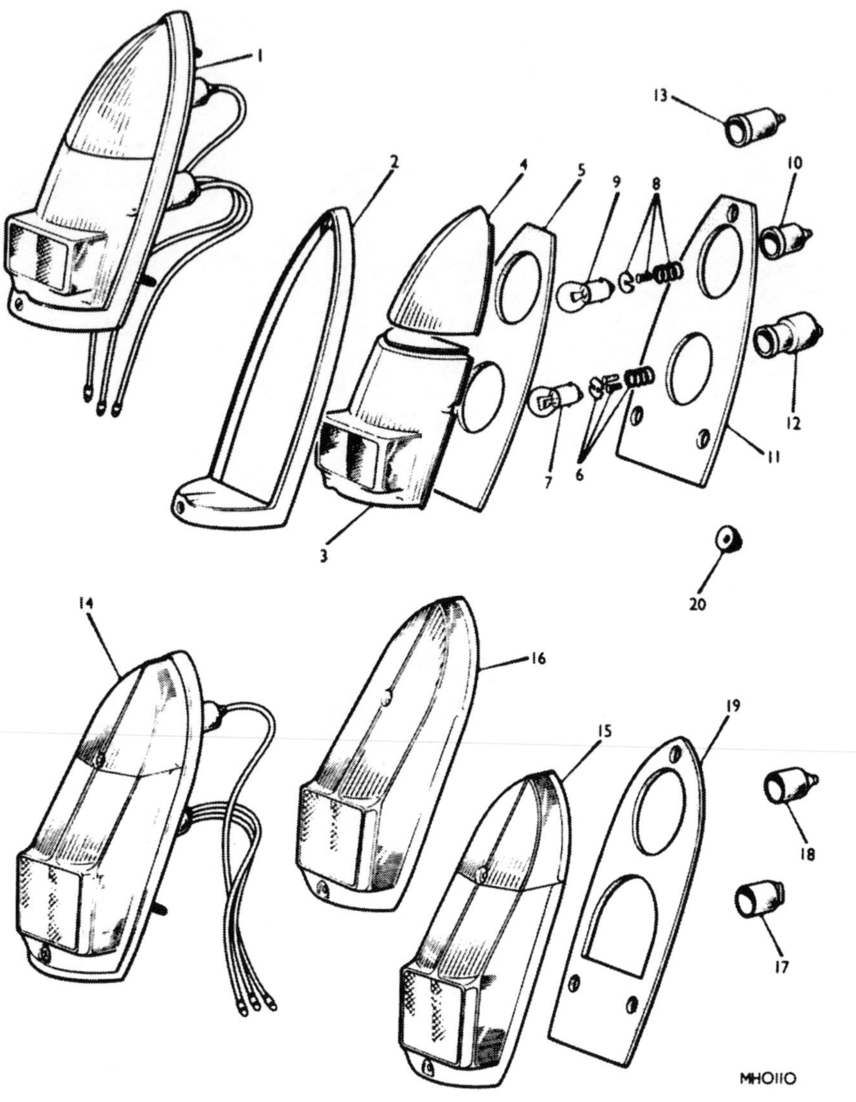

AUSTIN-HEALEY SPRITE MK. 3 AND MK. 4 & MG MIDGET MK. 2 AND MK. 3

NO.	PART NO.	DESCRIPTION	QTY	CHANGE POINT	REMARKS
		STOP/TAIL LAMPS			
1	BHA 4175	LAMP ASSEMBLY-STOP/TAIL FLASHER AND REFLEX-AMBER FLASHER	2	(C)H-AN8-38829 TO 5019.Germany	Except USA, Canada and W.Germany
1	BHA 4176	LAMP ASSEMBLY-STOP/TAIL FLASHER AND REFLEX-RED FLASHER $	NLA	(C)H-AN8-38829 TO 64734.Except Germany (C)H-AN9-64735 TO 85286 (C)G AN3-25788 To 38969.GERMANY (C)G-AN3-25788 To 52389.Except Germany (C)G-AN4-52390 To 74885	Use BHA 4175 With Lens 57H 5359 USA,Canada and W.Germany.
2	57H 5355	Rim	2		
	RMP 308	Screw	2		
3	57H 5357	Lens-stop/tail	2		
4	57H 5354	Lens-flasher-Amber	2		
4	57H 5359	Lens-flasher-Red $	2		
5	57H 5356	Gasket-lens seating	2		
7	GLB 380	Bulb-stop/tail	2		
8	37H 5452	Interior-bulb holder-flasher	2		
9	GLB 382	Bulb-flasher	2		
10	37H 5525	Grommet-cable	4		
11	57H 5358	Gasket-lamp seating	2		
	BHA 4488	LAMP ASSEMBLY-STOP/TAIL-FLASHER AND REFLEX-AMBER FLASHER	NLA	(C)H-AN8-50192 TO 64734 (C)H-AN9-64735 TO 85286 (C)G-AN3-38970 TO 52389 (C)G-AN4-52390 TO 74885	W.Germany
2	57H 5355	Rim	2		
	RMP 308	Screw-rim fixing	2		
3	57H 5357	Lens-stop/tail	2		
4	57H 5354	Lens-flasher	2		
5	57H 5356	Gasket-lens seating	2		
6	37H 5459	Interior-bulb holder-stop/tail	2		
8	37H 5452	Interior-bulb holder-flasher	2		
12	57H 5496	Grommet-stop/tail-lamp cable	2		
13	57H 5465	Grommet-flasher-lamp cable	NLA		
11	57H 5358	Gasket-lamp seating	2		

$ This item is subject to safety regulations

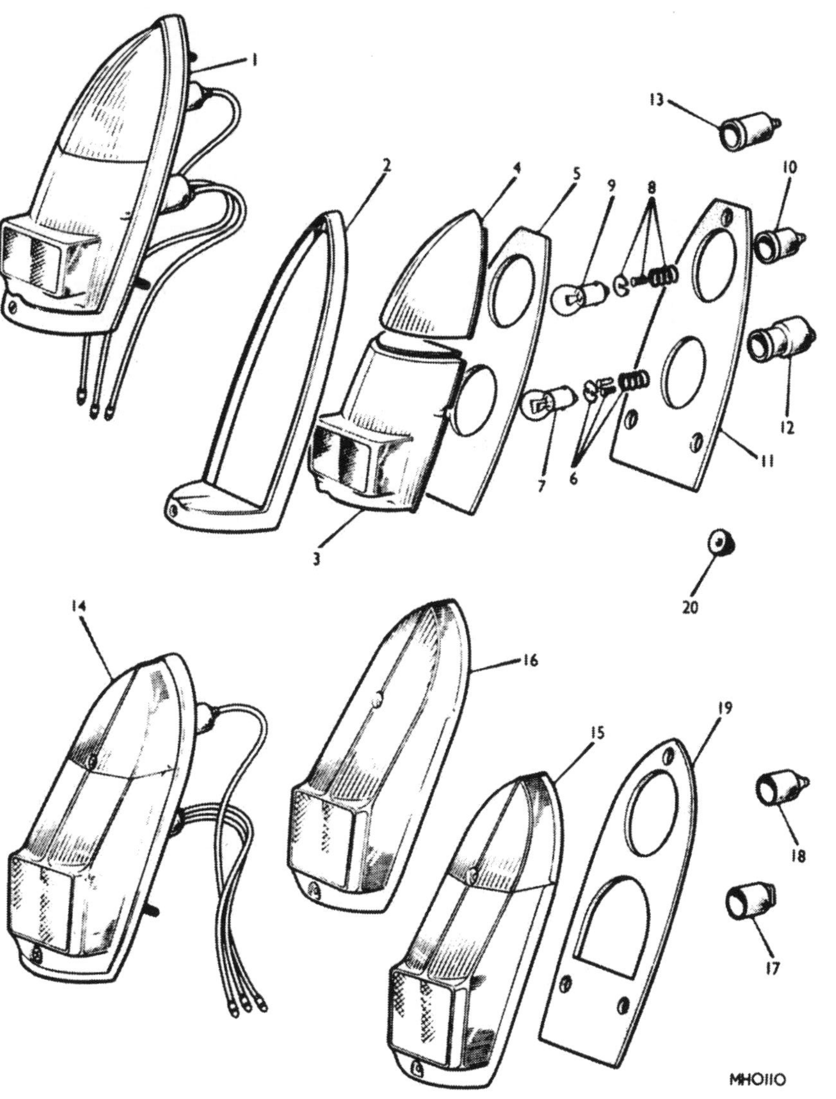

AUSTIN-HEALEY SPRITE MK. 3 AND MK. 4 & MG MIDGET MK. 2 AND MK. 3

NO.	PART NO.	DESCRIPTION	QTY	CHANGE POINT	REMARKS
		STOP/TAIL LAMPS-continued			
14	BHA 4973	LAMP ASSEMBLY-STOP/TAIL-FLASHER AND REFLEX-AMBER FLASHER	2	(C)H-AN10-85287 TO 86803 (C)A-AN10-86804 TO 87824 (C)G-AN5-74886 ON	Except USA and Canada
15	37H 4737	Lens-Amber/Red	2		
6	37H 5459	Interior-bulb holder	2		
7	GLB 380	Bulb-stop/tail	2		
8	37H 5452	Interior-bulb holder	2		
9	GLB 382	Bulb-flasher	2		
17	37H 2687	Grommet-cable-stop/tail	NLA		
18	37H 2688	Grommet-cable-flasher	NLA		
19	37H 4679	Gasket-lamp seating	2		
14	BHA 4902	LAMP ASSEMBLY-STOP/TAIL-FLASHER AND REFLEX-AMBER FLASHER	NLA	(C)H-AN10-85287 TO 86803 (C)A-AN10-86804 TO 87824 (C)G-AN5-74886 TO 129950	Use BHA 5260
16	37H 7119	Lens-Red/Amber	2		
6	37H 5459	Interior-bulbholder	2		
7	GLB 380	Bulb-stop/tail	2		
8	37H 5452	Interior-bulb holder	2		
9	GLB 382	Bulb-flasher	2		
17	37H 2687	Grommet-cable-stop/tail	NLA		
18	37H 2688	Grommet-cable flasher	NLA		
19	37H 4679	Gasket-lamp seating	2		USA and Canada
14	BHA 5260	LAMP ASSEMBLY-STOP/TAIL-FLASHER AND REFLEX-AMBER FLASHER	2	(C)G-AN5-129951 ON	
16	37H 7119	Lens-Red/Amber	2		
6	37H 5459	Interior-bulb holder	2		
7	GLB 380	Bulb-stop/tail	2		
8	37H 5452	Interior-bulb holder	2		
9	GLB 382	Bulb-flasher	2		
17	37H 2687	Grommet-cable	NLA		
18	37H 2688	Grommet	NLA		
19	37H 4679	Gasket-lamp seating	2		

AUSTIN-HEALEY SPRITE MK. 3 AND MK. 4 & MG MIDGET MK. 2 AND MK. 3

NO.	PART NO.	DESCRIPTION	QTY	CHANGE POINT	REMARKS
		LAMP-REVERSE			
1	BHA 5167	LAMP ASSEMBLY-REVERSE $	2	(C)H-AN9-70268 TO 85286 (C)H-AN10-85287 TO 86803 (C)A-AN10-86804 TO 87824 (C)G-AN4-58112 TO 74885 (C)G-AN5-74886 TO 113616 America 74886 ON except N.America	Except France
2	37H 1760	LENS ASSEMBLY $	2		
3	27H 8811	Screw-lens fixing	NLA		Use 37H 3751.
3	37H 3751	Screw-lens fixing	4		
4	37H 1759	Gasket-lens seating	2		
5	GLB 273	Bulb	2		
	BHA 5167	LAMP ASSEMBLY-REVERSE $	2	(C)G-AN5-113617 TO 129950	USA and Canada
	37H 7512	Lens $	2		
	37H 1759	Gasket-seating	2		
	GLB 270	Bulb	2		
	BHA 5262	LAMP ASSEMBLY-REVERSE $	2	(C)G-AN5-129951 ON	
	37H 7512	Lens $	2		
	GLB 270	Bulb-festoon	2		
	37H 1759	Gasket-seating	2		
1	BHA 4621	LAMP ASSEMBLY-REVERSE	2	(C)H-AN9-70268 TO 85286 (C)H-AN10-85287 TO 86803 (C)A-AN10-86804 TO 87824 (C)G-AN4-58112 TO 74885 (C)G-AN5-74886 ON	France
2	37H 3400	LENS ASSEMBLY	2		
3	27H 8811	Screw-lens	4		
4	37H 1759	Gasket-seating	2		
5	37H 1547	Bulb	2		

$ This item is subject to safety regulations

MHOIII

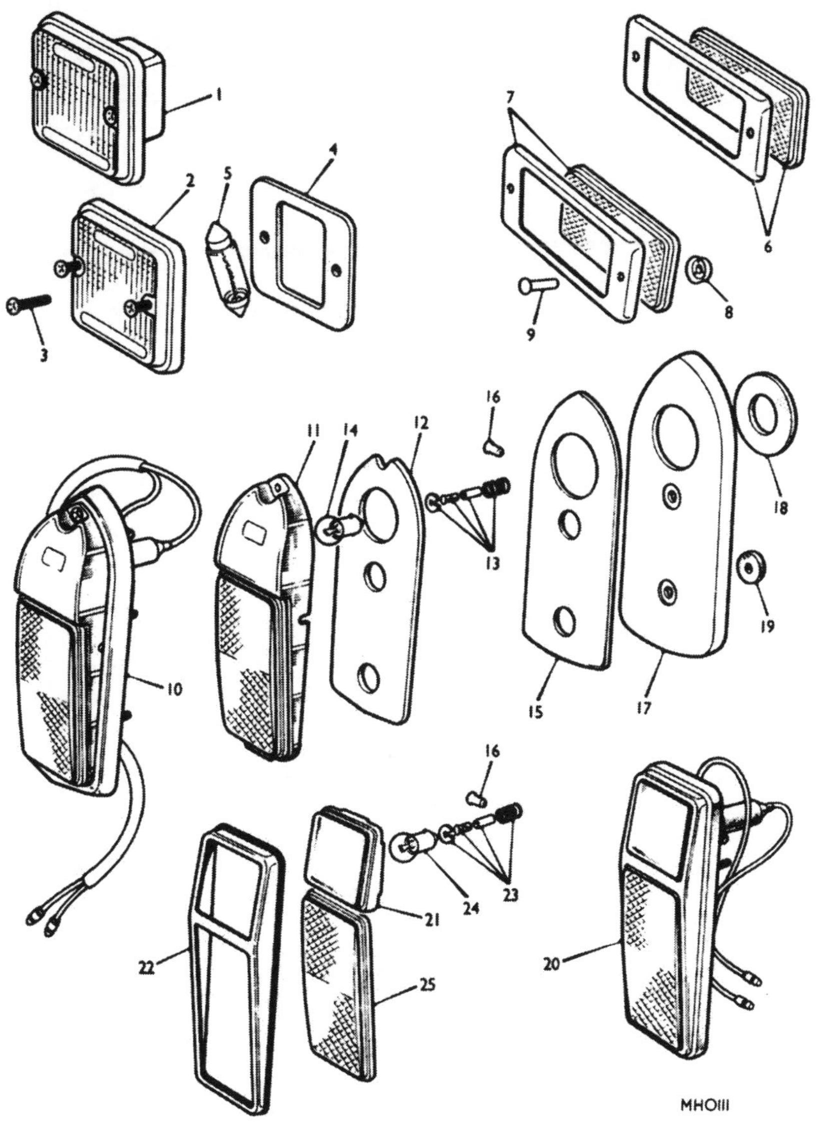

AUSTIN-HEALEY SPRITE MK. 3 AND MK. 4 & MG MIDGET MK. 2 AND MK. 3

NO.	PART NO.	DESCRIPTION	QTY	CHANGE POINT	REMARKS
		LAMP-REFLEX			
6	13H 4689	Reflector-reflex-Amber-front wing	2	Use prior to BHA 4968 and BHA 4969	USA,Canada AND Sweden
7	BCA 4568	Reflector-reflex-Red-rear wing	2		
8	BHA 4843	Push-on-fix	NLA		
9	AHH 8783	Rivet	8		
10	BHA 4968	LAMP ASSEMBLY-REFLEX-SIDE MARKER-FRONT-RH	1	(C)G-AN5-74886 ON	USA and Canada
	BHA 4969	LAMP ASSEMBLY-REFLEX-SIDE MARKER-FRONT-LH	1		
11	11727	Lens-Amber-RH	1		
	11730	Lens-Amber-LH	1		
12	37H 4753	Gasket-lens seating	2		
13	244700	Interior-bulb holder	2		
14	GLB 989	Bulb	2		
15	37H 4752	Gasket-lamp seating	2		
16	27H 6713	Sleeve-terminal	NLA		
17	AHA 9338	Plinth-side marker-RH	1		
	AHA 9339	Plinth-side marker-LH	1		
18	AHA 9485	Seal-plinth	NLA		
19	AHA 9484	Washer-sealing	NLA		
	PWZ 203	Washer-plain	4		
	LNZ 203	Lock-nut	4		
20	BHA 4972	LAMP ASSEMBLY-REFLEX SIDE MARKER-REAR	2		
21	608224	Lens-Red	2		
22	519364	Rim	2		
23	244700	Interior-bulb holder	2		
24	GLB 989	Bulb	2		
25	47H 5279	REFLEX-REFLECTOR	2		
	27H 6713	Sleeve-terminal	NLA		
16	CNZ 102	Nut	6		
	LWZ 202	Washer-spring	6		

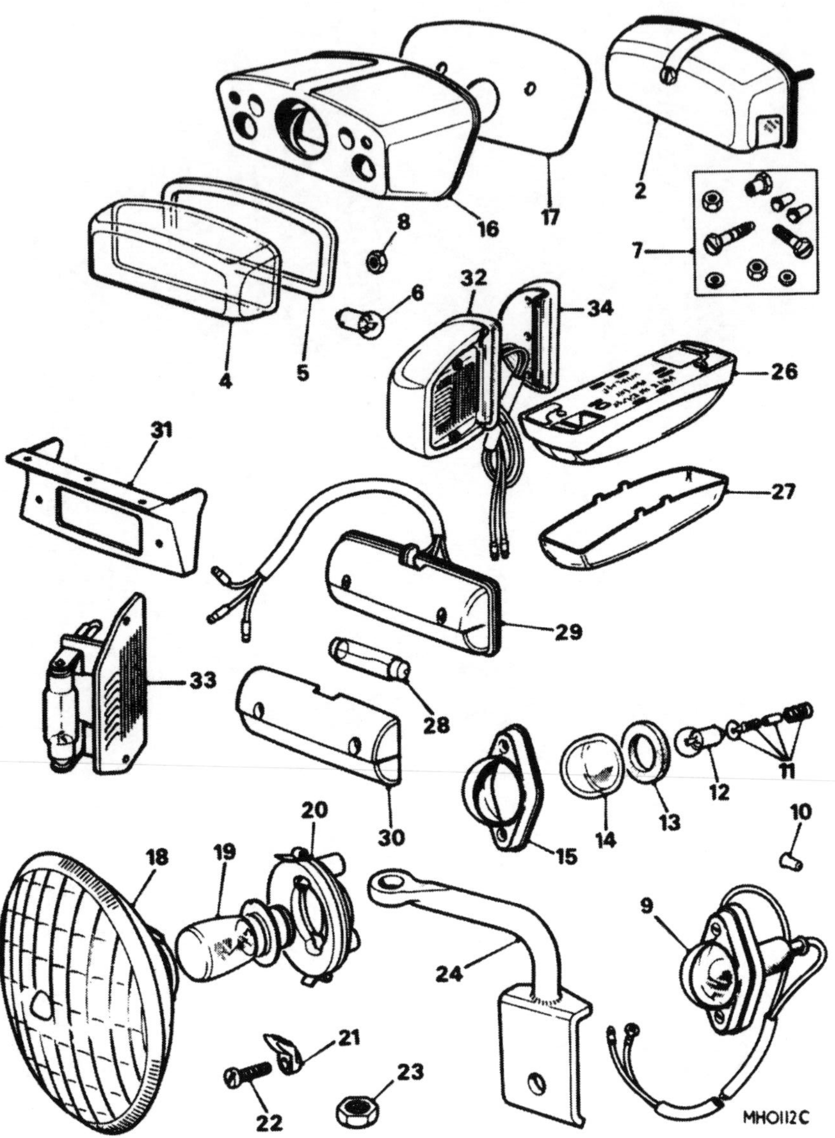

AUSTIN-HEALEY SPRITE MK. 3 AND MK. 4 & MG MIDGET MK. 2 AND MK. 3

NUMBER PLATE LAMPS AND FOGLAMP

NO.	PART NO.	DESCRIPTION	QTY	CHANGE POINT	REMARKS
	BHA 4494	LAMP ASSEMBLY-NUMBER PLATE	NLA	Use prior to 2A 9119	West Germany
2	BHA 4153	LAMP ASSEMBLY-NUMBER PLATE $	1		
4	601721	Lens	1		
5	57H 5368	Gasket-lens seating	NLA		
6	GLB 989	Bulb	2		
7	7H 5123	Sundry parts	1SET		
8	AJD 8052	Nut	4		Use with BHA 4494
9	2A 9119	LAMP ASSEMBLY-NUMBER PLATE $	2	(C)H-AN10-85287 TO 86803 (C)A-AN10-86804 TO 87824 (C)G-AN5-74886 TO 143354 USA AND Canada,74886 TO 154100 Except USA and Canada	
10	27H 6713	Sleeve-terminal	NLA		
11	244700	Interior-bulb holder	2		
12	GLB 989	Bulb	2		
13	17H 5302	Gasket-glass-seating	2		
14	606078	Glass	2		
15	37H 5426	Cover	2		
	127916	LAMP ASSEMBLY-NUMBER PLATE-RHD	1	(C)G-AN6-154101 ON	
32	BHA 5303	LAMP ASSEMBLY-NUMBER PLATE	2	(C)G-AN5-143355 TO 154100 (C)G-AN6-154101 To 179462	USA And Canada
23	13H 5991	Lens and bulb support	2		
28	GLB 254	Bulb	2		
34	13H 9016	Grommet-base	2		
	WA 702101	Washer	4		
	LNZ 203	Nut-lamp to mounting plate	4		
	AAU 2143	LAMP ASSEMBLY-NUMBER PLATE $	2	(C)G-AN6-179463 On	
	AAU 5113	Lens $	2		
	GLB 254	Bulb	2		
	NH 105041	Nut	4		
	WL 105001	Washer-spring	4		
16	AHA 9200	Plinth-number plate lamp	1	(C)H-AN10-85287 TO 86803 (C)A-AN10-86804 TO 87824 (C)G-AN5-74886 ON	
17	AHA 9202	Seal-plinth to body	1		
	PWZ 104	Washer-spring	2		
	LNZ 204	Locknut	2		

$ This item is subject to safety regulations

AUSTIN-HEALEY SPRITE MK. 3 AND MK. 4 & MG MIDGET MK. 2 AND MK. 3

NUMBER PLATE LAMPS AND FOGLAMP-continued.

NO.	PART NO.	DESCRIPTION	QTY	CHANGE POINT	REMARKS
	37H 5314	LAMP ASSEMBLY-FOG	NLA		
18	ACG 5179	Unit-light	2		
19	BFS 323	Bulb	2		
20	57H 5336	Adaptor	2		
21	AJH 5057	Catch-rim	2		
21	AJH 5057	Catch-rim	2		
22	17H 5400	Screw-catch	2		
23	27H 6767	Nut-lamp-spigot	2		
24	AHA 6368	Bracket-fog lamp mounting-RH	1		
25	AHA 6369	Bracket-fog lamp mounting-LH	NLA		
26	BHA 5040	COURTESY LIGHT ASSEMBLY-BOOT	1		
27	37H 5923	Lens	1		
28	GLB 254	Bulb	1		
	PTZ 606	Screw-courtesy light-trunk	2		
	PWZ 202	Washer	2		
29	BHA 5138	COURTESY LIGHT ASSEMLBY-INTERIOR	1		Was AVB 494.
30	27H 3590	Lens	1		
28	GLB 254	Bulb	1		
	PMZ 207	Screw-light to bracket	2		
	LWZ 202	Washer	2		
	AHA 9767	Bracket-interior light	1		USA Only
31	AHA 9769	Bracket-interior light	1		] Except USA
	PMZ 207	Screw-bracket	3		
	LWZ 202	Washer	3		

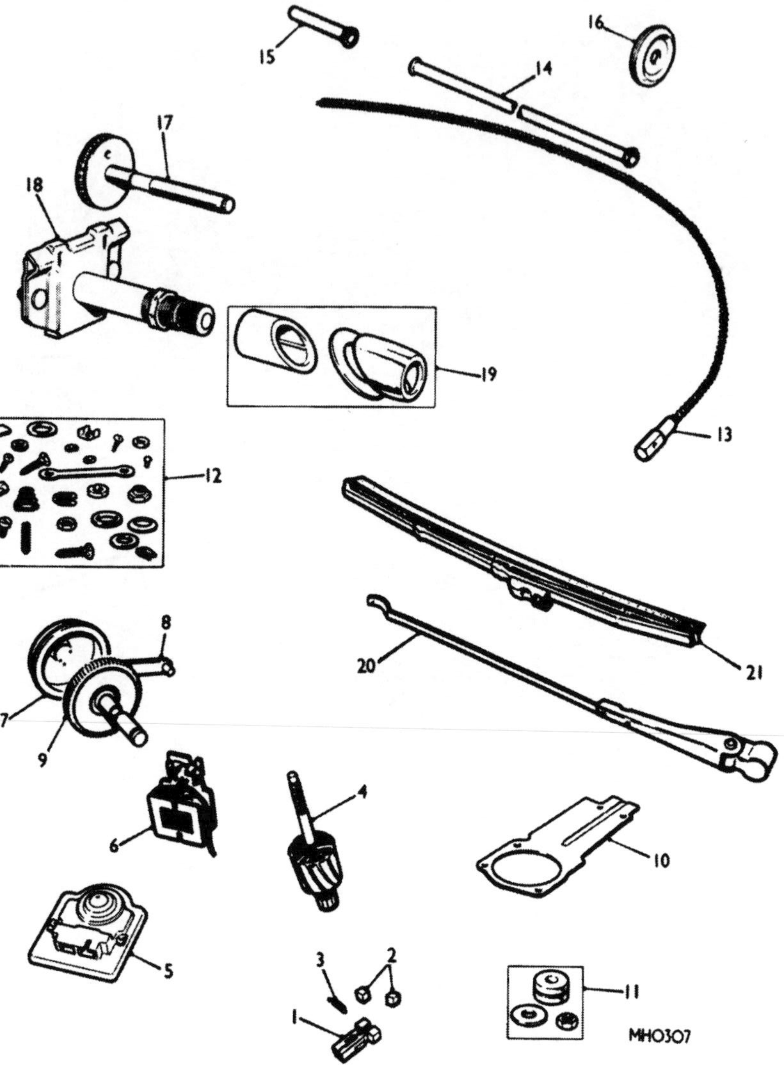

AUSTIN-HEALEY SPRITE MK. 3 AND MK. 4 & MG MIDGET MK. 2 AND MK. 3

WINDSCREEN WIPERS-2 BLADE SYSTEM

NO.	PART NO.	DESCRIPTION	QTY	CHANGE POINT	REMARKS
	27H 3542	MOTOR ASSEMBLY-WINDSCREEN WIPER	NLA	(C)H-AN8-38829 TO 64734 (C)H-AN9-64735 TO 72040 (C)G-AN3-25788 TO 52389 (C)G-AN4-52390 TO 60459	
1	17H 5396	BRUSH GEAR ASSEMBLY	1		For use with early type motor 57H 5555
2	7H 5130	Brush	1SET		
3	27H 5309	Spring-brush	1		
	27H 4463	BRUSH GEAR ASSEMBLY	NLA		Use with 27H 3542
2	27H 4464	Brush	NLA		
3	27H 5309	Spring-brush	1		
4	27H 5374	Armature	1		
5	7H 5991	Cover-armature(with bearing)	1		
7	57H 5559	Switch-parking	1		
8	17H 2458	Rod-connecting	1		
9	57H 5589	Shaft and gear	1		
10	27H 9070	Cover-gearbox	1		
11	17H 5431	Fixing parts	3STS		
12	17H 5449	Sundry parts	NLA		
13	37H 5169	Cross-head and rack	1		
15	13H 5412	Casing-outer-wheelbox to extension	1		
16	C 5574	Grommet-casing through dash	1		
	BHA 4151	WHEELBOX ASSEMLY	NLA		Use wheelbox 37H 6316 with 1 off bush kit 18G 8851
17	AJH 5079	Spindle and gear	2		
18	37H 6316	Wheelbox(less bushes)	2		
19	18G 8851	Kit-bush	1		
20	13H 66	Arm-wiper-RHD	2		
	13H 68	Arm-wiper-LHD	2		
21	GWB 159	Blade-wiper	2		

AUSTIN-HEALEY SPRITE MK. 3 AND MK. 4 & MG MIDGET MK. 2 AND MK. 3

NO.	PART NO.	DESCRIPTION	QTY	CHANGE POINT	REMARKS
		WINDSCREEN WIPERS-2 BLADE SYSTEM-continued			
1	37H 8221	MOTOR ASSEMBLY-WINDSCREEN WIPER(LESS GEAR) A/B AND D	1		Was 37H 2732
2	517644	Brush A/B	1SET	(C)H-AN9-72041 TO 85286	
3	37H 8222	Armature	1	(C)H-AN10-85287 TO 86803	Was 37H 2735
4	37H 2734	Switch-parking A/B	1	(C)A-AN10-86804 TO 87824	
	RTC 198	Brush D	1	(C)G-AN4-60460 TO 74885	
	37H 6784	Switch-parking D	1	(C)G-AN5-74886 ON	
5	AHH 8766	Packing-wiper motor	NLA		
6	BHA 4790	Strap-wiper motor	1		
7	150844	Pad	1		
8	608092	Gear-wiper motor-LHD.	1		
9	37H 5208	Rack-96.85cm(38")long	1		
9	37H 5169	Rack-82.62cm(32")long	1		N.America
10	AHA 8696	Casing-outer-wheelbox to wheelbox	1		
10	13H 5412	Casing-outer-wheelbox to extension	1		
11	C 5574	Grommet-casing through dash	2		
	BHA 4774	WHEELBOX ASSEMBLY $	NLA		Use wheelbox 37H 6314 with 1 off bush kit 18G 8851
	27H 2330	Spindle and gear $	2		
	FNZ 103	Nut	2		
	37H 6314	Wheelbox(less bushes)	2	Use prior to 37H 7738.	
	37H 7738	Wheelbox(less bushes)	2	(C)G-AN6-156798 ON	
	18G 8851	Kit-bush	2		

$ This item is subject to safety regulations

NOTE:
Reference must be made to the suffix letter of the manufacturers part number stamped on the motor to ensure that the correct component parts are ordered.

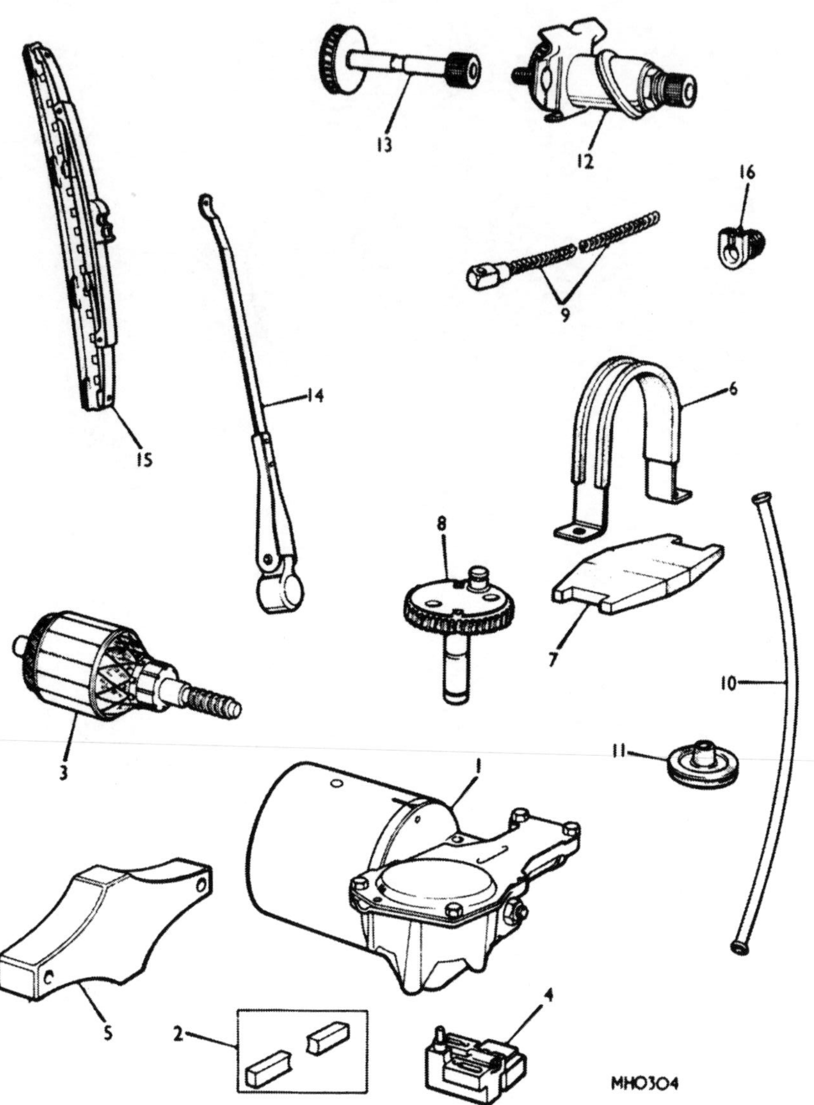

AUSTIN-HEALEY SPRITE MK. 3 AND MK. 4 & MG MIDGET MK. 2 AND MK. 3

WINDSCREEN WIPER-2 BLADE SYSTEM-continued

NO.	PART NO.	DESCRIPTION	QTY	CHANGE POINT	REMARKS
14	BHA 4776	Arm-windscreen wiper-RHD	2	(C)H-AN9-72041 TO 77590 (C)G-AN4-60460 TO 66225	
	BHA 4778	Arm-windscreen wiper-LHD	2		
15	GWB 159	Blade-windscreen wiper	2		
14	BHA 4894	Arm-windscreen wiper-RHD $	2	(C)H-AN9-77591 TO 85286 (C)H-AN10-85287 TO 86803 (C)A-AN10-86804 TO 87824 (C)G-AN4-66226 TO 74885 (C)G-AN5-74886 TO 123750	
	BHA 4893	Arm-windscreen wiper-LHD $	2		
15	GWB 145	Blade-windscreen wiper $	2		
14	BHA 5208	Arm-windscreen wiper-RHD $	2	(C)G-AN5-123751 ON	
	BHA 5207	Arm-windscreen wiper-LHD $	2		
15	GWB 164	Blade-windscreen wiper $	2		
	HBZ 411	Screw	2	(C)H-AN9-72041 TO 85286 (C)H-AN10-85287 TO 86803 (C)A-AN10-86804 TO 87824 (C)G-AN4-60460 TO 74885 (C)G-AN5-74886 ON	
	PWZ 204	Washer-plain	2		
	LWZ 204	Washer-spring	2		
	NH 604041	Nut	2		

$ This item is subject to safety regulations

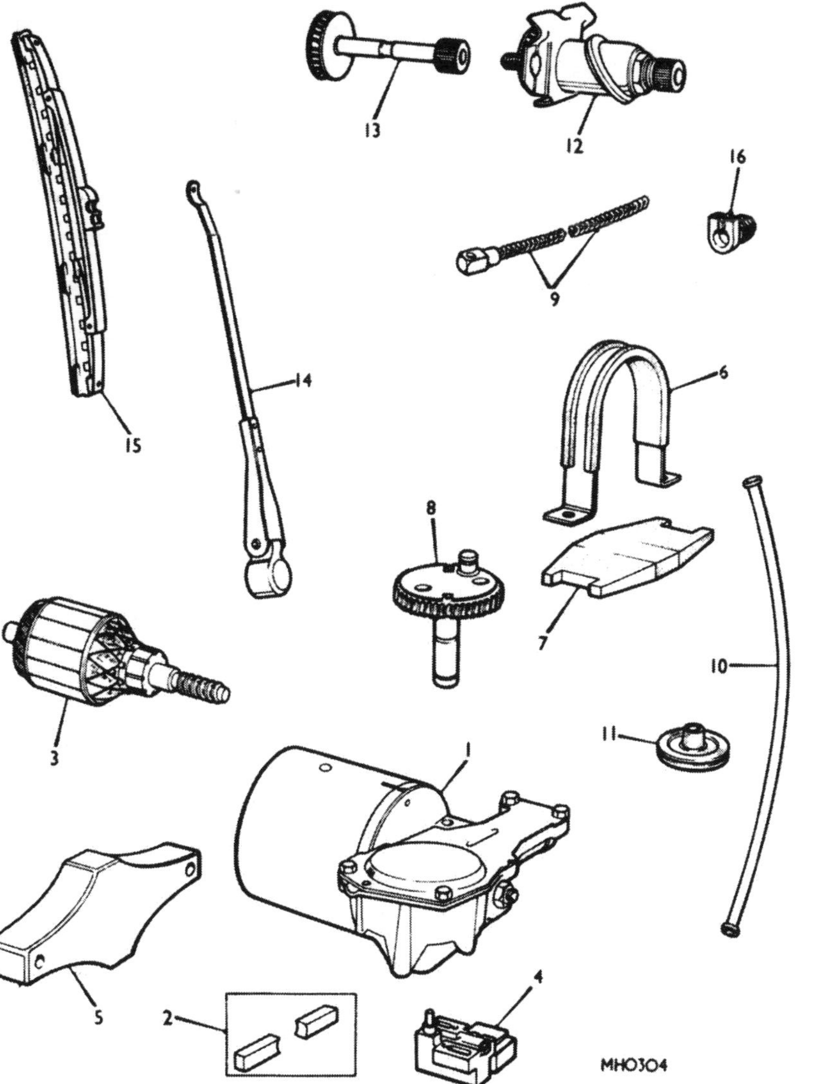

AUSTIN-HEALEY SPRITE MK. 3 AND MK. 4 & MG MIDGET MK. 2 AND MK. 3

WINDSCREEN WIPERS-3 BLADE SYSTEM

NO.	PART NO.	DESCRIPTION	QTY	CHANGE POINT	REMARKS
1	37H 2732	MOTOR ASSEMBLY-WINDSCREEN WIPER(LESS GEAR) AB/D	NLA		Use GEU 708
1	GEU 708	MOTOR ASSEMBLY-WINDSCREEN WIPER(LESS GEAR)	1		
2	517644	Brush AB	1SET		
3	37H 2735	Armature	1		
4	37H 2734	Switch-parking AB	1		
	RTC 198	Brush D	1SET		
	37H 6784	Switch-parking D	1		
16	37H 3694	Ferrule-casing retaining	1		
5	AHH 8766	Packing-wiper motor	NLA		
6	BHA 4790	Strap-wiper motor	1		
7	150844	Pad	1		
10	AHA 8696	Casing-outer-wheelbox to wheelbox	1		
10	13H 5412	Casing-wheelbox extension	1		
11	C 5574	Grommet-casing through dash	1		
8	37H 3045	Gear-wiper motor	1		
9	RTC 702	Rack-55"(140.73cm)long	1		
	BHA 4774	WHEELBOX ASSEMBLY $	NLA		Use wheelbox 37H 6314 with 1 off bush kit 18G 8851
13	27H 2330	Spindle and gear $	3		
	FNZ 103	Nut	6		
	37H 6314	Wheelbox(less bushes)	3	Use prior to 37H 7738.	
	37H 7738	Wheelbox(less bushes)	3	(C)G-AN6-156798 ON	
	18G 8851	Kit-bush	3		
14	BHA 4893	Arm-windscreen wiper $	3	Use prior to BHA 5207 and	
15	GWB 145	Blade-windscreen wiper $	3	GWB 164	
14	BHA 5207	Arm-windscreen wiper $	3	(C)G-AN5-123751 ON	
15	GWB 164	Blade-windscreen wiper $	3		
	HBZ 411	Screw	2		
	PWZ 204	Washer-plain	2		
	LWZ 204	Washer-spring	2		

$ This item is subject to safety regulations

NOTE:
Reference must be made to the suffix letter of the manufacturers part number stamped on the motor to ensure that the correct component parts are ordered.

MHO308A

AUSTIN-HEALEY SPRITE MK. 3 AND MK. 4 & MG MIDGET MK. 2 AND MK. 3

NO.	PART NO.	DESCRIPTION	QTY	CHANGE POINT	REMARKS
		SPEEDOMETER			
		SPEEDOMETER			
1	BHA 4634	KPH(SN6142/02)West Germany	1	(C)H-AN8-38829 TO 64734	For vehicles fitted with 145-13 tyres
1	BHA 4652	MPH(SN6142/04)West Germany	NLA	(C)H-AN9-64735 TO 77590	
1	BHA 4635	KPH(SN6142/03)West Germany	NLA	(C)G-AN3-24788 TO 52389	For vehicles fitted with 520-13 tyres
1	BHA 4653	MPH(SN6142/05)West Germany	NLA	(C)G-AN4-52390 TO 66225	
1	BHA 4437	KPH(SN6142/01)	1		
1	BHA 4436	MPH(SN6142/00)	1	Use prior to BHA 4844	Not USA.Canada or Sweden
1	BHA 4844	MPH(SN6142/06)	1	(C)H-AN9-77591 TO 85286	
1	BHA 4845	KPH(SN6142/07)Except Germany	NLA	(C)H-AN10-85257 TO 86803	
1	BHA 4846	KPH(SN6142/08)Germany only	1	(C)A-AN10-86804 TO 87824 (C)G-AN4-66226 TO 74885 (C)G-AN5-74886 TO 141411	
	BHA 5277	MPH(SN6142/06 BS)	1	(C)G-AN5-141412 TO 154100	
	BHA 5341	MPH(SN6142/09S)	1	(C)G-AN6-154101 ON	
1	BHA 4929	KPH(SN5226/10A)	NLA		Sweden
5	BHA 4689	MPH(SN5226/06)	NLA	Use prior to BHA 4863	USA and Canada
5	BHA 4863	MPH(SN5226/09)	1	(C)H-AN9-77591 TO 85286 (C)H-AN10-85287 TO 87284 (C)G-AN4-66226 TO 105500	
5	BHA 5094	MPH(SN5230/02)	1	(C)G-AN5-105501 TO 119495	
5	BHA 5166	MPH(SN5230/05)	1	(C)G-AN5-119496 TO 154100	
	BHA 5339	MPH(SN5230/12S)	1	(C)G-AN6-154101 ON	
6	BHA 4771	Control-remote	NLA		
7	BHA 4602	Stabilizer-voltage	1		
	PTZ 803	Screw	1		
22	BHA 4794	Angle drive-speedometer	1	(C)G-AN6-154101 ON	RHD

AUSTIN-HEALEY SPRITE MK. 3 AND MK. 4 & MG MIDGET MK. 2 AND MK. 3

NO.	PART NO.	DESCRIPTION	QTY	CHANGE POINT	REMARKS
		SPEEDOMETER CABLE			
8	GSD 118	CABLE ASSEMBLY-SPEEDOMETER-5'2"(157.48cm)-RHD	1		Midget Mk.2 Sprite Mk.3
9	17H 844	Cable-inner	1		
8	GSD 114	CABLE ASSEMBLY-SPEEDOMETER-5'6"(167.64cm)-RHD	1	Use prior to GSD 288	Midget Mk.3 Sprite Mk.4
9	17H 756	Cable-inner	1		
	GSD 288	Cable-speedometer-6'6"(210.8cm)	1	(C)G-AN6-154101 ON	RHD
8	GSD 104	CABLE ASSEMBLY-SPEEDOMETER-4'6"(137.16cm) LONG	1	Finished at (C)G-AN5-154100	LHD except USA Canada
9	17H 843	Cable-inner	1		
8	GSD 145	CABLE ASSEMBLY-SPEEDOMETER-3'11"(119.38cm) LONG	1	Use prior to BHA 5370/3 Inclusive	USA,Canada, Sweden,Germany
9	37H 2777	Cable-inner	1		
23	BHA 5370	Cable-speedometer-gearbox to single service interval counter	1	(C)G-AN6-154101 ON (USA) 154101 TO 175273(Canada)	USA and Canada (Except California)
	BHA 5371	Cable-speedometer-gearbox to double service interval counter	1	(C)G-AN6-154101 ON	California
	BHA 5372	Cable-speedometer service interval counter to service interval counter	1		
24	BHA 5373	Cable-speedometer-service interval counter to speedo head	1	(C)G-AN6-154101 ON (USA)-154101 TO 175273(Canada)	USA and CANADA
25	UKC 4260	Counter-service interval-EGR	1		
	13H 9407	Counter-service interval-Catalyst	1		California
	PMZ 307	Screw-indicator to bracket	4		
	WL 700101	Washer-spring	4		
	PMZ 306	Screw-indicator bracket	2		
	WL 700101	Washer-spring	2		
	PWZ 103	Washer-plain	2		
	13H 2567	Angle-drive-S.I.C	1		California
8	AAU 3499	Cable assembly-speedometer 6'3"(160.0cm)long	1	(C)G-AN6-175274 ON (Canada)	
10	AHA 8755	Bracket-remote trip flex	1		
11	PCR 709	Clip-cable to bulkhead	NLA		
12	ACH 8529	Sleeve-clip(rubber)	1		
	NH 604041	Nut	1		
	LWZ 204	Washer-spring	1		
13	RFR 305	Grommet-cable through foot-well	1		
13	RFR 503	Grommet-sic cable through bulkhead	1		

AUSTIN-HEALEY SPRITE MK. 3 AND MK. 4 & MG MIDGET MK. 2 AND MK. 3

NO.	PART NO.	DESCRIPTION	QTY	CHANGE POINT	REMARKS
		TACHOMETER			
14	BHA 4380	Tachometer(RVI 2401/00B)	1	Use prior to BHA 4639	
14	BHA 4639	TACHOMETER ASSEMBLY (RVI 2401/01)	1	(C)H-AN9-64734 TO 72033 (C)G-AN4-52390 TO 60440	
15	27H 8215	Core(metal)	1		
16	13H 784	Loop-sleeve(nylon)	1		
18	BHA 4690	Tachometer(RVI 1433/01) $	1	(C)H-AN9-72034 TO 85286 (C)H-AN10-85287 TO 86803 (C)A-AN10-86804 TO 87824 (C)G-AN4-60441 TO 74885 (C)G-AN5-74886 TO 105500	N.America,Sweden and Germany
18	BHA 5095	Tachometer(RVI 1439/01) $	1	(C)G-AN5-105501 TO 123730	N.America,Sweden and Germany
18	BHA 5221	Tachometer(RVC 1410/01AF)	1	(C)G-AN5-123731 ON	N.America,Sweden and Germany
18	BHA 4710	Tachometer(RVI 2430/01)	1	(C)H-AN9-72034 TO 85286 (C)H-AN10-85287 TO 86803 (C)A-AN10-86804 TO 87824 (C)G-AN4-60441 TO 74885 (C)G-AN5-74886 TO 128262	Except N.America Sweden,and Germany
18	BHA 5222	Tachometer(RVC 2415/01AR)	1	(C)G-AN5-128263 ON	Except N.America Sweden,and Germany
		BODY AND LENS			
19	BCA 4780	Oil filter warning light	1	Use prior to BHA 5122 and BHA 5123	USA,Canada, Sweden and Germany
19	BCA 4780	Ignition warning light-red $	1	Use prior to BHA 5122 and BHA 5123	USA,Canada, Sweden and Germany
19	27H 8052	Main beam warning light -blue $	1	Use prior to BHA 5122 and BHA 5123	USA,Canada, Sweden and Germany
20	BHA 5122	Main beam warning light-blue $	1	(C)G-AN5-105501 ON	USA,Canada, Sweden and Germany
20	BHA 5123	Ignition warning light-red $	1	(C)G-AN5-105501 ON	USA,Canada, Sweden and Germany
21	BHA 5125	Washer-retaining	2	(C)G-AN5-105501 ON	USA,Canada, Sweden and Germany

$ This item is subject to safety regulations.

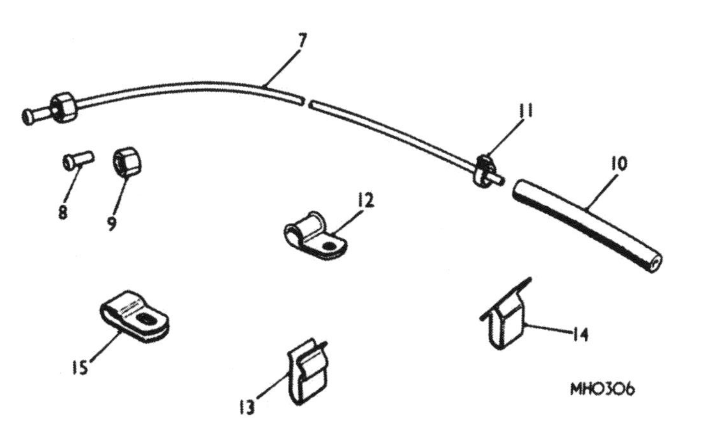

AUSTIN-HEALEY SPRITE MK. 3 AND MK. 4 & MG MIDGET MK. 2 AND MK. 3

NO.	PART NO.	DESCRIPTION	QTY	CHANGE POINT	REMARKS
		GAUGE-FUEL			
1	BHA 4381	Gauge-fuel	1	Use prior to BHA 4685 and BHA 4736	
2	BHA 4685	Gauge-fuel $	1	(C)H-AN9-72033 TO 85286 (C)H-AN10-85287 TO 86803 (C)A-AN10-86804 TO 87824 (C)G-AN4-60441 TO 74885 (C)G-AN5-74886 TO 105500	USA,Canada,Sweden and Germany
2	BHA 4736	Gauge-fuel $	1	(C)G-AN5-105501 TO 154100 (C)G-AN6-154101 ON Except California	USA,Canada,Sweden and Germany
	BHA 5342	Gauge-fuel(Unleaded)	1		California
2	BHA 4736	Gauge-fuel $	1	(C)H-AN9-72040 TO 85286 (C)H-AN10-85287 TO 86803 (C)A-AN10-86804 TO 87824 (C)G-AN4-60459 TO 74885 (C)G-AN5-74886 ON	Except USA, Canada,Sweden and Germany.

$ This item is subject to safety regulations.

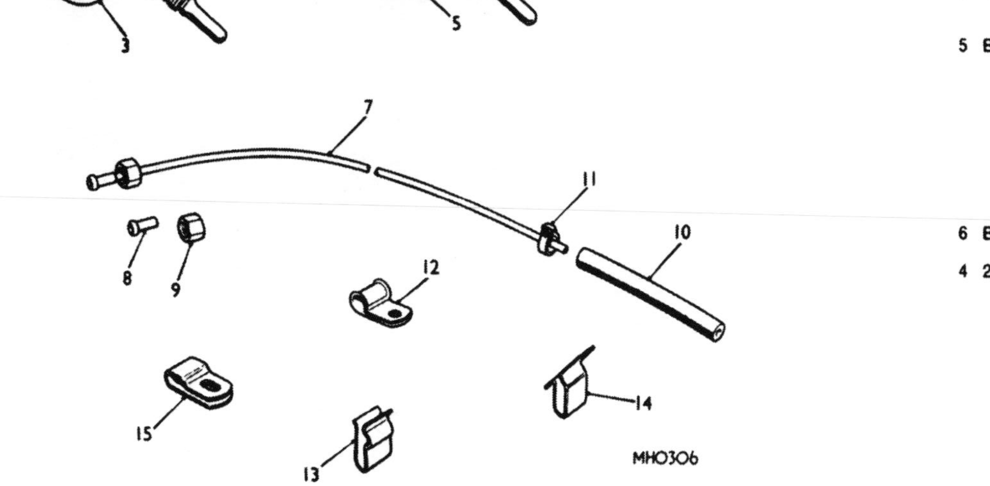

AUSTIN-HEALEY SPRITE MK. 3 AND MK. 4 & MG MIDGET MK. 2 AND MK. 3

NO.	PART NO.	DESCRIPTION	QTY	CHANGE POINT	REMARKS
		GAUGE-OIL PRESSURE AND WATER TEMPERATURE			
3	BHA 4587	GAUGE ASSEMBLY-OIL PRESSURE AND WATER TEMPERATURE-CENTIGRADE	1		
3	BHA 4586	GAUGE ASSEMBLY-OIL PRESSURE AND WATER TEMPERATURE-FAHRENHEIT	1	Use prior to BHA 4824 and BHA 4900.	
4	27H 7877	Restrictor	1		
5	BHA 4824	GAUGE ASSEMBLY-OIL PRESSURE AND WATER TEMPERATURE-FAHRENHEIT	1	(C)H-AN9-72033 TO 85286 (C)H-AN10-85287 TO 86803 (C)A-AN10-86804 TO 87824 (C)G-AN4-60441 TO 74885 (C)G-AN5-74886 TO 105500	USA and Canada
5	BHA 4900	GAUGE ASSEMBLY-OIL PRESSURE AND WATER TEMPERATURE-H,N,C.	1	(C)G-AN5-105501 TO 154100 (C)G-AN6- 154101 ON	USA and Canada
5	AAU 2641	GAUGE ASSEMBLY-OIL PRESSURE AND WATER TEMPERTURE-HNC	1	(C)G-AN6-154101 ON	USA and CANADA refer TSB75-A-6.
5	BHA 4900	GAUGE ASSEMBLY-OIL PRESSURE AND WATER TEMPERATURE-H,N,C.	1	(C)H-AN9-72040 TO 85286 (C)H-AN10-85287 TO 86803 (C)A-AN10-86803 TO 87824 (C)G-AN4-60459 TO 74885 (C)G-AN5-74886 ON	Except USA, Canada and Sweden
6	BHA 4931	GAUGE ASSEMBLY-OIL PRESSURE AND WATER TEMPERATURE-H,N,C.	1		Sweden
4	27H 7877	Restrictor	1		

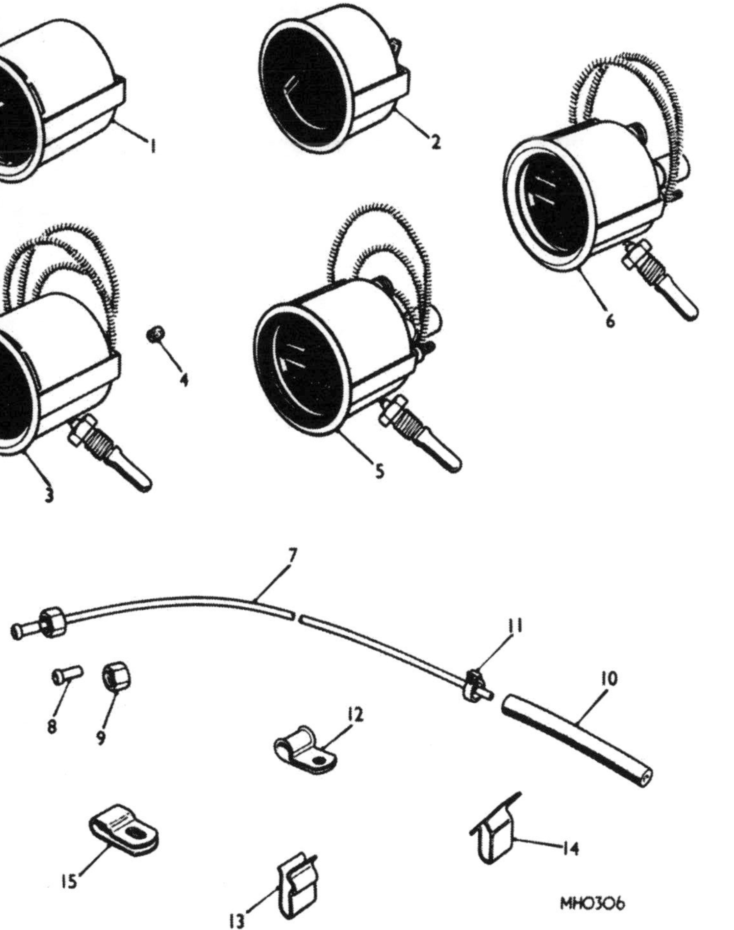

AUSTIN-HEALEY SPRITE MK. 3 AND MK. 4 & MG MIDGET MK. 2 AND MK. 3

NO.	PART NO.	DESCRIPTION	QTY	CHANGE POINT	REMARKS
		OIL PRESSURE GAUGE PIPES AND FITTINGS-EXCEPT MIDGET 1500			
7	2A 5635	PIPE ASSEMBLY-GAUGE TO FLEXIBLE PIPE(21"long)	1		
7	AHA 8756	PIPE ASSEMBLY-GAUGE TO FLEXIBLE PIPE(34"long)	1		USA,Canada and W.Germany.
8	51K 2824	Union	1		
9	11B 2037	Nut	1		
10	AHA 6331	Pipe-flexible	1		
11	88G 308	Clip-flexible	2		
7	AHA 6392	PIPE ASSEMBLY-FLEXIBLE PIPE TO ENGINE	1		
8	ACA 5422	Nipple	1		
9	ACA 5421	Nut	1		
12	PCR 307	Clip-thermometer capillary	A/R		
13	1G 9529	Clip-thermoter capillary to retainer	1		
14	BMK 385	Clip-thermometer capillary to vacuum pipe	1		
15	AHA 8683	Clip-thermometer capillary and heat control cable	NLA		
	PMZ 310	Screw-clip to wheelarch-front	1		
	PMZ 308	Screw-clip to wheelarch-rear	1		
	PMZ 306	Screw-clip to foot-well	1		
	PMZ 307	Screw-clip to foot-well	1		
	PWZ 103	Washer-plain	1		

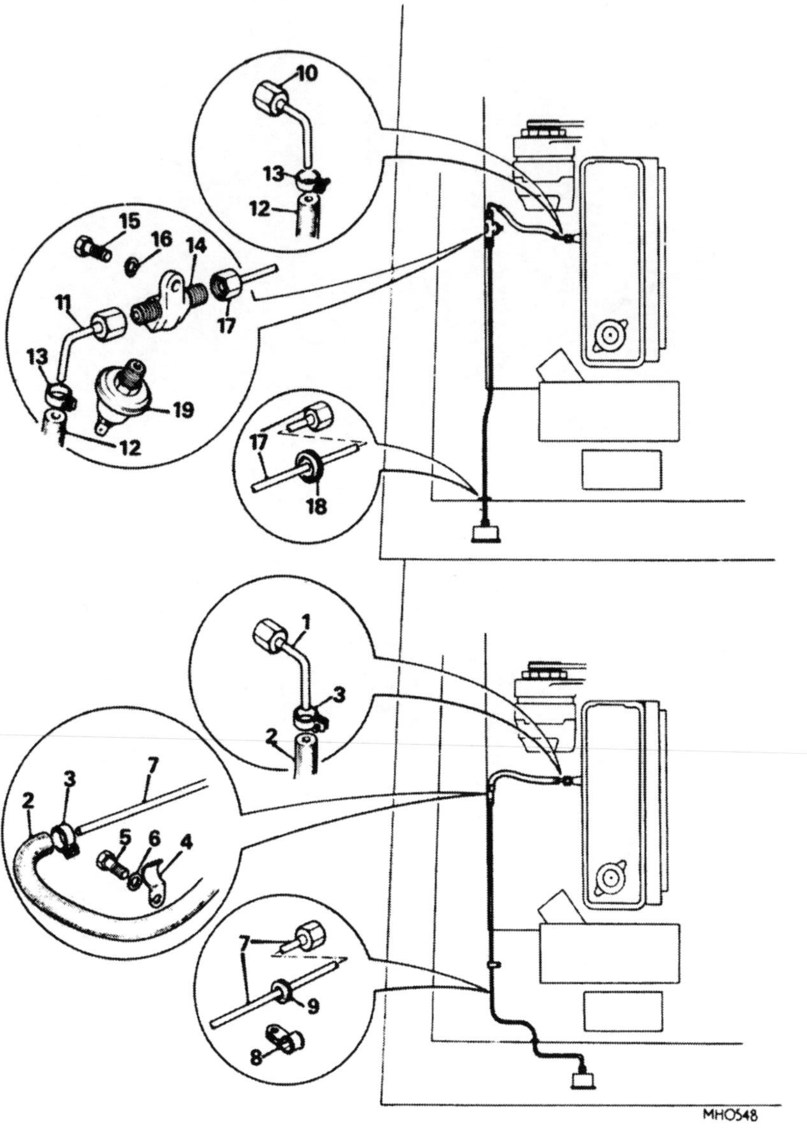

AUSTIN-HEALEY SPRITE MK. 3 AND MK. 4 & MG MIDGET MK. 2 AND MK. 3

OIL PRESSURE GAUGE PIPES AND FITTINGS-MIDGET 1500.

NO.	PART NO.	DESCRIPTION	QTY	CHANGE POINT	REMARKS
1	AHA 6392	Pipe-engine to hose	1		UK Only.
2	AHA 6331	Hose-flexible	1	Use prior to CHA 600.	UK Only.
2	CHA 600	Hose-flexible	1	(C)G-AN6-173709 ON	UK Only.
3	88G 308	Clip-flexible hose	2		UK Only.
4	PCR 809	Clip-flexible hose to body	1		UK Only.
5	SH 604041	Screw-clip	1		UK Only.
6	WL 600041	Washer-spring	1		UK Only.
7	BHH 1281	Pipe-gauge to flexible hose	1		UK Only.
8	PCR 809	Clip-pipe to footwell	1		UK Only.
9	RFR 102	Ferrule-pipe	1		UK Only.
10	AHA 6392	Pipe-adaptor to hose	1		USA and Canada.
11	AHA 6392	Pipe-'T'piece to hose	1		USA and Canada.
12	AHA 6331	Hose-flexible	1	Use prior to CHA 600.	USA and Canada.
12	CHA 600	Hose-flexible	1	(C)G-AN6-173709 ON.	USA and Canada.
13	88G 308	Clip-hose	2		USA and Canada.
14	BHH 649	'T' piece-anti run-on switch	1		USA and Canada.
15	SH 604051	Screw-'T' piece to body	1		USA and Canada.
16	WL 600041	Washer-spring	1		USA and Canada.
17	AHH 6678	Pipe-'T' piece to gauge	1		USA and Canada.
18	AHC 805	Grommet-pipe	NLA		USA and Canada.
19	BHA 5197	Switch-oil pressure-anti run-on valve	1		USA and Canada.

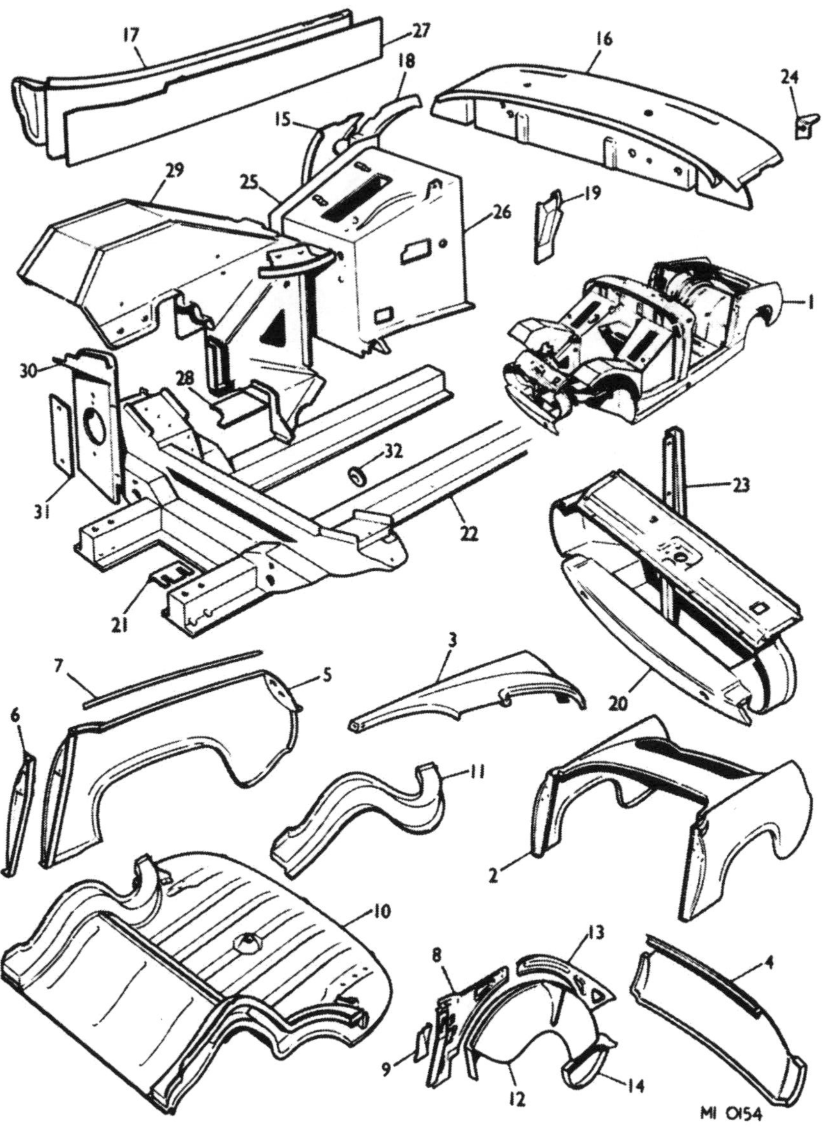

AUSTIN-HEALEY SPRITE MK. 3 AND MK. 4 & MG MIDGET MK. 2 AND MK. 3

NO.	PART NO.	DESCRIPTION	QTY	CHANGE POINT	REMARKS
		BODY SHELL-SPRITE MK 3 AND MIDGET MK 2			
1	AHA 7190	BODY SHELL AND UNDERFRAME ASSEMBLY(LESS BOOT LID, BONNET TOP,DOORS AND FRONT WINGS)	NLA		
2	AHA 7248	PANEL ASSEMBLY-BODY REAR	1		
3	AHA 5756	Panel-wing inner-RH	1		
	AHA 5757	Panel-wing inner-LH	NLA		
4	CZJ 70	Panel-body rear-lower	1		
5	AHA 7212	WING ASSEMBLY-REAR-RH	1		
	AHA 7213	WING ASSEMBLY-REAR-LH	1		
6	AHA 7229	'B'post-RH	1		
	AHA 7230	'B'post-LH	1		
7	AHA 5755	Moulding-rear wing to panel	NLA		
	AHA 7301	Reinforcement-'B'post to wheelarch-upper-LH	1		
9	AHA 7304	Reinforcement-'B'post to wheelarch-lower-RH	NLA		
	AHA 7305	Reinforcement-'B'post to wheelarch-lower-LH	1		
10	AHA 8055	PANEL ASSEMBLY-LUGGAGE FLOOR	1		
11	AHA 7240	Reinforcement member-RH	1		
	AHA 7241	Reinforcement member-LH	1		
12	AHA 5731	Panel-rear wheelarch-RH	NLA		
	AHA 5732	Panel-rear wheelarch-LH	NLA		
13	AHA 5729	Gusset-wheelarch to luggage floor-RH	1		
	AHA 5730	Gusset-wheelarch to luggage floor-LH	1		
14	AHA 5837	Extension-luggage floor-RH	1		
	AHA 5388	Extension-luggage floor-LH	1		

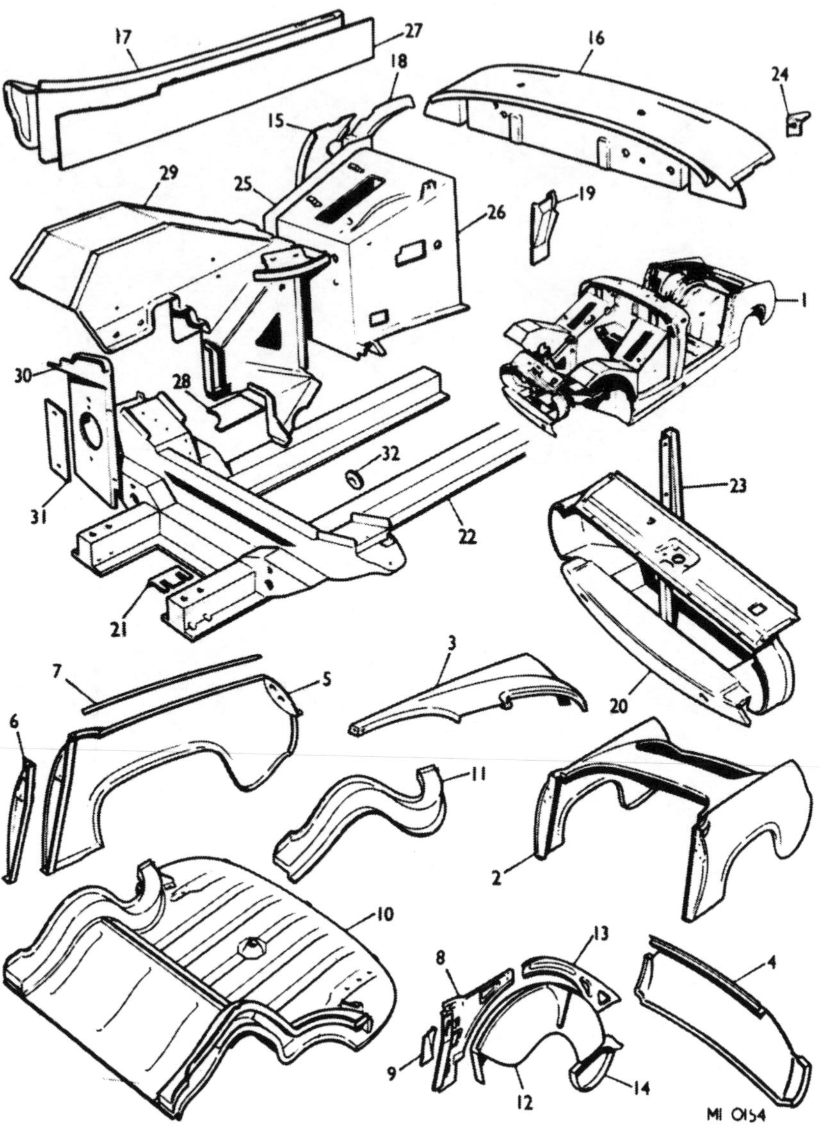

AUSTIN-HEALEY SPRITE MK. 3 AND MK. 4 & MG MIDGET MK. 2 AND MK. 3

NO.	PART NO.	DESCRIPTION	QTY	CHANGE POINT	REMARKS
		BODY SHELL-SPRITE MK 3 AND MIDGET MK 2-continued			
15	AHA 7955	Panel-Shroud side-RH	1		
	AHA 7956	Panel-Shroud side-LH	1		
16	AJA 5118	Panel-Shroud and dash top	1		
17	AHA 5552	Panel-Sill outer-RH	1		
	AHA 5553	Panel-Sill outer-LH	1		
18	AHA 7238	'A'post-RH	1		
	AHA 7239	'A'post-LH	1		
19	AHA 7423	Extension-'A'post to scuttle-LH	1		
20	AHA 5549	End-front	1		
21	AHA 5642	Shim-front end to underframe	A/R		Maximum of 4 used
	SH 604061	Screw	10		
	PWZ 104	Washer-plain	6		
	PWZ 204	Washer-plain	4		
	LWZ 204	Washer-spring	10		
22	28G 118	Front suspension and main beam	1		
23	AHA 5624	Bracket-radiator mounting-RH	1		
	AHA 5626	Bracket-radiator mounting-LH	1		
24	2A 5509	Bracket-handbrake abutment	1		
25	AHA 5620	Panel-footwell outer-RH	1		
	AHA 5622	Panel-footwell outer-LH	1		
26	28G 121	Panel-footwell front and inner side-RH	1		
	28G 122	Panel-footwell front and inner side-LH	1		
27	CZJ 176	Plate-sill side-RH $	1		
	CZJ 177	Plate-sill side-LH $	1		
28	AHA 5465	Plate-splash-RH	NLA		
	AHA 5466	Plate-splash-LH	1		
29	CZJ 432	Wheelarch-front-RH	1		
	CZJ 433	Wheelarch-front-LH	1		
30	CHA 224	Shield-mud-RH	1		
	AHA 6206	Shield-mud-LH	1		
31	AHA 6223	Plate-blanking-mud shield	NLA		Use when heater OR Fresh-air UNIT IS NOT FITTED
	PMZ 306	Screw	2		
	LWZ 203	Washer-spring	2		
	FNZ 103	Nut	2		

$ This item is subject to safety regulations

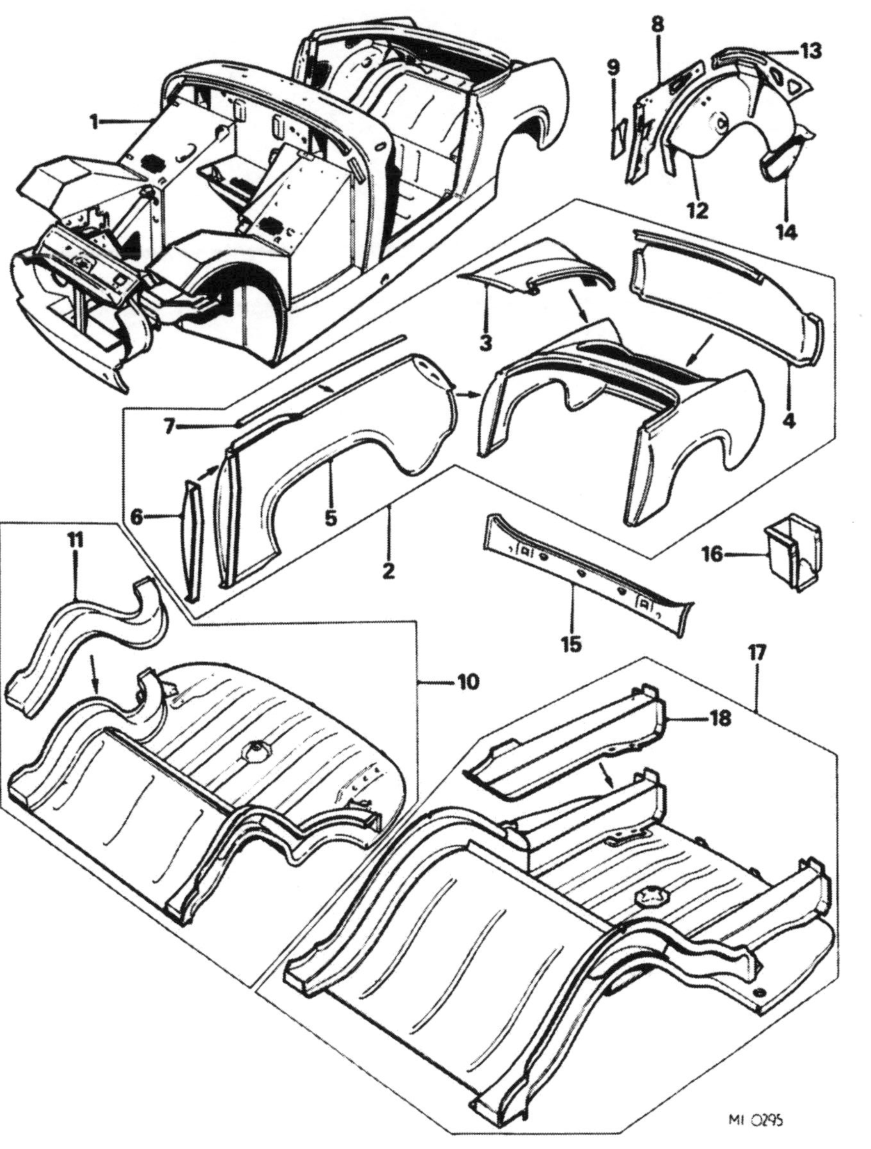

AUSTIN-HEALEY SPRITE MK. 3 AND MK. 4 & MG MIDGET MK. 2 AND MK. 3

BODY SHELL-SPRITE MK 4 AND MIDGET MK 3

NO.	PART NO.	DESCRIPTION	QTY	CHANGE POINT	REMARKS
1	CZJ 365	BODYSHELL AND UNDERFRAME ASSEMBLY(LESS BOOT LID, BONNET PANEL,DOORS AND FRONT WINGS)	NLA	Use prior to CZJ 494	Except N.America and Sweden
1	CZJ 494	BODYSHELL AND UNDERFRAME ASSEMBLY(LESS BOOT LID, BONNET PANEL,DOORS AND FRONT WINGS)	NLA	(C)G-AN5-138801 TO 154100	Except N.America and Sweden
1	CZJ 663	BODYSHELL AND UNDERFRAME ASSEMBLY(LESS BOOT LID, BONNET PANEL,DOORS AND FRONT WINGS) $	1	(C)G-AN6-154101 ON	Was CZJ 605 Except N.America.
1	AHA 8602	BODYSHELL AND UNDERFRAME ASSEMBLY(LESS BOOT LID, BONNET PANEL,DOORS AND FRONT WINGS) $	1	Use prior to CZJ 140	N.America,Sweden
1	CZJ 140	BODYSHELL AND UNDERFRAME ASSEMBLY(LESS BOOT LID, BONNET PANEL,DOORS AND FRONT WINGS) $	1	(C)H-AN9-77591 TO 85286	N.America,Sweden
2	CZJ 347	PANEL ASSEMBLY-BODY REAR	1	Use prior to CZJ 391	Except N.America and Sweden.
2	CZJ 391	PANEL ASSEMBLY-BODY REAR	1	(C)G-AN5-105501 TO 154100	Except N.America and Sweden.
2	CZJ 599	PANEL ASSEMBLY-BODY REAR	1	(C)G-AN6-154101 ON	Except N.America.
3	AHA 8023	Panel-wing inner-RH	1		
	AHA 8024	Panel-wing inner-LH	1		
4	CZJ 70	Panel-body rear-lower	1	Use prior to CZJ 598.	Except N.America.
4	CZJ 598	Panel-body rear-lower	1	(C)G-AN6-154101 ON	Except N.America.
4	CZJ 70	Panel-body rear-lower	1	Use prior to CZJ 475	N.America.
4	CZJ 475	Panel-body rear-lower	1	(C)G-AN5-138801 TO 154100	N.America.
4	CZJ 642	Panel-body rear-lower	1	(C)G-AN6-154101 ON	N.America.

$ This item is subject to safety regulations.

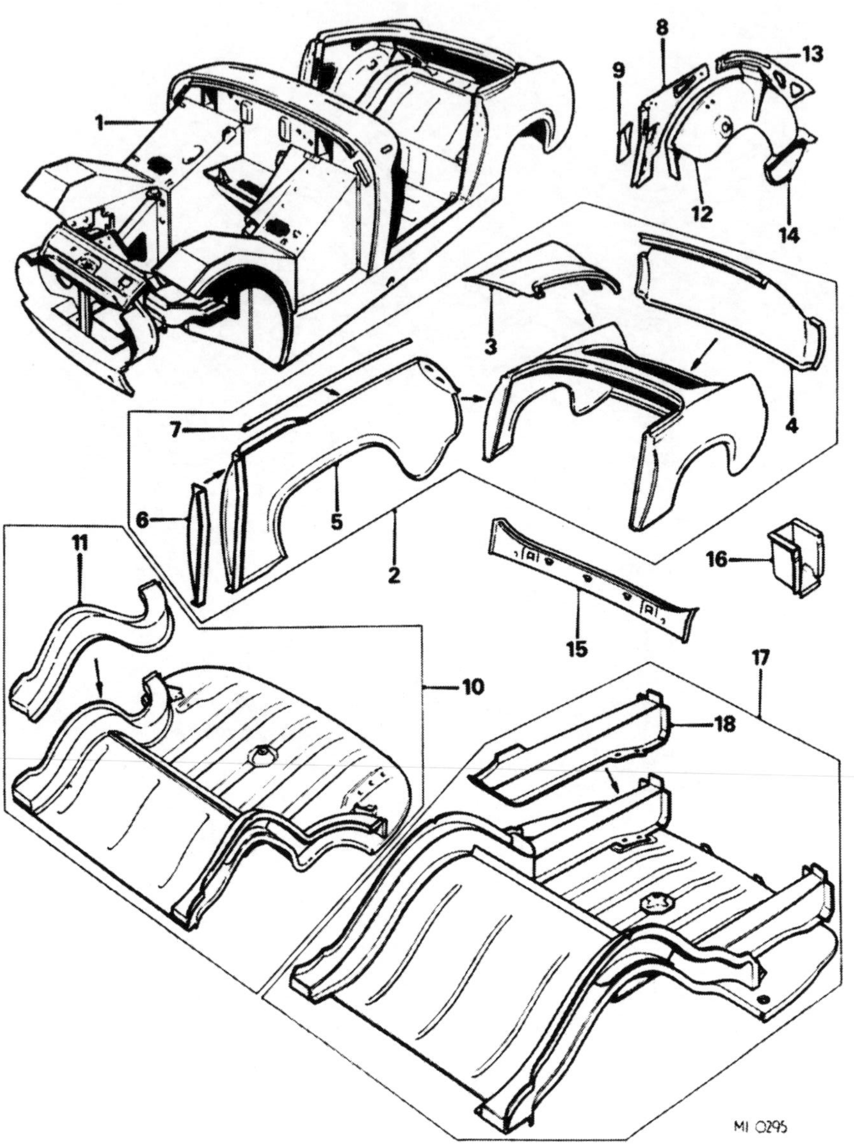

AUSTIN-HEALEY SPRITE MK. 3 AND MK. 4 & MG MIDGET MK. 2 AND MK. 3

BODY SHELL-SPRITE MK 4 AND MIDGET MK 3-continued

NO.	PART NO.	DESCRIPTION	QTY	CHANGE POINT	REMARKS
5	CZJ 220	WING ASSEMBLY-REAR-RH $	1	Use prior to CZJ 408 and 409	
	CZJ 221	WING ASSEMBLY-REAR-LH $	1		
5	CZJ 408	WING ASSEMBLY-REAR-RH	1	(C)G-AN5-105501 TO 123730 N.America (C)G-AN5-105501 TO 154100(except N.America)	
	CZJ 409	WING ASSEMBLY-REAR-LH	1		
5	CZJ 590	WING ASSEMBLY-REAR-RH $	1	(C)G-AN6-154101 ON	Except N.America.
	CZJ 591	WING ASSEMBLY-REAR-LH $	1		
6	AHA 7229	'B'post-RH $	1		
	AHA 7230	'B'post-LH $	1		
7	AHA 8025	Moulding-rear wing to panel	2		
5	CZJ 464	WING ASSEMBLY-REAR-RH $	1	(C)G-AN5-123731 TO 154100	North America.
	CZJ 465	WING ASSEMBLY-REAR-LH $	1		
5	CZJ 592	WING ASSEMBLY-REAR-RH $	1	(C)G-AN6-154101 ON	
	CZJ 593	WING ASSEMBLY-REAR-LH $	1		
6	CZJ 458	'B'post-RH	1	(C)G-AN5-123731 TO 154100	
	CZJ 459	'B'posr-LH	1		
7	AHA 8025	Moulding-rear wing to panel	1	(C)G-AN6-154101 ON	
8	AHA 8014	Reinforcement-'B'post to wheelarch-upper-RH	1		
	AHA 8015	Reinforcement-'B'post to wheelarch-upper-LH	1		
9	AHA 7304	Reinforcement-'B'post to wheelarch-lower-RH	NLA		
	AHA 7305	Reinforcement-'B'post to wheelarch-lower-LH	1		

$ This item is subject to safety regulations.

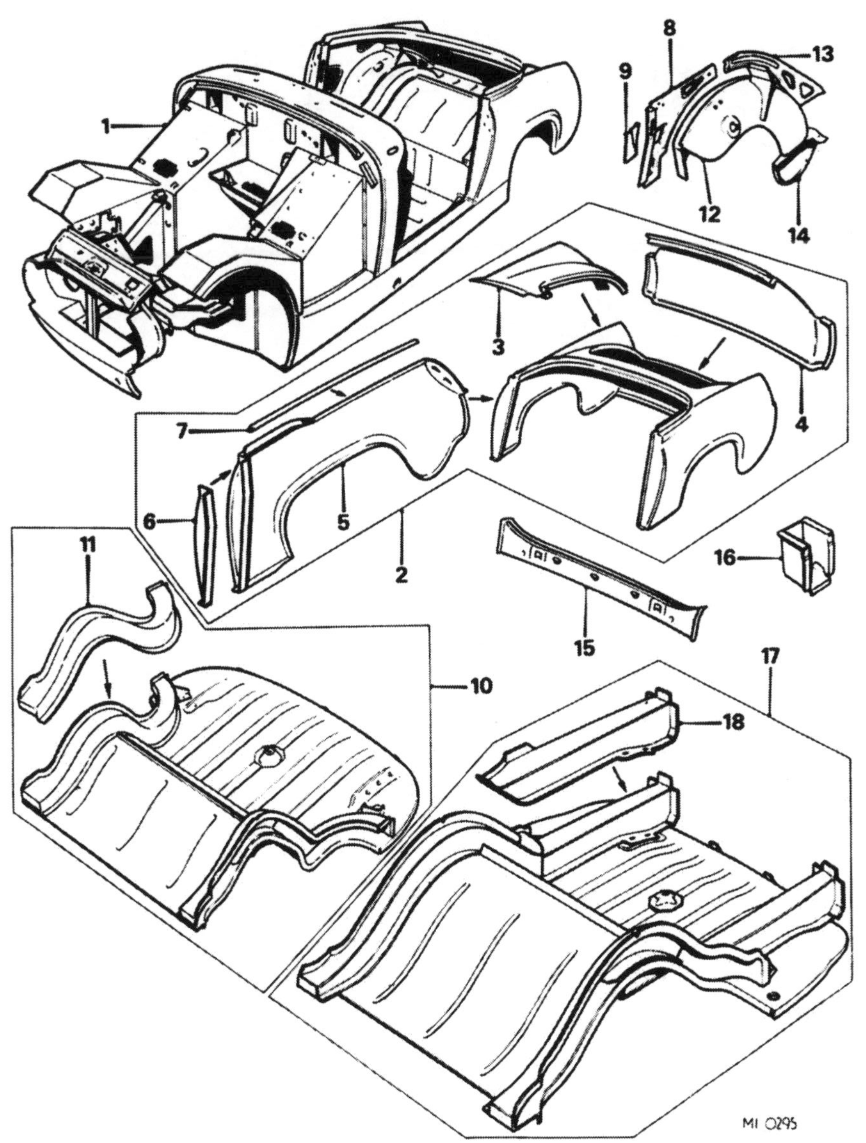

AUSTIN-HEALEY SPRITE MK. 3 AND MK. 4 & MG MIDGET MK. 2 AND MK. 3

NO.	PART NO.	DESCRIPTION	QTY	CHANGE POINT	REMARKS
		BODY SHELL-SPRITE MK.4 AND MIDGET MK.3-continued			
10	AHA 8055	PANEL ASSEMBLY-LUGGAGE FLOOR	1	Use prior to CZJ 267	
10	CZJ 267	PANEL ASSEMBLY-LUGGAGE FLOOR	1	(C)H-AN10-85287 TO 86803 (C)A-AN10-86804 TO 87824 (C)G-AN5-74886 TO 138800	
10	CZJ 34	PANEL ASSEMBLY-LUGGAGE FLOOR	1	(C)G-AN5-138801 TO 154100	
17	CZJ 569	PANEL ASSEMBLY-LUGGAGE FLOOR $	1	(C)G-AN6-154101 ON	
18	CZJ 644	Beam-mounting-rear bumper-RH	1		
	CZJ 645	Beam-mounting-rear bumper-LH	1		
11	AHA 7240	Reinforcement member-RH	1		
	AHA 7241	Reinforcement member-LH	1		
12	AHA 8033	Panel-rear wheelarch-RH	1	Use prior to CZJ 400 and CZJ 401	
	AHA 8034	Panel-rear wheelarch-LH	1		
12	CZJ 400	Panel-rear wheelarch-RH	1	(C)G-AN5-105501 TO 138800-UK and TO 154100 Not UK.	
	CZJ 401	Panel-rear wheelarch-LH	1		
12	CZJ 150	Panel-rear wheelarch-RH	1	(C)G-AN5-138801 TO 154100-UK.	
	CZJ 151	Panel-rear wheelarch-LH	1		
12	CZJ 614	Panel-rear wheelarch-RH $	1	(C)G-AN6-154101 ON	Except N.America
	CZJ 615	Panel-rear wheelarch-LH $	1		
12	CZJ 616	Panel-rear wheelarch-RH $	1		N.America.
	CZJ 617	Panel-rear wheelarch-LH $	1		
13	AHA 8035	Gusset-wheelarch to luggage floor-RH	1		
	AHA 8036	Gusset-wheelarch to luggage floor-LH	1		
14	AHA 5837	Extension-luggage floor-RH	1		
	AHA 5838	Extension-luggage floor-LH	1		
15	AHA 8017	Stiffener-cockpit-rear	1		
16	CZJ 258	Bracket-check strap	NLA		

$ This item is subject to safety regulations.

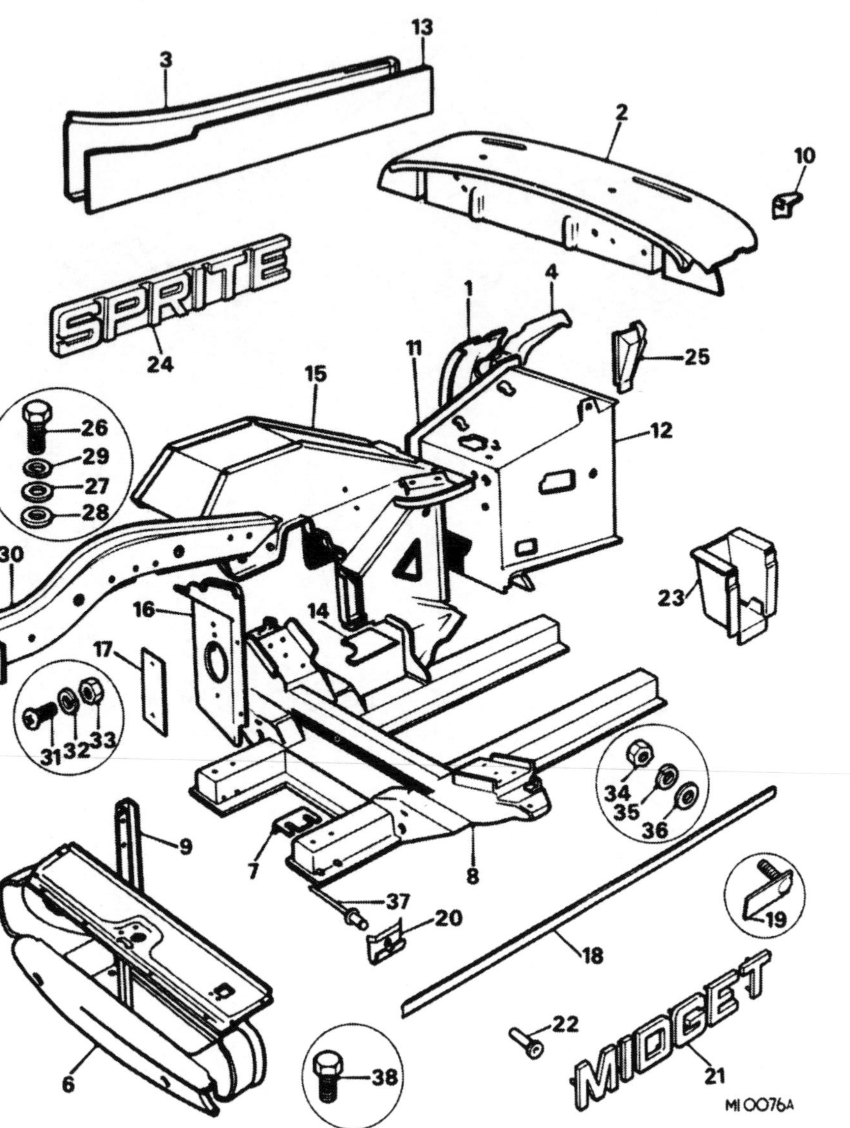

AUSTIN-HEALEY SPRITE MK. 3 AND MK. 4 & MG MIDGET MK. 2 AND MK. 3

BODY SHELL-SPRITE MK.4 AND MIDGET MK.3-continued

NO.	PART NO.	DESCRIPTION	QTY	CHANGE POINT	REMARKS
1	AHA 7955	Panel-shroud side-RH	1		
	AHA 7956	Panel-shroud side-LH	1		
2	AJA 5118	Panel-shroud and dash top	1		
2	AHA 8615	Panel-shroud and dash top	1		N.America and Sweden
3	AHA 5552	Panel-sill outer-RH	1	Use prior to CZJ 694/5.	
	AHA 5553	Panel-sill outer-LH	1		
3	CZJ 694	Panel-sill outer-RH	1	(C)G-AN6-157672 ON	
	CZJ 695	Panel-sill outer-LH	1		
4	AHA 7238	'A'post-RH	1		
	AHA 7239	'A'post-LH	1		
25	AHA 7423	Extension-'A'post to scuttle-LH	1		
6	AHA 5549	End-front	1	Use prior to CZJ 565.	
	CZJ 565	End-front	1	(C)G-AN6-154101 ON	
7	AHA 5642	Shim-front end to underframe	NLA		
26	SH 604061	Screw	10		
27	PWZ 104	Washer-plain	6		
28	PWZ 204	Washer-plain	4		
29	LWZ 204	Washer-spring	10		
8	28G 118	Front suspension and main beam	1	Use prior to CZJ 676.	
	CZJ 676	Front suspension and main beam	1	(C)G-AN6-154101 ON	
9	AHA 5624	Bracket-radiator mounting-RH	1		
	AHA 5626	Bracket-radiator mounting-LH	1		
10	2A 5509	Bracket-hand brake abutment	1		
11	AHA 5620	Panel-footwell outer-RH	1		
	AHA 5622	Panel-footwell outer-LH	1		
12	AHA 8284	Panel-footwell front and inner side-RH	1		
	AHA 8285	Panel-footwell front and inner side-LH	1		
	AHA 8860	Panel-footwell front and inner side-LH	1		Use with collapsible type steering column
13	CZJ 176	Panel-sill side-RH $	1		
	CZJ 177	Panel-sill side-LH $	1		
14	AHA 5465	Plate-splash-RH	1		
	AHA 5466	Plate-splash-LH	1		
15	CZJ 432	Wheelarch-front-RH	1	Use prior to CZJ 682/3.	
	CZJ 433	Wheelarch-front-LH	1		
15	CZJ 682	Wheelarch-front-RH	1	(C)G-AN6-154101 ON	
	CZJ 683	Wheelarch-front-LH	1		
30	CZJ 586	Beam-mounting-front bumper-RH	1		Except N.America
	CZJ 587	Beam-mounting-front bumper-LH	1		
	CZJ 638	Beam-mounting-front bumper-RH	1		N.America.
	CZJ 639	Beam-mounting-front bumper-LH	1		

$ This item is subject to safety regulations.

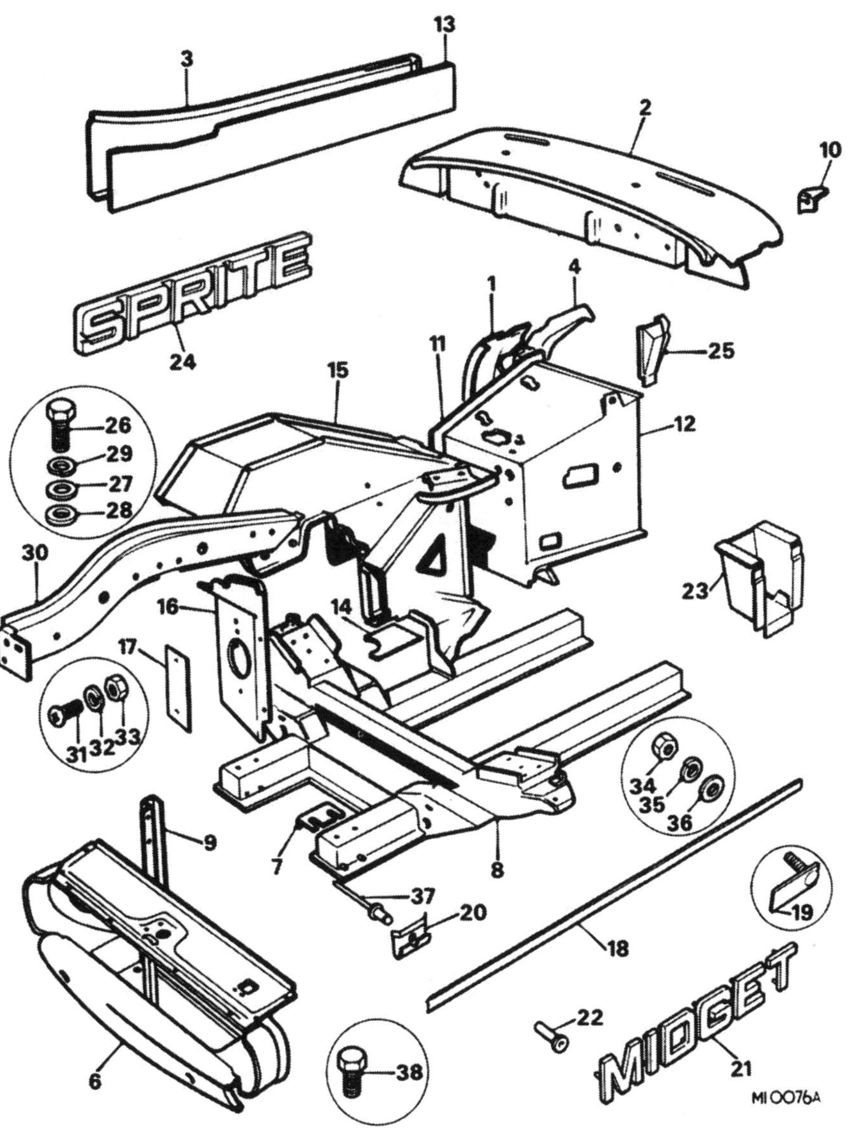

AUSTIN-HEALEY SPRITE MK. 3 AND MK. 4 & MG MIDGET MK. 2 AND MK. 3

BODY SHELL-SPRITE MK4 AND MIDGET MK3-continued.

NO.	PART NO.	DESCRIPTION	QTY	CHANGE POINT	REMARKS
16	AHA 8387	Shield-mud-RH	NLA	Use prior to CHA 224/225	Use CHA 224
	AHA 6206	Shield-mud-LH	1		
16	CHA 224	Shield-mud-RH	1	(C)G-AN5-138801 TO 154100	
	CHA 225	Shield-mud-LH	1		
17	AHA 6223	Plate-blanking-mud shield	NLA	Use prior to (C)G-AN6-154101	Use when heater OR FRESH-AIR UNIT IS NOT FITTED.
31	PMZ 306	Screw	2		
32	LWZ 203	Washer-spring	2		
33	FNZ 103	Nut	2		
18	AHA 9440	Moulding-sill	2	(C)H-AN10-85287 TO 86803 (C)A-AN10-86804 TO 87824 (C)G-AN5-74886 TO 154100 (C)G-AN6-154101 ON	
19	AHA 9447	Stud-plate	2		
34	FNZ 103	Nut-stud plate	2		
35	LWZ 203	Washer-spring	2		
36	PWZ 103	Washer-plain	2		
20	ALA 3647	Clip-moulding	14		
37	DMP 721	Rivet	14		
21	18G 8761	Motif 'Midget'(sill)	2STS		
22	BDA 500	Fastener-motif	24		
23	CZJ 258	Bracket-check strap	2		N.America and Sweden.
38	HZS 405	Screw-front end	10		
24	AHA 9658	Motif 'Sprite'(sill)	2		

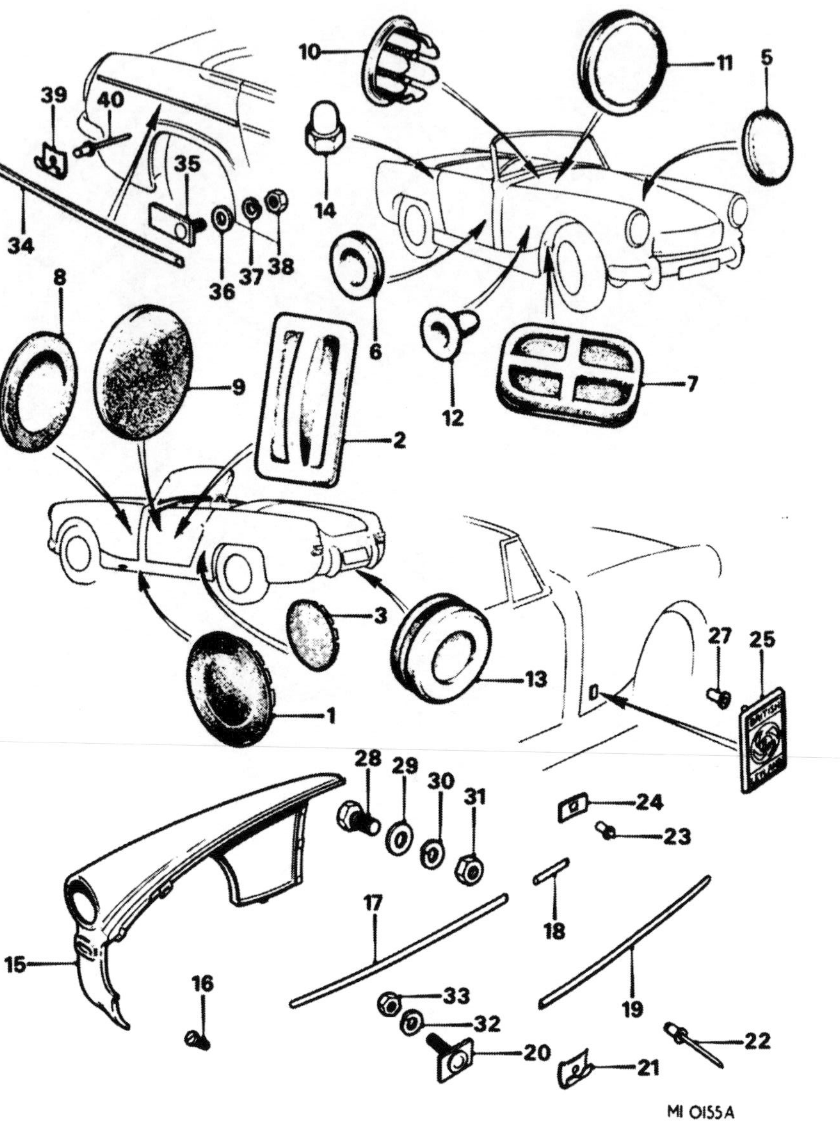

AUSTIN-HEALEY SPRITE MK. 3 AND MK. 4 & MG MIDGET MK. 2 AND MK. 3

NO.	PART NO.	DESCRIPTION	QTY	CHANGE POINT	REMARKS
		BODY SHELL BLANKING PLUGS.			
1	2H 8198	Plug-blanking-Sill outer panel	2/4		
2	4G 4920	Plug-blanking-Gearbox filler hole	1	Finished at (C)G-AN6-175959 (N.America) (C)G-AN6-182084 (UK).	
3	4G 1851	Plug-blanking-Propeller shaft oiling hole	1		
5	RFR 210	Plug-blanking-LH foot-well	2		
5	RFR 210	Plug-blanking-bulkhead	1		When Automatic Choke fitted
6	RFR 207	Plug-blanking-Safety strap hole in tunnel	2		
7	AHA 6296	Plug-blanking-Toe-box side-RH	1	Finished at (C)G-AN6-175959 (N.America) (C)G-AN6-182084 (UK).	
8	BHA 4536	Plug-blanking-Steering-column hole	1		
9	4G 9763	Plug-blanking-Demister outlet hole	2		Use when heater is not fitted.
10	AHH 5514	Plug-blanking-hole in fascia panel-heater switch or fresh-air unit control	1		Used when heater or fresh-air unit IS NOT FITTED.
11	CFP 625	Plug-blanking-hole in dash	A/R		
12	ADA 2493	Plug-blanking-foot-well side panel	2		
13	AHA 8401	Plug-blanking-Mud-shield	2		
14	14B 2685	Nut-dome-safety strap weld bolt on rear wheelarch	4		
	PWZ 105	Washer-plain	4		
	WL 600051	Washer-spring	4		

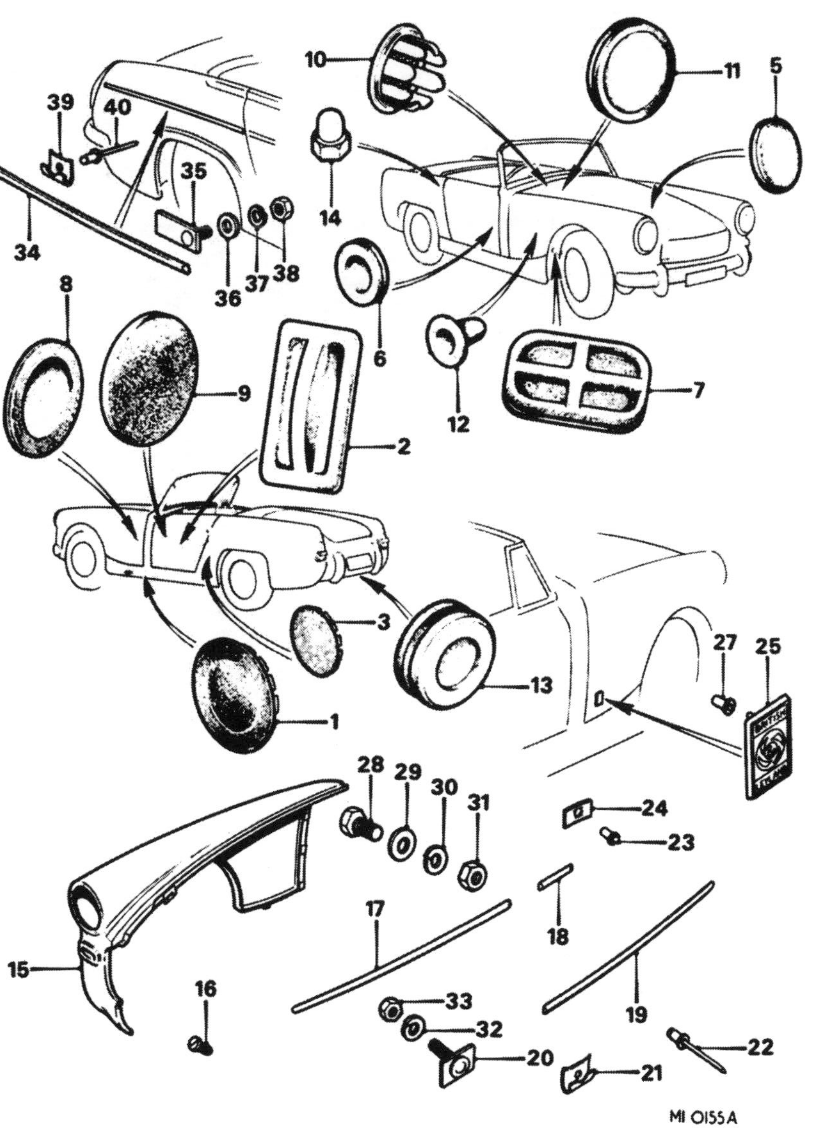

AUSTIN-HEALEY SPRITE MK. 3 AND MK. 4 & MG MIDGET MK. 2 AND MK. 3

WING DETAILS

NO.	PART NO.	DESCRIPTION	QTY	CHANGE POINT	REMARKS
15	AHA 7393	Wing-front-RH	1	Use prior to CZJ 361 and CZJ 279	
	AHA 5546	Wing-front-LH	1		
15	CZJ 361	Wing-front-RH	1	(C)H-AN9-77591 TO 85286 (C)H-AN10-85287 TO 86803 (C)A-AN10-86804 TO 87824 (C)G-AN4-66226 TO 74885 (C)G-AN5-74886 TO 154100	
	CZJ 279	Wing-front-LH	1		
15	CZJ 594	Wing-front-RH	1	(C)G-AN6-154101 ON	
	CZJ 595	Wing-front-LH	1		

NOTE: For Rear Wing details see Body Shell Section

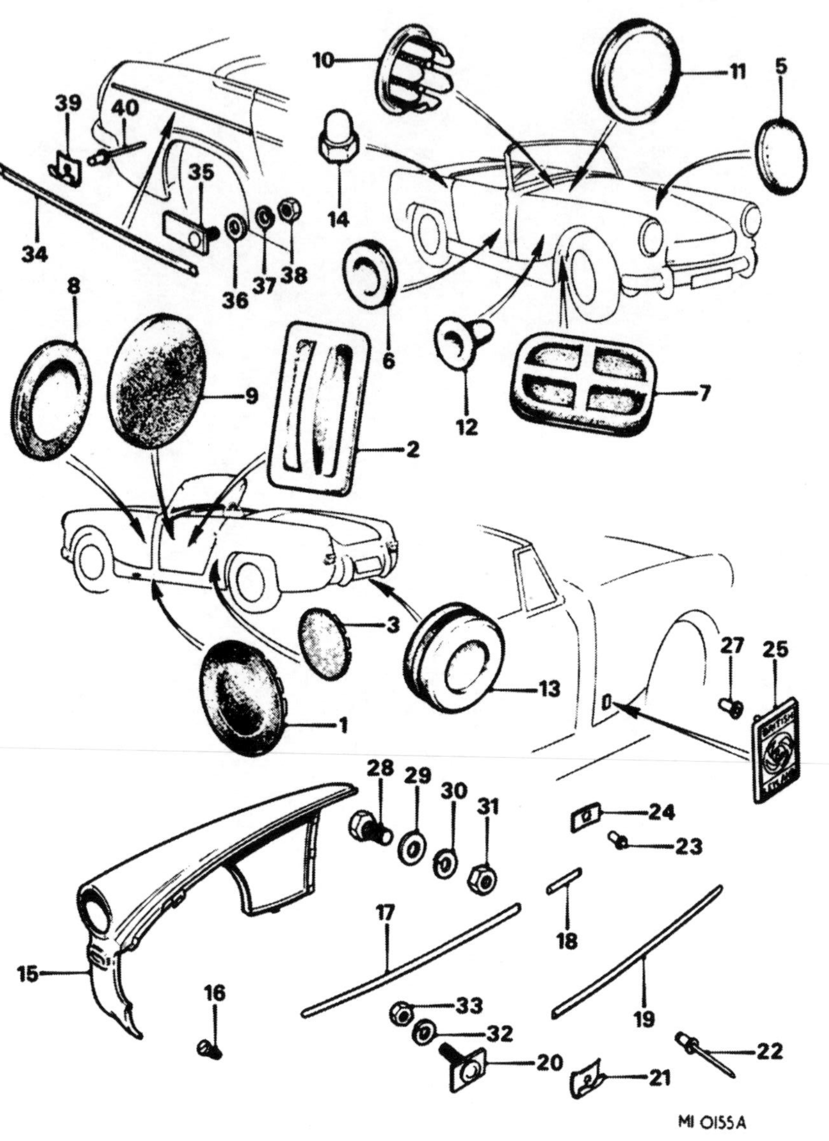

AUSTIN-HEALEY SPRITE MK. 3 AND MK. 4 & MG MIDGET MK. 2 AND MK. 3

NO.	PART NO.	DESCRIPTION	QTY	CHANGE POINT	REMARKS
		WING DETAILS-continued			
16	AHA 6352	Screw-front wing(round head)	NLA		
28	HZS 405	Screw-front wing(hexagon head)	16		
29	PWZ 104	Washer-plain-screw	28		
30	LWZ 204	Washer-spring-screw	22		
31	NH 604041	Nut-screw	6		
17	AHA 5825	Moulding-front wing	2	Use prior to (C)H-AN9-85286 (C)G-AN4-74885	Midget
18	AHA 5822	Moulding-shroud side panel	2		
19	AHA 5818	Moulding-rear wing	2		
20	AHA 5817	Stud plate-wing moulding	4		
32	LWZ 203	Washer-spring-stud plate	4		
33	FNZ 103	Nut-stud plate	4		
21	ALA 3647	Clip-wing moulding	30		
22	DMP 721	Rivet-clip	30		
23	BCA 4590	Clip-speed-shroud side panel moulding	2		
24	BHA 4082	Push-on-fix-shroud side panel moulding	2		
25	CZH 657	Badge-British Leyland	2	(C)H-AN10-85287 TO 86803 (C)A-AN10-86804 TO 87824 (C)G-AN5-74886 TO 118598	Except Arab countries
27	13H 217	Fix-badge to wing	4		
25	CZH 2717	Badge-British Leyland	1	(C)G-AN5-118599 TO 154100 (C)G-AN6-154101 ON	
34	CHA 347	Moulding-rear wing-RH	1	(C)G-AN6-154101 ON	
	CHA 348	Moulding-rear wing-LH	1		
35	AHA 9447	Stud-plate-wing moulding	2		
36	WA 702101	Washer-plain	2		
37	WL 700101	Washer-spring	2		
38	FNZ 103	Nut-stud plate	2		
39	ALA 3647	Clip-moulding	6		
40	DMP 721	Rivet-clip	6		

AUSTIN-HEALEY SPRITE MK. 3 AND MK. 4 & MG MIDGET MK. 2 AND MK. 3

DOORS AND FITTINGS.

NO.	PART NO.	DESCRIPTION	QTY	CHANGE POINT	REMARKS
1	AHA 8518	DOOR ASSEMBLY-RH	NLA	Use prior to AHA 8436 and AHA 8437	
	AHA 8519	DOOR ASSEMBLY-LH	NLA		
1	AHA 8436	DOOR ASSEMBLY-RH $	1	(C)H-AN9-72041 TO 85286 (C)H-AN10-85287 TO 86803 (C)A-AN10-86804 TO 87824 (C)G-AN4-60460 TO 74885 (C)G-AN5-74886 TO 123730 N.America (C)G-AN5-74886 TO 138000 except N.America	
	AHA 8437	DOOR ASSEMBLY-LH $	1		
1	CZJ 478	DOOR ASSEMBLY-RH $	1	(C)G-AN5-138001 TO 154100 (C)G-AN6-154101 ON	Except USA and Canada.
	CZJ 479	DOOR ASSEMBLY-LH $	1		
1	CZJ 452	DOOR ASSEMBLY-RH $	1	(C)G-AN5-123731 TO 138000	USA and Canada.
	CZJ 453	DOOR ASSEMBLY-LH $	1		
1	CZJ 480	DOOR ASSEMBLY-RH $	1	(C)G-AN5-138001 TO 154100 (C)G-AN6-154101 ON	
	CZJ 481	DOOR ASSEMBLY-LH $	1		
2	AHA 7428	Hinge $	4		
	HZS 505	Screw	8		
	LWZ 505	Washer-shakeproof	8		
	PMZ 408	Screw	12		
	LWZ 404	Washer-shakeproof	12		
3	AHA 5823	Moulding-side-door-RH	1	Use prior to (C)G-AN4-74885	Midget.
	AHA 5824	Moulding-side-door-LH	1		
4	AHA 5817	Stud plate-moulding	2		
	LWZ 203	Washer-spring	2		
	FNZ 103	Nut	2		
5	ALA 3647	Clip-moulding	10		
6	DMP 721	Rivet	10		
7	4B 3479	Pull-door	2	See(1)foot of page	
8	CZA 2365	End-door pull-RH	2	(C)H-AN9-72041 TO 85286 (C)H-AN10-85287 TO 86803 (C)A-AN10-86804 TO 87824 (C)G-AN4-60460 TO 74885 (C)G-AN5-74886 TO 105500	
	CZA 2366	End-door pull-LH	2		
9	CZA 2364	Handle-door pull	2		
	RMP 310	Screw	4		

$ This item is subject to safety regulations.

CHANGE POINTS.
(1).(C)H-AN8-30829 TO 64734,(C)H-AN9-64735 TO 70240,(C)G-AN3-25788 TO 52389,
(C)G-AN4-52390 TO 60459.

1
2
3
4
5
6
7
8
9
10
11
12
13
14
MJO064

AUSTIN-HEALEY SPRITE MK. 3 AND MK. 4 & MG MIDGET MK. 2 AND MK. 3

NO.	PART NO.	DESCRIPTION	QTY	CHANGE POINT	REMARKS
		DOORS AND FITTINGS-continued.			
10	AHA 7634	Seal-waist-door outer-RH	1		
	AHA 7635	Seal-waist-door outer-LH	1		
11	14A 6797	Clip-seal	14		
12	AHA 7719	Weatherstrip-door inner-RH $	1		
	AHA 7720	Weatherstrip-door inner-LH $	1		
13	AHA 7838	Clip-weatherstrip	12		
14	37H 1811	Door-seal-front-upper	2	(C)H-AN9-69428 TO 85286 (C)H-AN10-85287 TO 86803 (C)A-AN10-86804 TO 87824 (C)G-AN4-56971 TO 74885 (C)G-AN5-74886 TO 154100 (C)G-AN6-154101 ON	
	GWS 121	Tape-sealing	A/R		Supplied in 50 metre rolls.

$ This item is subject to safety regulations.

AUSTIN-HEALEY SPRITE MK. 3 AND MK. 4 & MG MIDGET MK. 2 AND MK. 3

NO.	PART NO.	DESCRIPTION	QTY	CHANGE POINT	REMARKS
		DOOR LOCKS AND HANDLES			
1	AHA 7144	Remote control-lock-RH $	1		
	AHA 7145	Remote control-lock-LH $	1		
	PMZ 308	Screw	6		
	PWZ 103	Washer-plain	6		
	LWZ 203	Washer-spring	6		
2	AHA 7033	Lock-door-RH	1	See(1)foot of page	
	AHA 7034	Lock-door-LH	1		
2	AHA 9173	Lock-door-RH $	1	(C)H-AN9-72041 TO 85286 (C)H-AN10-85287 TO 86803 (C)A-AN10-86804 TO 87824 (C)G-AN4-60460 TO 74885 (C)G-AN5-74886 TO 154100 (C)G-AN6-154101 ON	
	AHA 9174	Lock-door-LH $	1		
3	AHA 8433	Handle-remote control $	2		
	LWZ 203	Washer-spring	4		
	PMZ 308	Screw-handle to remote control	2		
3	AHA 7037	Handle-remote control	2	See(1)foot of page	
	CMZ 416	Screw-lock to door	6		
4	AHA 7040	Escutcheon-handle-locking-RH	1		Locking handles fitted to both doors from (C)H-AN9-69049 (C)G-AN4-56715
	AHA 7041	Escutcheon-handle-locking-LH	1		
	MTP 402	Screw	4		
5	AHA 7157	HANDLE ASSEMBLY-DOOR	2	See(1)foot of page	
6	AHA 7188	Button-push	2		
	LWN 403	Washer-shakeproof	2		
	LWZ 203	Washer-spring	2		
5	AHA 8530	HANDLE ASSEMBLY-DOOR $	2	(C)H-AN9-72041 TO 85286 (C)H-AN10-85287 TO 86803 (C)A-AN10-86804 TO 87824 (C)G-AN4-60460 TO 74885 (C)G-AN5-74886 TO 154100 (C)G-AN6-154101 ON	
8	37H 3717	Button-push $	2		
	AJD 8012 Z	Nut-lock	2		
9	14G 2792	Washer-seating $	2		
9	14G 2792	Washer-handle to door-rear(fibre) $	2		
	FNZ 103	Nut	2		
	53K 126	Screw	2		
	PWZ 103	Washer-plain	4		
	LWZ 203	Washer-spring	4		

$ This item is subject to safety regulations

CHANGE POINTS
(1) (C)H-AN8-38829 TO 64734, (C)H-AN9-64735 TO 70240, (C)G-AN3-25788 TO 52389, (C)G-AN4-52390 TO 60459

AUSTIN-HEALEY SPRITE MK. 3 AND MK. 4 & MG MIDGET MK. 2 AND MK. 3

DOOR LOCKS AND HANDLES-continued

NO.	PART NO.	DESCRIPTION	QTY	CHANGE POINT	REMARKS
10	AHA 7035	Striker-lock-RH	NLA	See(1)foot of page	
	AHA 7036	Striker-lock-LH	1		
10	CZA 3310	Striker-lock-RH $	1	(C)H-AN9-72041 TO 85286 (C)H-AN10-85287 TO 86803 (C)A-AN10-86804 TO 87824 (C)G-AN4-60460 TO 74885 (C)G-AN5-74886 TO 154100 (C)G-AN6-154101 ON	
	CZA 3311	Striker-lock-LH $	1		
		SHIM-STRIKER			
11	AHH 8715	.06"(1.6mm) $	A/R		
11	BHH 342	.03"(.80mm) $	A/R		
12	AHH 8589	Plate-tapping-lower-striker	NLA		
13	AHA 7085	Plate-tapping-upper-striker $	2		
	CMZ 402	Screw-long	2	Use prior to AHH 9239	
14	AHH 9239	Screw-long	2	(C)H-AN9-78137 TO 85286 (C)H-AN10-85287 TO 86803 (C)A-AN10-86804 TO 87824 (C)G-AN4-66667 TO 74885 (C)G-AN5-74886 TO 154100 (C)G-AN6-154101 ON	
	CMZ 410	Screw-short	4		
15	AHA 7378	LOCK-PRIVATE-RH	1	See(1)foot of page	
	AHA 7379	LOCK-PRIVATE-LH	1		
15	AHA 8531	LOCK-PRIVATE-RH $	1	(C)H-AN9-72041 TO 85286 (C)H-AN10-85287 TO 86803 (C)A-AN10-86804 TO 87824 (C)G-AN4-60460 TO 74885 (C)G-AN5-74886 TO 154100 (C)G-AN6-154101 ON	
	AHA 8532	LOCK-PRIVATE-LH $	1		
	AHA 7405	Clip-private lock	1		
16	AHA 7404	Barrel-lock $	NLA		
18	AHA 7408	Clip-retaining	2		

$ This item is subject to safety regulations

CHANGE POINTS
(1).(C)H-AN8-38829 TO 64734,(C)H-AN9-64735 TO 72040,(C)G-AN3-25788 TO 52389,,
(C)G-AN4-52390 TO 60459.

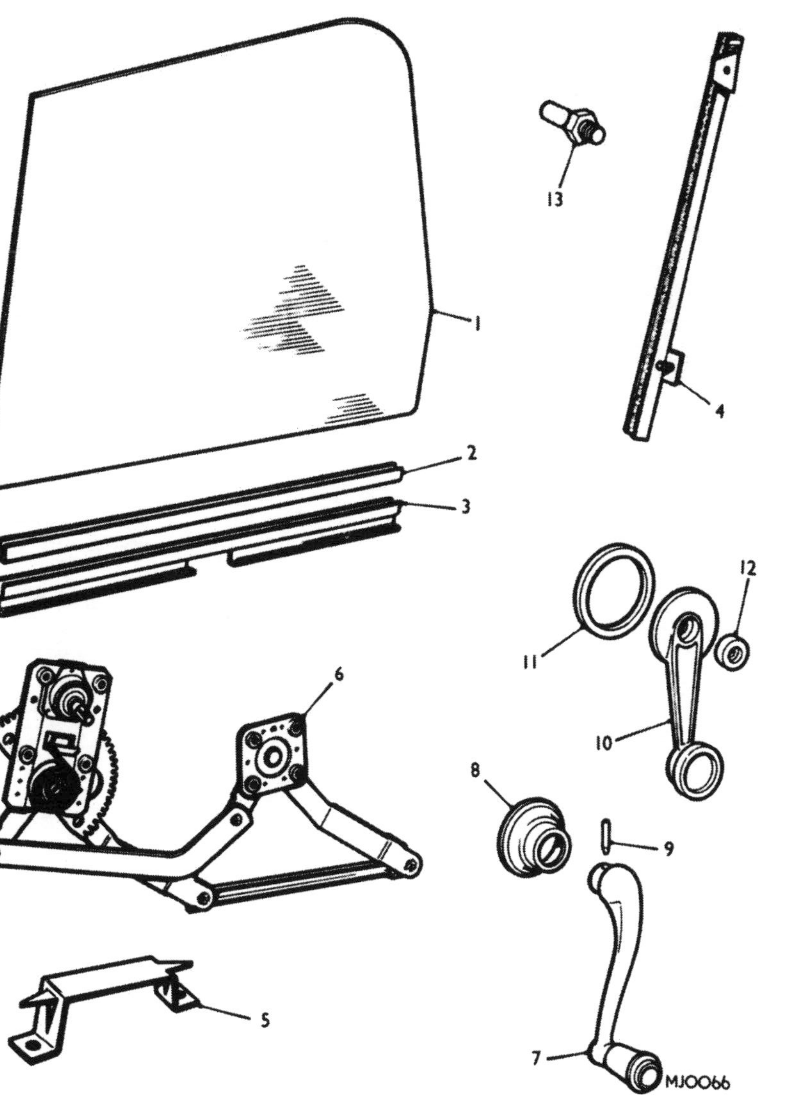

AUSTIN-HEALEY SPRITE MK. 3 AND MK. 4 & MG MIDGET MK. 2 AND MK. 3

NO.	PART NO.	DESCRIPTION	QTY	CHANGE POINT	REMARKS
		WINDOWS AND WINDOW REGULATORS			
1	AHA 7056	Glass-door-RH $	1	See(1)foot of page	
	AHA 7057	Glass-door-LH $	1		
1	AHA 8431	Glass-door-RH $	1	(C)H-AN9-72041 TO 85286 (C)H-AN10-85287 TO 86803 (C)A-AN10-86804 TO 87824 (C)G-AN4-60460 TO 74885 (C)G-AN5-74886 TO 154100 (C)G-AN6-154101 ON	
	AHA 8432	Glass-door-LH $	1		
2	37H 4297	Channel-glazing-46.7cm-18.375"	A/R		Supplied in multiples of feet (30.5cm)
3	AHA 7042	Channel-lower	2		
4	AHA 8405	CHANNEL ASSEMBLY-REAR-RH	1		
	AHA 8406	CHANNEL ASSEMBLY-REAR-LH	1		
	HZS 404	Screw-bracket and channel top to door	6		
	NH 604041	Nut-channel to bracket	2		
	PWZ 104	Washer-plain	8		
	LWZ 204	Washer-spring	8		
5	AHA 7431	Bracket-glass stop	NLA		
	PTZ 1004	Screw-bracket to door	4		
	PFS 410	Nut-spring-screw	4		
6	AHA 7038	Regulator-window-RH	1	See(1)foot of page	
	AHA 7039	Regulator-window-LH	1		
6	AHA 8533	Regulator-window-RH $	1	(C)H-AN9-72041 TO 85286 (C)H-AN10-85287 TO 86803 (C)A-AN10-86804 TO 87824 (C)G-AN4-60460 TO 74885 (C)G-AN5-74886 TO 154100 (C)G-AN6-154101 ON	
	AHA 8534	Regulator-window-LH $	1		

$ This item is subject to safety regulations

CHANGE POINTS.
(1) (C)H-AN8-38829 TO 64734,(C)H-AN9-64735 TO 72040,(C)G-AN3-25788 TO 523899, (C)G-AN4-52390 TO 60459

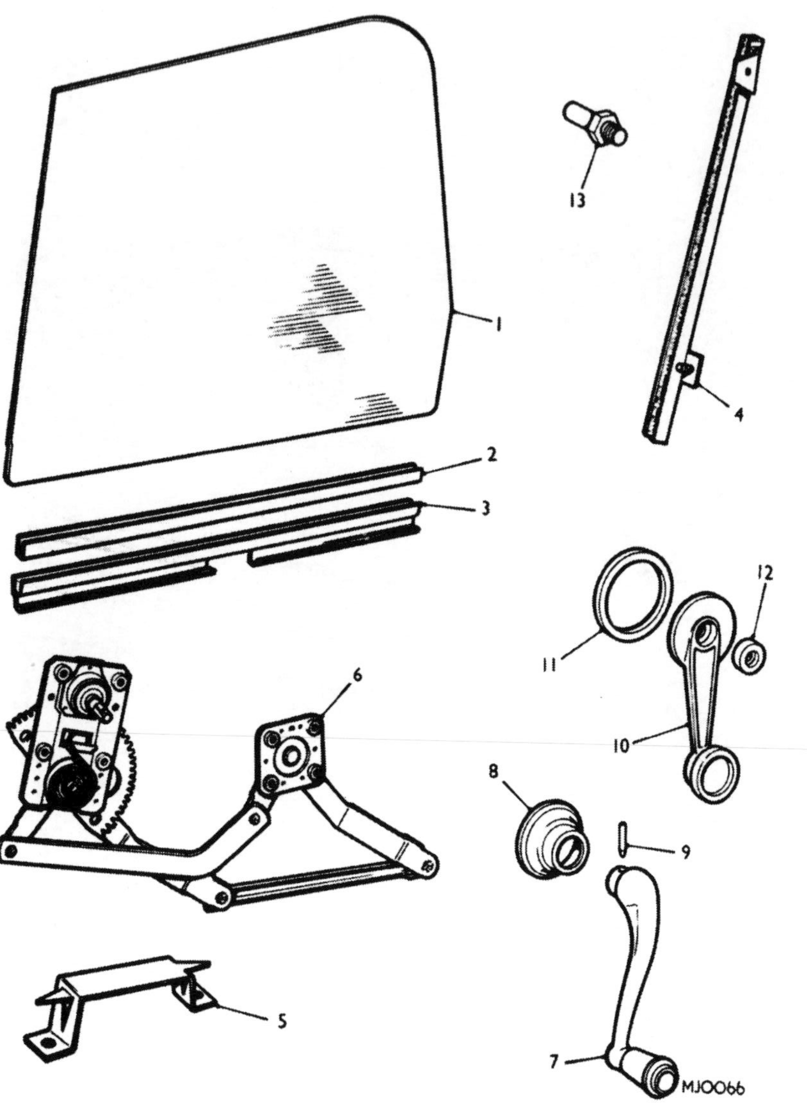

AUSTIN-HEALEY SPRITE MK. 3 AND MK. 4 & MG MIDGET MK. 2 AND MK. 3

NO.	PART NO.	DESCRIPTION	QTY	CHANGE POINT	REMARKS
		WINDOWS AND WINDOW REGULATORS-continued			
	HZS 404	Screw-regulator to door	8		
	PWZ 204	Washer-plain-screw	8		
	LWZ 204	Washer-spring-screw	8		
7	ADH 5481	Handle-regulator	2	See(1)foot of page	
8	ADB 709	Esctucheon-handle	2	See(1)foot of page	
9	ALH 1527	Pin-handle to regulator	2	See(1)foot of page	
10	CZA 7109	Handle-regulator $	2	(C)H-AN9-72041 TO 85286 (C)H-AN10-85287 TO 86803 (C)A-AN10-86804 TO 87824 (C)G-AN4-60460 TO 74885 (C)G-AN5-74886 TO 154100 (C)G-AN6-154101 ON	
11	AHA 8517	Escutcheon-handle to door	2	(as above)	
	CZA 7194	Screw-flanged	2	(as above)	
	PMZ 308	Screw-handle to regulator	2	(as above)	
	LWZ 203	Washer-spring	2	(as above)	
13	AHA 7703	Stop-regulator arm	NLA		
	NH 605041	Nut-stop to door	2		
	PWZ 105	Washer-plain-nut	2		
	LWZ 505	Washer-shakeproof-nut	2		

$ This item is subject to safety regulations

CHANGE POINTS.
(1).(C)H-AN8-38829 TO 64734,(C)H-AN9-64735 TO 72040,(C)G-AN3-25788 TO 52389, (C)G-AN4-52390 TO 60459

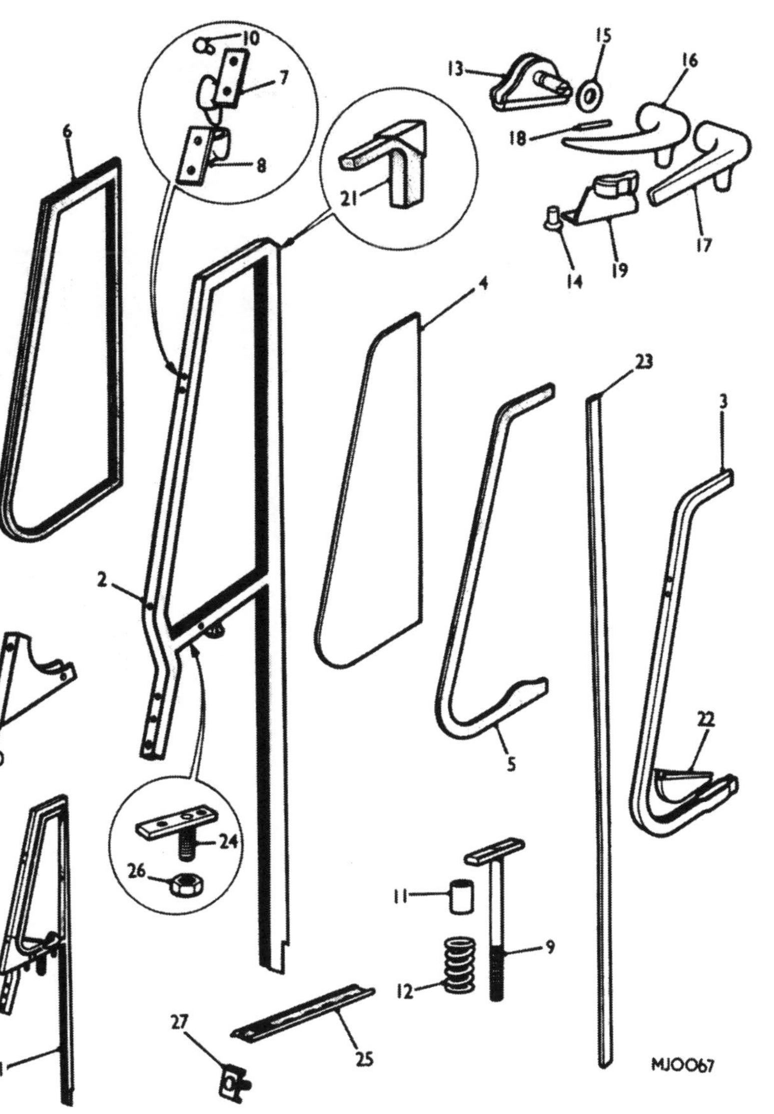

AUSTIN-HEALEY SPRITE MK. 3 AND MK. 4 & MG MIDGET MK. 2 AND MK. 3

NO.	PART NO.	DESCRIPTION	QTY	CHANGE POINT	REMARKS
		WINDOW VENTILATORS			
1	18G 8466	VENTILATOR ASSEMBLY(WITH CURVED LOCKING HANDLE) DOOR-RH $	1		
	18G 8467	VENTILATOR ASSEMBLY(WITH CURVED LOCKING HANDLE) DOOR-LH $	1		
1	18G 8468	VENTILATOR ASSEMBLY(WITH FLAT LOCKING HANDLE) DOOR-RH $	1	Use prior to AHA 9973 and AHA 9974	
	18G 8469	VENTILATOR ASSEMBLY(WITH FLAT LOCKING HANDLE) DOOR-LH $	NLA		Use AHA 9974
1	AHA 9973	VENTILATOR ASSEMBLY-RH $	1	(C)G-AN5-121650 TO 154100 (C)G-AN6-154101 ON	
	AHA 9974	VENTILATOR ASSEMBLY-LH $	1		
2	AHA 7402	Frame-outer-RH	1	Use prior to AHA 9991,AHA 9992, AHA 9989 and AHA 9990	
	AHA 7403	Frame-outer-LH	1		
3	AHA 7480	Frame-inner-RH	1		
	AHA 7481	Frame-inner-LH	1		
2	AHA 9991	Frame-outer-RH	1	(C)G-AN5-121650 TO 154100 (C)G-AN6-154101 ON	
	AHA 9992	Frame-outer-LH	1		
3	AHA 9989	Frame-inner-RH	1		
	AHA 9990	Frame-inner-LH	1		
4	AHA 7482	Glass-RH $	1		
	AHA 7483	Glass-LH $	1		
5	27H 8705 M	Rubber-glazing-19"(49cm)	A/R		Supplied in multiples of metres(39.37")
6	AHA 7416	Rubber-sealing-outer frame-RH	1		
	AHA 7417	Rubber-sealing-outer frame-LH	1		
7	AHA 7463	Pivot-top-upper half-RH	1	Use prior to AHA 9982,AHA 9983 AHA 9984,AHA 9985 and AHA 9981.	
	AHA 7464	Pivot-top-upper half-LH	NLA		
8	AHA 7465	Pivot-top-lower half-RH	NLA		
	AHA 7466	Pivot-top-lower half-LH	1		
9	AHA 7468	Pivot-bottom	2		
7	AHA 9982	Pivot-upper half-RH	1	(C)G-AN5-121650 TO 154100 (C)G-AN6-154101 ON	
	AHA 9983	Pivot-upper half-LH	1		
8	AHA 9984	Pivot-lower half-RH	1		
	AHA 9985	Pivot-lower half-LH	1		
9	AHA 9981	Pivot-lower	2		
10	AHA 7775	Rivet-top pivot to inner frame	4		
11	AHA 7467	Distance-tube-bottom pivot	2		
12	AHA 7544	Spring-bottom pivot	2		
	PWZ 104	Washer-plain-bottom pivot	4		
	LWZ 204	Washer-spring-bottom pivot	2		
	NH 604041	Nut-bottom pivot to frame	4		
13	27H 3351	Bracket curved locking handle(with pivot)	NLA		
13	37H 4347	Bracket flat locking handle (with pivot)	NLA		
14	AHA 7554	Rivet-bracket to inner frame	2		
15	AHA 7473	Washer-waved	2		

$ This item is subject to safety regulations.

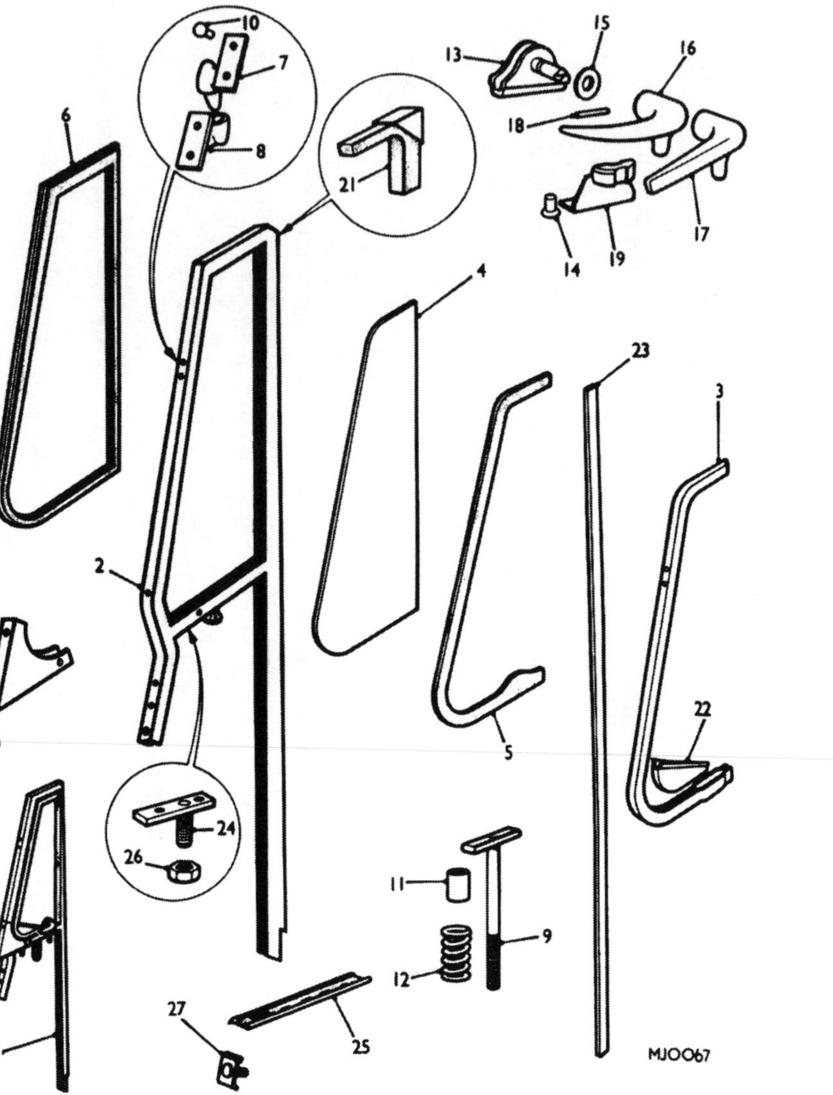

AUSTIN-HEALEY SPRITE MK. 3 AND MK. 4 & MG MIDGET MK. 2 AND MK. 3

WINDOW VENTILATORS-continued

NO.	PART NO.	DESCRIPTION	QTY	CHANGE POINT	REMARKS
16	AHA 7469	Handle-curved locking-RH	NLA		
	AHA 7470	Handle-curved locking-LH	1		
17	AHA 8446	Handle-flat locking-RH $	1		
	AHA 8447	Handle-flat locking-LH $	1		
18	AHA 7474	Pin-locking handle $	2		
19	AHA 7475	Plate-catch-locking handle-RH $	1		
	AHA 7476	Plate-catch-locking handle-LH $	1		
20	AHA 7484	Capping-front corner-RH	1	Use prior to AHA 9993 and AHA 9994	
	AHA 7485	Capping-front corner-LH	1		
20	AHA 9993	Capping-corner-RH	1	(C)G-AN5-121650 TO 154100 (C)G-AN6-154101 ON	
	AHA 9994	Capping-corner-LH	1		
	CZP 404	Screw-capping to frame-side	2		
21	AHH 8935	Block-top corner(rubber)	2	Use prior to AHA 9986,AHA 9987 and AHA 9988.	
22	AHA 7477	Channel-drain-RH	1		
	AHA 7478	Channel-drain-LH	1		
21	AHA 9986	Block-corner	2	(C)G-AN5-121650 TO 154100 (C)G-AN6-154101 ON	
22	AHA 9987	Channel-drain-RH	1		
	AHA 9988	Channel-drain-LH	1		
23	AHH 7448	Channel-door glass	2		
24	AHA 7543	Plate-stud-ventilator	NLA		
25	AHA 7746	Seal-ventilator to door-RH	1		
	AHA 7747	Seal-ventilator to door-LH	1		
26	AHH 6343	Nut-ventilator to door waist	NLA		
	PWZ 204	Washer-plain-nut	4		
	LWZ 304	Washer-spring-nut	4		
	HZS 507	Screw-ventilator to door front lower	4		
	WL 600051	Washer-spring	4		
	KXR 416	Rivet-packing to frame foot	2		
	HZS 404	Screw-bracket to door	4		
	PWZ 104	Washer-plain-screw	4		
	LWZ 204	Washer-spring-screw	4		
	PWZ 104	Washer-plain-stud plate	2		
	LWZ 204	Washer-spring-stud plate	2		
	NH 604041	Nut-stud plate	2		

$ This item is subject to safety regulations.

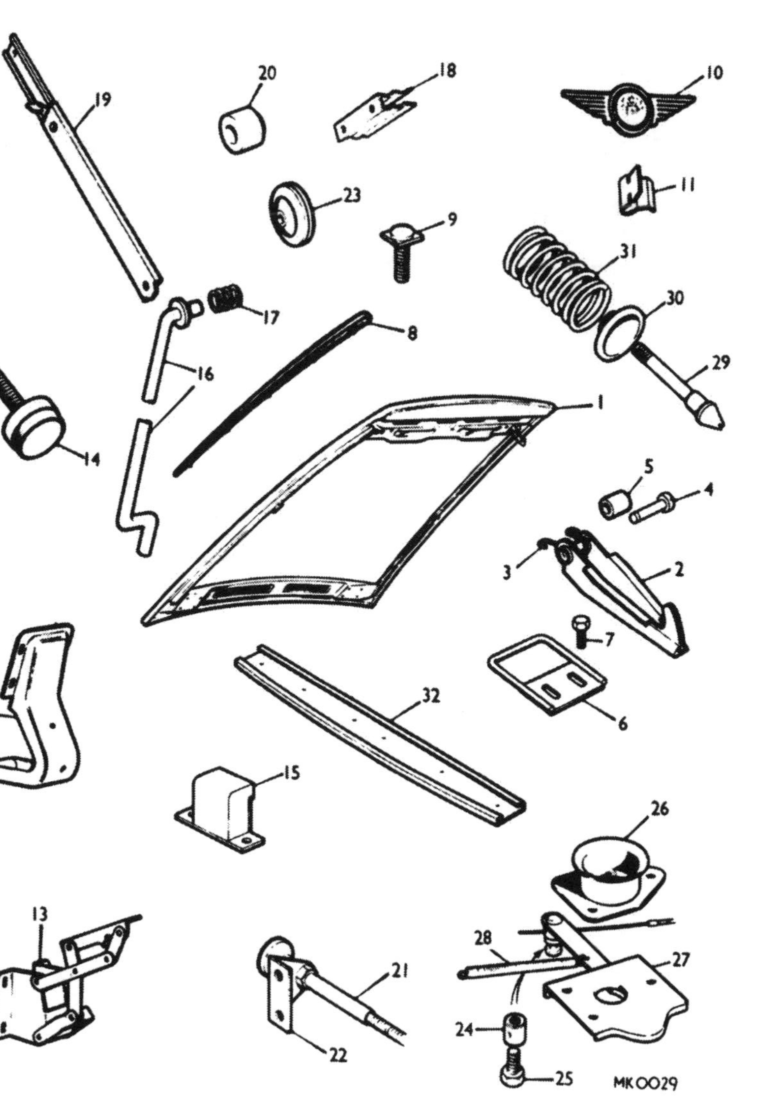

AUSTIN-HEALEY SPRITE MK. 3 AND MK. 4 & MG MIDGET MK. 2 AND MK. 3

BONNET AND CONTROL.

NO.	PART NO.	DESCRIPTION	QTY	CHANGE POINT	REMARKS
	AJA 5117	BONNET ASSEMBLY $	NLA		Use CZJ 380
2	14A 366	CATCH ASSEMBLY-SAFETY $	1		
3	4B 8646	Spring $	1		
1	CZJ 380	Panel-bonnet $	1	Use prior to CZJ 704	
1	CZJ 704	Panel-bonnet	1	(C)G-AN6-183740 ON	
2	4B 8644	Hook-bonnet	1	(C)H-AN10-86301 TO 86803 (C)A-AN10-86804 TO 87824 (C)G-AN5-89501 TO 154100 (C)G-AN6-154101 ON	
3	4B 8646	Spring $	1		
4	4B 8769	Pin	NLA		
5	4B 8768	Piece-distance	1		
6	AHA 5617	Bracket-safety catch $	1		
	PWZ 103	Washer-plain	2		
	LWZ 203	Washer-spring	2		
8	14A 7074	Moulding-bonnet centre	1	(C)G-AN3-25788 TO 52389 (C)G-AN4-52390 TO 66225	Midget.
9	AHA 5700	Stud plate-moulding-front	2		
9	AHA 5701	Stud plate-moulding-No.3	1		
9	AHA 6257	Stud plate-moulding-No.4	1		
9	AHA 5702	Stud plate-moulding-rear	1		
	FNZ 103	Nut	3		
	LWZ 203	Washer-spring	3		
	CNZ 102	Nut	2		
	LWZ 202	Washer-spring	2		
10	AHA 5518	Badge-bonnet	1		Sprite.
11	14A 5542	Clip-badge to bonnet	4		
12	14A 4684	Hinge-bonnet $	2		Except N.America And Sweden
13	CZJ 104	Hinge-bonnet-RH $	1		N.America and Sweden.
	CZJ 105	Hinge-bonnet-LH $	1		
32	AHA 5514	Finisher-grille surround-upper	1	Use prior to (C)G-AN6-154101	
	HZS 405	Screw	8		
	PWZ 104	Washer-plain	8		
	LWZ 204	Washer-spring	8		
	HBZ 524	Bolt	2		
	LNZ 405	Locknut	2		
14	AHA 5654	Buffer-side	2	Use prior to CZG 1668	
	CZG 1668	Buffer-side	2	(C)G-AN6-183740 ON	
	FNZ 205	Locknut	2		
15	AHA 5674	Buffer-side	2		
	PMZ 306	Screw	4		
	LWZ 203	Washer-spring	4		
	FNZ 103	Nut	4		

$ This item is subject to safety regulations.

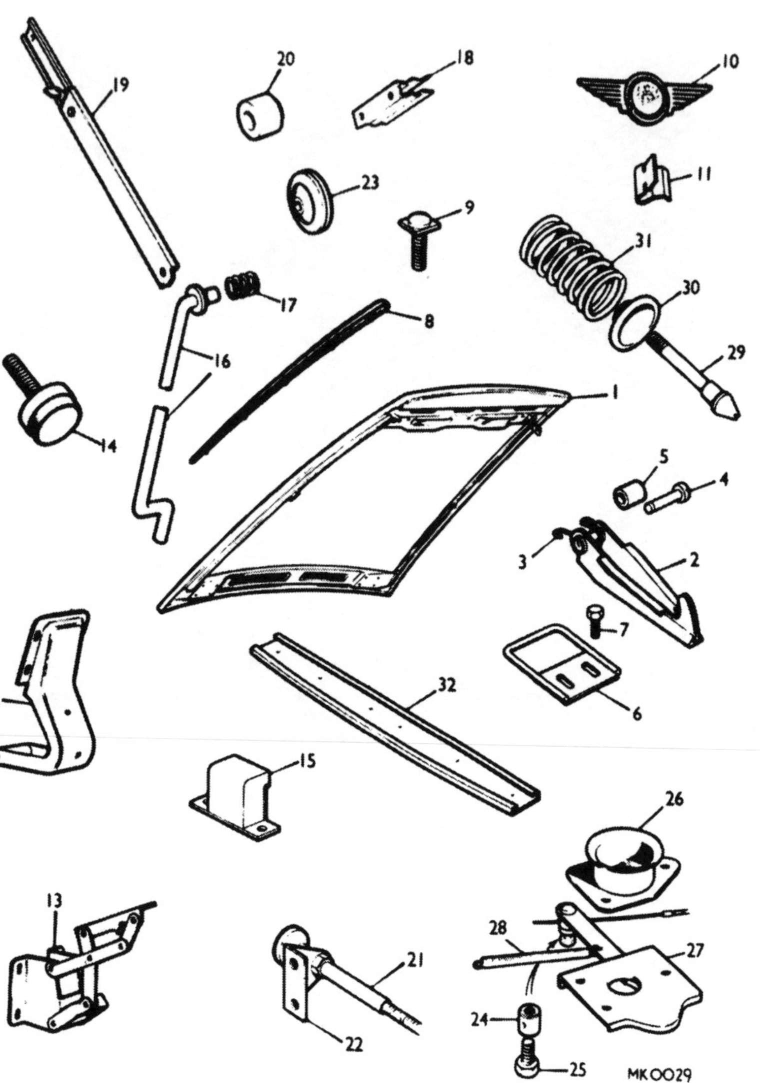

AUSTIN-HEALEY SPRITE MK. 3 AND MK. 4 & MG MIDGET MK. 2 AND MK. 3

BONNET AND CONTROL-continued.

NO.	PART NO.	DESCRIPTION	QTY	CHANGE POINT	REMARKS
16	AHA 8746	Rod-bonnet prop	NLA	Use prior to AHA 9717 and AHA 9718	
17	AAA 2398	Spring-prop rod to bonnet	1		
	PWZ 105	Washer-plain	1		
	PMZ 306	Screw	2		
	LWZ 203	Washer-spring	2		
	FNZ 103	Nut	2		
19	AHA 9717	Support-bonnet	1		Not USA.
	AHA 9800	Support-bonnet	1	(C)H-AN10-86301 TO 86803 (C)A-AN10-86804 TO 87824 (C)G-AN5-89501 TO 154100 (C)G-AN6-154101 ON	USA.
20	AHA 9718	Spacer-support	2		
	HZS 407	Screw	2		
	AJD 7742	Washer-spring	2		
	PWZ 104	Washer-plain	2		
	LWZ 204	Washer-spring	2		
	PWZ 106	Washer-plain	2		
	NH 604041	Nut	2		
21	AHA 5653	Cable-bonnet release $	1		
22	AHA 5517	Bracket-cable	NLA		
	PMZ 306	Screw	2		
	LWZ 203	Washer-spring	2		
	PCR 307	Clip	2		
	PMZ 308	Screw	2		
	LWZ 203	Washer-spring	2		
	FNZ 103	Nut	2		
	AB 610041	Screw-cable clip to bumper mounting beam	1		
23	3H 2615	Grommet-cable through mud-shield	1		
24	24G 1052	Clamp-cable to lock $	1		
25	53K 1016	Screw	1		
26	AHA 5543	Cup-lock locating $	1		
27	4G 3035	Plate-catch $	1		
28	4G 2494	Spring-catch plate return $	1		
	HZS 405	Screw	3		
	PWZ 104	Washer-plain	3		
	LWZ 204	Washer-spring	3		
29	14G 2444	Pin-bonnet lock $	1		
30	4G 3676	Thimble-pin $	1		
31	4G 1588	Spring-pin $	1		
	LWZ 206	Washer-spring	1		
	FNZ 206	Locknut	1		

AUSTIN-HEALEY SPRITE MK. 3 AND MK. 4 & MG MIDGET MK. 2 AND MK. 3

NO.	PART NO.	DESCRIPTION	QTY	CHANGE POINT	REMARKS
		BOOT LID AND FITTINGS			
1	CZJ 351	Lid-boot	1		
2	AHA 5699	Motif'Sprite'	1		
3	AHA 5683	Motif'Midget'	1		
4	BHA 4082	Push-on-fix-motif	2		
5	BHA 4558	Push-on-fix-motif	2		
6	AHH 5261	Surround-letters'MG'	1		Midget.
7	ADH 2475	Letter'M'	1		Midget.
8	ADH 2476	Letter'G'	1		Midget.
9	PFS 103	Nut-spire-surround and letters	13		Midget.
5	BHA 4558	Push-on-fix-surround and letters	13		Midget.
10	34G 252	Badge-boot lid-Silver letters	1	Use prior to CHA 545 (C)G-AN6-171431 ON	Midget.
10	CHA 545	Badge-boot lid-Silver letters	1		Midget.
10	CHA 508	Badge-boot lid-Gold letters	1		Midget.
9	PFS 106	Push-on-fix	3		Midget.
11	AHA 9665	Badge-heraldic'Austin-Healey'	NLA		Use AHA 9916
12	AHA 9916	Badge-heraldic'Austin'	NLA		
9	PFS 106	Push-on-fix	3		

MKO028A

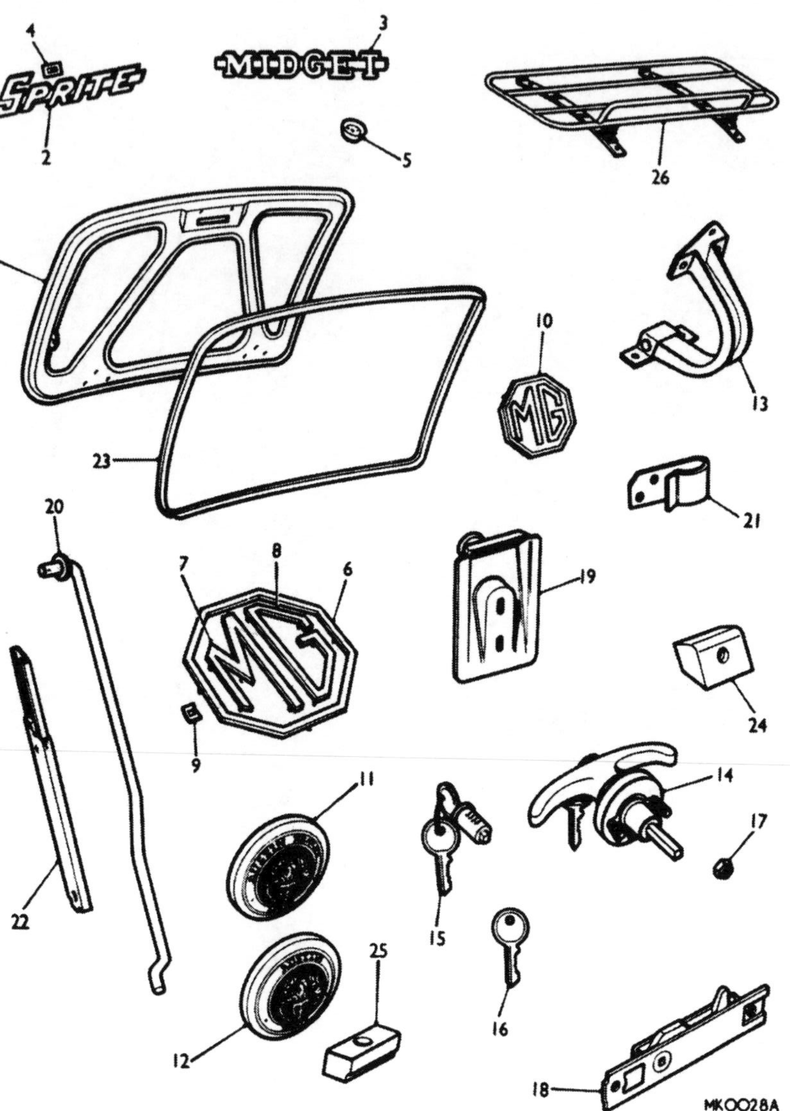

AUSTIN-HEALEY SPRITE MK. 3 AND MK. 4 & MG MIDGET MK. 2 AND MK. 3

BOOT LID AND FITTINGS-continued

NO.	PART NO.	DESCRIPTION	QTY	CHANGE POINT	REMARKS
13	AHA 6314	Hinge-boot lid-RH	1		
	AHA 6315	Hinge-boot lid-LH	1		
	HZS 405	Screw-hinge	10		
	LWZ 204	Washer-spring	10		
14	AHA 6357	HANDLE ASSEMBLY-LOCKING	1		
15	ADH 4492	Barrel-lock	1		
17	53K 1420	Locknut-handle to boot lid	2		
18	AHA 5807	Lock	1		
	SH 605051	Screw-lock to boot lid	2		
	WL 600051	Washer-spring	2		
	NH 605041	Nut	2		
19	AHA 5810	Plate-striker	1		
	PMZ 308	Screw-plate to body	2		
	PWZ 103	Washer-plain	2		
	LWZ 203	Washer-spring	2		
20	AHA 5811	Rod-boot lid prop	1	Use prior to AHA 9716	
	PWZ 104	Washer-plain	2		
21	AAA 1524	Clip	1		
	PTZ 603	Screw	2		
22	AHA 9716	Support-boot lid	1	(C)H-AN10-86301 TO 86803 (C)A-AN10-86804 TO 87824 (C)G-AN5-89501 TO 154100 (C)G-AN6-154101 ON	
	HZS 405	Screw	2		
	PWZ 104	Washer	4		
	LNZ 204	Nut	2		
23	AHA 6399	Rubber-sealing	1	Use prior to CHA 149	
23	CHA 149	Rubber-sealing	1	(C)G-AN5-127605 TO 154100 (C)G-AN6-154101 ON	
24	AHA 6213	Buffer-boot lid-front	2		
25	AHA 6207	Buffer-boot lid-rear	2		
	LWZ 202	Washer-spring	4		
	CNZ 102	Nut-screw	4		
26	AHA 6252	CARRIER ASSEMBLY-LUGGAGE	NLA		
	PMP 516	Screw	4		
	PWZ 105	Washer-plain	4		
	LWZ 205	Locknut	4		

MKO049

AUSTIN-HEALEY SPRITE MK. 3 AND MK. 4 & MG MIDGET MK. 2 AND MK. 3

NO.	PART NO.	DESCRIPTION	QTY	CHANGE POINT	REMARKS
		HOOD-SPRITE MK.3 AND MIDGET MK.2			
		COVER ASSEMBLY(WITH HEADER RAIL)			
1	AHA 7368	Red	1		
1	AHA 7370	Grey	1		
1	AHA 7371	Black	1		
2	TFS 106	Socket-fastener-peg	2		
3	14A 6537	Eyelet-turn-button	2		
4	BHA 4461	Washer-eyelet	2		
5	7H 9866	Socket-fastener-stud	4		
6	7H 9864	Button-socket	4		
7	CTZ 604	Screw	2		
	FWP 206	Washer-cup	2		
7	AHH 6438	Sealheader rail	1		
8	AHA 7350	Retainer-seal	1		
9	DAP 829	Rivet	15		
10	AHH 6439	Pad-header rail	2		
	CTZ 604	Screw-pad to header rail	4		
11	AHA 7709	Fastener-hood $	2		
12	53K 126	Screw	4		
	LWZ 203	Washer-spring	4		
13	AHA 7645	Frame-hood-RH	1		
	AHA 7646	Frame-hood-LH	NLA		
14	14A 6536	Turn-button	2		
15	14B 1730	Retainer-hood cover	2		
16	11K 5564	Collar-distance-retainer	2		
	PMZ 305	Screw	4		
	PWZ 203	Washer-plain	2		
	LWZ 203	Washer-spring	4		
18	AHA 5217	Strap-stowage bag	NLA		
19	TFP 1006	Peg-rear decking panel	2		
20	2K 4936	Washer-joint	2		
	LWZ 203	Washer-spring	2		
	FNZ 103	Nut	2		
21	ADB 4811	Stud-socket	2		
22	DMP 829	Rivet	2		

$ This item is subject to safety regulations

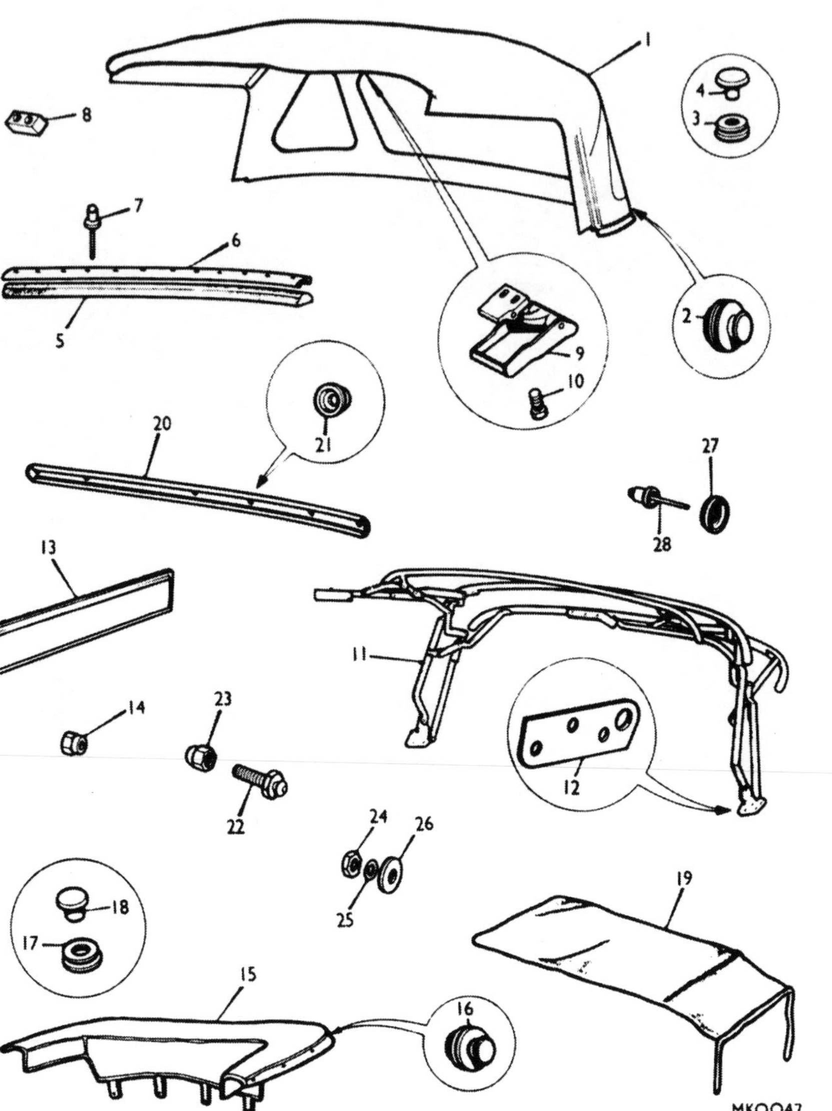

AUSTIN-HEALEY SPRITE MK. 3 AND MK. 4 & MG MIDGET MK. 2 AND MK. 3

NO.	PART NO.	DESCRIPTION	QTY	CHANGE POINT	REMARKS
		HOOD-SPRITE MK.4 AND MIDGET MK.3			
	AHA 8188	COVER ASSEMBLY-HOOD(WITH HEADER RAIL)BLACK	NLA	(C)H-AN9-64735 TO 77590	Use CHA 86 with 2 off AHA 9054
1	CHA 86	COVER ASSEMBLY-HOOD(WITH HEADER RAIL)BLACK	1	(C)G-AN4-52390 TO 66225 (C)H-AN9-77591 TO 85286 (C)H-AN10-85287 TO 86803 (C)A-AN10-86804 TO 87824 (C)G-AN4-66226 TO 74885 (C)G-AN5-74886 TO 154100 (C)G-AN6-154101 ON	
2	TFS 106	Socket-fastener-peg	8		
3	7H 9866	Socket-fastener-stud	A/R		
4	7H 9864	Button	A/R		
	CTZ 604	Screw-hood to header rail	2		
	FWZ 206	Washer-cup	2		
5	AHA 8355	Seal-header rail	1		
6	AHA 7350	Retainer-seal	1		
7	DAP 829	Rivet-retainer	15		
8	AHH 6439	Pad-header rail	2		
	CTZ 604	Screw-pad to header rail	4		
9	AHA 7709	Fastener-hood $	2	(C)H-AN9-64735 TO 72033 (C)G-AN4-52390 TO 60440	
9	AHA 8491	Fastener-hood $	2	(C)H-AN9-72034 TO 85286 (C)H-AN10-85287 TO 86803 (C)A-AN10-86804 TO 87824 (C)G-AN4-60441 TO 74885 (C)G-AN5-74886 TO 154100 (C)G-AN6-154101 ON	

AUSTIN-HEALEY SPRITE MK. 3 AND MK. 4 & MG MIDGET MK. 2 AND MK. 3

HOOD-SPRITE MK.4 AND MIDGET MK.3-continued

NO.	PART NO.	DESCRIPTION	QTY	CHANGE POINT	REMARKS
10	53K 126	Screw-fastener to header rail	4		
	LWZ 203	Washer-spring	4		
11	AHA 9051	Frame-hood $	1		
	SH 605081	Screw-frame to body	6		
	WL 600051	Washer-spring	6		
	PWZ 105	Washer-plain	6		
12	AHA 8295	Piece-packing-frame to body $	2		
	CMZ 410	Screw-hood to frame	6		
13	AHA 9054	Hoop-velcro	2	(C)H-AN9-77591 TO 85286 (C)H-AN10-85287 TO 86803 (C)A-AN10-86804 TO 87824 (C)G-AN4-66226 TO 74885 (C)G-AN5-74886 TO 154100 (C)G-AN6-154101 ON	
	RMP 212	Screw-'B' post finisher and Velcro to body	2		
14	AHA 9061	Nut-dome	2		
	PWZ 102	Washer-plain	2		
	LWZ 202	Washer-spring	2		
	RTP 604	Screw-'B' post finisher and Velcro to body	2		

$ This item is subject to safety regulations

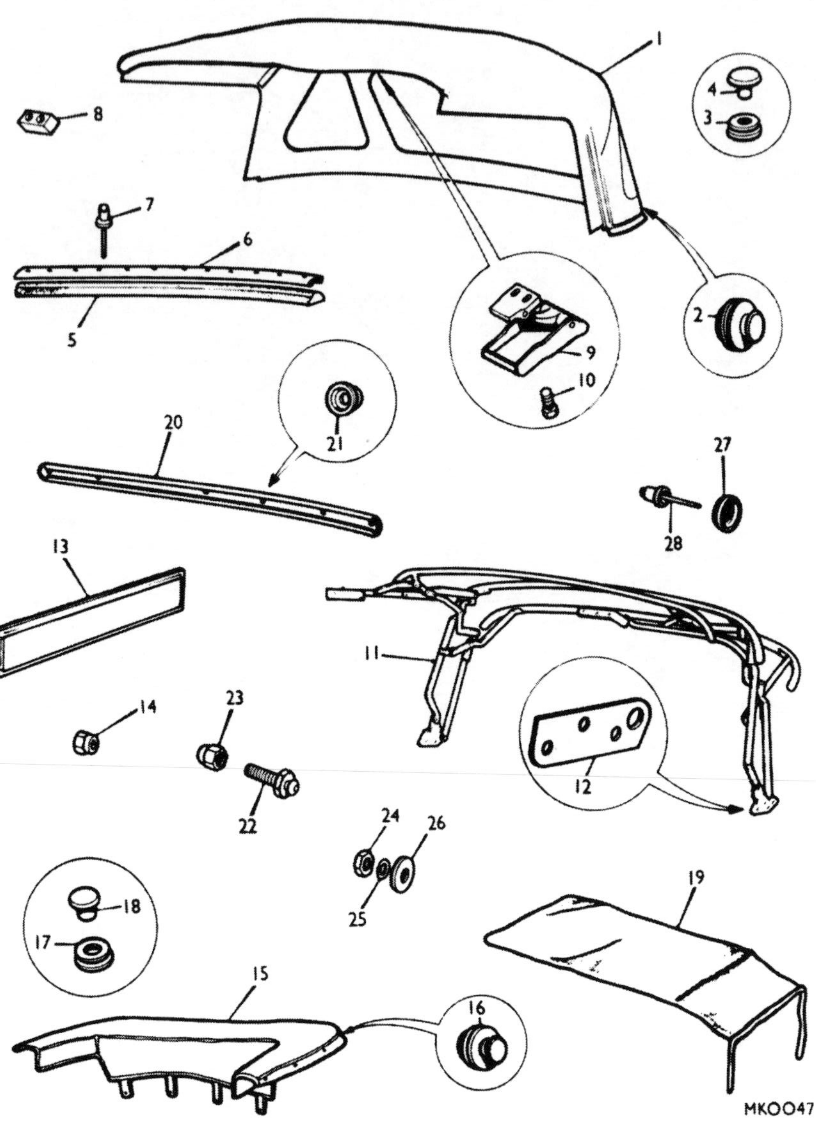

AUSTIN-HEALEY SPRITE MK. 3 AND MK. 4 & MG MIDGET MK. 2 AND MK. 3

HOOD-SPRITE MK.4 AND MIDGET MK.3-continued

NO.	PART NO.	DESCRIPTION	QTY	CHANGE POINT	REMARKS
15	AHA 9190	COVER ASSEMBLY-HOOD STOWAGE	1	Use prior to CHA 15	When supplying prior to (C)H-AN9-77590 (C)G-AN4-66225 Supply also 2 off AHA 9054
15	CHA 93	COVER ASSEMBLY-HOOD STOWAGE $	1	(C)G-AN5-112276 TO 154100 (C)G-AN6-154101 ON	
16	TFS 106	Socket-fastener-peg	A/R		
17	7H 9866	Socket-fastener-stud	A/R		
18	7H 9864	Button-socket	A/R		
19	AHA 8324	Bag-stowage-hood stowage cover	1	Use prior to CHA 128	
19	CHA 128	Bag-stowage-hood stowage cover $	1	(C)G-AN5-123731 TO 154100 (C)G-AN6-154101 ON	
20	AHA 8185	Retainer-hood-rear	1		
	ZCT 605	Screw-retainer to body	7		
21	ADB 4811	Stud-screw	7		
22	TFP 1010	Peg-rear cockpit flange	2	(C)H-AN9-64735 TO 77590 (C)G-AN4-52390 TO 66225	
	LWZ 203	Washer-spring	2		
23	14B 7889	Nut-peg	2		
22	TFP 1006	Peg-rear cockpit flange	6		
24	BHA 4631	Fastener-peg	6		
22	AHA 8369	Peg-rear cockpit flange	6		
25	AHA 8309	Piece-distance flange finisher	6		
26	AHA 8310	Washer-flange finisher	6		
27	ADB 4811	Stud-hood cover to'B'post	2	(C)H-AN9-64735 TO 77590 (C)G-AN4-52390 TO 66225	
28	DMP 835	Rivet-stud	2		

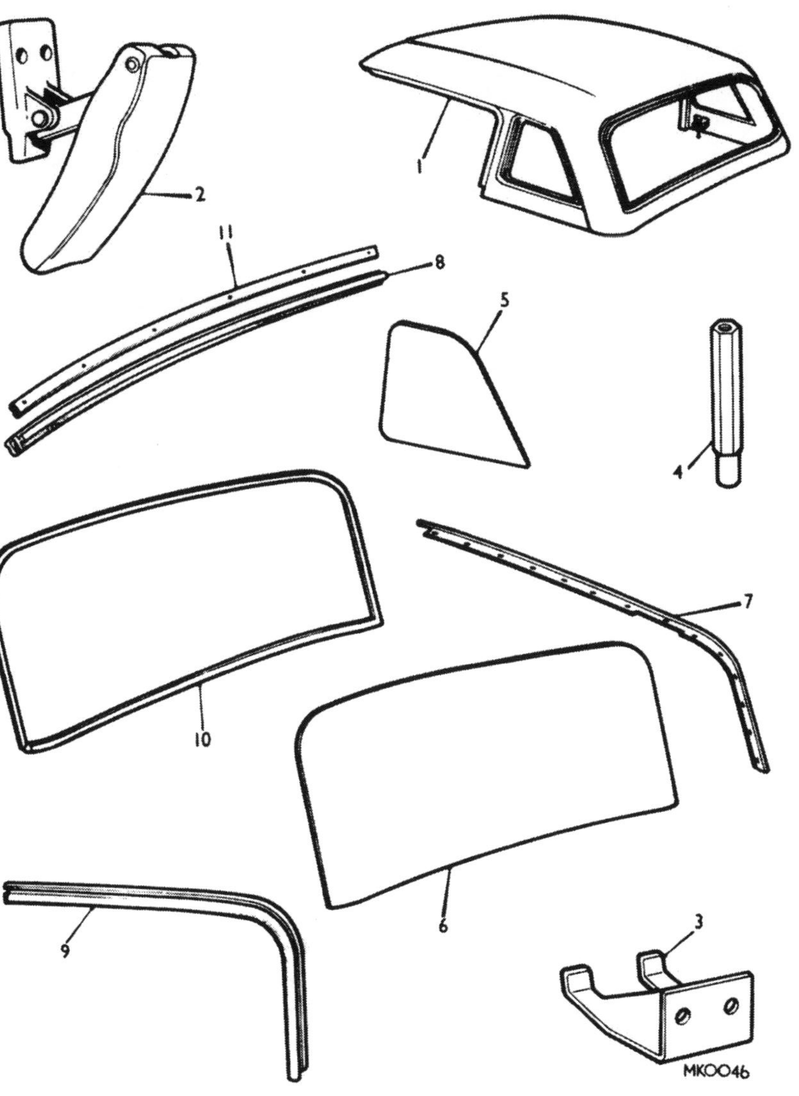

AUSTIN-HEALEY SPRITE MK. 3 AND MK. 4 & MG MIDGET MK. 2 AND MK. 3

NO.	PART NO.	DESCRIPTION	QTY	CHANGE POINT	REMARKS
		HARD TOP-SPRITE MK.3 AND MIDGET MK.2-OPTIONAL EXTRA			
1	AHA 7814	HARD TOP ASSEMBLY-PRIMED	1		
2	AHA 7709	Fastener-hard top to windscreen $	2		
	LWZ 203	Washer-spring	4		
	PMP 308	Screw	2		
	LWZ 203	Washer-spring	2		
	HZS 405	Screw	6		
	LWZ 204	Washer-spring	6		
	HZS 507	Screw	2		
	PWZ 105	Washer-plain	8		
4	AHA 7837	Spacer	2		
	PWZ 108	Washer-plain	2		
	HBZ 526	Bolt	2		
	PWZ 205	Washer-plain	2		
	WL 600051	Washer-spring	2		
	HZS 405	Screw	4		
	PWZ 104	Washer-plain	4		
	LWZ 204	Washer-spring	4		
7	AHA 7845	Moulding-drip-RH	1		
	AHA 7846	Moulding-drip-LH	1		
8	AHH 6438	Rubber-sealing-hard top to windscreen	1		
9	37H 2508	Rubber-sealing-door(30") 76.2cm	A/R		
10	27H 4798	Finisher-backlight sealing rubber	A/R		
	RTP 403	Screw	4		
	FWP 106	Washer-cup	NLA		Use FWP 206
	FWP 206	Washer cup	4		
11	AHA 7350	Retainer-sealing-rubber-hard top to windscreen	1		

$ This item is subject to safety regulations.

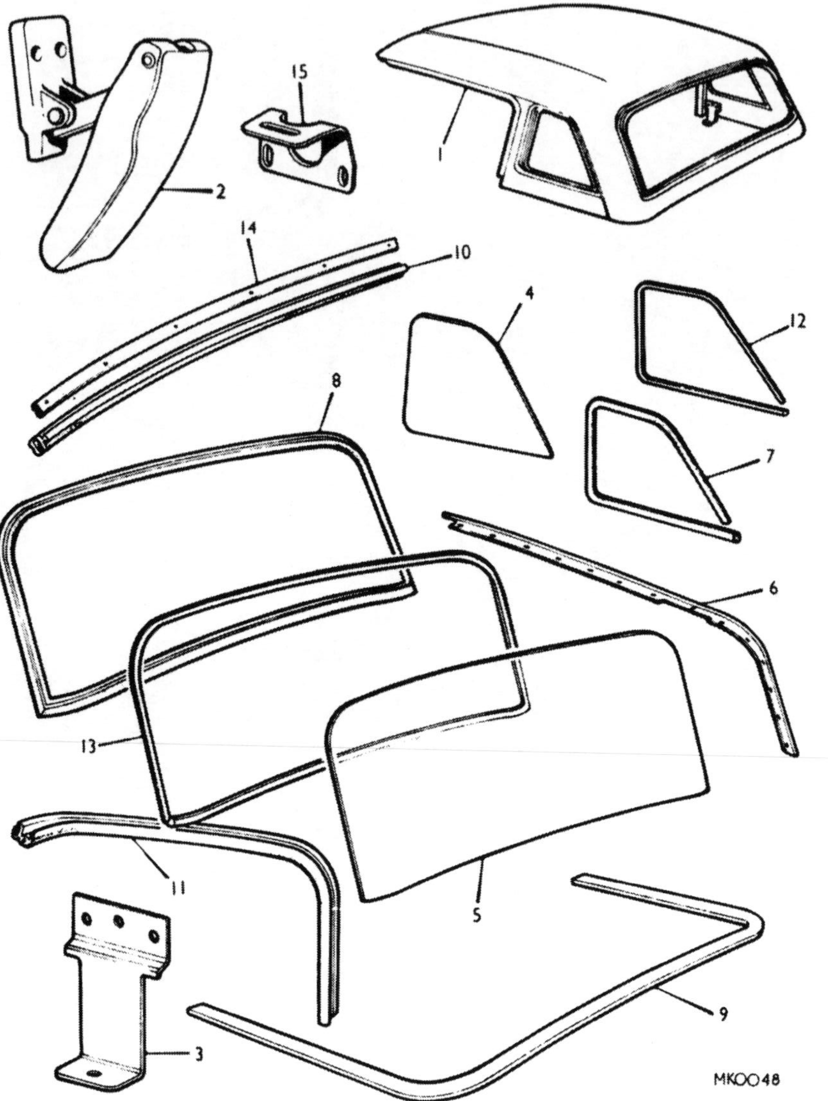

AUSTIN-HEALEY SPRITE MK. 3 AND MK. 4 & MG MIDGET MK. 2 AND MK. 3

HARD TOP-SPRITE MK.4 AND MIDGET MK.3-OPTIONAL EXTRA

NO.	PART NO.	DESCRIPTION	QTY	CHANGE POINT	REMARKS
1	GSS 156	HARD TOP ASSEMBLY-PRIMED	1		
2	AHA 7709	Fastener-hard top $	2	Use prior to AHA 8491	
2	AHA 8491	Fastener-hard top $	2	(C)H-AN9-72034 TO 85286 (C)H-AN10-85287 TO 86803 (C)A-AN10-86804 TO 87824 (C)G-AN4-60441 TO 74885 (C)G-AN5-74886 TO 154100 (C)G-AN6-154101 ON	
	LWZ 203	Washer-spring	4		
	PMP 308	Screw	2		
	LWZ 203	Washer-spring	2		
3	AHA 8083	Bracket-side	2		
	HZS 405	Screw	6		
	LWZ 204	Washer-spring	6		
4	AHA 8086	Glass-quarter-light $	2		
5	AHA 8064	Glass-back-light $	1		
6	AHA 7845	Moulding-drip-RH	1		
	AHA 7846	Moulding-drip-LH	1		
	CTP 404	Screw	28		
7	AHA 8084	Rubber-sealing-quarter-light-RH	1		
	AHA 8085	Rubber-sealing-quarter-light-LH	1		
8	AHA 8087	Rubber-sealing-back-light	1		
9	AHA 8315	Rubber-sealing-hard top to body	1		
10	AHA 8355	Seal-header rail	1		

$ This item is subject to safety regulations.

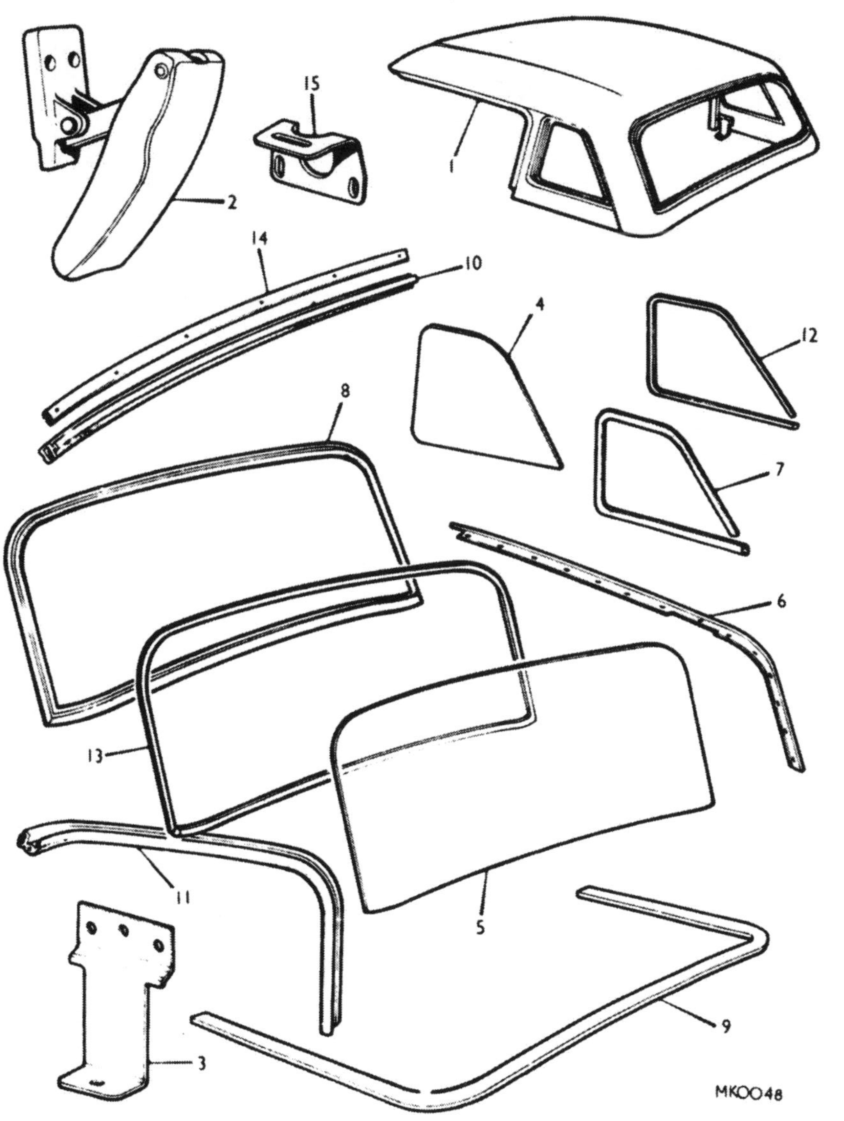

AUSTIN-HEALEY SPRITE MK. 3 AND MK. 4 & MG MIDGET MK. 2 AND MK. 3

HARD TOP-SPRITE MK4 AND MIDGET MK3-OPTIONAL EXTRA-continued.

NO.	PART NO.	DESCRIPTION	QTY	CHANGE POINT	REMARKS
11	37H 2508	Rubber-sealing-door-76.2cm (30")	A/R	(C)H-AN9-67435 TO 72537 (C)G-AN4-52390 TO 61809	Supplied in 22 metre(24 yard) roll.
11	BHH 1139	Rubber-sealing-door	2	(C)H-AN9-72538 TO 85286 (C)H-AN10-85287 TO 86803 (C)A-AN10-86804 TO 87824 (C)G-AN4-61810 TO 74885 (C)G-AN5-74886 TO 154100 (C)G-AN6-154101 ON	
12	37H 3227	Finisher-quarter-window sealing rubber	A/R		Supplied in MULTIPLES OF metres(39.37").
13	37H 3226 M	Finisher-back-light sealing rubber	A/R		Supplied in MULTIPLES OF metres(39.37").
	RTP 403	Screw-door sealing rubber to hard top	4		
	FWP 106	Washer-cup	NLA		Use FWP 206
	FWP 206	Washer-cup	4		
14	AHA 7350	Retainer-sealing-rubber-hard top to windscreen	1		
15	AHA 8082	Bracket-side	2		
	HZS 509	Screw	2		
	WL 600051	Washer-spring	2		
	NH 605041	Nut	2		

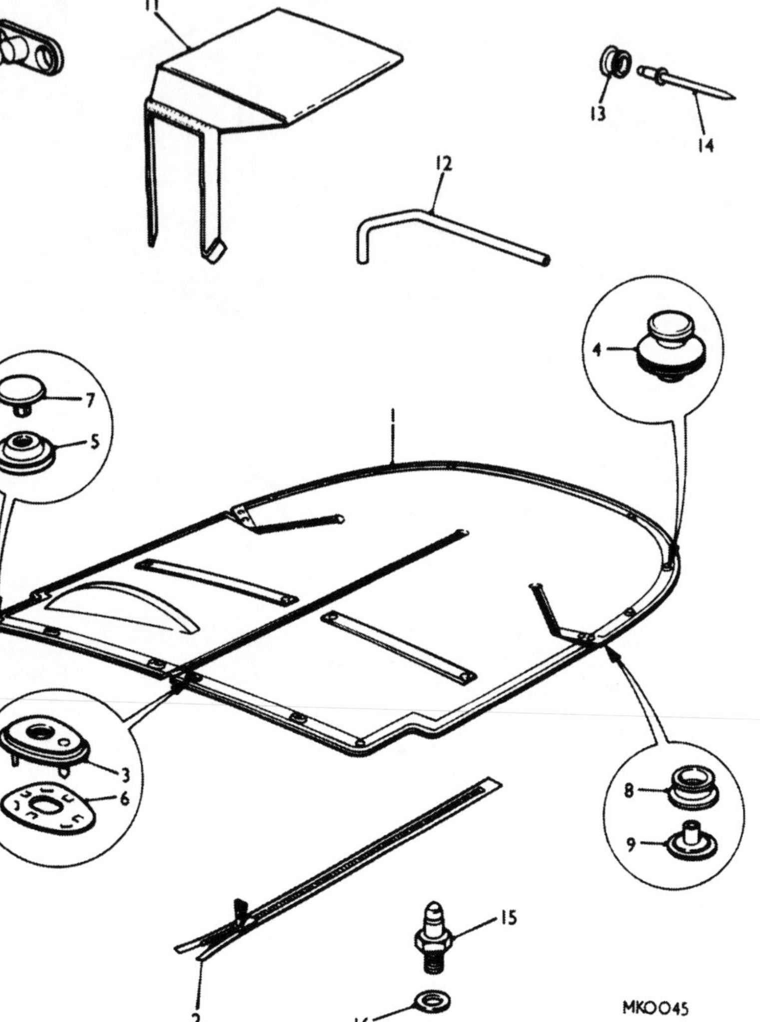

AUSTIN-HEALEY SPRITE MK. 3 AND MK. 4 & MG MIDGET MK. 2 AND MK. 3

TONNEAU COVER-SPRITE MK3 AND MIDGET MK2-OPTIONAL EXTRA.

NO.	PART NO.	DESCRIPTION	QTY	CHANGE POINT	REMARKS
		COVER ASSEMBLY-TONNEAU			
1	AHA 7785	Blue-RHD	1		
	AHA 7787	Red-LHD	1		
	AHA 7786	Black-LHD	1		
3	LFS 107	Socket-fastener-Dash panel and heelboard peg	8		
4	TFS 106	Socket-fastener-Rear decking panel peg	2		
5	7H 9866	Socket-fastener-Stud	10		
6	LFS 100	Washer-dash panel and heelboard peg socket	8		
7	7H 9864	Button-stud socket	10		
8	ADB 4811	Stud-socket	2		
9	7H 9568	Eyelet-stud	2		
10	LFP 6	Peg-base plate-heelboard	4		
	RTP 604	Screw	8		
11	AHA 9166	Bag-tonneau cover stowage	1		
13	ADB 4811	Stud-socket	4		
14	DMP 829	Rivet	4		
15	97H 717	Peg-dash panel	4		
16	2K 4936	Washer-joint	4		
	LWZ 203	Washer-spring	4		
	AJD 8012 Z	Nut	4		

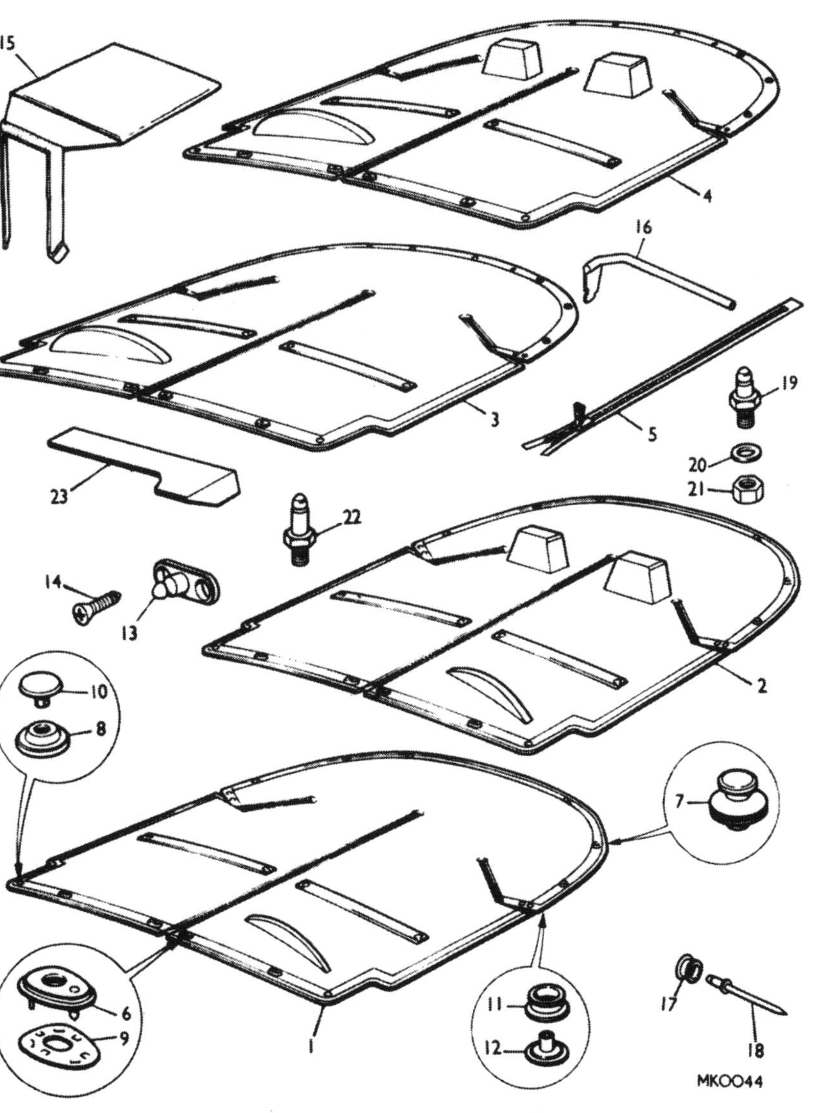

AUSTIN-HEALEY SPRITE MK. 3 AND MK. 4 & MG MIDGET MK. 2 AND MK. 3

TONNEAU COVER-SPRITE MK 4 AND MIDGET MK 3

NO.	PART NO.	DESCRIPTION	QTY	CHANGE POINT	REMARKS
		COVER ASSEMBLY-TONNEAU			
1	AHA 8758	BLACK-N.AMERICA AND SWEDEN	1	Use prior to AHA 6153 for N.America and AHA 9719 for Sweden	No head restraint
1	AHA 9719	BLACK-SWEDEN AND GERMANY	1	(C)G-AN5-74886 TO 154100	No head restraint
2	AHA 9153	BLACK-N.AMERICA	NLA	(C)G-AN6-154101 ON	Use with head restraint with double pole fixing
2	CHA 70	N.AMERICA,SWEDEN,GERMANY AND NORWAY $	1		Use with head restraint with single pole fixing.
3	CHA 119	BLACK-RHD $	1		No head restraint. Use CHA 121.
1	AHA 9157	BLACK-LHD NOT N.AMERICA, SWEDEN,GERMANY OR NORWAY	NLA	Use prior to CHA 121	
1	CHA 121	BLACK-LHD NOT N.AMERICA SWEDEN OR NORWAY $	1	(C)G-AN5-123731 TO 154100 (C)G-AN6-154101 ON	

$ This item is subject to safety regulations

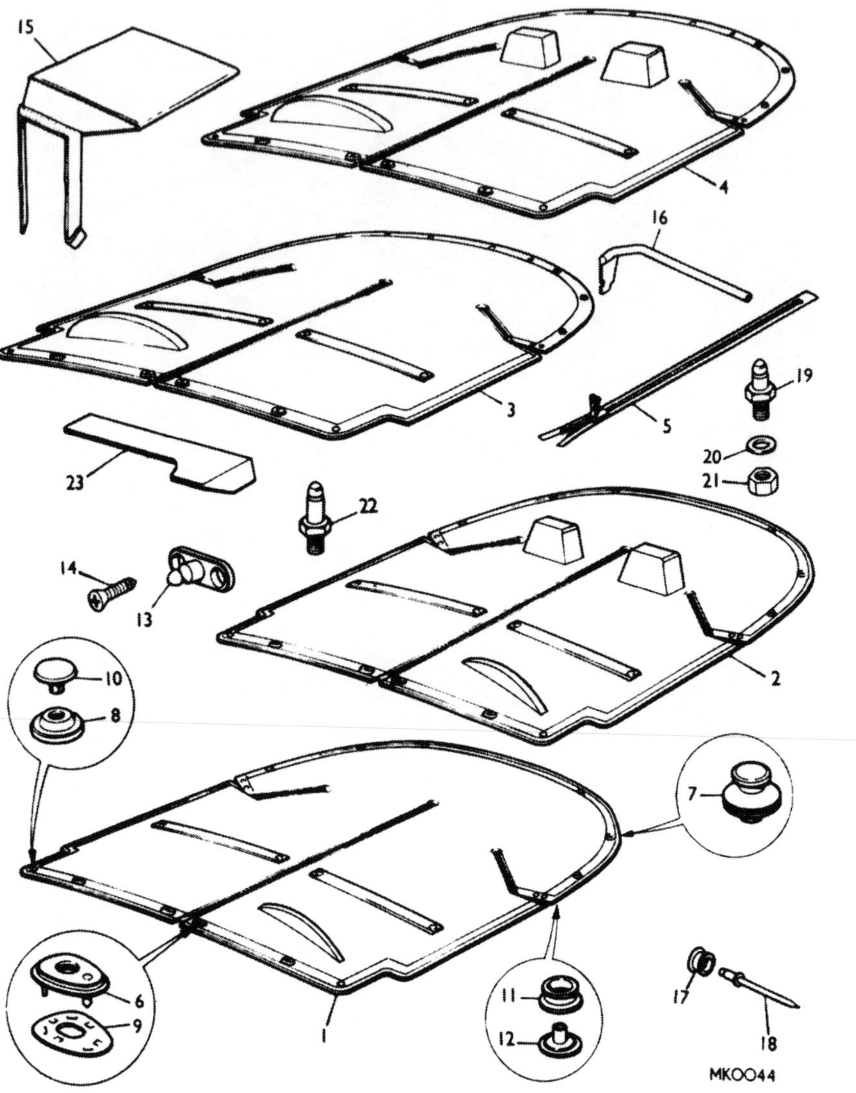

AUSTIN-HEALEY SPRITE MK. 3 AND MK. 4 & MG MIDGET MK. 2 AND MK. 3

NO.	PART NO.	DESCRIPTION	QTY	CHANGE POINT	REMARKS
		TONNEAU COVER-SPRITE MK 4 AND MIDGET MK 3-continued			
		COVER ASSEMBLY-TONNEAU			
4	CHA 123	BLACK-RHD $	1		Was AHA 9918
2	AHA 9919	BLACK-LHD NOT N.AMERICA, SWEDEN,GERMANY OR NORWAY	1	Use prior to CHA 125	Use with head RESTRAINT WITH single pole fixing
2	CHA 125	BLACK-LHD NOT N.AMERICA, SWEDEN,GERMANY OR NORWAY $	1	(C)G-AN5-123731 TO 154100 (C)G-AN6-154101 ON	
		FASTENER-ZIP			
5	AHA 7792	33"(83.82cm)	NLA		
5	AHA 9158	35"(88.9cm)	NLA		When head restraint is not fitted
5	AHA 9159	6"(15.24cm)	NLA		When head restraint is fitted
6	LFS 107	Socket-fastener-dash panel and heelboard peg	A/R		
7	TFS 106	Socket-fastener-rear decking panel peg	A/R		
8	7H 9866	Socket-fastener-stud	A/R		
9	LFS 100	Washer-dash panel and heelboard peg socket	A/R		
10	7H 9864	Button-stud socket	A/R		
11	ADB 4811	Stud-socket	2		
10	BHA 4645	Stud-socket	1		Use with AHA 9655

$ This item is subject to safety regulations

MKO044

AUSTIN-HEALEY SPRITE MK. 3 AND MK. 4 & MG MIDGET MK. 2 AND MK. 3

TONNEAU COVER-SPRITE MK4 AND MIDGET MK3-continued.

NO.	PART NO.	DESCRIPTION	QTY	CHANGE POINT	REMARKS
12	7H 9868	Eyelet stud	2		
13	LFP 116	Peg-base plate-heelboard	A/R		
14	RTP 604	Screw	A/R		
15	AHA 9166	Bag-tonneau cover stowage	1	Use prior to CHA 127	
15	CHA 127	Bag-tonneau cover stowage $	1	(C)G-AN5-123731 TO 154100 (C)G-AN6-154101 ON	
		RAIL ASSEMBLY-TONNEAU COVER SUPPORT			
16	AHA 8313	RH	NLA	(C)H-AN9-64735 TO 77590 (C)G-AN4-52390 TO 66225	Use AHA 9086 with AHA 9087
	AHA 8314	LH	NLA		Use AHA 9087 With AHA 9086
16	AHA 9086	RH	1	(C)H-AN9-77591 TO 85286 (C)H-AN10-85287 TO 86803 (C)A-AN10-86804 TO 87824 (C)G-AN4-66226 TO 74885 (C)G-AN5-74886 TO 154100 Except N.America (C)G-AN6-154101 ON except N.America	
	AHA 9087	LH	1		
17	BHA 4645	Stud-tonneau cover fixing	2		
18	DMP 2840	Rivet-stud	2		
19	97H 717	Peg-dash	A/R		
20	2K 4936	Washer-joint	A/R		
	LWZ 203	Washer-spring	A/R		
21	AJD 8012 Z	Nut	A/R		
22	BHA 5009	Stud-shroud panel	1	(C)H-AN10-85287 TO 86803 (C)A-AN10-86804 TO 87824 (C)G-AN5-74886 TO 154100 (C)G-AN6-154101 ON	
23	AHA 9160	Bag-tonneau rail stowage	1		

$ This item is subject to safety regulations.

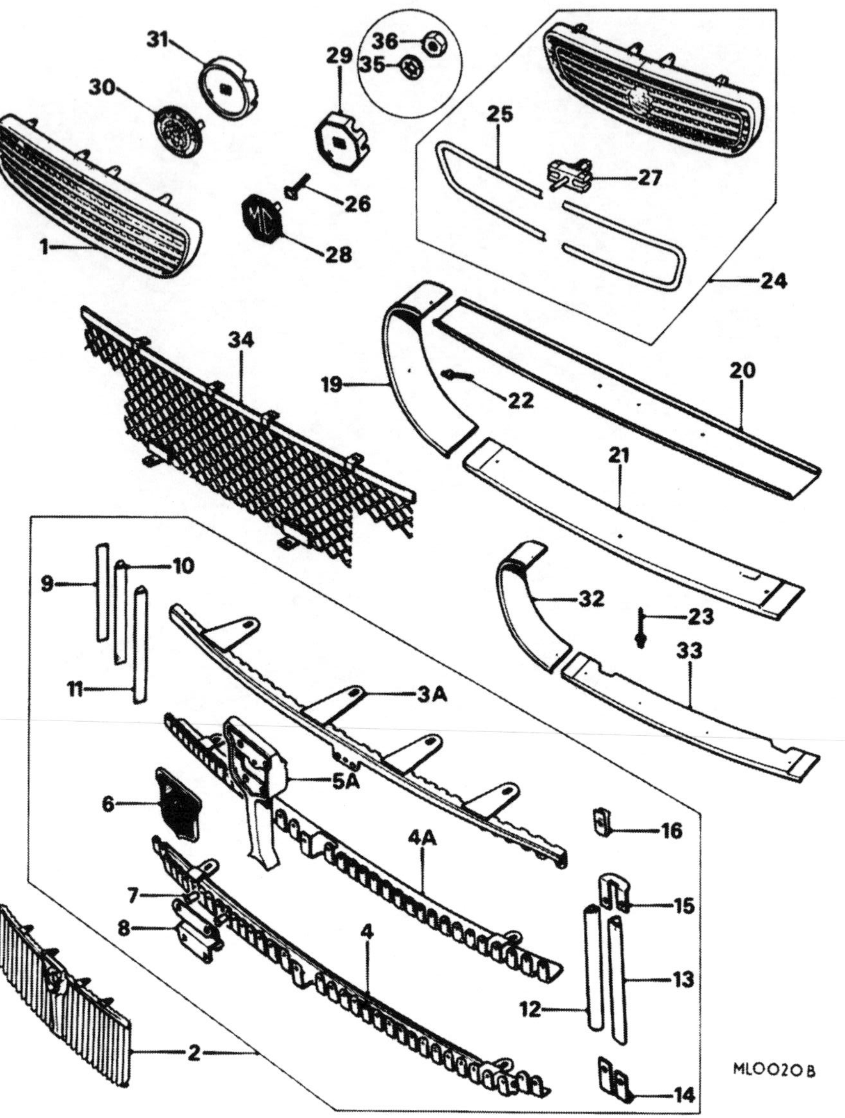

AUSTIN-HEALEY SPRITE MK. 3 AND MK. 4 & MG MIDGET MK. 2 AND MK. 3

RADIATOR GRILLE.

NO.	PART NO.	DESCRIPTION	QTY	CHANGE POINT	REMARKS
1	AHA 8098	Grille-radiator-Sprite	1		Use prior to AHA 9925.
2	ARA 249	GRILLE ASSEMBLY-RADIATOR-MIDGET	1		
3A	ARA 2070	Bar-grille-upper	NLA		
4	ARA 1205	Bar-grille-lower	1	(C)G-AN3-25788 TO 52389	
4A	ARA 2175	Bar-grille-lower	NLA	(C)G-AN4-52390 TO 74885	
5A	ARA 2069	Bar-grille-centre	1		
	FNZ 103	Nut-centre bar to grille	3	(C)G-AN3-25788 TO 49678	
	LWZ 203	Washer-spring-nut	3		
	PZZ 1006	Screw-centre bar to grille	2		
6	ARA 2148	Badge	1		
7	CZG 1864	Fix-badge to bracket	4		
8	ARA 1218	Bracket-badge mounting	1		
	PJZ 804	Screw-bracket to centre bar	1		
	PFS 308	Nut-spring-screw	1		
9	ARA 1208	Slat-grille-RH No.1	1		
10	ARA 1215	Slat-grille-RH No.2	1		
11	ARA 1210	Slat-grille Nos.3 to 34	32		
12	ARA 1216	Slat-grille-LH No.35	1		
13	ARA 1209	Slat-grille-LH No.36	1		
14	ARA 1206	Link-slat-lower LH upper RH	2		
15	ARA 1207	Link-slat-upper LH lower RH	2		
16	ARH 596	Clip-slat	76		
	PZZ 606	Screw clip	NLA		
	PMZ 408	Screw	4	Finished at (C)G-AN5-154100	
	PMZ 410	Screw	NLA		Use SE 604051
	SE 604051	Screw	2		
	PWZ 104	Washer-plain-screw	A/R		
	LWZ 204	Washer-spring-screw	A/R		
	NH 604041	Nut-screw	4		
	PJZ 1004	Nut-grille to body	2		
	PFS 310	Nut-grille to body	2		
19	AHA 5512	Finishers-grille surround-RH	1		Use with grilles AHA 8098 and ARA 249.
	AHA 5513	Finishers-grille surround-LH	1		
20	AHA 5514	Finishers-grille surround-upper	1		
21	AHA 5515	Finishers-grille surround-lower	1		
22	DMP 829	Rivet-side finishers	6		
23	DMP 819	Rivet-upper and lower finishers	10		

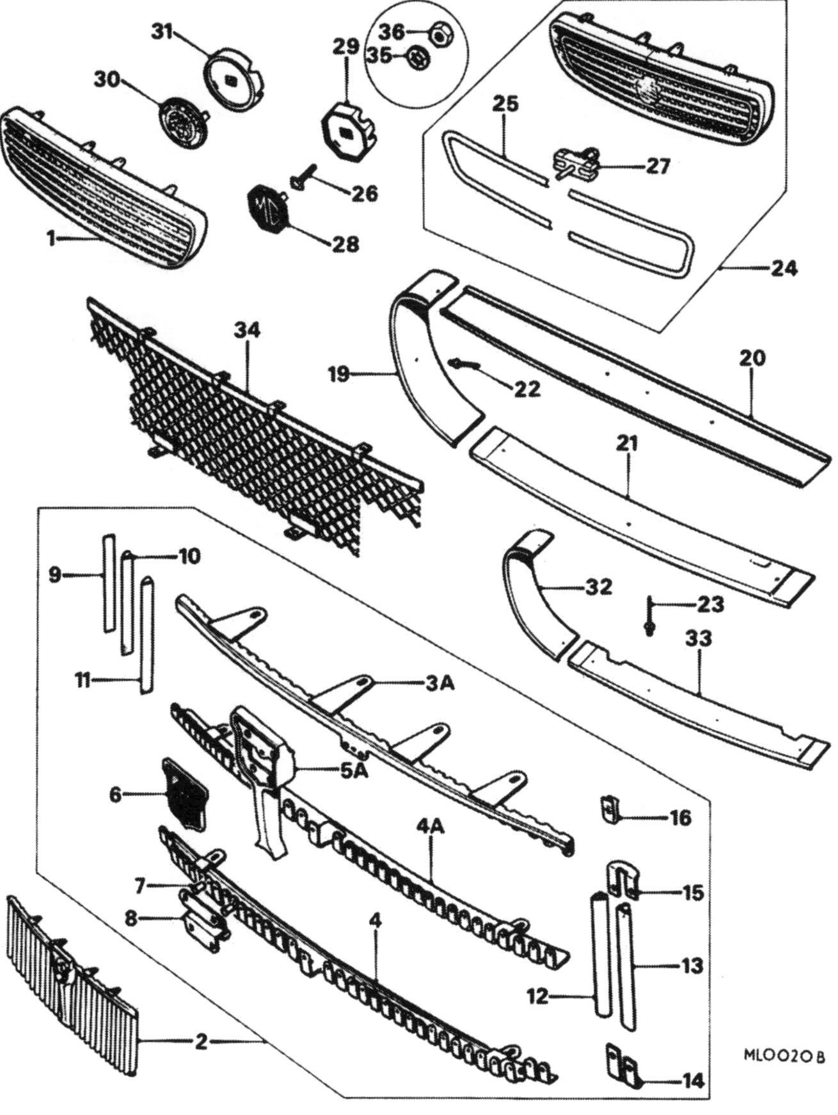

AUSTIN-HEALEY SPRITE MK. 3 AND MK. 4 & MG MIDGET MK. 2 AND MK. 3

RADIATOR GRILLE-continued.

NO.	PART NO.	DESCRIPTION	QTY	CHANGE POINT	REMARKS
24	AHA 9925	GRILLE ASSEMBLY-RADIATOR (LESS MOTIF)	1		
25	AHA 9315	Finisher-grille-RH	1		
	AHA 9316	Finisher-grille-LH	1		
27	BHA 5008	Clip-fastener	8		
28	AHA 9318	Motif-grille-MG	1		Midget.
29	AHA 9319	Plinth-motif	1		Midget.
30	AHA 9915	Motif-grille-Austin	1		Austin-Healey.
31	AHA 9661	Plinth	1		Austin-Healey.
26	AHA 9482	Stud-plate	3		
35	LWZ 402	Washer-lock	3	(C)H-AN10-85287 TO	
36	ANZ 102	Nut	3	87824	
32	AHA 9450	Finisher-grille surround-RH	1	(C)G-AN5-74886 TO	
	AHA 9451	Finisher-grille surround-LH	1	154100	
33	AHA 9449	Finisher-grille-lower	1		
22	DMP 829	Rivet-slide-finisher	10		
	PMZ 408	Screw	4		
	PMZ 410	Screw	NLA		Use SE 604051
	SE 604051	Screw	2		
	PWZ 104	Washer-plain	A/R		
	LWZ 204	Washer-spring	A/R		
	NH 604041	Nut-screw	4		
	PJZ 1004	Nut-grille to body	2		
	PFS 310	Nut-grille to body	2		
34	CHA 478	GRILLE ASSEMBLY-AIR INTAKE	1	(C)G-AN6-154101 ON	
	AB 608041	Screw-grille to bonnet locking platform	4		

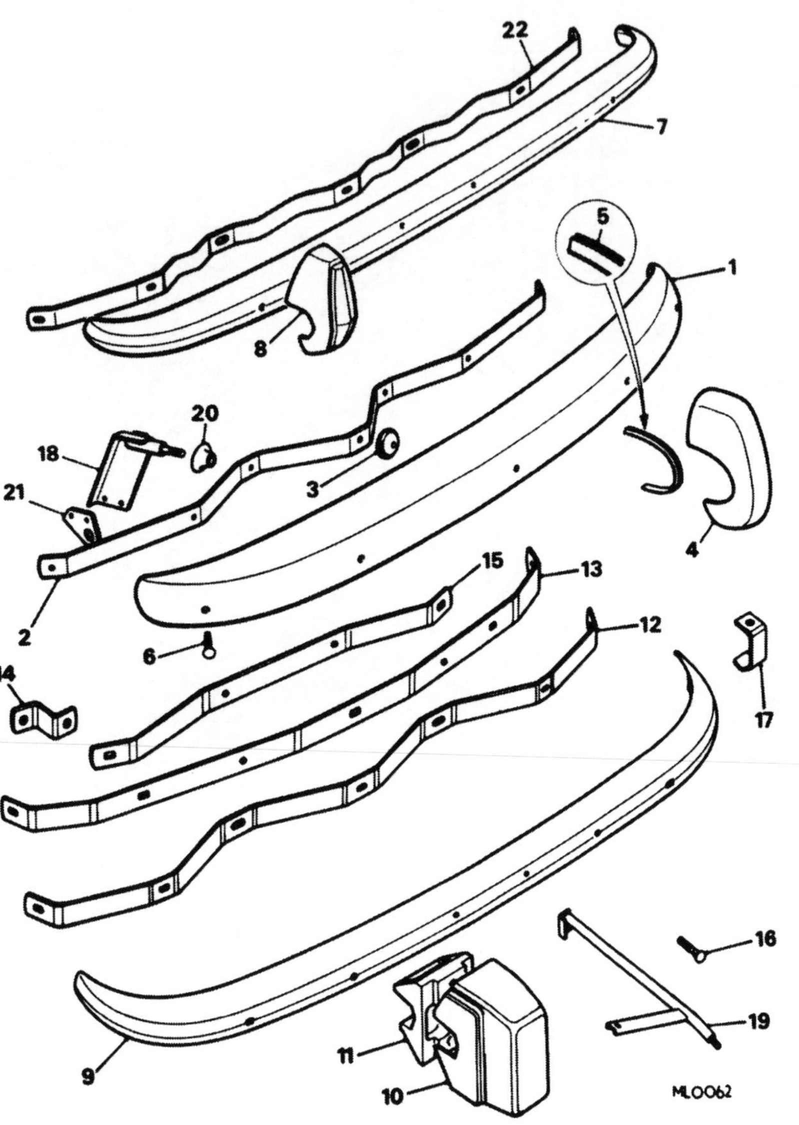

AUSTIN-HEALEY SPRITE MK. 3 AND MK. 4 & MG MIDGET MK. 2 AND MK. 3

NO.	PART NO.	DESCRIPTION	QTY	CHANGE POINT	REMARKS
		FRONT BUMPERS			
1	AHA 5695	Bar-bumper-front	1		
2	AHA 5696	Spring-bar	1		
3	11B 5721	Piece-packing-bar to spring	5		
4	AHA 5686	Over-rider	2		
5	37H 9871 M	Moulding-over-rider-13cm(5")	A/R	Use prior to AHA 9453	Supplied in multiples of metres(39.37")
6	ACH 9287	Bolt-bar to spring	3		
	WA 110061	Washer-plain	5		
	LWZ 206	Washer-spring	5		
	FNZ 106	Nut	3		
7	AHA 9453	Bar-bumper-front	1	(C)H-AN10-85287 TO 86803	
8	AHA 9633	Over-rider	2		
5	37H 9871 M	Moulding-over-rider-9cm(3.5")	A/R	(C)A-AN10-86804 TO 87824 (C)G-AN5-74886 TO 154100	Supplied in multiples of metres(39.37")
	BH 606161	Bolt	2	Except USA and	
	WA 110061	Washer-plain	2	Canada TO 143354	
	WL 600061	Washer-spring	2		
9	CHA 201	Bar-bumper	1		
10	CHA 207	Over-rider-RH $	1		
	CHA 208	Over-rider-LH $	1		
11	CHA 187	Bracket-mounting support casting-RH	1	(C)G-AN5-143355 TO 154100	North America.
	CHA 188	Bracket-mounting support casting-LH	1		
	BH 606261	Bolt-over-rider to bumper	2		
	WL 600061	Washer-spring	2		
22	AHA 9455	Spring-bar	1	(C)H-AN10-85287 TO 86803 (C)A-AN10-86804 TO 87824 (C)G-AN5-74886 TO 123730	

$ This item is subject to safety regulations.

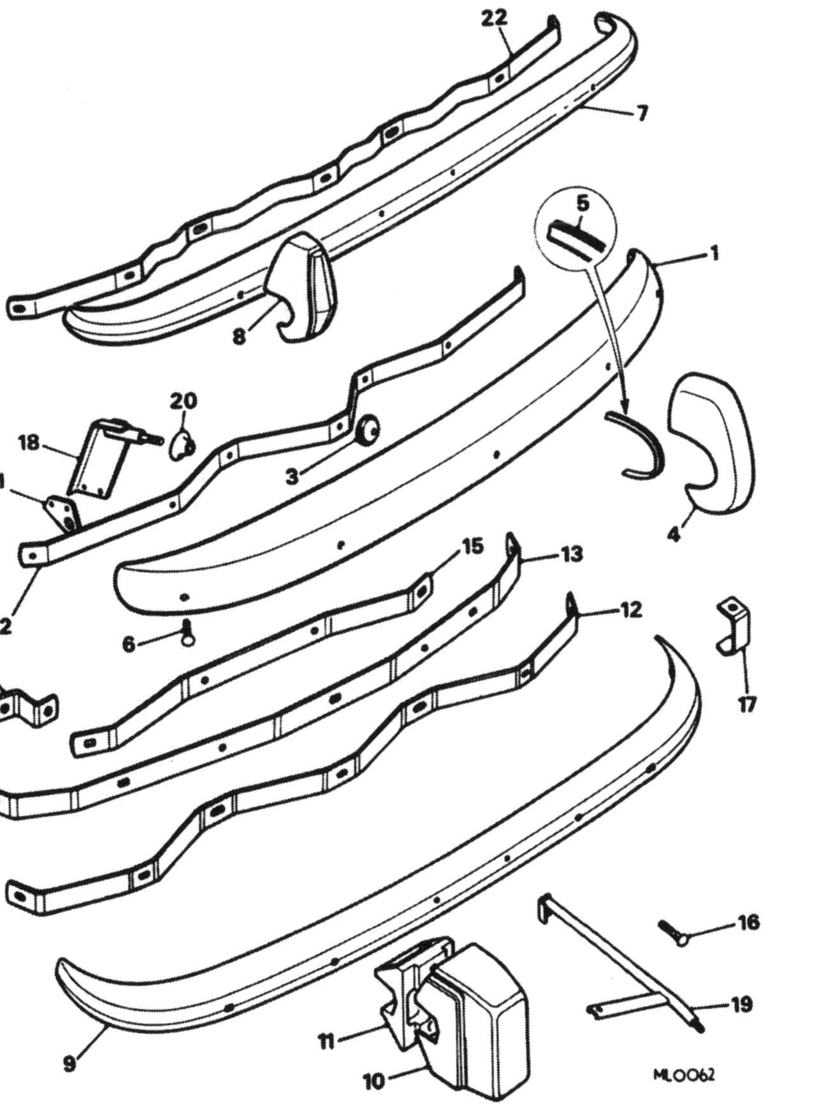

AUSTIN-HEALEY SPRITE MK. 3 AND MK. 4 & MG MIDGET MK. 2 AND MK. 3

NO.	PART NO.	DESCRIPTION	QTY	CHANGE POINT	REMARKS
		FRONT BUMPERS-continued			
12	CHA 42	Mainspring-front bumper	1	(C)G-AN5-123731 TO 154100-Except N.America TO 143354-N.America	
13	CHA 190	Mainspring-front bumper $	1	(C)G-AN5-143355 TO 154100	North America.
14	CHA 191	Bracket-reinforcement $	2		
15	CHA 192	Spring-support $	1		
16	CHA 212	Bolt-spring and outer spacer to bumper	2		
	WA 108051	Washer-plain	2		
	WL 600051	Washer-spring	2		
	NH 605041	Nut	2		
17	CHA 43	Bracket-reinforcement-front bumper mounting	2	(C)G-AN5-123731 TO 154100	
	HZS 506	Screw	2	(C)H-AN10-85287 TO 86803 (C)A-AN10-86804 TO 87824 (C)G-AN5-74886 TO 123730	
	HZS 507	Screw	1		
	PWZ 105	Washer-plain	1		
	WL 600051	Washer-spring	1		
18	AHA 5521	Bracket-bumper mounting-RH	1	Use prior to CHA 182/183	
	AHA 5522	Bracket-bumper mounting-LH	1		
19	CHA 182	Bracket-front bumper mounting-RH $	1	(C)G-AN5-138801 TO 154100	
	CHA 183	Bracket-front bumper mounting-LH $	1		
	SH 604051	Screw-bracket to radiator support and crossmember	4		
	WL 600041	Washer-spring	4		
20	AAA 1645	Grommet-bracket(rubber)	2	Use prior to (C)G-AN6-154101	
	NH 608041	Nut	2		
	WL 600081	Washer-spring	2		
	SH 606061	Screw	4		
21	AHA 6498	Eye-towing	2		
	SH 606081	Screw	4		
	WA 110061	Washer-plain	4		
	WL 600061	Washer-spring	4		

$ This item is subject to safety regulations.

AUSTIN-HEALEY SPRITE MK. 3 AND MK. 4 & MG MIDGET MK. 2 AND MK. 3

NO.	PART NO.	DESCRIPTION	QTY	CHANGE POINT	REMARKS
		REAR BUMPERS			
1	AHA 5673	Bar-bumper-rear	1	Use prior to AHA 9458 and AHA 9459	
2	AHA 5675	Spring-bar	2		
3	11B 5721	Piece-packing-bar to spring	4		
4	AHA 5686	Over-rider	2		
23	37H 9871 M	Moulding-over-rider-5"(13cm)	A/R		Supplied in multiples of metres(39.37")
5	ACH 9287	Bolt-bar spring	2		
	HBZ 611	Bolt	2		
	WA 110061	Washer-plain	4		
	LWZ 206	Washer-spring	4		
	FNZ 106	Nut	2		
6	AHA 9458	Bar-bumper-rear-RH	1	(C)H-AN10-85287 TO 86803 (C)A-AN10-86804 TO 87824 (C)G-AN5-74886 TO 154100 Except USA and Canada 74886 TO 143354 USA and Canada	
	AHA 9459	Bar-bumper-rear-LH	1		
7	AHA 9633	Over-rider	2		
8	AHA 9465	Spring-bar $	2		
	SH 605061	Screw	2		
	WA 108051	Washer-plain	2		
	WL 600051	Washer-spring	2		
9	CHA 203	Bar-RH	1	(C)G-AN5-143355 TO 154100	North America.
	CHA 204	Bar-LH	1		
10	CHA 184	Mainspring $	2		
11	CHA 217	Bolt-main spring and outer spacer to bumper bar	1		
	WA 108051	Washer-plain	1		
	WL 600051	Washer-spring	1		
	NH 605041	Nut	1		
12	CHA 208	Over-rider-RH bumper $	1		
	CHA 207	Over-rider-LH bumper $	1		
13	CHA 188	Bracket-mounting support casting-RH bumper	1		
	CHA 187	Bracket-mounting support casting-LH bumper	1		
14	CHA 209	Gasket-mounting bracket	4		

$ This item is subject to safety regulations.

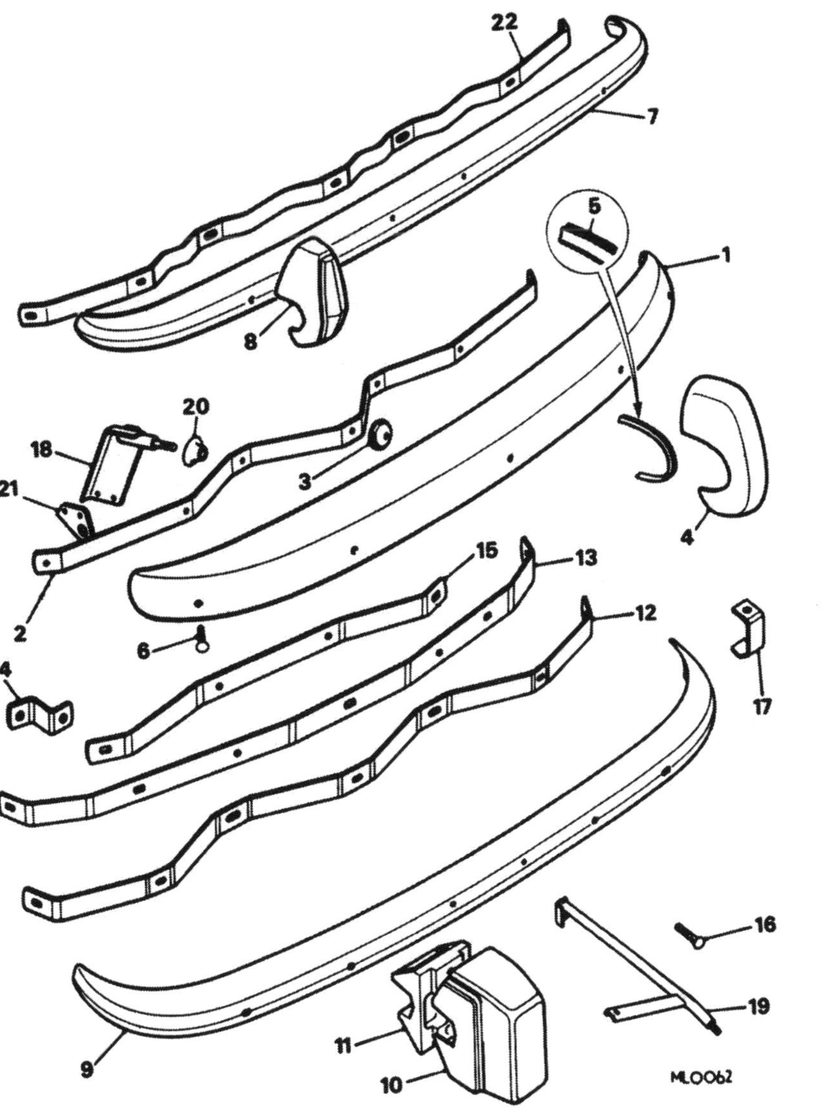

AUSTIN-HEALEY SPRITE MK. 3 AND MK. 4 & MG MIDGET MK. 2 AND MK. 3

NO.	PART NO.	DESCRIPTION	QTY	CHANGE POINT	REMARKS
		REAR BUMPERS-continued			
15	37H 9871 M	Moulding-over-rider-3.5"(9cm)	A/R	Use prior to (C)G-AN6-154101	Supplied in multiples of metres(39.37")
	SH 605081	Screw	2	(C)H-AN10-85287 TO 86803 (C)A-AN10-86804 TO 87824 (C)G-AN5-74886 TO 154100	
	WA 108051	Washer-plain	2		
	WL 600051	Washer-spring	2		
	BH 606161	Bolt	2		
	WA 110061	Washer-plain	4		
	WL 600061	Washer-spring	4		
	SH 606071	Screw	2		
16	AHA 9468	Bracket-mounting-bumper	2	Use prior to CHA 172	
17	CHA 172	Bracket-mounting-bumper $	NLA	(C)G-AN5-138801 TO 154100-except USA and Canada. 138801 TO 143354-USA and Canada.	
18	CHA 185	Bracket-mounting-bumper $	2	(C)G-AN5-143355 TO 154100	North America.

$ This item is subject to safety regulations.

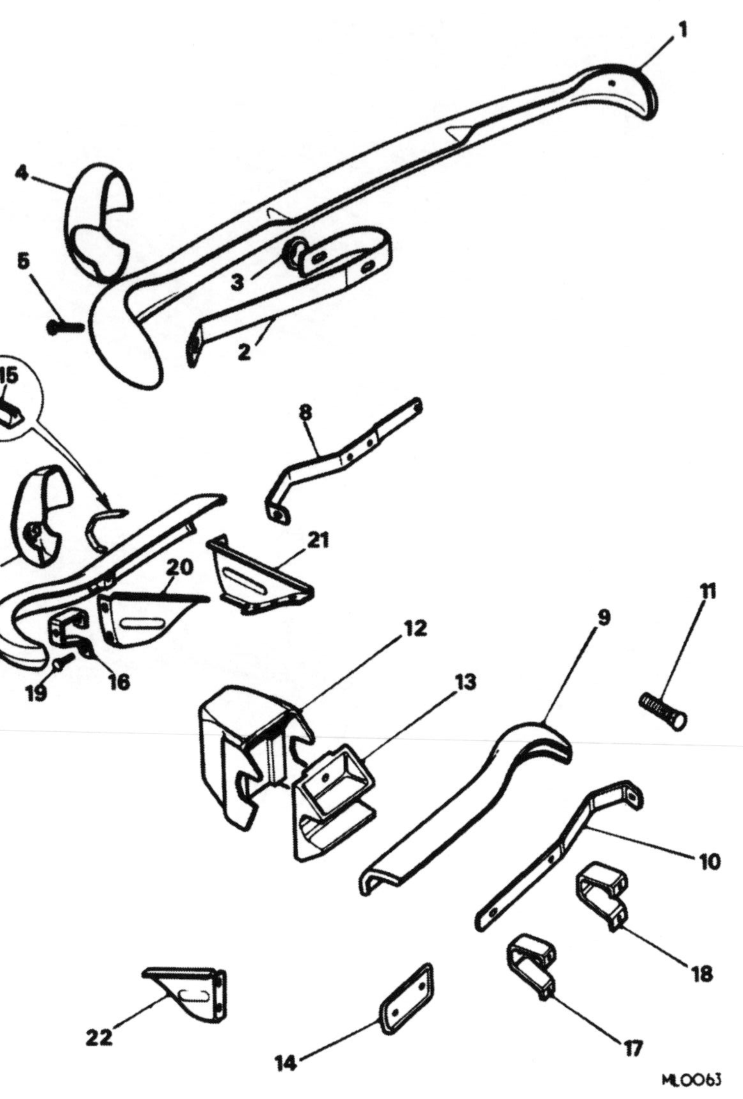

AUSTIN-HEALEY SPRITE MK. 3 AND MK. 4 & MG MIDGET MK. 2 AND MK. 3

NO.	PART NO.	DESCRIPTION	QTY	CHANGE POINT	REMARKS
		REAR BUMPERS-continued			
	FNZ 106	Nut	2	(C)H-AN10-85287 TO 86803 (C)A-AN10-86804 TO 87824 (C)G-AN5-74886 TO 138800	
19	BHA 4991	Bolt-bumper to body	8		
	PWZ 205	Washer-plain	8		
	WL 600051	Washer-spring	8		
	NH 605041	Nut	8		
	SH 605081	Screw-rear bumper to body	8	(C)G-AN5-138801 TO 154100	
	WA 108051	Washer-plain	8		
	PWZ 205	Washer-plain	8		
	LNZ 205	Nut	8		
	WL 600051	Washer-spring	4		N.America
		Reinforcement-bumper fixing			
20	CZJ 334	Outer-RH	1	(C)H-AN10-85287 TO 86803 (C)A-AN10-86804 TO 87824 (C)G-AN5-74886 TO 154100	Except N.America
	CZJ 335	Outer-LH	1		
21	CZJ 336	Inner-RH	1		
	CZJ 337	Inner-LH	1		
	SH 605061	Screw-reinforcement to luggage floor	12		
	WL 600051	Washer-spring	12		
	PWZ 205	Washer-plain	12		
		Reiforcement-bumper fixing			
21	CZJ 336	Inner-RH	1	(C)H-AN10-85287 TO 86803 (C)A-AN10-86804 TO 87824 (C)G-AN5-74886 TO 138800	N.America
	CZJ 337	Inner-LH	1		
22	CZJ 482	Inner-RH	NLA	(C)G-AN5-138801 TO 154100	
	CZJ 483	Inner-LH	NLA		
20	CZJ 334	Outer-RH	1	(C)H-AN10-85287 TO 86803 (C)A-AN10-86804 TO 87824 (C)G-AN5-74886 TO 154100	
	CZJ 335	Outer-LH	1		
	SH 605061	Screw-reinforcement to luggage floor	12		
	WL 600051	Washer-spring	12		
	PWZ 205	Washer-plain	12		

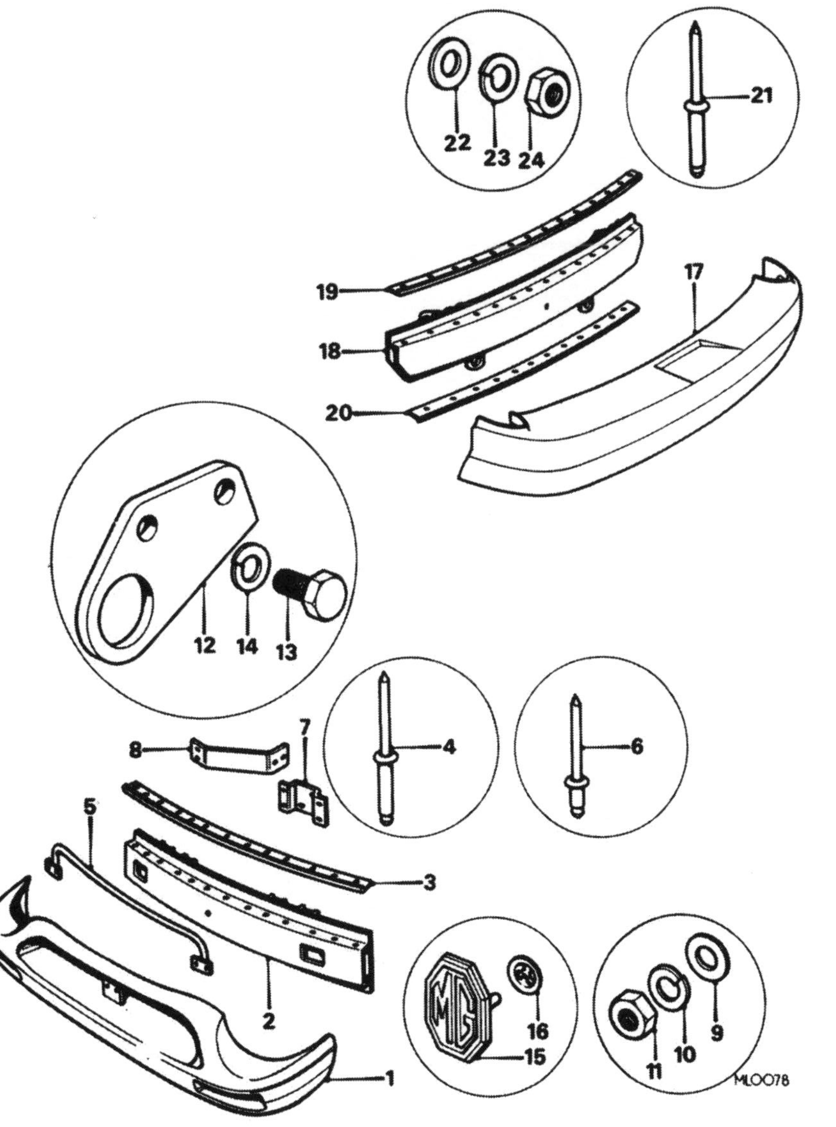

AUSTIN-HEALEY SPRITE MK. 3 AND MK. 4 & MG MIDGET MK. 2 AND MK. 3

NO.	PART NO.	DESCRIPTION	QTY	CHANGE POINT	REMARKS
		BUMPERS-FRONT AND REAR-(C)G-AN6-154101 ON.			
1	BHM 538	BAR ASSEMBLY-BUMPER-FRONT $	1		
4	CHA 307	Rivet-front bumper	26		
2	CHA 238	Armature-front bumper $	1	Use prior to CHA 534	
2	CHA 534	Armature-front bumper $	1	(C)G-AN6-158716 ON	
3	CHA 254	Plate-clamping	2		
5	CHA 321	Tube-support	1		
6	CHA 365	Rivet-support tube to armature	4		
7	CHA 298	Spring-inner-RH	1		
	CHA 299	Spring-inner-LH	1		
8	CHA 250	Spring-outer $	2	Finished at (C)G-AN6-158715	
9	WC 110061	Washer-plain-springs	12		
10	WL 600061	Washer-spring-springs	12		
11	NH 606041	Nut-spring-inner to body	4		
12	AHA 6498	Eye-towing	2		
15	CHA 344	Motif-front bumper-Silver letters	1	Use prior to CHA 544	
15	CHA 544	Motif-front bumper-Silver letters	1	(C)G-AN6-171431 ON	
15	CHA 507	Motif-front bumper-Gold letters	1		
16	PFR 106	Push-on-fix-motif	2		
17	BHM 539	BAR ASSEMBLY-BUMPER-REAR $	1		
21	CHA 307	Rivet-rear bumper	28		
18	CHA 244	Armature-rear bumper $	1	Use prior to CHA 536	
18	CHA 536	Armature-rear bumper $	1	(C)G-AN6-158716 ON	
19	CHA 252	Plate-clamping-upper	1		
20	CHA 253	Plate-clamping-lower	1		
23	WL 600061	Washer-spring	4		
24	NH 606041	Nut-bumper to body	4		

$ This item is subject to safety regulations.

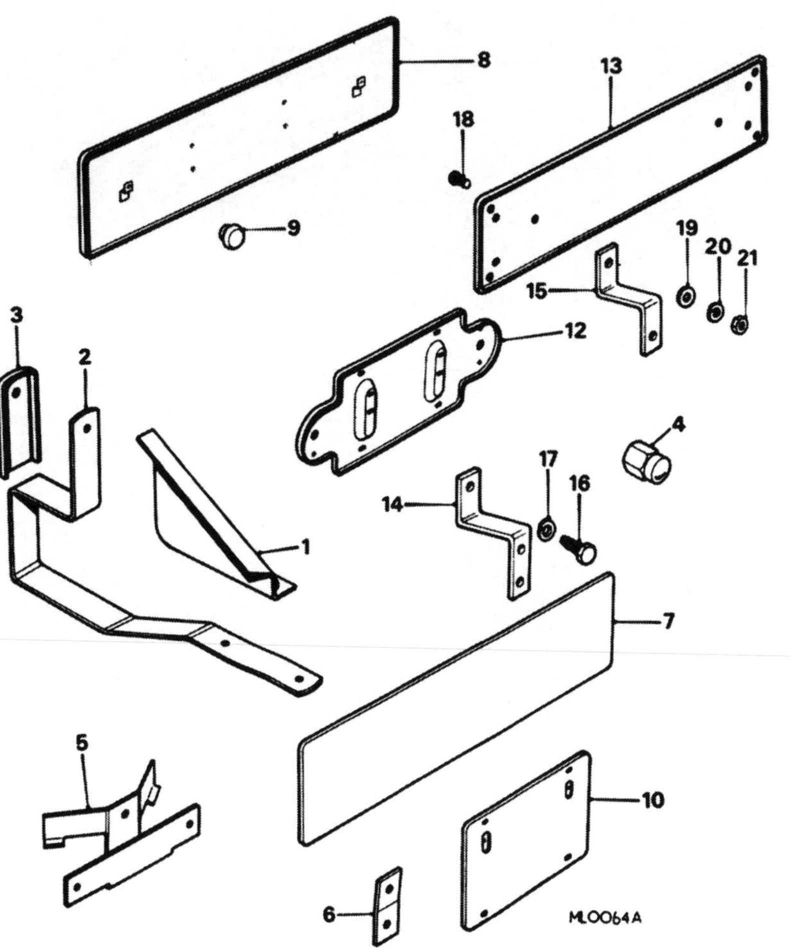

AUSTIN-HEALEY SPRITE MK. 3 AND MK. 4 & MG MIDGET MK. 2 AND MK. 3

BUMPER FIXINGS AND NUMBER PLATES.

NO.	PART NO.	DESCRIPTION	QTY	CHANGE POINT	REMARKS
1	AHA 5765	Bracket-bumper mounting	2	Use prior to AHA 5211	
2	AHA 5677	Bracket-bumper support-RH	1		
	AHA 5678	Bracket-bumper support-LH	1		
3	AHA 5679	Finisher-support bracket	NLA		
	HZS 608	Screw	2		
	WA 110061	Washer-plain	2		
	LWZ 206	Washer-spring	2		
	FNZ 106	Nut	2		
	HZS 506	Screw	8		
	PWZ 105	Washer-plain	A/R		
	WL 600051	Washer-spring	8		
4	14B 2685	Nut-dome	2		
15	AHA 5533	Bracket-front number-plate mounting	1	(C)H-AN8-38829 TO 58700 (C)G-AN3-25788 TO 46561	
6	AHH 8177	Bracket-mounting front number-plate	2	(C)H-AN3-58701 TO 64734 (C)H-AN9-64735 ON (C)G-AN3-46562 TO 52389 (C)G-AN4-52390 ON	Except N.America
7	ALK 3268	Number-plate-front	1	(C)H-AN8-38829 TO 64374 (C)H-AN9-64735 TO 85286 (C)G-AN3-25788 TO 52389 (C)G-AN4-52390 TO 74885	
8	AHA 5791	Number-plate-rear	1		
9	AHA 5804	Buffer-rear number-plate	2		
10	AHA 5211	Support-rear number plate	1	(C)H-AN10-85287 TO 86803 (C)A-AN10-86804 TO 87824 (C)G-AN5-74886 TO 154100	
	PMZ 416	Screw-number plate to bumper	NLA		
	WL 600041	Washer-spring	2		
	NH 604041	Nut	2		

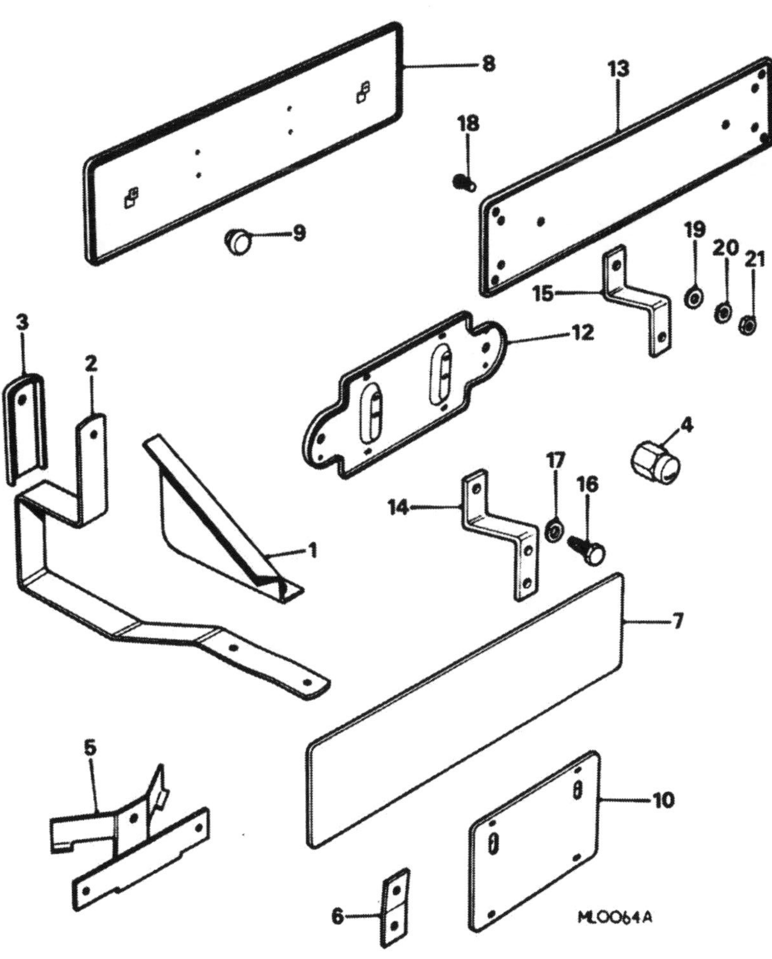

AUSTIN-HEALEY SPRITE MK. 3 AND MK. 4 & MG MIDGET MK. 2 AND MK. 3

BUMPER FIXINGS AND NUMBER PLATES-continued.

NO.	PART NO.	DESCRIPTION	QTY	CHANGE POINT	REMARKS
10	AHA 5211	Support-number plate-front and rear	2	(C)G-AN5-143355 TO 154100	North America.
10	AHA 5211	Support-number plate-front	1	(C)G-AN6-154101 ON	
	CHA 594	Piece-distance	2		
	AAU 2499	Nut-rawl	2		
	SE 106501	Screw-number plate to bumber	2		
	WL 106001	Washer-spring	2		
	WA 106041	Washer-plain	2		
12	CZK 3693	Plate-mounting-number plate rear	1		
	WL 600041	Washer-spring	2		
	WA 106041	Washer-plain	2		
	NH 604041	Nut	2		
9	AHA 5804	Buffer-bracket	2		West Germany.
	LNZ 204	Nut-Nyloc	2	Use prior to (C)G-AN6-154101	
	SE 604051	Screw	4		
	PMZ 416	Screw	NLA		
	WL 600041	Washer-spring	4		
	NH 604041	Nut	4		
13	14A 7552	Number-plate-rear	1	(C)G-AN6-154101 ON (Except N.America).	
14	BHH 1642	Bracket-front number-plate	2		
15	CHA 363	Bracket-rear number-plate	2		
16	CZK 3721	Screw-bracket to armature	4		
17	WL 600041	Washer-spring	4		
18	SE 604061	Screw-number-plates	4		
19	WA 106041	Washer-plain	4		
20	WL 600041	Washer-spring	4		
21	NH 604041	Nut	4		

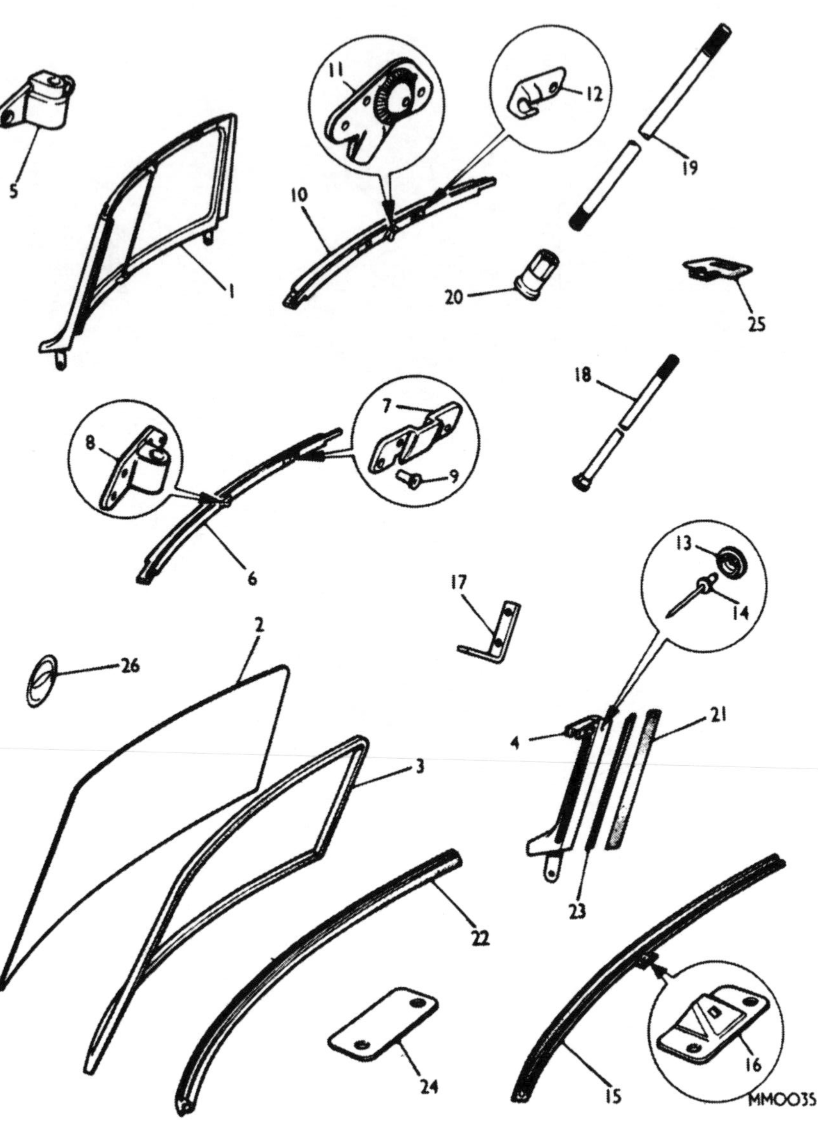

AUSTIN-HEALEY SPRITE MK. 3 AND MK. 4 & MG MIDGET MK. 2 AND MK. 3

WINDSCREEN AND WINDSCREEN FIXINGS.

NO.	PART NO.	DESCRIPTION	QTY	CHANGE POINT	REMARKS
		WINDSCREEN ASSEMBLY			
1	AHA 7074	Zone toughened-RHD	NLA	See(1)below	Alternatives Use AHA 9692
1	AHA 7960	Zone toughened-RHD(Expoxy Black)	NLA	See(1)below	Alternatives Use AHA 9692
1	AHA 9692	Zone toughened-RHD	1	See(2)below	
1	AHA 7075	Laminated LHD(Ex.N.America)	NLA	See(3)below	Use AHA 9684
1	AHA 8007	High impact laminated $ (N.America)	NLA	See(3)below	Use AHA 9681
1	AHA 8476	High impact laminated $ (N.America)	NLA	See(4)below	Use AHA 9681
1	AHA 9684	Laminted LHD(Ex.N.America & Sweden)	1	See(5)below	
1	AHA 9681	High impact laminated $ (N.America & Sweden)	1	See(5)below	
2	AHA 7959	Glass-windscreen-zone toughened-RHD	1		
2	AHA 8008	Glass-windscreen-laminated-high impact $ LHD	1		Optional fit RHD
3	88G 455	Rubber-glazing	1		

CHANGE POINTS:
(1).(C)H-AN8-38829 TO 64734,(C)H-AN9-64735 TO 85286,(C)H-AN10-85287 TO 85307, (C)G-AN3-25788 TO 52389,(C)G-AN4-52390 TO 74885,(C)G-AN5-74885 TO 77803.
(2).(C)H-AN10-85308 TO 87824,(C)G-AN5-74886 TO 154100,(C)G-AN6-154101 ON.
(3).(C)H-AN8-38829 TO 64734,(C)H-AN9-64735 TO 72033(N.America), 85286(Ex.N.America),(C)G-AN3-25788 TO 52389, (C)G-AN4-52390 TO 60440(N.America),74885(Ex.N.America).
(4).(C)H-AN9-72034 TO 85286,(C)G-AN4-60441 TO 74885.
(5).(C)H-AN10-85287 TO 86803,(C)A-AN10-86804 TO 87824, (C)G-AN5-74886 TO 154100,(C)G-AN6-154101 ON.

AUSTIN-HEALEY SPRITE MK. 3 AND MK. 4 & MG MIDGET MK. 2 AND MK. 3

WINDSCREEN AND WINDSCREEN FIXINGS-continued.

NO.	PART NO.	DESCRIPTION	QTY	CHANGE POINT	REMARKS
		PILLAR ASSEMBLY			
4	AHA 9537	RH	NLA		RHD-Black finish.
	AHA 9538	LH	NLA		
4	AHA 7063	RH	1		RHD and LHD (Except N.America And Sweden)
	AHA 7064	LH	1		
4	AHA 8559	RH-$	NLA		N.America and Sweden.
	AHA 8560	LH-$	NLA		
5	AHH 8758	Bracket-sun visor pivot $	2		
	CMP 308	Screw-pillar to top rail 12.7mm(.5")	NLA		
	CMP 310	Screw-pillar to top rail 15.87mm(.625)	NLA		
6	AHA 7065	RAIL ASSEMBLY-TOP	1	See(1)below	
7	AHH 6267	Bracket-hood fastener	NLA		
9	AHH 7138	Rivet-bracket to rail	12		
10	AHA 8479	RAIL ASSEMBLY-TOP $	1	See(4)below	
7	AHA 8483	Bracket-hood fastener $	2		
11	AHH 8846	Bracket-mirror $	1		
12	AHA 8557	Bracket-anchor-sun visor $	2		
9	AHH 7138	Rivet-bracket	12		
10	AHA 9539	RAIL ASSEMBLY-TOP	NLA		RHD-Black finish.
7	AHA 8483	Bracket-hood fastener	2		
9	AHH 7138	Rivet-bracket to rail	8		
10	AHA 9685	RAIL ASSEMBLY-TOP	1	See(2)below RHD See(3)and(5) Below LHD (Ex.N.America and Sweden)	
7	AHH 6267	Bracket-hood fastener	NLA		
9	AHH 7138	Rivet-bracket	8		
	BHA 4963	Bracket-mirror	1		
	AHH 7138	Rivet	4		
10	AHA 9682	RAIL ASSEMBLY-TOP $	NLA	See(5)below (N.America and Sweden)	
7	AHA 8483	Bracket-hood fastener $	2		
12	AHH 9838	Bracket-anchor-sun visor $	2		
9	AHH 7138	Rivet-bracket	12		
	PWZ 102	Washer-visor to rail	4		
13	ADB 4811	Stud-socket fastener-hood and tonneau cover	4	See(1)(3)and (4)	
13	BHA 4645	Stud-socket fastener	4	See(2)below RHD And(5)below	

CHANGE POINTS:
(1).(C)H-AN8-38829 TO 64734,(C)H-AN9-64735 TO 85286,(C)H-AN10-85287 TO 85307 (C)G-AN3-25788 TO 52389,(C)G-AN4-52390 TO 74885,(C)G-AN5-74885 TO 77803.
(2).(C)H-AN10-85308 TO 87824,(C)G-AN5-74886 TO 154100,(C)G-AN6-154101 ON.
(3).(C)H-AN8-38829 TO 64734,(C)H-AN9-64735 TO 72033(N.America) 85286(Ex.N.America),(C)G-AN3-25788 TO 52389, (C)G-AN4-52390 TO 60440(N.America),74885(Ex.N.America).
(4).(C)H-AN9-72034 TO 85286,(C)G-AN4-60441 TO 74885.
(5).(C)H-AN10-85287 TO 86803,(C)A-AN10-86804 TO 87824, (C)G-AN5-74886 TO 154100,(C)G-AN6-154101 ON.

$ This item is subject to safety regulations.

AUSTIN-HEALEY SPRITE MK. 3 AND MK. 4 & MG MIDGET MK. 2 AND MK. 3

WINDSCREEN AND WINDSCREEN FIXINGS-continued

NO.	PART NO.	DESCRIPTION	QTY	CHANGE POINT	REMARKS
15	AHA 7067	RAIL ASSEMBLY-BOTTOM	1	See(1)below	
16	AHA 7060	Bracket-centre rod	NLA		
9	AHH 7138	Rivet-bracket to rail	2		
15	AHA 9541	RAIL ASSEMBLY-BOTTOM	1		RHD Black finish
16	AHA 8486	Bracket-centre rod $	NLA		
9	AHH 7138	Rivet	3		
15	AHA 8484	RAIL ASSEMBLY-BOTTOM $	1	See(3)(4)and (5) Below.(N.America And Sweden	
16	AHA 8486	Bracket-centre rod $	NLA		
9	AHH 7138	Rivet	3		
15	AHA 9687	RAIL ASSEMBLY-BOTTOM	1	See(2)below RHD And(5)below (Except N.America And Sweden	
16	AHA 8486	Bracket-centre rod	NLA		
9	AHH 7138	Rivet	2		
	CMP 305	Screw-bottom rail to reinforcement	NLA		
17	AHA 7070	Reinforcement-bottom corner-RH	NLA		
	AHA 7071	Reinforcement-bottom corner-LH	NLA		
18	AHA 7061	Rod-centre	1		
19	AHA 8561	Rod-centre $	NLA		RHD Black finish
20	AHH 8749	Nut-centre rod $	NLA		
	FNP 103	Nut-rod	1		
	LWZ 203	Washer-spring	1		
21	AHA 7091	Seal-pillar-RH	NLA		Use AHA 7092.
	AHA 7092	Seal-pillar-RH and LH	2		
22	AHA 7698	Seal-windscreen to body	1		
23	AHA 7080	Retainer-pillar seal-RH	1		
	AHA 7081	Retainer-pillar seal-LH	1		
9	AHH 7138	Rivet-seal and retainer to pillar	12		
	PWZ 202	Washer-plain-rivet	2		
24	AHA 7779	Packing-centre fixing-windscreen to body	1		
	HPS 408	Screw-centre fixing-windscreen to body	1		
	LWZ 204	Washer-spring-screw	2		
	ZCS 609	Screw-pillar foot to body-upper	2		
	PWZ 306	Washer-plain-screw and bolt	4		
	LWZ 206	Washer-spring-screw and bolt	4		
	FNZ 106	Nut-bolt	2		
25	AHA 7093	Grommet-seal-pillar foot-RH	1		
	AHA 7094	Grommet-seal-pillar foot-LH	1		

$ This item is subject to safety regulations.

CHANGE POINTS:
(1).(C)H-AN8-38829 TO 64734,(C)H-AN9-64735 TO 85286,(C)H-AN10-85287 TO 85307 , (C)G-AN3-25788 TO 52389,(C)G-AN4-52390 TO 74885,(C)G-AN5-74885 TO 77803.
(2).(C)H-AN10-85308 TO 87824,(C)G-AN5-74886 TO 154100,(C)G-AN6-154101 ON.
(3).(C)H-AN8-38829 TO 64734,(C)H-AN9-64735 TO 72033(N.America), 85286(Ex.N.America),(C)G-AN3-25788 TO 52389, (C)G-AN4-52390 TO 60440(N.America),74885(Ex.N.America).
(4).(C)H-AN9-72034 TO 85286,(C)G-AN4-60441 TO 74885.
(5).(C)H-AN10-85287 TO 86803,(C)A-AN10-86804 TO 87824, (C)G-AN5-74886 TO 154100,(C)G-AN6-154101 ON.

MMO035

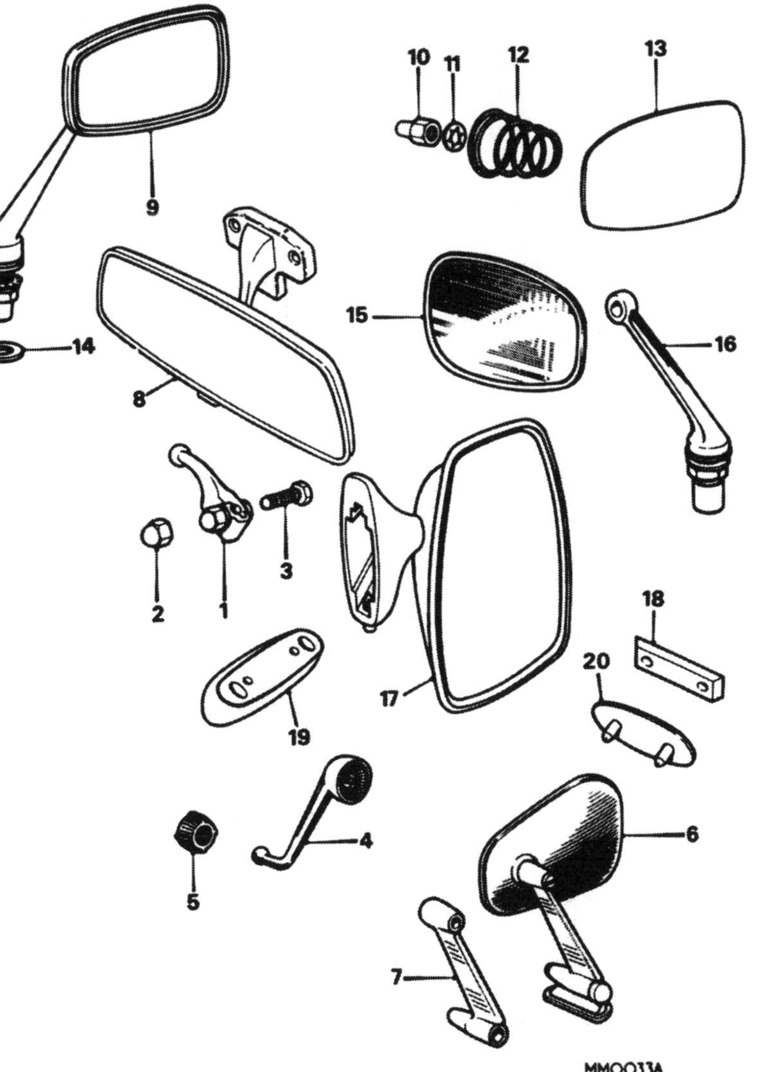

AUSTIN-HEALEY SPRITE MK. 3 AND MK. 4 & MG MIDGET MK. 2 AND MK. 3

NO.	PART NO.	DESCRIPTION	QTY	CHANGE POINT	REMARKS
		MIRRORS			
1	AHH 6940	STEM ASSEMBLY	1		
	LWZ 203	Washer-spring	1		
2	14B 7889	Nut-dome	1		
1	AHH 6940	STEM ASSEMBLY	1	(C)H-AN9-74462 TO 85286 (C)G-AN4-63075 TO 74885	Except N.America
3	AHH 6951	Screw	1		
	LWZ 203	Washer-spring	1		
2	14B 7889	Nut-dome	1		
4	BHA 4801	Stem-mirror $	1	(C)H-AN9-72034 TO 85286 (C)G-AN4-60441 TO 74885 (C)G-AN5-74886 TO 138800	N.America and Sweden
5	BHA 4783	Nut $	1		
6	BHA 4735	MIRROR ASSEMBLY-DOOR $	1		
7	37H 2502	Stem $	1		
8	BHA 4960	Mirror-interior-dipping $	1	(C)G-AN10-85287 TO 86803 (C)A-AN10-86804 TO 87824 (C)G-AN5-74886 TO 154100 (C)G-AN6-154101 ON	
	RMP 2307	Screw-mirror to windscreen rail	2		
9	GAM 101	MIRROR-WING-BOOMERANG TYPE-OPTIONAL EXTRA	2		Except N.America
9	GAM 102	MIRROR-WING-BOOMERANG TYPE-OPTIONAL EXTRA $	1		N.America
10	37H 9967	Nut-dome $	NLA		
11	37H 9968	Washer-shakeproof $	NLA		
12	17H 8148	Spring $	NLA		
13	GAM 113	Glass $	2		Was 17H 8146
	37H 9946	ARM ASSEMBLY $	NLA		
14	37H 9971	Washer(rubber)$	2		Alternative to GAM 101 in pairs and GAM 102 singly also standard fitment for Switzerland only
15	37H 4579	Head-mirror(with nut) $	2/1		
16	47H 9518	Arm-mirror $	2/1		
17	BHH 1395	Mirror-door-anti-glare-RH $	1	(C)G-AN5-138801 TO 154100 (C)G-AN6-154101 TO 175833	
	BHH 1396	Mirror-door-anti-glare-LH $	1		
18	CZK 6342	Plate-fixing-door mirror	2		
	AC 610061	Screw-mirror to door	4		
19	CZH 3521	Base plinth-door mirror	2		
20	CHA 176	Plate-mounting-door mirror	2		
	SM 105161	Screw-fixing plate to plinth	4		
17	HZA 5074	Mirror-door-anti-glare-RH $	1	(C)G-AN6-175834 ON	
	HZA 5075	Mirror-door-anti-glare-LH $	1		
	DZB 5208	Plate-fixing(breakout)	2		
	AC 610061	Screw-mirror to door	4		
19	CZM 3521	Base-plinth	2		
20	CHA 176	Plate-mounting	2		
	SM 105161	Screw-fixing plinth	4		

$ This item is subject to safety regulations.

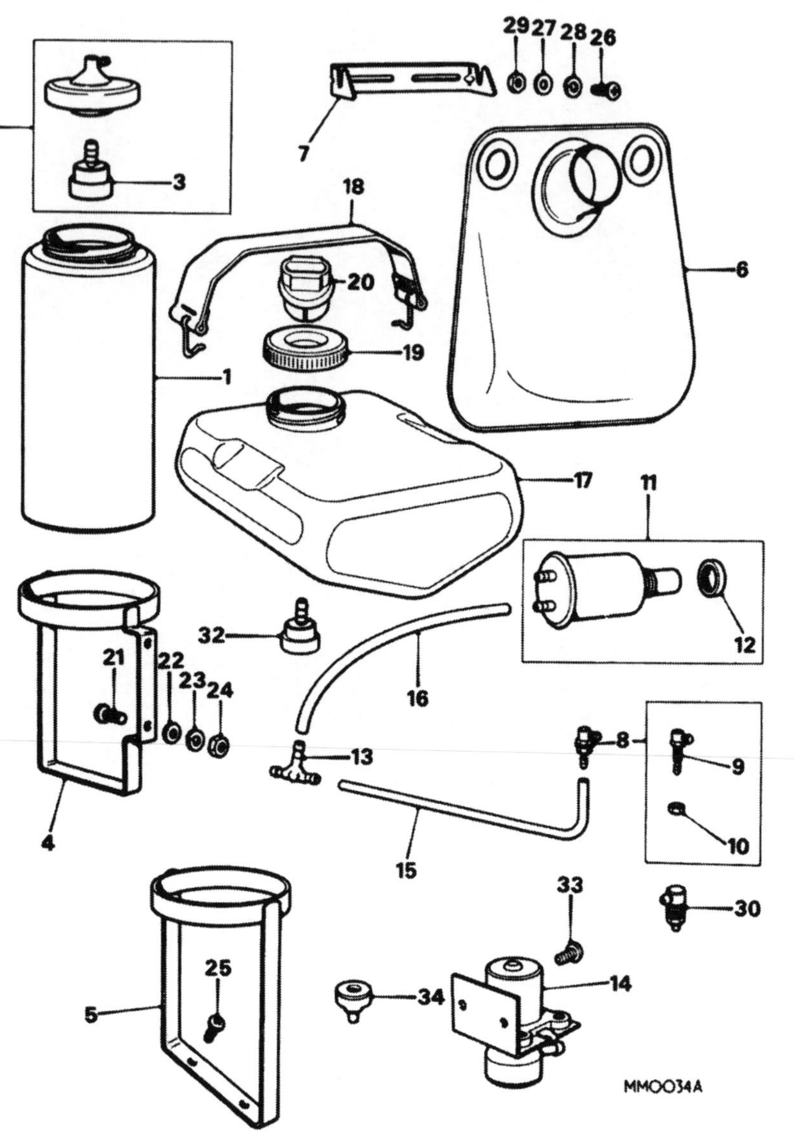

AUSTIN-HEALEY SPRITE MK. 3 AND MK. 4 & MG MIDGET MK. 2 AND MK. 3

WINDSCREEN WASHER

NO.	PART NO.	DESCRIPTION	QTY	CHANGE POINT	REMARKS
1	13H 227	Container	1	Use prior to CHA 434.	
17	CHA 434	Container	1	(C)G-AN6-154101 ON	
18	CHA 458	Strap-container	1		
	BHA 5232	Container $	1	(C)G-AN6-166301 ON	North America
2	AHH 6848	CAP ASSEMBLY-CONTAINER	1	Use prior to 34G 1290	Except Sweden
3	13H 6473	Valve-foot	1		
19	34G 1290	Cap-container	1	(C)G-AN5-134186 TO 154100	
20	34G 1289	Plug-filler	1	(C)G-AN6-154101 ON	
2	AHH 6848	CAP ASSEMBLY-CONTAINER	1		Sweden
3	13H 6473	Valve-foot	1		
4	13H 232	Bracket-container mounting	1		
21	PMZ 306	Screw-bracket to mudshield	2		
22	PWZ 103	Washer-plain	2		
23	LWZ 203	Washer-spring	2		
24	FNZ 103	Nut	2		
5	AHA 8729	Bracket-container mounting	1	Use prior to CHA 458.	
25	PTZ 1004	Screw-bracket to footwell	2		
6	BHA 4920	Container	1		Sweden
2	AHH 6848	CAP ASSEMBLY-CONTAINER	1		
3	13H 6473	Valve-foot	1		
7	BHA 4919	Bracket-container	NLA		
26	PMZ 308	Screw	2		
27	PWZ 203	Washer-plain	2		
28	LWZ 203	Washer-spring	2		
29	FNZ 103	Nut	2		
8	13H 231	JET ASSEMBLY	2	Use prior to CZD 1593	
9	27H 9623	Jet	2		
10	AJD 9012 Z	Nut	2		
30	CZD 1593	Jet	2	(C)G-AN5-134186 TO 154100 (C)G-AN6-154101 ON	
11	BHA 4510	CONTROL ASSEMBLY	1		Manually operated washer
12	17H 2669	Ring-locking	1		
13	BHA 4361	Connection-3 way	1	Use prior to 13H 6472	
13	13H 6472	Connection-3 way	1	(C)G-AN5-134186 TO 154100	
32	13H 6473	Valve-foot	1	(C)G-AN6-154101 ON	
14	BHA 5146	Control-windscreen washer $	1	Use prior to 13H 7553	Electrically operated washer.
14	13H 7553	Control-windscreen washer $	1	(C)G-AN5-139307 TO 154100 (C)G-AN6-154101 ON	
33	PTZ 1004	Screw-control	2		
34	13H 7846	Filter-foot	1	(C)G-AN5-134186 TO 154100 (C)G-AN6-154101 ON	
13	34G 1295	Connection-3 way	1		
15	17H 8579	Tubing-.187"(4.8mm)O/D	A/R		Supplied in multiples of metres(39.37")
16	97H 2679 M	Tubing-.25"(6.4mm)O/D	A/R		

$ This item is subject to safety regulations.

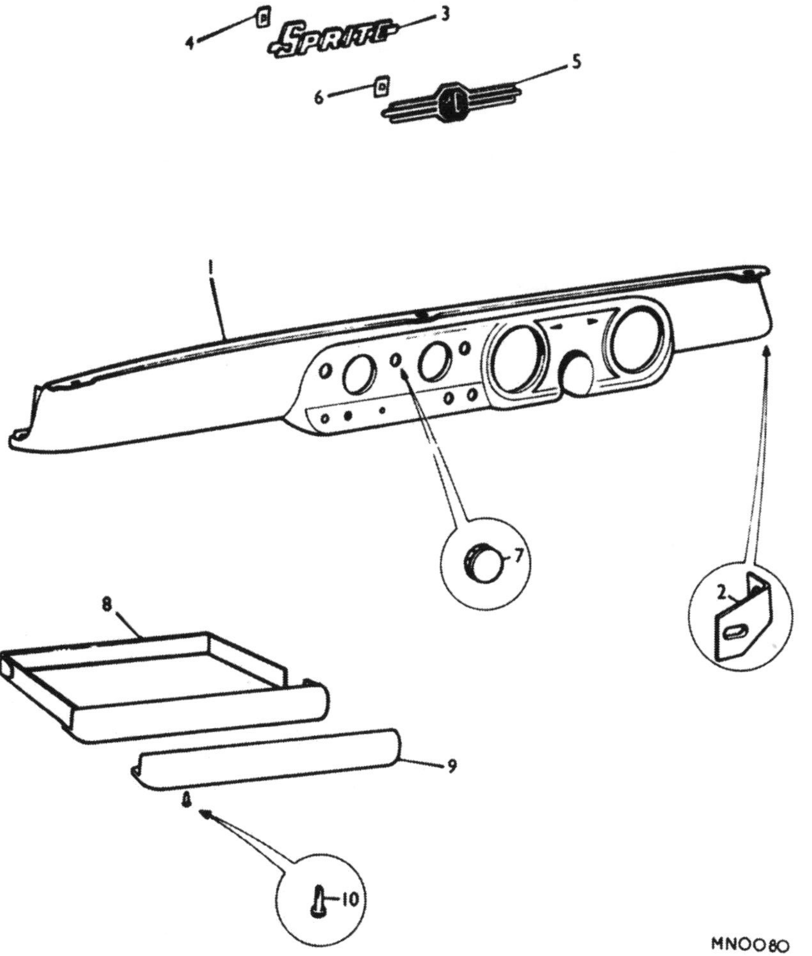

AUSTIN-HEALEY SPRITE MK. 3 AND MK. 4 & MG MIDGET MK. 2 AND MK. 3

FASCIA DETAILS-NOT N.AMERICA AND SWEDEN.

NO.	PART NO.	DESCRIPTION	QTY	CHANGE POINT	REMARKS
1	CZJ 422	Panel-fascia-RHD	1	Use prior to CZJ 488	When supplying prior to (C)G-AN5-105501 supply also 1 off BHA 5111,BHA 5109 and BHA 5112-switches
	CZJ 423	Panel-fascia-LHD	NLA	(C)G-AN5-74886 TO 138800	
1	CZJ 488	Panel-fascia-RHD	1	(C)G-AN5-138801 TO 154100	
1	CZJ 662	Panel-fascia-RHD	1	(C)G-AN6-154101 TO 182000	
1	CHA 660	Panel-fascia-RHD	1	(C)G-AN6-182001 ON	
2	AHA 7438	Bracket-fascia panel to 'A'post-RH	1		
	AHA 7439	Bracket-fascia panel to 'A'post-LH	1		
	PFS 512	Nut-spring	2		
	HZS 405	Screw	2		
	PMZ 408	Screw	2		
	PWZ 104	Washer-plain	7		
	LWZ 204	Washer-spring	5		
	PTZ 1003	Screw	4		
3	AHA 5799	Motif-'Sprite'	1		
4	BHA 4082	Push-on-fix-motif to fascia panel	2		
5	AHH 5258	Motif-'MG'	1		
6	ADB 509	Nut-spire	2		
7	ACH 9373	Plug-blanking-ignition switch hole	1		
8	AHA 8275	TRAY ASSEMBLY-PARCEL-RHD	1		
	AHA 8276	TRAY ASSEMBLY-PARCEL-LHD	1		
9	AHA 7541	Moulding	1		
	FWZ 210	Washer-cup	4		
	FWP 710	Washer-cup	5		

AUSTIN-HEALEY SPRITE MK. 3 AND MK. 4 & MG MIDGET MK. 2 AND MK. 3

NO.	PART NO.	DESCRIPTION	QTY	CHANGE POINT	REMARKS
		FASCIA DETAILS-N.AMERICA AND SWEDEN			
1	AHA 8780	Panel-fascia $	1	Use prior to AHA 8866	
1	AHA 8866	Panel-fascia $	1	(C)G-AN5-105501 TO 154100 (C)G-AN6-154101 ON	
	NH 604041	Nut-fascia to shroud	4		
	PWZ 104	Washer-plain	4		
	LWZ 204	Washer-spring	4		
2	AHA 8606	Plate-support-fascia to dash-LH	1		
	PTZ 1003	Screw-support plates	3		
	LWZ 203	Washer-spring	A/R		
	FNZ 103	Nut	A/R		
	HZA 5025	Badge-anniversary-fascia panel	1		
3	AHA 8570	Nacelle-switches	1		
4	J2A 9599	Panel-radio mounting	1	(C)G-AN5-74886 TO 112275	
4	J2A 9966	Panel-radio mounting	1	(C)G-AN5-112276 TO 123730	
4	CHA 59	Panel-radio mounting	1	(C)G-AN5-123731 TO 154100 (C)G-AN6-154101 ON	
5	AHH 5255	Bezel-radio aperture	1		
6	ARH 59	Plate-blanking-Black	1	Use prior to CHA 659	
4	CHA 659	Plate-blanking-Grey	1	(C)G-AN6-182001 ON	
7	BHH 364	Clip-blanking plate and motif	2		
8	AHA 8706	Screw-nacelle	4		
9	AHA 8763	Screw-nacelle	NLA		
	FWP 706	Washer-cup	NLA		
10	BHA 4823	Bezel-nacelle	1		
11	AJD 8014 Z	Nut-bezel	8		
	PWZ 103	Washer-plain	4		
12	AHH 5258	Motif-'MG'	1		
13	ADB 509	Nut-spire-motif	2		
14	AHA 5699	Motif-'Sprite'	1		
	PFS 104	Push-on-fix-motif	2		
15	BHA 5102	Clip-retaining panel	2		
	FWP 710	Washer-cup	5		
	13H 7986	Light-warning-'fasten belts'	1	(C)G-AN5-112276 TO 154100 (C)G-AN6-154101 ON	USA and Canada

$ This item is subject to safety regulations.

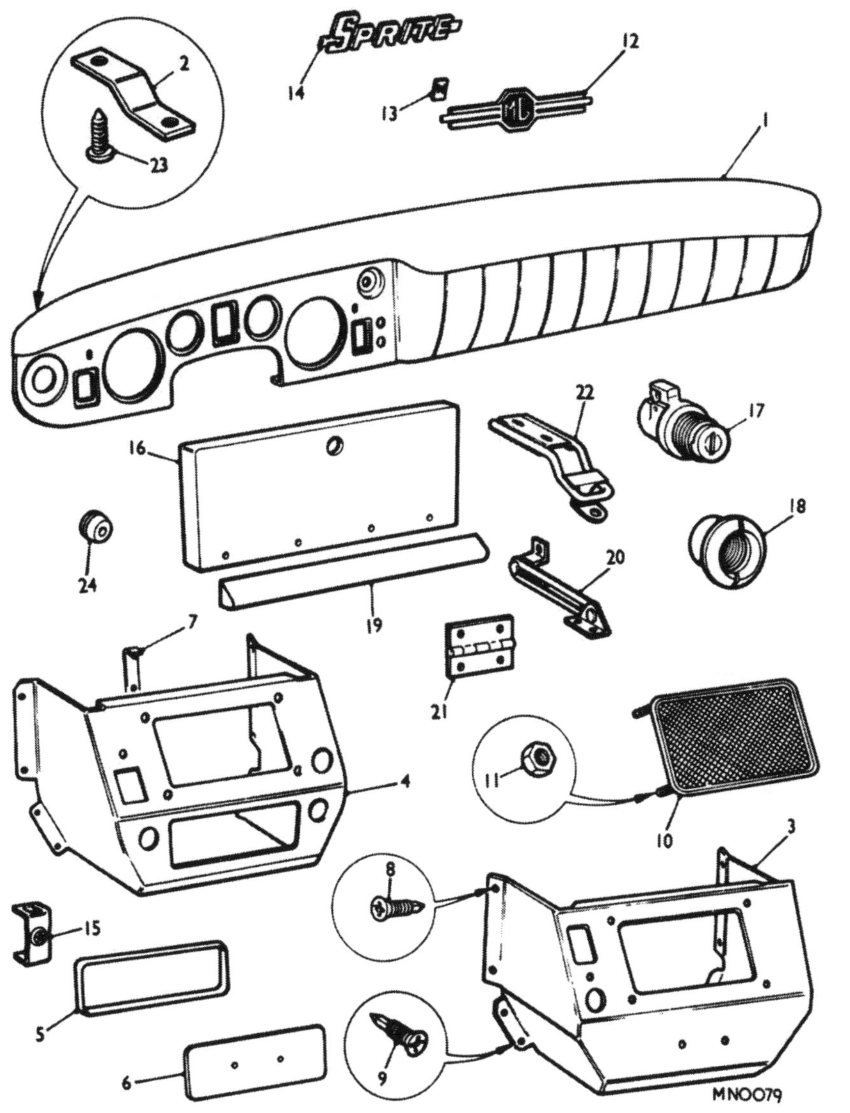

AUSTIN-HEALEY SPRITE MK. 3 AND MK. 4 & MG MIDGET MK. 2 AND MK. 3

NO.	PART NO.	DESCRIPTION	QTY	CHANGE POINT	REMARKS
		FASCIA DETAILS-N.AMERICA AND SWEDEN-continued			
16	AHA 9965	Lid-cubby box	NLA	(C)G-AN5-105501 TO 123730	Use CHA 55
16	CHA 55	Lid-cubby box $	1	(C)G-AN5-123731 TO 154100 (C)G-AN6-154101 ON	
17	AHA 9802	Lock-lid	1	(C)G-AN5-105501 TO 154100 (C)G-AN6-154101 ON	
18	AHA 9809	Bezel-lock	1		
	PTZ 804	Screw	2		
19	AHA 9812	Moulding-lid	1	(C)G-AN5-105501 TO 123730	
19	CHA 54	Moulding-lid $	1	(C)G-AN5-123731 TO 154100 (C)G-AN6-154101 ON	
20	AHA 9813	Stay-support-lid	NLA	(C)G-AN5-105501 TO 154100 (C)G-AN6-154101 ON	
	PTZ 804	Screw-stay	2		
	PTZ 806	Screw-stay	2		
21	AHA 9805	Hinge-lid	NLA		
	PTZ 804	Screw-hinge	4		
22	AHA 9807	Striker-lock	1		
	PWZ 203	Washer-plain	2		
	LWZ 203	Washer-spring	2		
23	53K 126	Screw	2		
24	BHA 5103	Buffer-lid	NLA		

$ This item is subject to safety regulations.

MNO076

AUSTIN-HEALEY SPRITE MK. 3 AND MK. 4 & MG MIDGET MK. 2 AND MK. 3

HEATER UNIT.

NO.	PART NO.	DESCRIPTION	QTY	CHANGE POINT	REMARKS
2	AHA 8090	HEATER UNIT ASSEMBLY	1	(C)H-AN9-64735 TO 72033 (C)G-AN4-52390 TO 60440	
1	17H 1590	Matrix(with seals)	1		
4	27H 1253	Washer-water pipe	NLA		
2	BHA 4744	HEATER UNIT ASSEMBLY $	NLA	(C)H-AN9-72034 AND G-AN4-60441 TO (B)GUN-151300 AND (B)GBE-100650	
1	37H 2797	Matrix(with seals)	1		
4	27H 1253	Washer-water pipe	NLA		
5	4B 9713	Seal-heater base	NLA		
	PMZ 410	Screw	4		
	WA 106041	Washer-plain	4		
	WL 600041	Washer-spring	4		
6	AHA 9727	HEATER UNIT ASSEMBLY	1	(B)GUN-151301 AND (B)GBE-100651 TO (C)G-AN5-154100	
7	37H 6193	Motor and mounting plate	1		
8	37H 6194	Matrix	1		
	CHA 345	HEATER UNIT ASSEMBLY	1	(C)G-AN6-154101 ON	
	37H 4583	Motor and mounting plate	1		
	37H 8818	Matrix	1		
	PJZ 1005	Screw-heater to platform	6		
	PWZ 103	Washer	6		
9	88G 588	Tap-water control	1	Use prior to 12H 1293,CHA 349 AND 12H 3868.	
10	AAA 836	Washer-tap	1		
11	ACA 5456	Adaptor-tap	1		
	12H 1293	Tap-water control	1	(C)G-AN6-154101 ON	
	CHA 349	Elbow-tap	1		
	12H 3868	Gasket-tap	1		
	SE 604081	Screw-elbow to bracket	2		
	WL 600041	Washer-spring	2		
	NH 604041	Nut	2		
12	88G 221	Gasket-adaptor to cylinder head	1		
	SH 604061	Screw	2		
14	AHA 8782	Hose-heater to control tap	1	Use prior to AHA 9782	
16	AHA 8331	Hose-heater to blower	1		
14	AHA 9782	Hose-heater to control tap	1	(B)GBE-100651 AND (B)GUN-151301 TO (C)G-AN5-154100	
	CHA 352	Hose-control tap to manifold	1	(C)G-AN6-154101 ON	North America except California.
	CHA 351	Hose-heater to control tap	1		Except N.America.
	CHA 359	Hose-control tap to manifold	1		
	GHC 709	Clip-hose	4		
	CHA 448	Pipe-heater by-pass	1	(C)G-AN6-160160 ON	California only.
	CHA 449	Hose-pipe to manifold	1		
	CHA 450	Hose-elbow to pipe	1		
	CHA 521	Hose-automatic choke	2		
17	AHH 8394	Hose-demister	2		
18	12G 1785	Pipe-heater hose to radiator hose	1		
19	GHC 507	Clip	A/R		
20	PCR 809	Clip	2		

$ This item is subject to safety regulations.

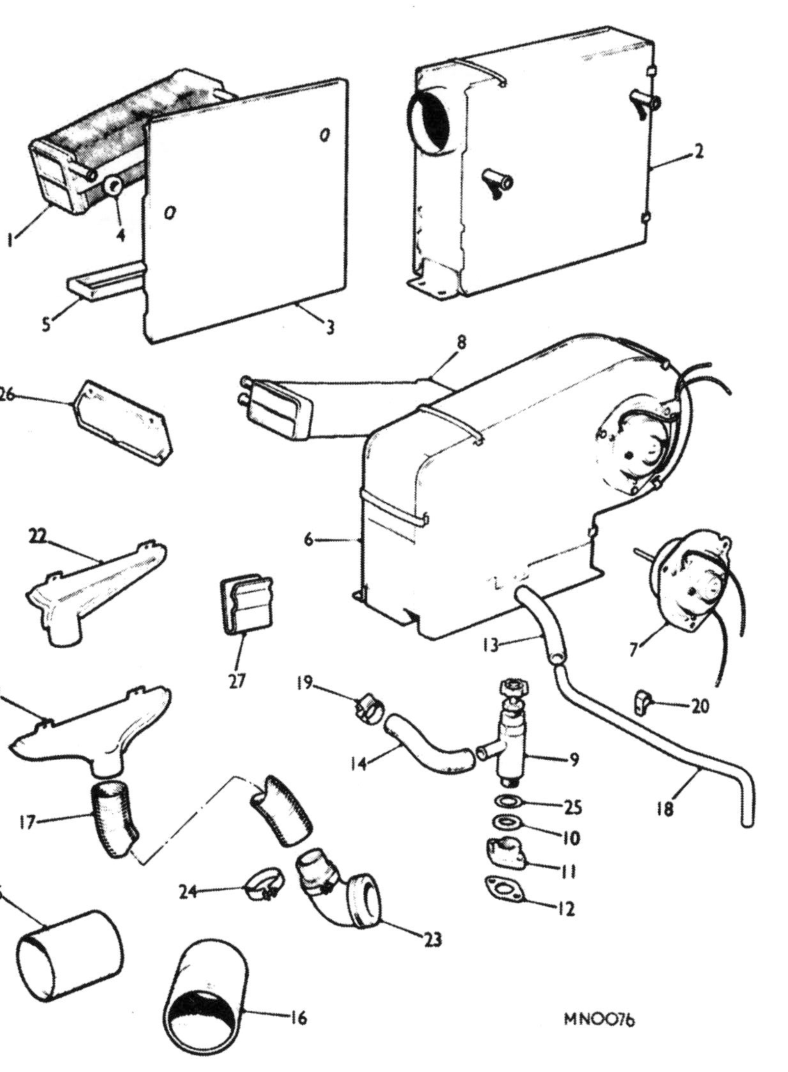

AUSTIN-HEALEY SPRITE MK. 3 AND MK. 4 & MG MIDGET MK. 2 AND MK. 3

NO.	PART NO.	DESCRIPTION	QTY	CHANGE POINT	REMARKS
		HEATER UNIT-continued.			
21	14A 1162	Nozzle-demister	NLA		Except N.America.
22	AHA 8565	Nozzle-demister-RH	NLA		] N.America.
	AHA 8566	Nozzle-demister-LH	NLA		]
	PTP 603	Screw	4		
23	14G 3499	ELBOW ASSEMBLY-DEMISTER	2		
24	BMK 924	Clip $	2		
26	13H 59	Door-heater outlet	NLA		
	AB 606031	Screw	8		
27	1G 9529	Clip-spring-pipe to heater tap	1		
13	GRH 1003 M	Hose-water outlet	A/R	] Use prior to CHA 430	Supplied in MULTIPLES OF metres.
	GHC 709	Clip-hose	1	]	
	CHA 430	Hose-heater to water pump pipe	1	] (C)G-AN6-154101-ON	
	GHC 709	Clip-hose	2	]	

$ This item is subject to safety regulations.

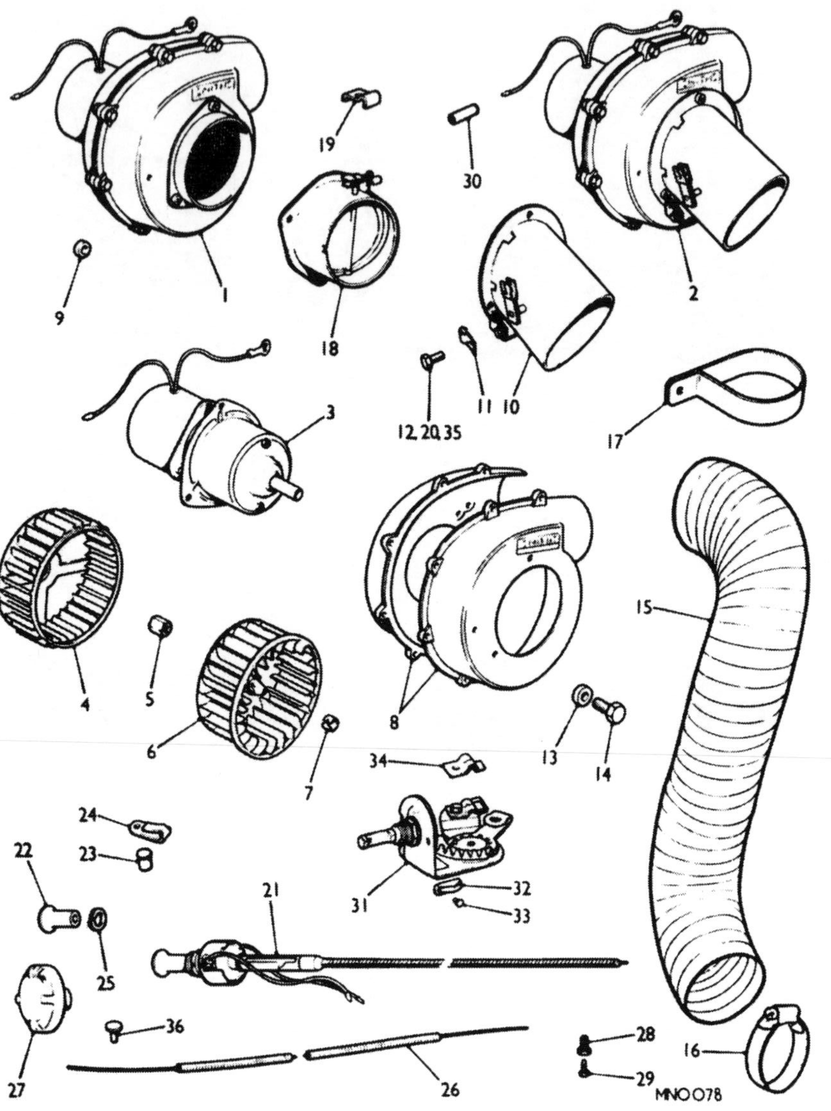

AUSTIN-HEALEY SPRITE MK. 3 AND MK. 4 & MG MIDGET MK. 2 AND MK. 3

NO.	PART NO.	DESCRIPTION	QTY	CHANGE POINT	REMARKS
		HEATER UNIT-continued.			
1	13H 51	BLOWER ASSEMBLY	1	Use prior to AHA 8091	
1	AHA 8091	BLOWER ASSEMBLY	NLA	(C)H-AN9-64735 TO 71120 (C)G-AN4-52390 TO 58853	
2	AHA 8415	BLOWER ASSEMBLY	NLA	(C)H-AN9-71121 TO 72033 (C)G-AN4-58854 TO 60440	
2	BHA 4745	BLOWER ASSEMBLY	1	(C)H-AN9-72034 and (C)G-AN4-60441 TO (B)GUN 151300 AND (B)GBE 100650	
3	17H 1455	Motor	1	Use prior to BHA 4745 and 37H 4708	
4	17H 1574	ROTOR(METAL)	1		
5	27H 602	Nut-collet	NLA		
7	17H 6836	Ring-compression	1		
8	17H 819	Casing	1		
	HZS 404	Screw	3		
	PWZ 204	Washer-plain	3		
	WL 600041	Washer-spring	3		
3	37H 4708	Motor and mounting plate	1	(C)H-AN9-72034 AND (C)G-AN4-60441 TO (B)GUN 151300 AND (B)GBE 100650	
8	17H 819	Casing	1		
13	27H 1258	Spacer-bracket	3		
	PWZ 204	Washer-bracket	3		
14	53K 126	Screw-bracket	6		
9	27H 1232	Grommet	NLA		
	FNZ 103	Nut	6		
	LWZ 403	Washer-shakeproof	6		
	WL 600041	Washer-bolt	3		
	NH 604041	Nut-bolt	3		
18	AHA 8092	TUBE ASSEMBLY-AIR INTAKE	1	(C)H-AN9-64735 TO 71120 (C)G-AN4-52390 TO 58853	
20	53K 126	Screw-clamp	1		
	LWZ 403	Washer-screw	1		
	PMZ 306	Screw	3		
	WL 700101	Washer-spring	3		
	FNZ 103	Nut	3		
10	AHA 8416	TUBE ASSEMBLY-AIR INTAKE	NLA	(C)H-AN9-71121 AND (C)G-AN4-58854 TO (B)GBE 100650 AND (B)GUN 151300	
11	27H 1193	Clamp-cable	1		
12	53K 126	Screw-clamp	1		
	LWZ 403	Washer-screw	1		

AUSTIN-HEALEY SPRITE MK. 3 AND MK. 4 & MG MIDGET MK. 2 AND MK. 3

NO.	PART NO.	DESCRIPTION	QTY	CHANGE POINT	REMARKS
		HEATER UNIT-continued.			
15	13H 58	Hose-blower to inlet	1	Use prior to AHA 8501	
15	AHA 8501	Hose-blower to inlet	1	(C)H-AN9-71121 TO 85286 (C)H-AN10-85287 TO 86803 (C)A-AN10-86804 TO 87824 (C)G-AN4-58854 TO 74885 (C)G-AN5-74886 TO 154100	
	CHA 290	Hose-blower to inlet	1	(C)G-AN6-154101 ON	
16	GHC 3036	Clip-hose	2/1		
	PMZ 310	Screw	1		
	WA 702101	Washer-plain	1		
	WL 700101	Washer-spring	1		
	FNZ 103	Nut	1		
21	BHA 4205	SWITCH ASSEMBLY-HEATER	1	Use prior to AHA 8317	
21	AHA 8317	SWITCH ASSEMBLY-HEATER	1	(C)H-AN9-64735 TO 71120 (C)G-AN4-52390 TO 58853	
21	AHA 8417	SWITCH ASSEMBLY-HEATER $	1	(C)H-AN9-71121 TO 85286 (C)H-AN10-85287 TO 86803 (C)A-AN10-86804 TO 87824 (C)G-AN4-58854 TO 74885 (C)G-AN5-74886 TO 154100 (C)G-AN6-154101 ON	
22	17H 1602	Knob $	1		
23	17H 1603	Pin-knob	1		
24	17H 1601	Clip-knob	1		

$ This item is subject to safety regulations.

MNO078

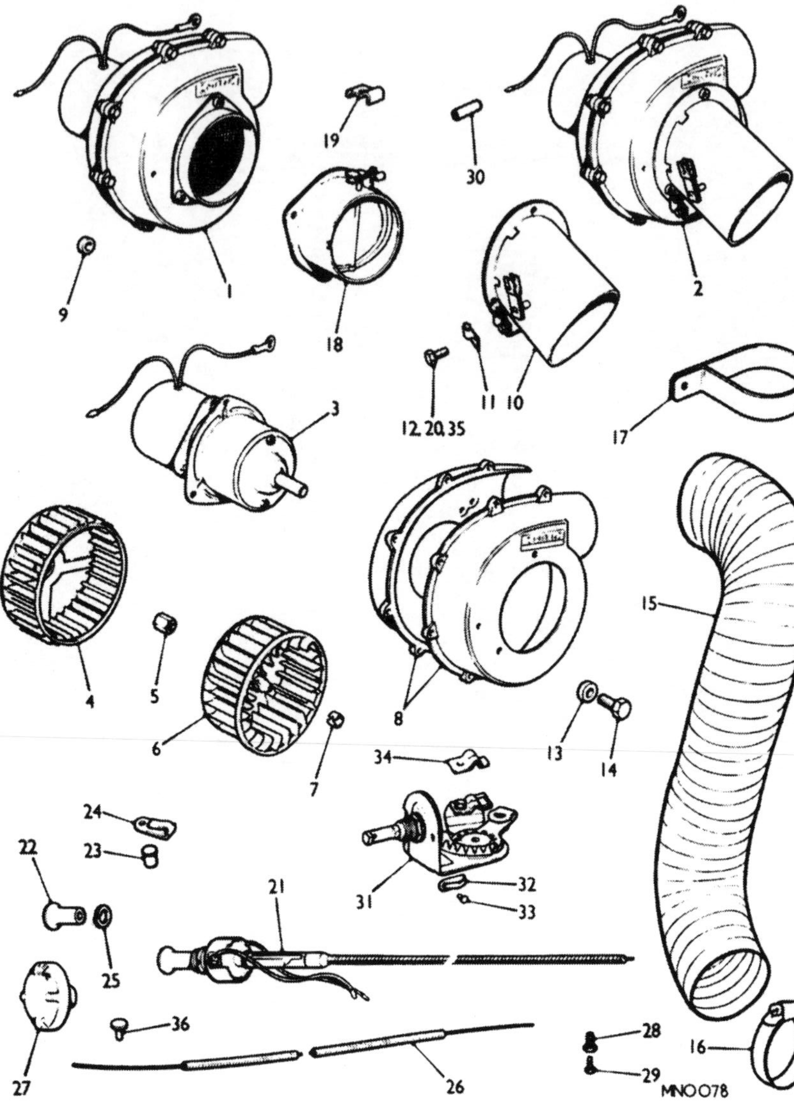

AUSTIN-HEALEY SPRITE MK. 3 AND MK. 4 & MG MIDGET MK. 2 AND MK. 3

NO.	PART NO.	DESCRIPTION	QTY	CHANGE POINT	REMARKS
		HEATER FIXINGS.			
26	AHC 752	Cable-air control $	1	Use prior to CHA 447	
26	CHA 447	Cable-air control $	1	(C)G-AN6-154101 ON	North America.
27	AHA 8716	Knob-rotary control-air $	1	Use prior to AHA 9721	
27	AHA 9721	Knob-rotary control-air $	1	(C)H-AN10-86301 TO 86803 (C)A-AN10-86804 TO 87824 (C)G-AN5-89501 TO 112275	
27	CHA 1	Knob-rotary control-air	NLA	(C)G-AN5-112276 TO 123730	N.America
27	BHH 1012	Knob-rotary control-air $	1	(C)G-AN5-123731 TO 154100	N.America
	CHA 111	Dial-illuminated-air $	1	(C)G-AN6-154101 ON	N.America
28	24G 1482	Trunnion-control cable	1		
29	53K 1016	Screw-trunnion	1		
30	104618	Connector-snap-switch to blower	1		
31	BHA 4792	CONTROL ASSEMBLY-ROTARY-AIR VALVE	1	Use prior to AHA 9720	
31	AHA 9720	CONTROL ASSEMBLY-ROTARY-AIR VALVE	1	(C)H-AN10-86301 TO 86803 (C)A-AN10-86804 TO 87824 (C)G-AN5-89501 TO 123730	N.America.
31	BHA 4792	CONTROL ASSEMBLY-ROTARY-AIR VALVE	1	(C)G-AN5-123731 TO 154100 (C)G-AN6-154101 ON	N.America.
32	17H 1601	Clip-knob	1		
33	17H 1603	Pin-knob	1		
34	27H 1193	Clamp-cable	1		
35	53K 126	Screw-clamp	1		
	LWZ 403	Washer-shakeproof	1		
36	AHH 8971	Rivet-control	NLA		
	WA 704061	Washer-rivet	1		

$ This item is subject to safety regulations.

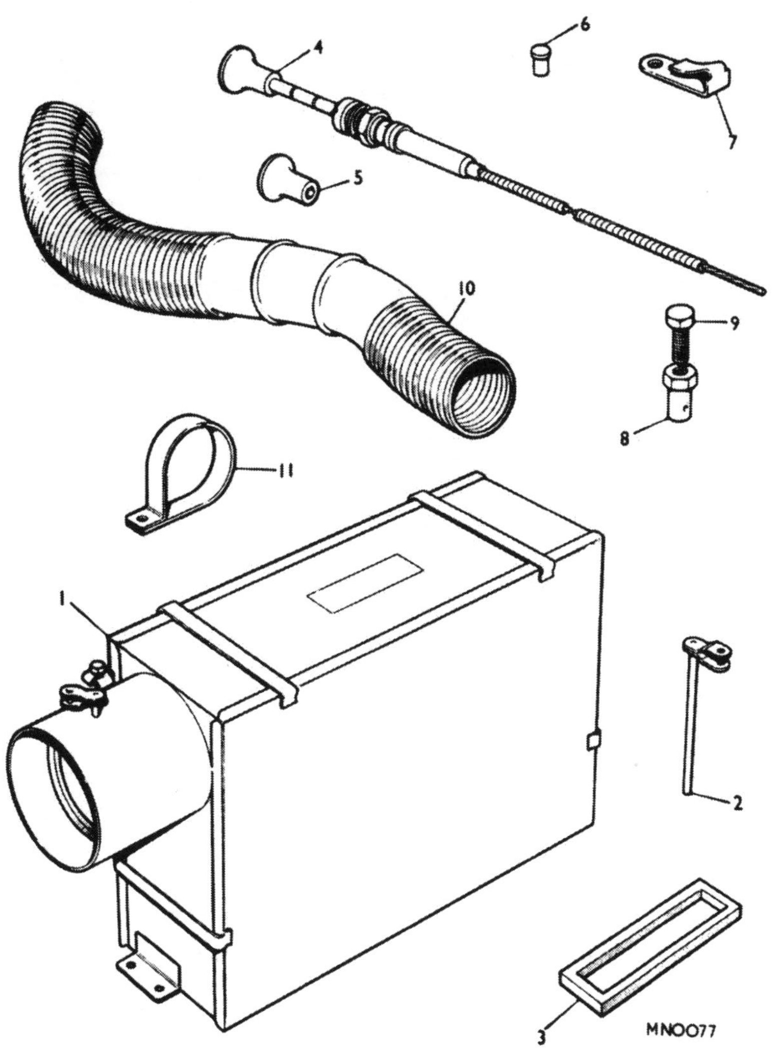

AUSTIN-HEALEY SPRITE MK. 3 AND MK. 4 & MG MIDGET MK. 2 AND MK. 3

NO.	PART NO.	DESCRIPTION	QTY	CHANGE POINT	REMARKS
		FRESH-AIR UNIT-OPTIONAL EXTRA			
1	13H 56	FRESH-AIR UNIT ASSEMBLY	NLA		
3	4B 9713	Seal-fresh-air unit base	NLA		
	HZS 404	Screw	4		
	WA 106041	Washer-plain	4		
	WL 600041	Washer-spring	4		
4	13H 57	CONTROL ASSEMBLY-PUSH-PULL	1		
5	14A 5772	Knob	NLA		
6	17H 1603	Pin-knob	1		
7	17H 1601	Clip-knob	1		
8	14G 6451	Trunnion-control cable	1		
9	AHH 5593	Screw-trunnion	1		
10	AHA 9172	Hose-fresh-air unit to inlet	1		
11	AHA 8768	Clip-hose	NLA		
	PMZ 316	Screw-clip to wheel arch	1		
	WL 700101	Washer-spring	2		
	PMZ 310	Screw	1		
	PWZ 103	Washer-plain	1		
	WL 700101	Washer-spring	1		
	FNZ 103	Nut	1		

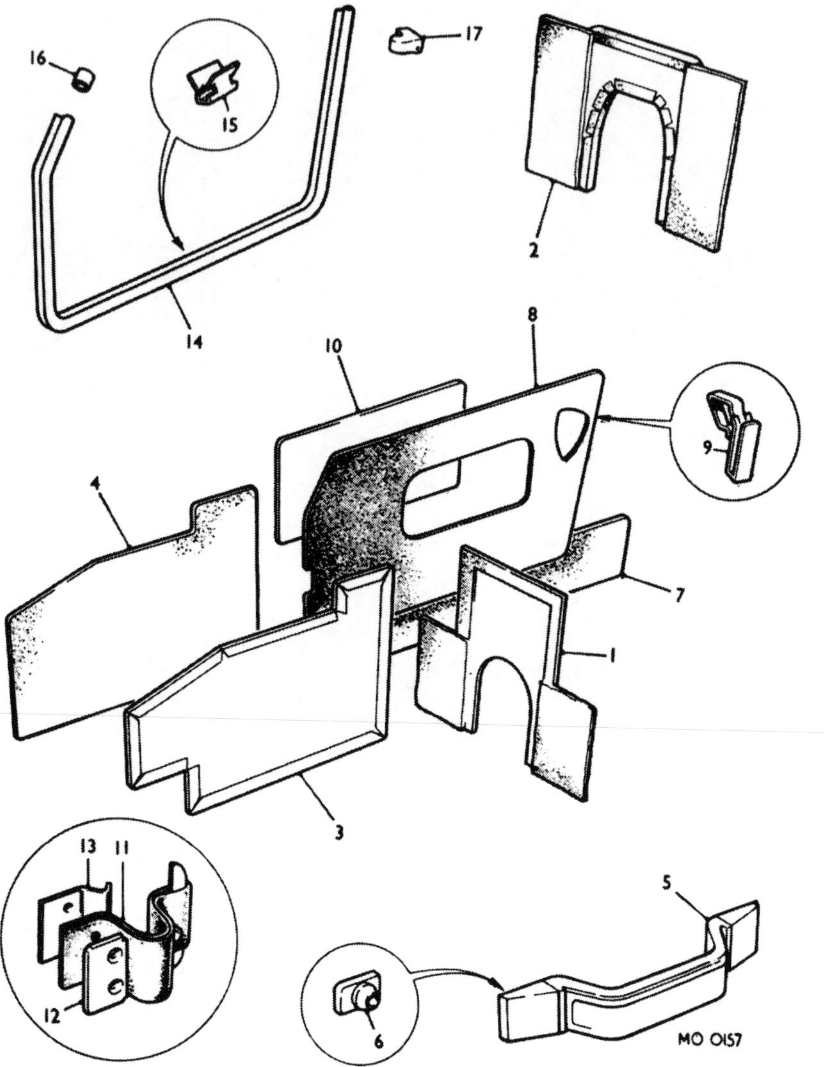

AUSTIN-HEALEY SPRITE MK. 3 AND MK. 4 & MG MIDGET MK. 2 AND MK. 3

NO.	PART NO.	DESCRIPTION	QTY	CHANGE POINT	REMARKS
		TRIM LINERS			
		LINER-FOOTWELL			
1	AHA 8964	Front	NLA		
3	AHA 7750	Side-RH	NLA	See(1)foot of page	
	AHA 7751	Side-LH	NLA		
	FWP 906	Washer-cup	8		
		LINER-SCUTTLE			
4	J2A 9573	Black-RH	NLA	See(2)foot of page	
	J2A 9575	Black-LH	NLA		
	FWP 906	Washer-cup	6		
		PULL-DOOR			
5	RGK 6476	Autumn Leaf $	2	(C)G-AN5-105501 TO 123730	
5	RGN 6476	Navy $	2		
5	XGT 2456	Ochre $	2		
	XGK 2456	Autumn Leaf $	2	(C)G-AN5-138801 TO 154100 (C)G-AN6-154101 ON	
	XGA 2456	Black $	2		
	AB 612061	Screw-door pull	4		
6	CZG 782	Locknut	4		

$ This item is subject to safety regulations.

CHANGE POINTS:
(1).(C)H-AN8-38829 TO 64734.(C)H-AN9-64735 TO 77590.(C)G-AN3-25788 TO 52389.
(C)G-AN4-52390 TO 66225.
(2).(C)H-AN10-85287 TO 86803.(C)A-AN10-86804 TO 87824.(C)G-AN5-74886 TO 105500.

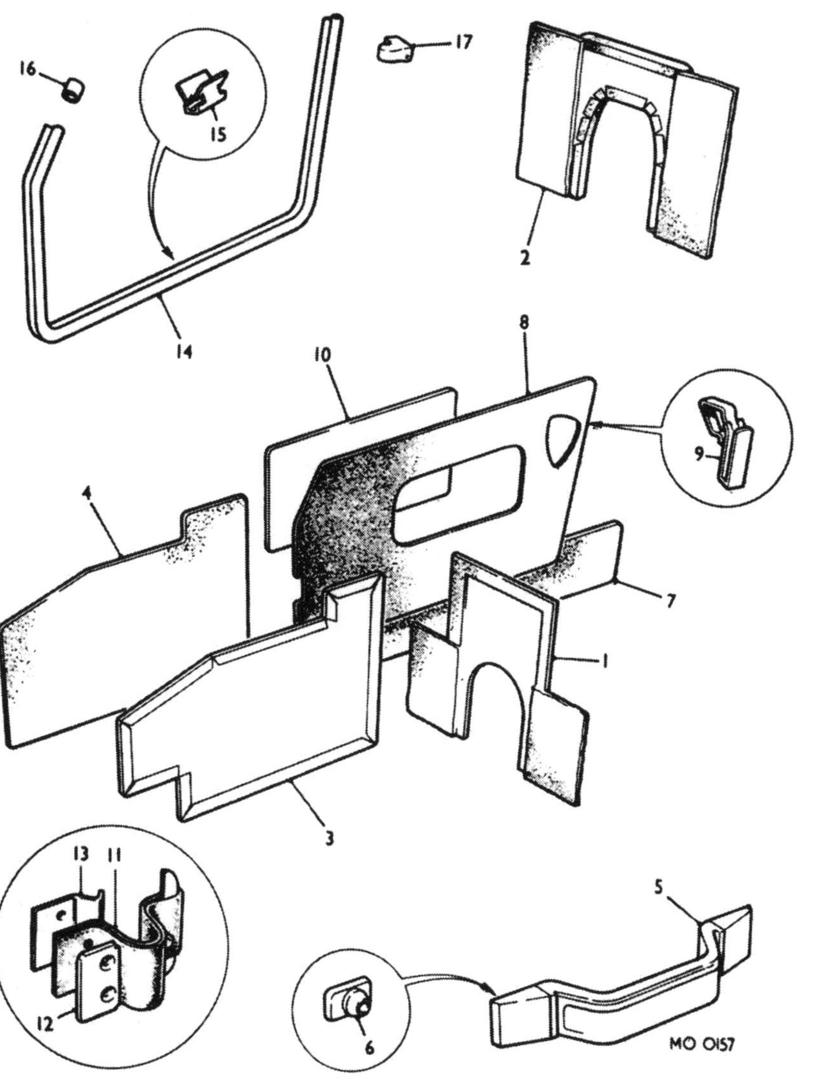

AUSTIN-HEALEY SPRITE MK. 3 AND MK. 4 & MG MIDGET MK. 2 AND MK. 3

TRIM LINERS-continued

NO.	PART NO.	DESCRIPTION	QTY	CHANGE POINT	REMARKS
7	NLA	LINER-SILL	NLA		
	FWP 906	Washer-cup	8		
		LINER ASSEMBLY-DOOR			
8	AHA 7617	Black-RH	NLA	See(1)foot of page	
	AHA 7618	Black-LH	NLA		
8	AHA 8905	Black-RH	NLA	(C)H-AN9-77591 TO 85286 (C)G-AN4-66226 TO 74885	
	AHA 8906	Black-LH	NLA		
8	J2A 9475	Black-RH	NLA	See(2)foot of page	
	J2A 9476	Black-LH	1		
8	J2K 9475	Autumn Leaf-RH	NLA		
	J2K 9476	Autumn Leaf-LH	NLA		
8	X2K 2119	Autumn Leaf-RH	NLA	(C)G-AN5-105501 TO 123730	
	X2K 2120	Autumn Leaf-LH	NLA		
8	X2N 2119	Navy-RH	1		
	X2N 2120	Navy-LH	1		
8	X2N 2768	Navy-RH $	1	(C)G-AN5-123731 TO 138800	
	X2N 2769	Navy-LH $	1		
8	X2T 2768	Ochre-RH $	1		
	X2T 2769	Ochre-LH $	NLA		
8	X2K 2768	Autumn Leaf-RH $	1	(C)G-AN5-138801 TO 154100 (C)G-AN6-154101 ON	
	X2K 2769	Autumn Leaf-LH $	1		
8	X2A 2768	Black-RH $	1		
	X2A 2769	Black-LH $	1		
9	ADA 1874	Clip-liner	A/R		
10	AHA 7434	Panel-door trim-inner-RH	NLA		
	AHA 7435	Panel-door trim-inner-LH	NLA		

$ This item is subject to safety regulations.

CHANGE POINTS:
(1).(C)H-AN8-38829 TO 64734.(C)H-AN9-64735 TO 72040.(C)G-AN3-25788 TO 52389.
(C)G-AN4-52390 TO 60459.
(2).(C)H-AN10-85287 TO 86803.(C)A-AN10-86804 TO 87824.(C)G-AN5-74886 TO 105500.

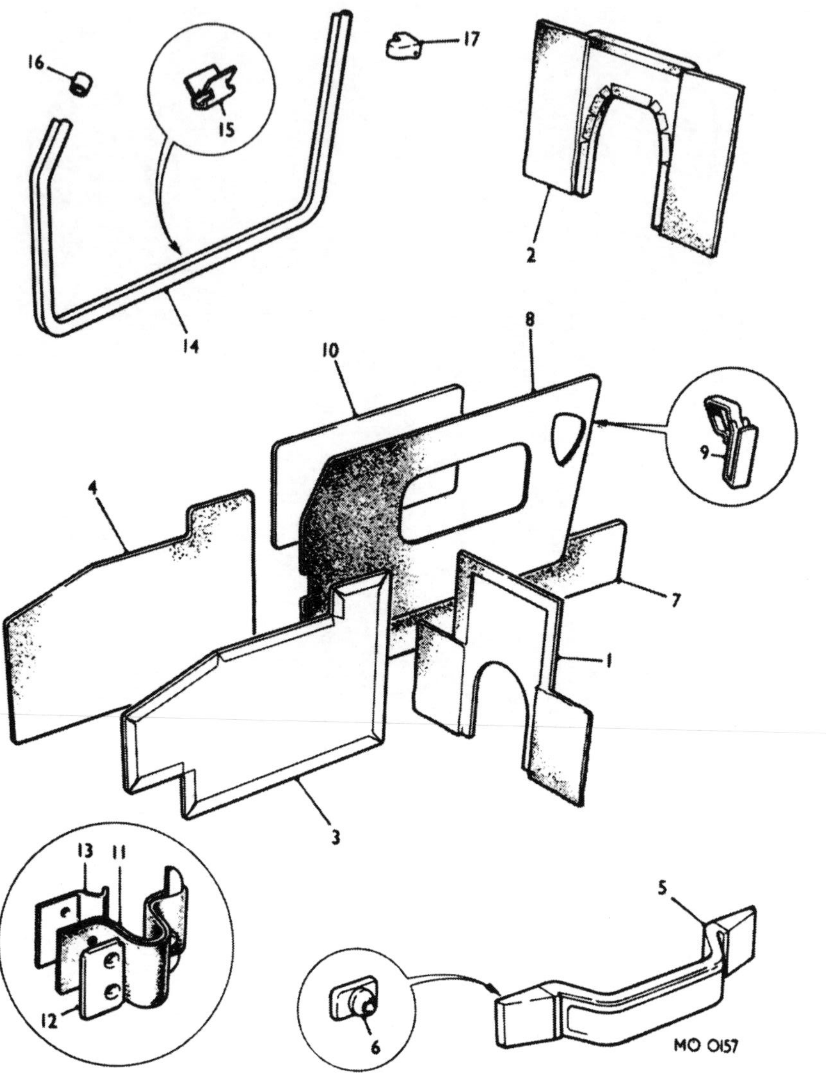

AUSTIN-HEALEY SPRITE MK. 3 AND MK. 4 & MG MIDGET MK. 2 AND MK. 3

NO.	PART NO.	DESCRIPTION	QTY	CHANGE POINT	REMARKS
		DOOR CHECK STRAP AND DRAUGHT EXCLUDER			
		STRAP-DOOR CHECK			
11	AHA 6881	Red	NLA		
11	X2A 3220	Black $	2		
11	J2K 9564	Autumn Leaf	NLA	Use prior to X2T 3220 and X2N 3220.	
11	J2N 9564	Navy	2		
11	X2N 3220	Navy $	2	(C)G-AN5-123731 TO 138800	
11	X2T 3220	Ochre $	2	(C)G-AN5-138801 TO 154100	
11	X2K 3220	Autumn Leaf $	2	(C)G-AN6-154101 ON	
		RETAINER-STRAP			
12	14A 764	Black	2		
12	AHA 9931	Navy	NLA		
12	AHA 9793	Autumn Leaf	2		
12	CHA 130	Ochre	NLA		
		BRACKET-STRAP			
13	14A 6745	Black	2		
13	AHA 9794	Autumn Leaf	NLA		
13	CHA 131	Ochre	NLA		
		DRAUGHT EXCLUDER-DOOR-60"(152.4mm)			
14	XGN 3223	Navy	2		
14	XGT 3223	Ochre	2		
14	37H 6112 M	Autumn Leaf	A/R		Supplied in multiples of metres(39.37")
14	XGK 3223	Autumn Leaf	2	(C)G-AN5-138801 TO 154100	
14	XGA 3223	Black	2	(C)G-AN6-154101 ON	
15	13H 4014	Clip-draught excluder	A/R		
		FINISHER-DRAUGHT EXCLUDER			
16	AHB 9656	Front	2		
17	AHA 8162	Rear-RH	1		
	AHA 8163	Rear-LH	1		
	AB 606033	Screw	4		

$ This item is subject to safety regulations.

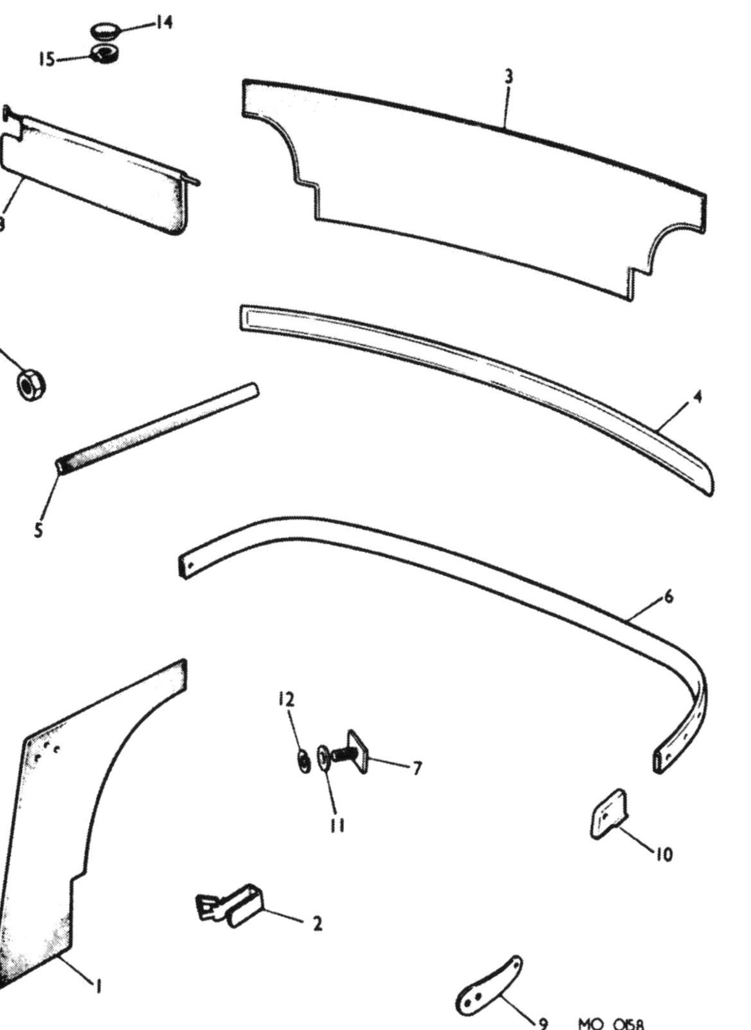

AUSTIN-HEALEY SPRITE MK. 3 AND MK. 4 & MG MIDGET MK. 2 AND MK. 3

NO.	PART NO.	DESCRIPTION	QTY	CHANGE POINT	REMARKS
		REAR LINERS			
		LINER ASSEMBLY-REAR QUARTER			
1	J2A 9579	Black-RH	NLA	(C)H-AN10-85287 TO 86803 (C)A-AN10-86804 TO 87824 (C)G-AN5-74886 TO 105500	
	J2A 9581	Black-LH	NLA		
1	J2K 9579	Autumn Leaf-RH	NLA	(C)H-AN10-86301 TO 86803 (C)A-AN10-86804 TO 87824 (C)G-AN5-89501 TO 105500	
	J2K 9581	Autumn Leaf-LH	NLA		
1	X2K 2095	Autumn Leaf-RH	NLA	(C)G-AN5-105501 TO 123730	
	X2K 2096	Autumn Leaf-LH	NLA		
1	X2N 2095	Navy-RH	NLA		Use X2N 2750
	X2N 2096	Navy-LH	NLA		Use X2N 2751.
1	X2N 2750	Navy-RH $	1	(C)G-AN5-123731 TO 138800	
	X2N 2751	Navy-LH $	1		
1	X2T 2750	Ochre-RH $	NLA		
	X2T 2751	Ochre-LH $	1		
1	X2K 2750	Autumn Leaf-RH $	1	(C)G-AN5-138801 TO 154100 (C)G-AN6-154101 ON	
	X2K 2751	Autumn Leaf-LH $	1		
1	X2A 2750	Black-RH $	1		
	X2A 2751	Black-LH $	1		
2	ADA 1874	Clip-rear quarter liner	6		

$ This item is subject to safety regulations

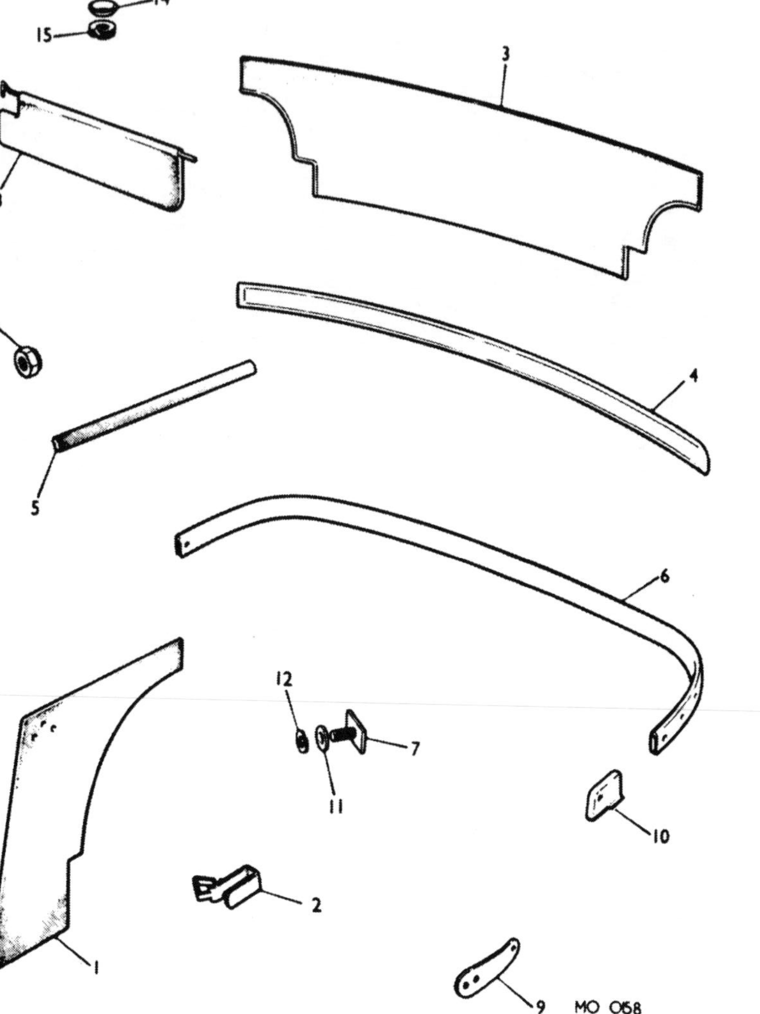

AUSTIN-HEALEY SPRITE MK. 3 AND MK. 4 & MG MIDGET MK. 2 AND MK. 3

NO.	PART NO.	DESCRIPTION	QTY	CHANGE POINT	REMARKS
		REAR LINERS-continued			
		LINER ASSEMBLY-REAR BULKHEAD			
3	AHA 6785	Black	NLA	(C)H-AN8-38829 TO 64734 (C)G-AN3-25788 TO 52389	
3	J2A 9590	Black	NLA	(C)H-AN10-85287 TO 86803 (C)A-AN10-86804 TO 87824 (C)G-AN5-74885 TO 105500	
3	J2K 9590	Autumn Leaf	1	(C)H-AN10-86301 TO 86803 (C)A-AN10-86804 TO 87824 (C)G-AN5-74885 TO 105500	
3	X2K 2116	Autumn Leaf	1	(C)G-AN5-105501 TO 123731	
3	X2N 2116	Navy	1	(C)G-AN5-105501 TO 123730	
3	X2N 2755	Navy $	1	(C)G-AN5-123731 TO 138800	
3	X2T 2755	Ochre $	1		
3	X2K 2755	Autumn Leaf $	1	(C)G-AN5-138801 TO 154100	
3	X2A 2755	Black $	1	(C)G-AN6-154101 ON	
2	ADA 1874	Clip-liner	2		
	FWP 906	Washer-cup	8		
4	AHA 9028	Trim-roll-black-fascia	NLA		

$ This item is subject to safety regulations.

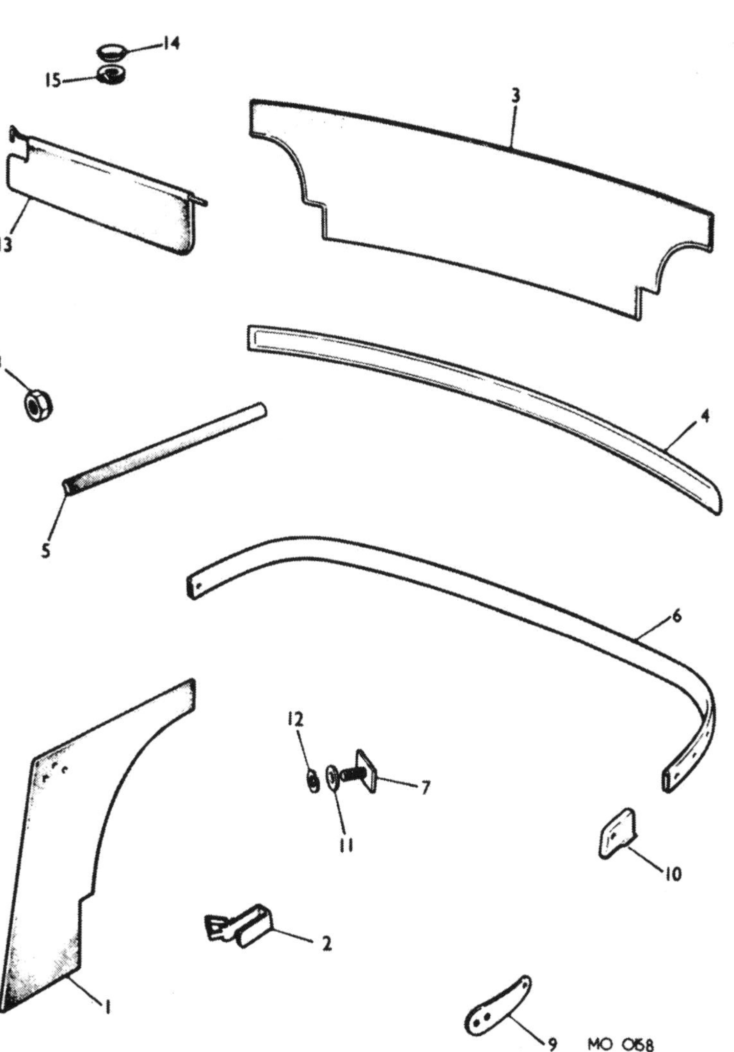

AUSTIN-HEALEY SPRITE MK. 3 AND MK. 4 & MG MIDGET MK. 2 AND MK. 3

REAR COCKPIT FINISHER AND SUN VISOR

NO.	PART NO.	DESCRIPTION	QTY	CHANGE POINT	REMARKS
5	AHA 7412	Moulding-door top-RH	1		
	AHA 7413	Moulding-door top-LH	1		
6	AHA 8058	Moulding-cockpit rear	NLA	(C)H-AN9-64735 TO 77590 (C)G-AN4-52390 TO 66225	
6	AHA 9167	Moulding-cockpit rear-Black $	1	(C)H-AN9-77591 TO 85286 (C)H-AN10-85287 TO 86803 (C)A-AN10-86804 TO 87824 (C)G-AN4-66226 TO 74885 (C)G-AN5-74886 TO 154100 (C)G-AN6-154101 ON	
7	AHH 6417	Stud plate-trim rolls and cockpit rear mouldings	10		
	PWZ 203	Washer-plain	19		
	WL 700101	Washer-spring	A/R		
	WE 702101	Washer-shakeproof	7		
	FNZ 103	Nut	A/R		
7	AHA 5701	Stud plate-door top moulding	4		
	WA 702101	Washer-plain	4		
8	53K 1420	Locknut	4		
10	AHA 8140	Finisher-rear cockpit-flange-RH	1		
	AHA 8141	Finisher-rear cockpit flange-LH	1		
11	AHA 8309	Piece-distance-flange finisher	6		
12	AHA 8310	Washer-flange finisher	6		
13	AHA 9694	Visor-sun-RH $	1	(C)G-AN5-81742 TO 123730	N.America Sweden and Germany
	AHA 9695	Visor-sun-LH $	1		
13	CHA 64	Visor-sun-RH $	1	(C)G-AN5-123731 TO 154100 (C)G-AN6-154101 ON (N.America only	
	CHA 65	Visor-sun-LH $	1		
14	AHH 8799	Washer-spherical	2		
15	AJD 7721	Washer-spring-DC	2		
	LNZ 203	Locknut	2		

$ This item is subject to safety regulations

MO O105A

AUSTIN-HEALEY SPRITE MK. 3 AND MK. 4 & MG MIDGET MK. 2 AND MK. 3

NO.	PART NO.	DESCRIPTION	QTY	CHANGE POINT	REMARKS
		CARPETS.			
		CARPET ASSEMBLY-FRONT-RH-RHD			
1	AHA 9224	Black	1	Use prior to XGN 2022	
1	JGK 9224	Autumn Leaf	1		
1	XGK 2022	Autumn Leaf	1	(C)G-AN5-105501 TO 123730	
1	XGN 2022	Navy	1		
1	XGN 2777	Navy $	1	(C)G-AN5-123731 TO 138800	
1	XGT 2777	Ochre $	1		
1	XGK 2777	Autumn Leaf $	NLA	(C)G-AN5-138801 TO 154100	Use XGK 2778
1	XGA 2777	Black $	NLA	(C)G-AN6-154101 ON	Use XGA 2778
		CARPET ASSEMBLY-FRONT-LH-RHD			
2	AHA 9225	Black	1	Use prior to XGN 2023	
2	XGN 2023	Navy	1	(C)G-AN5-15501 TO 123730	
2	XGN 2786	Navy $	1	(C)G-AN5-123731 TO 138800	
2	JGK 9225	Autumn Leaf	NLA	(C)H-AN10-86301 TO 86803 (C)A-AN10-86804 TO 87824 (C)G-AN5-89501 TO 105500	Use XGK 2023
2	XGK 2023	Autumn Leaf	1	(C)G-AN5-105501 TO 123730	
2	XGT 2786	Ochre $	NLA		
2	XGK 2786	Autumn Leaf $	1	(C)G-AN5-138801 TO 154100	
2	XGA 2786	Black $	1	(C)G-AN6-154101 ON	
		CARPET ASSEMBLY-FRONT-RH-LHD			
	AHA 9226	Black	1	Use prior to XGN 2024	
	XGN 2024	Navy	NLA	(C)G-AN5-105501 TO 123730	Use XGN 2778
	XGN 2778	Navy $	1	(C)G-AN5-123731 TO 138800	
	JGK 9226	Autumn Leaf	NLA		Use XGK 2024
	XGK 2024	Autumn Leaf	1		
	XGT 2778	Ochre	NLA		
	XGK 2778	Autumn Leaf $	1	(C)G-AN5-138801 TO 154100	
	XGA 2778	Black $	1	(C)G-AN6-154101 ON	

$ This item is subject to safety regulations.

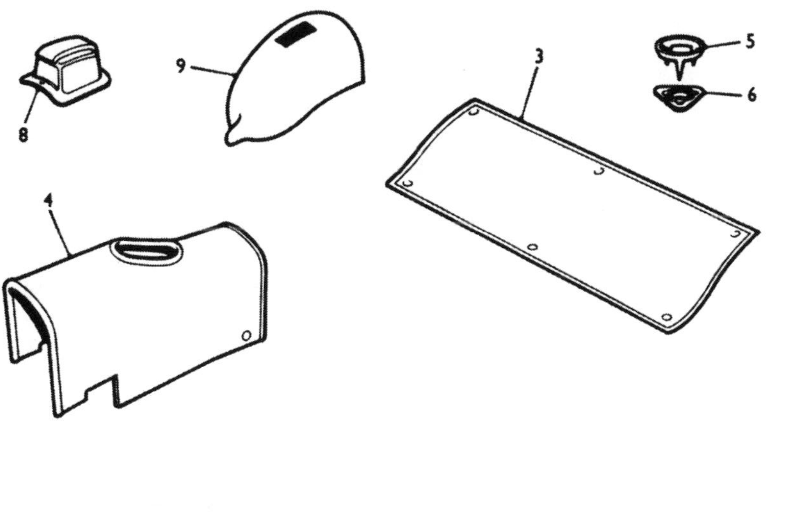

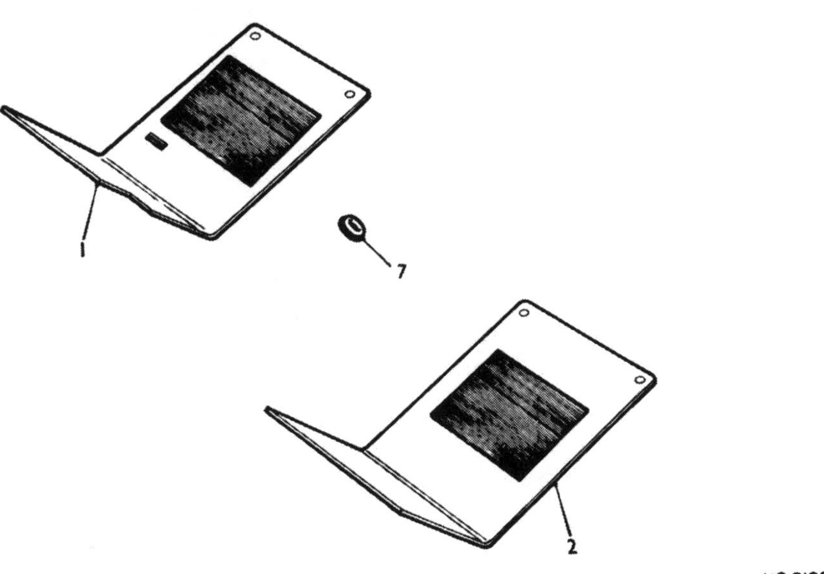

AUSTIN-HEALEY SPRITE MK. 3 AND MK. 4 & MG MIDGET MK. 2 AND MK. 3

NO.	PART NO.	DESCRIPTION	QTY	CHANGE POINT	REMARKS
		CARPETS-continued.			
		CARPET ASSEMBLY-FRONT-LH-LHD			
	AHA 8724	Red	NLA		
	AHA 9228	Black	NLA	] Use prior to	
	JGK 9228	Autumn Leaf	1	] XGN 2025,XGK 2025	
	XGN 2025	Navy	1	] (C)G-AN5-105501 TO	
	XGK 2025	Autumn Leaf	1	] 123730	
	XGT 2787	Ochre $	NLA		
	XGN 2787	Navy	NLA	(C)G-AN5-123731 TO 138800	
	XGK 2787	Autumn Leaf $	1	] (C)G-AN5-138801 TO 154100	
	XGA 2787	Black $	1	] (C)G-AN6-154101 ON	

$ This item is subject to safety regulations.

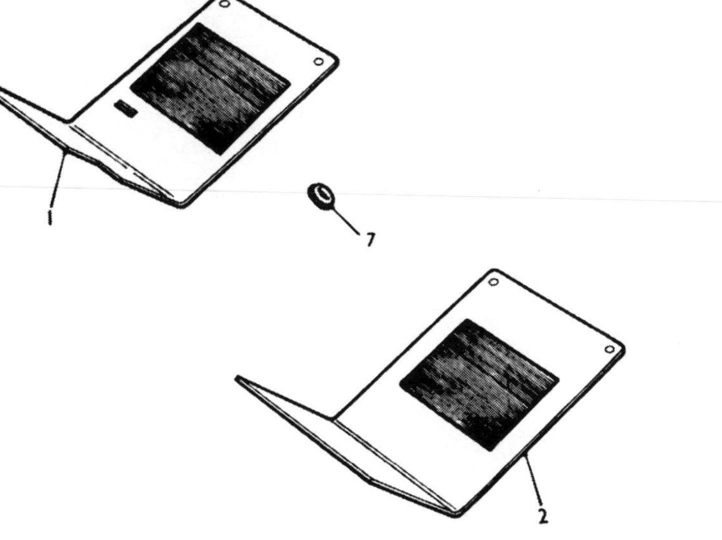

AUSTIN-HEALEY SPRITE MK. 3 AND MK. 4 & MG MIDGET MK. 2 AND MK. 3

NO.	PART NO.	DESCRIPTION	QTY	CHANGE POINT	REMARKS
		CARPETS-continued			
		CARPET ASSEMBLY-REAR COMPARTMENT-CENTRE			
3	JGK 9216	Autumn Leaf	1	(C)H-AN10-86301 TO 86803 (C)A-AN10-86804 TO 87824 (C)G-AN5-89501 TO 105500	
3	XGK 2027	Autumn Leaf	1	(C)G-AN5-105501 TO 123730	
3	XGT 2781	Ochre $	1		
3	XGN 2781	Navy $	1		
3	XGK 2781	Autumn Leaf $	1	(C)G-AN5-138801 TO 154100 (C)G-AN6-154101 ON	
3	XGA 2781	Black $	1		
		CARPET ASSEMBLY-TUNNEL-FRONT			
4	AHA 9240	Black	1		
4	XGK 2021	Autumn leaf	1		
4	XGT 2772	Ochre $	NLA		
4	XGN 2021	Navy	1	(C)G-AN5-105501 TO 123730	
4	XGN 2772	Navy $	1	(C)G-AN5-123731 TO 138800	
4	XGK 2772	Autumn Leaf $	1	(C)G-AN5-138801 TO 154100 (C)G-AN6-154101 ON	
4	XGA 2772	Black $	1		
5	2H 8445	Fastener-carpet	18		
6	14G 8736	Ring-fastener to carpet	18		
7	ADB 4811	Fastener-floor	18		
	AC 606041	Screw-fastener to floor	20		
8	AHA 9728	Ashtray-tunnel	1		
	AB 606043	Screw	2		

$ This item is subject to safetry regulations.

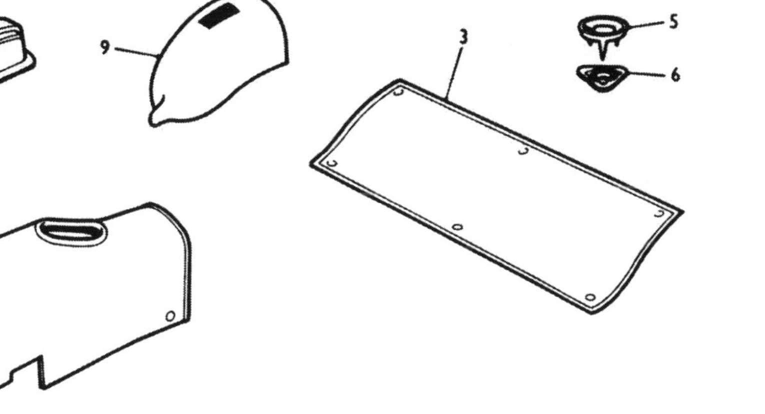

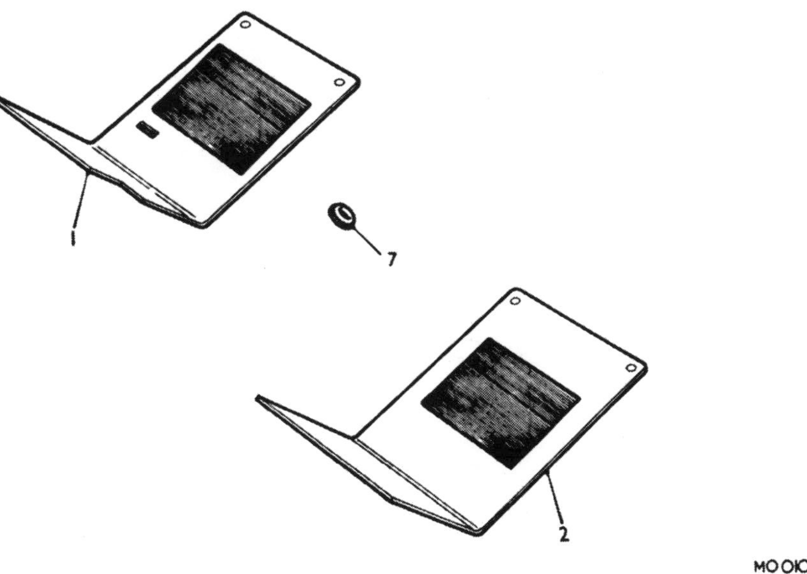

AUSTIN-HEALEY SPRITE MK. 3 AND MK. 4 & MG MIDGET MK. 2 AND MK. 3

NO.	PART NO.	DESCRIPTION	QTY	CHANGE POINT	REMARKS
		CARPETS-continued			
		CARPET-REAR WHEELARCH			
9	AHA 9220	Black-RH	NLA		
	AHA 9221	Black-LH	NLA		
9	JGK 9220	Autumn Leaf-RH	NLA	Use prior to XGK 2028/9	Use XGK 2028
	JGK 9221	Autumn Leaf-LH	1		
9	XGK 2028	Autumn Leaf-RH $	1	(C)G-AN5-105501 TO 154100 (C)G-AN6-154101 ON	
	XGK 2029	Autumn Leaf-LH $	1		
9	XGT 2028	Ochre-RH $	1		
	XGT 2029	Ochre-LH $	NLA		
9	XGN 2028	Navy-RH $	1		
	XGN 2029	Navy-LH $	NLA		

$ This item is subject to safety regulations.

AUSTIN-HEALEY SPRITE MK. 3 AND MK. 4 & MG MIDGET MK. 2 AND MK. 3

RECLINING SEATS-HEAD RESTRAINTS AND SEAT BELTS.

NO.	PART NO.	DESCRIPTION	QTY	CHANGE POINT	REMARKS
		SEAT ASSEMBLY			
13	J2A 9529	Black-RH	1	Finished at (C)H-AN9-85285 (C)G-AN4-66225	
	X2N 2122	Navy-LH	1		
13	J2K 9529	Autumn Leaf-RH	1		
	J2K 9530	Autumn Leaf-LH	1		
1	AHA 8896	Frame-RH	NLA	(C)H-AN9-77591 TO 85286(West Germany) (C)G-AN4-66226 TO 74885	
	AHA 8897	Frame-LH	NLA		
16	CHA 4	Frame-RH	1	Use prior to CHA 23,CHA 24	
	CHA 5	Frame-LH	1		
16	CHA 23	Frame-RH $	1	(C)G-AN5-119496 TO 154100 (C)G-AN6-154101 ON	
	CHA 24	Frame-LH $	1		
17	BHA 5140	Sensor-seat $	1	Use prior to BHA 5274	North America.
17	BHA 5274	Sensor-seat $	2	(C)G-AN5-138801 TO 154100 (C)G-AN6-154101 TO 159053	North America.
18	AHA 9928	DIAPHRAGM ASSEMBLY-CUSHION $	NLA		
3	BHA 5097	Hook-diaphragm	16		
19	CZA 4713	Roller-friction-head restraint	2	Use prior to CZH 2889	
	CZH 2889	Roller-friction-head restraint	2	(C)G-AN6-157177 ON	
	CHA 96	Pad-cushion $	2		
	CHA 97	Pad-squab-RH $	1		
	CHA 98	Pad-squab-LH $	1		

$ This item is subject to safety regulations

AUSTIN-HEALEY SPRITE MK. 3 AND MK. 4 & MG MIDGET MK. 2 AND MK. 3

RECLINING SEATS-HEAD RESTRAINTS AND SEAT BELTS-continued

NO.	PART NO.	DESCRIPTION	QTY	CHANGE POINT	REMARKS
		COVER-CUSHION			
4	AHA 9102	Black	NLA	(C)H-AN9-77591 TO 85286(West Germany) (C)G-AN4-66226 TO 74885	
20	J2A 9531	Black	2	Use prior to X2N 2794.	
20	X2N 2794	Navy $	2	(C)G-AN5-105501 TO 138800	
20	J2K 9531	Autumn Leaf	2	(C)H-AN10-85287 TO 86803 (C)A-AN10-86804 TO 87824 (C)G-AN5-74886 TO 123730	
20	X2T 2794	Ochre $	2	(C)G-AN5-138801 TO 154100 (C)G-AN6-154101 ON	
20	X2K 2794	Autumn Leaf $	2		
20	X2A 2794	Black $	2		
		COVER-SQUAB			
21	J2A 9532	Black-RH	NLA	Use prior to J2N 9532 and J2N 9533	
	J2A 9533	Black-LH	NLA		
21	J2N 9532	Navy-RH	1	(C)G-AN5-105501 TO 123730	
	J2N 9533	Navy-LH	1		
21	X2N 2795	Navy-RH $	1	(C)G-AN5-123731 TO 138800	
	X2N 2796	Navy-LH $	1		
21	J2K 9532	Autumn Leaf-RH	NLA	(C)H-AN10-85287 TO 86803 (C)A-AN10-86804 TO 87824 (C)G-AN5-74886 TO 123730	
	J2K 9533	Autumn Leaf-LH	NLA		
21	X2T 2795	Ochre-RH $	1		
	X2T 2796	Ochre-LH $	1		
21	X2K 2795	Autumn Leaf-RH $	1	(C)G-AN5-138801 TO 154100 (C)G-AN6-154101 ON	
	X2K 2796	Autumn Leaf-LH $	1		
21	X2A 2795	Black-RH $	1		
	X2A 2796	Black-LH $	1		
5	24B 4057	Handle-adjusting $	2		
6	54K 205	Screw-handle	2		
7	BHA 4339	Clip-trim	A/R		
8	14A 4497	Clip-spring $	6		

$ This item is subject to safety regulations.

AUSTIN-HEALEY SPRITE MK. 3 AND MK. 4 & MG MIDGET MK. 2 AND MK. 3

RECLINING SEATS-HEAD RESTRAINTS AND SEAT BELTS-continued

NO.	PART NO.	DESCRIPTION	QTY	CHANGE POINT	REMARKS
		RESTRAINT-HEAD			
22	J2K 9628	Autumn Leaf	NLA	Use prior to GLZ 133 and 127.	Use GLZ 133
22	J2N 9628	Navy	NLA		Use GLZ 127
22	GLZ 131	Ochre $	2	(C)G-AN5-112312 TO 138800	
22	GLZ 127	Navy $	2		
22	GLZ 133	Autumn Leaf $	2	(C)G-AN5-138801 TO 154100	
				(C)G-AN6-154101 ON	
22	GLZ 135	Black $	2		
		PLUG-HEAD RESTRAINT APERTURE			
23	BHA 4985	Black	2		
23	XGN 1953	Navy	2		
23	AHA 9779	Autumn Leaf	2		
23	XGT 1953	Ochre	2		
24	CZA 4500	Eyelet-head restraint	2		
25	CZA 4263	Washer-finisher-head restraint	2		
10	AHH 9711	Clip-retaining-restraint $	NLA	(C)H-AN9-77591 TO 85286	N. America.
	PMZ 306	Screw-clip	4		
11	AHH 9441	Bush-friction $	4	(C)G-AN4-66226 TO 74885	
12	AHH 9295	Sleeve-finishing	NLA		

$ This item is subject to safety regulations.

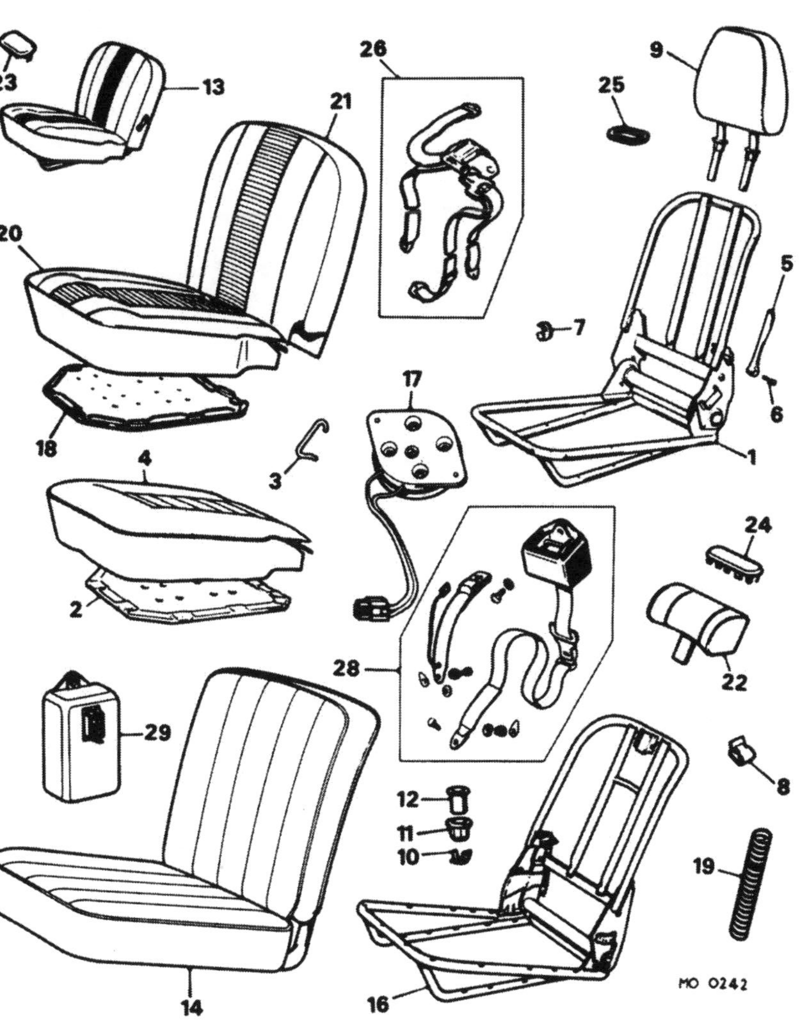

AUSTIN-HEALEY SPRITE MK. 3 AND MK. 4 & MG MIDGET MK. 2 AND MK. 3

NO.	PART NO.	DESCRIPTION	QTY	CHANGE POINT	REMARKS
		RECLINING SEATS-HEAD RESTRAINTS AND SEAT BELTS-continued.			
	14A 5519	Runner-seat(with catch)-top-RH $	1	Use prior to AHA 9946/7	
	14A 5520	Runner-seat(with catch)-top-LH	1		
	4G 877	Runner-seat(less catch)-top	2		
	AHA 7883	Runner-seat-bottom-RH $	NLA		
	AHA 7884	Runner-seat-bottom-LH $	2		
	SF 604101	Screw-top runner to seat	16		
	LNZ 104	Nut-lock	16		
	SH 604061	Screw-bottom runner to floor	4		
	PWZ 104	Washer-plain	4		
	WL 600041	Washer-spring	4		
	PWZ 205	Washer-plain	2		
	WA 108051	Washer-plain	2		
	LNZ 205	Nut	4		
	AHA 9946	Rail-seat-floor rack-RH $	2	(C)G-AN5-(+)TO 154100 (C)G-AN6-154101 ON	
	AHA 9947	Rail-seat-floor rack-LH $	2		
	AHA 9944	Slide-seat catch-RH $	1		
	AHA 9945	Slide-seat catch-LH $	1		
	AHA 9943	Slide-seat catch $	2		
26	CHA 38	Belt-seat set-static(Kangol)$	2	(C)A-AN10-86804 TO 87824 (C)G-AN5-96916 TO 154100 (C)G-AN6-154101 ON N.America TO 116169	
28	CHA 28	Belt-seat set(Kangol)$	2	(C)G-AN5-116170 TO 138800	N. America.
28	CHA 223	Belt-seat set(Kangol)$	2	(C)G-AN5-138801 TO 154100 (C)G-AN6-154101 TO 159053	
29	13H 9801	Unit-control-sequential seat system $	1		
	CHA 523	BELT-SEAT SET-RH(KANGOL) $	1	(C)G-AN6-159054 ON	
28	CHA 223	BELT-SEAT SET-LH(KANGOL) $	1		
	BHM 558	Kit-seat belt release button	1		
	AAU 3247	Tongue-stop-seat belt	2		
	AAU 1110	Unit-buzzer-time delay $	1		
		CUSHION-REAR COMPARTMENT			
	AHA 8939	Black	NLA	(C)H-AN9-77591 TO 85286 (C)G-AN4-66226 TO 74885	Optional extra.
	LFP 116	Peg-fastener-rear compartment cushion	2	(C)H-AN8-38829 TO 64734 (C)H-AN9-64735 TO 85286 (C)G-AN3-25788 TO 52389 (C)G-AN4-52390 TO 74885	
	AB 608061	Screw-rear compartment cushion to floor	4		

$ This item is subject to safety regulations.

(+) Change point not available.

ILLUSTRATION NOT USED

AUSTIN-HEALEY SPRITE MK. 3 AND MK. 4 & MG MIDGET MK. 2 AND MK. 3

NO.	PART NO.	DESCRIPTION	QTY	CHANGE POINT	REMARKS
		BULK MATERIALS			
		MATERIAL-LEATHERCLOTH			
	1KL 1113 M	Black	NLA	Use prior to 1KL 1115 M	
	1KL 1115 M	Black	A/R	(C)H-AN9-77591 TO 85286 (C)G-AN4-66226 TO 74885	
	1BL 116 M	Black	NLA	(C)H-AN10-85287 TO 86803 (C)A-AN10-86804 TO 87824 (C)G-AN5-74886 TO 154100 (C)G-AN6-154101 ON	Supplied in multiples of metres.
	1KL 3636 M	Autumn Leaf	NLA		
	1KL 5329 M	Navy	A/R		
	1AL 706 M	Ochre	A/R		
		MATERIAL-CARPET			
	37H 4314 M	Black	A/R		
	AKE 5621 M	Navy	A/R		
	AKE 5620 M	Autumn Leaf	A/R		
	AKE 5643 M	Ochre	A/R		
	AAA 743 M	Underfelt-mat	NLA		
	27H 6841	Material-anti-drum	1BOX		

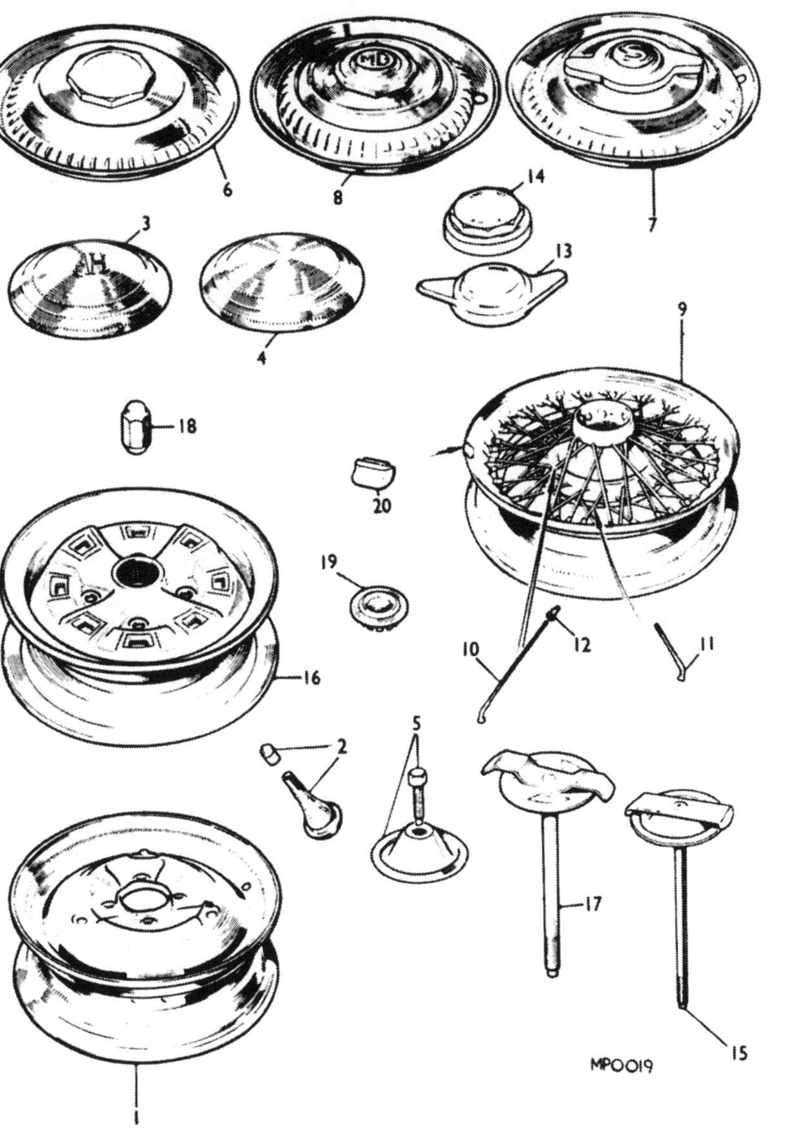

AUSTIN-HEALEY SPRITE MK. 3 AND MK. 4 & MG MIDGET MK. 2 AND MK. 3

NO.	PART NO.	DESCRIPTION	QTY	CHANGE POINT	REMARKS
		ROAD WHEELS			
1	AHA 6455	Wheel-disc $	5		Disc wheels
2	13H 412	Valve-tyre	5		Disc wheels
3	2A 8055	Cap-hub-SPRITE	NLA		Disc wheels
4	AHA 5660	Cap-hub-MIDGET	4		Disc wheels
5	24A 1032	Clamp-spare wheel	1		Disc wheels
6	BHA 4163	Disc-louvered-wheel-RH-SPRITE	2		Disc wheels
	BHA 4259	Disc-louvered-wheel-with centre motif'S'-LH-SPRITE	2		Disc wheels
8	BHA 4253	Disc-louvered-wheel-RH-MIDGET	NLA		Disc wheels
	BHA 4254	Disc-louvered-wheel-LH-MIDGET	2		Disc wheels
9	AHA 6377	WHEEL ASSEMBLY-WIRE(PRIMED) $	5	Fitted to N.American MARKETS PRIOR TO AHA 9524	All markets
10	17H 3613	Spoke-long	NLA		All markets
11	17H 3984	Spoke-short	40		All markets
12	7H 1709	Nipple-spoke	60		All markets
9	AHA 9524	WHEEL ASSEMBLY-WIRE(CHROME)	5	(C)G-AN5-74886 ON	N.America only
10	37H 4967	Spoke-long	20		N.America only
11	37H 4968	Spoke-short	40		N.America only
12	37H 3651	Nipple-spoke	60		N.America only
13	AHA 7373	Cap-wing-hub-RH	2		Wire wheels
	AHA 7374	Cap-wing-hub-LH	2		Wire wheels
14	88G 606	Cap-hub-RH $	2		Wire wheels
	88G 607	Cap-hub-LH $	2		Wire wheels
15	AHA 6664	Clamp-spare wheel	1		Wire wheels
16	AHA 8892	Wheel(Rostyle) $	5	Use prior to AHA 9881 and AHA 9940	
16	AHA 9881	Wheel(Rostyle) $	5	(C)G-AN5-105501 ON	
17	AHA 9940	Clamp-spare wheel	1		
18	AHA 8785	Nut-wheel stud-CP	16		
19	AHA 8950	Trim-wheel	4		
		WEIGHT-WHEEL BALANCE			
20	AKF 1446	0.5oz.(14.17gm)	A/R		
20	AKF 1447	1oz.(28.35gm)	A/R		
20	AKF 1448	1.5oz(42.52gm)	A/R		
20	AKF 1449	2oz(56.70gm)	A/R		
20	AKF 1450	2.50oz.(70.87gm)	A/R		
20	AKF 1451	3oz.(85.05gm)	A/R		
20	13H 8328	10g(0.353oz)	A/R		
20	13H 8329	15g(0.529g)	A/R		
20	13H 8330	20g(0.705oz)	A/R		
20	13H 8331	30g(1.058oz)	A/R		
20	13H 8332	40g(1.411oz)	A/R		
20	13H 8333	50g(1.764oz)	A/R		
20	13H 9334	60g(2.116oz)	A/R		
20	13H 8335	70g(2.469oz)	A/R		
20	13H 8336	80g(2.822oz)	A/R		
20	13H 8337	90g(3.175oz)	A/R		

$ This item is subject to safety regulations

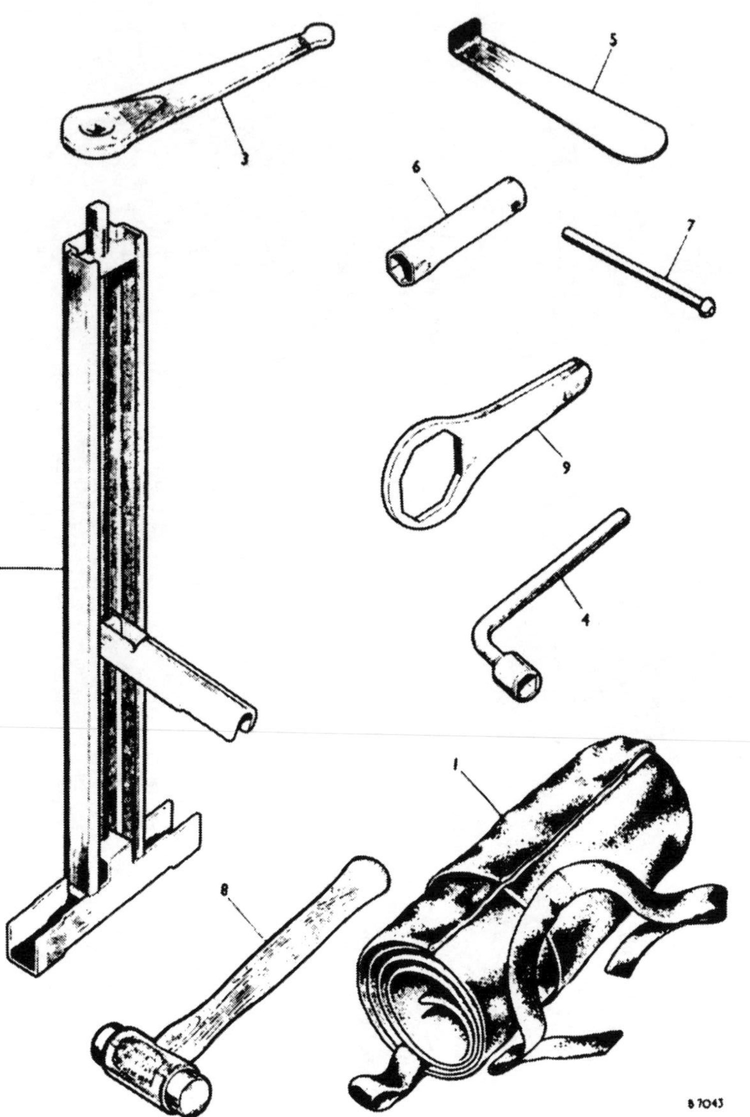

AUSTIN-HEALEY SPRITE MK. 3 AND MK. 4 & MG MIDGET MK. 2 AND MK. 3

NO.	PART NO.	DESCRIPTION	QTY	CHANGE POINT	REMARKS
		TOOLS			
1	AHA 5506	Bag-tool	NLA		
2	BHA 4964	Jack	1	Finished at (C)G-AN5-154100	
3	13H 6692	Spanner-ratchet-jack	1	Finished at (C)G-AN5-154100	
	BHA 5414	Jack(side lift)	1	(C)G-AN6-154101 TO 157671(except USA) 157682(USA)	
	BHA 5329	Jack(side lift)	1	(C)G-AN6-157672 ON (except USA) (C)G-AN6-157683 ON (USA)	
3	2A 5626	Brace-wheel	1		Disc wheels
5	31G 957	Lever-hub cap removal	1		Disc wheels
6	1B 8995	Spanner-box-sparking plug	1		
7	88G 570	Tommy-bar-box spanner	1		
8	88G 329	Hammer-hub cap	1		Wire wheels
9	AHH 5839	Spanner-hub cap-Not UK	1		Wire wheels

AUSTIN-HEALEY SPRITE MK. 3 AND MK. 4 & MG MIDGET MK. 2 AND MK. 3

NO.	PART NO.	DESCRIPTION	QTY	CHANGE POINT	REMARKS
		SPECIAL TUNING-ENGINE UNIT			
		PISTON ASSEMBLY-ENGINE SET-GRADE 3-9.75 : 1 COMPRESSION RATIO			
1	8G 2668	Standard	1SET		
1	8G 2668 20	.020"(.508mm)O/S	1SET		
		PISTON ASSEMBLY-ENGINE SET-GRADE 3-12 : 1 COMPRESSION RATIO			
1	8G 2432 3	Standard	1SET		
1	8G 2432 23	.020"(.508mm)O/S	1SET		
		RING-PISTON-ENGINE SET			
2	8G 2433	Standard	1SET		
2	8G 2433 20	.020"(.508mm)O/S	1SET		
3	AEG 189	Pin-gudgeon	4		
		PISTON ASSEMBLY-ENGINE SET-GRADE 3-9.75 : 1 COMPRESSION RATIO-LIGHTWEIGHT FORGED			C-MG
1	AJJ 3377 3	Standard	1SET		C-MG
1	AJJ 3377 23	.020"(.508mm)O/S	1SET		C-MG
1	AJJ 3377 43	.040"(1.016mm)O/S	1SET		C-MG
		CAMSHAFT			
4	88G 229	Tuning	1		C-MG,1098cc
4	AEA 731	Competition	1		C-MG,1098cc
4	AEA 648	Racing	1		C-MG,1098cc
5	2A 299	Pin-driving-oil pump	1		1098CC
		CAMSHAFT			
6	AEG 567	Road use	1		C-MG,1275cc
6	AEG 542	Rally	1		C-MG,1275cc
6	AEG 529	Racing	1		C-MG,1275cc
7	12G 729	Flange-driving-oil pump	1		1275CC
8	AEG 578	Gear-camshaft-lightened	1		C-MG,1275cc
	AHT 4013	MAIN BEARING SET	1		C-MG
	AEG 417	Main bearing nuts	NLA		Use with studs AEG 323 2 off and 12G 479-4 off.
	AHT 141	HEAD ASSEMBLY-POLISHED-COMPLETE	1		C-MG
	12A 186	Guides	8		
	12G 296	Valve-inlet	4		
	AEA 400	Valve-exhaust	4		1098CC ONLY.
	AEA 311	Springs-outer	8		
	AEA 401	Springs-inner	8		
	AEA 402	Cap-top	8		
	AEA 403	Washer-bottom	8		
	2A 879	Seals	8		
	2A 11	Cotters	8PRS		
	AHT 288	Washer-spring(Disc)	1SET		C-MG
	AHT 326	Crankshaft-Nitrided	1		C-MG

NOTE: All parts listed with the Remark C-MG are Competition parts and must be ordered direct from British Leyland Special Tuning Dept., Abingdon-on-Thames,Berkshire.

E2701

AUSTIN-HEALEY SPRITE MK. 3 AND MK. 4 & MG MIDGET MK. 2 AND MK. 3

NO.	PART NO.	DESCRIPTION	QTY	CHANGE POINT	REMARKS
		SPECIAL TUNING-ENGINE UNIT-continued			
		SPRING-VALVE			
9	AEA 494	Inner-150lb	8		C-MG,max.load 170 with cam AEA 648.
10	AEA 767	Outer-140lb	8		
9	AEA 494	Inner-165lb	8		C-MG,10CC
10	AEA 524	Outer-180lb	8		
11	AEA 653	Cup-bottom	8		C-MG
9	AEA 652	Spring-valve-inner-180lb	8		
10	AEA 524	Spring-valve-outer	8		C-MG,1275cc
12	AEA 654	Collar-locating	8		
13	AEG 544	Valve-inlet 1.401"(35.5mm dia)	4		
13	AEG 569	Valve-inlet-competition	4		
15	AEA 692	Screw-tappet adjusting	8		C-MG
14	AEA 399	SHAFT-VALVE ROCKER-STRENGTHENED	1		
17	6K 878	Plug-plain	1		
18	2K 4608	Plug-screwed	1		
		BRACKET-ROCKER SHAFT			
19	12G 1926	Plain	2		
2	12G 1926	With oil hole	1		
20	12G 1927	Tapped	1		
21	12G 1221	ROCKER-VALVE(FORGED)	8		
22	2A 21	Bush	8		
23	5C 2436	Rivet	8		
24	12H 2178	Washer-cylinder head nut	5		
25	AJJ 3325	KIT-CHAIN TIMING-DUPLEX	1		C-MG
	AEG 578	Sprocket-camshaft	1		C-MG,not 1275cc
	AEA 695	Sprocket-camshaft	1		
	2H 4905	Chain-timing	1		
	AEA 687	Screw-countersunk	2		
	AEG 392	Spacer-valve rocker	3		
26	AEA 539	Belt-fan-short	2		
		PLUG-SPARKING			C-MG
27	37H 4208	N64Y rally and road use	4		
27	27H 5982	N57R racing	4		
27	37H 2149	N62R racing	4		
27	37H 2148	N60Y racing	4		
28	88G 219	Gasket-plug	4		

NOTE: All parts listed with the Remark C-MG are Competition parts and must be ordered direct from British Leyland Special Tuning Dept., Abingdon-on-Thames,Berkshire.

AUSTIN-HEALEY SPRITE MK. 3 AND MK. 4 & MG MIDGET MK. 2 AND MK. 3

SPECIAL TUNING-ENGINE UNIT-continued

NO.	PART NO.	DESCRIPTION	QTY	CHANGE POINT	REMARKS
1	AJJ 3324	KIT-SUMP(DEEP)	1		
2	AHT 12	Sump	1		C-MG
3	AHT 14	Pipe-oil suction	1		C-MG, 1275cc only
4	HBZ 414	Bolt-bracket to strainer	2		
6	AHH 6162	Piece-distance	2		
7	6K 871	Spring	1		
8	GEG 501	Gasket	1		
	12G 3016	Seal-oil-main bearing cap-front	1		
	12G 1009	Seal-oil-main bearing cap-rear	1		
11	AHT 11	Manifold-exhaust large bore	1		
13	AEA 647	Gasket-cylinder head	1		C-MG
14	AEA 411	Gasket-manifold	1		
15	AEA 511	Gasket-rocker cover	1		
16	AJJ 3323	KIT-OIL COOLER	1		C-MG, 1275cc
17	ARH 186	Cooler-oil	1		
	AHA 8396	Bracket-support	1		
19	PMZ 410	Screw-bracket to cooler	4		
20	HZS 404	Screw-bracket to chassis	4		
21	LWZ 204	Washer-spring	8		
22	NH 604041	Nut	8		
	AHA 8778	Hose-flexible-block to cooler	1		
	AHA 8777	Hose-flexible-filter to cooler	1		
	AHA 8779	Bracket-pipe clip	1		
	HZS 407	Screw	2		
27	LWZ 204	Washer-spring	2		
28	FNZ 104	Nut	2		
29	AHH 6865	Strap	NLA		
	AHH 6866	Plate-clamp	2		
19	PMZ 408	Screw	2		
	NH 604041	Nut	2		
30	AHA 3390	Plate-clamp	1		
	PMZ 314	Screw	NLA		
	LWZ 203	Washer-spring	2		
33	AHA 6424	Adaptor-crankcase	1		
34	AHA 6423	Adaptor-filter	1		
35	12A 1768	Washer-adaptor	1		
37	AHA 8401	Grommet	4		
38	ARO 9809	Cooler-oil	1		Alternative to ARH 186 for racing. C-MG
39	AHT 181	Cover-oil cooler	1		

NOTE: All parts listed with the Remark C-MG are Competition parts and must be ordered direct from British Leyland Special Tuning Dept., Abingdon-on-Thames, Berkshire.

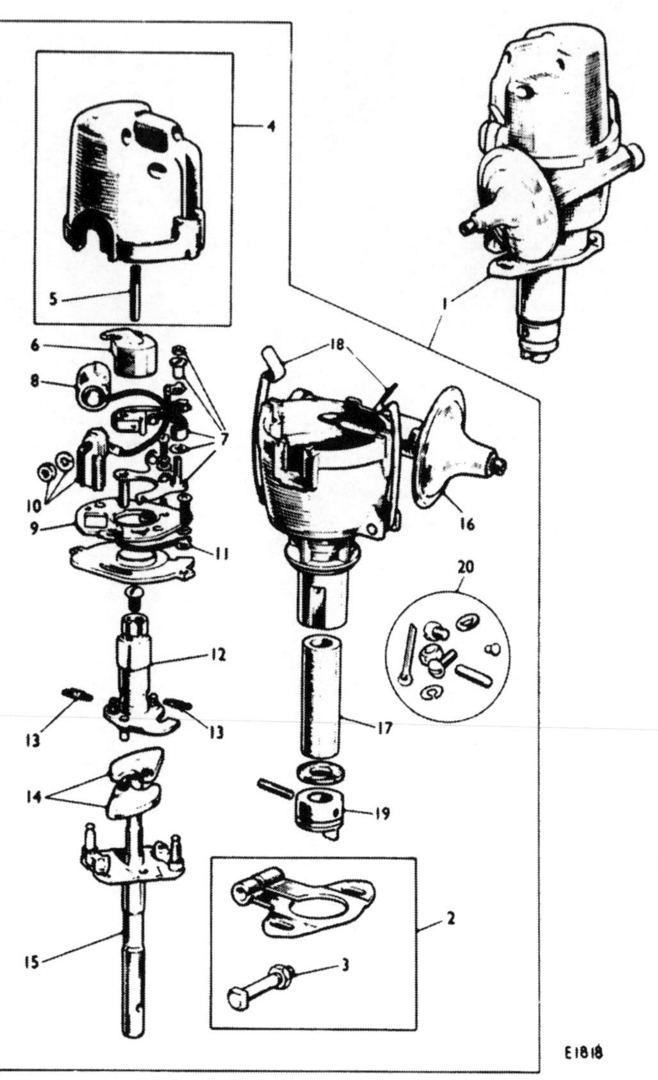

AUSTIN-HEALEY SPRITE MK. 3 AND MK. 4 & MG MIDGET MK. 2 AND MK. 3

SPECIAL TUNING-DISTRIBUTOR-IGNITION AND ENGINE ANCILLARIES.

NO.	PART NO.	DESCRIPTION	QTY	CHANGE POINT	REMARKS
1	27H 7766	DISTRIBUTOR	1		C-MG use with competion camshafts.
2	3H 2138	Plate-clamping	1		
4	GDC 102	COVER ASSEMBLY	1		
5	17H 5065	Brush and spring	1SET		
6	GRA 101	Arm-rotor	1		
7	GCS 101	Contacts	1SET		
8	GSC 101	Condenser	1		
10	37H 2981	Terminal-bush and lead	1		
13	27H 8022	Spring-automatic advance	1SET		C-MG.
16	47H 5555	Vacuum unit	1		
20	17H 5106	Sundry parts	1SET		
	AJJ 4010	KIT-HIGH TENSION-PLUG-WATER PROOFING	1		C-MG.
	AHT 265	Plug-cover-lodge	1		C-MG.
	AHT 266	Lead H.T. length 6 feet	1		C-MG.
	AHT 269	Coil	1		C-MG.
	8G 727	Cover-coil	1		
	AHT 332	SWITCH-IGNITION CUT-OUT	1		C-MG.
	AEA 535	Pulley-dynamo for reduced speed	1		C-MG.
	AHT 32	Bracket-alternator mounting	1		C-MG.
	AJJ 4012	KIT-BLANKING SLEEVE-THERMOSTAT BY-PASS	1		C-MG.
	11G 176	Blanking sleeve	1		
	GTG 101	Joint-thermostat	1		

NOTE.All parts listed with the remark C-MG are competition parts and must be ordered direct from British Leyland Special Tuning Dept., Abingdon-on-Thames,Berkshire.

AUSTIN-HEALEY SPRITE MK. 3 AND MK. 4 & MG MIDGET MK. 2 AND MK. 3

SPECIAL TUNING-FLYWHEEL,CLUTCH,GEARBOX,FINAL DRIVE AND AXLE SHAFT.

NO.	PART NO.	DESCRIPTION	QTY	CHANGE POINT	REMARKS
1	AHT 70	Flywheel-lightened-1275cc	1		
2	BHA 4448	Cover-assembly-1098cc	1		
3	BHA 4519	Plate-driven-clutch	1		
2	AEG 546	Cover-assembly-1275cc	1		
3	AEG 547	Plate-driven	1		
3	AHT 383	Plate-driven-6.5"	1		
	AHT 409	Plate-driven-race only	1		C-MG.
4	AJJ 3319	KIT-GEAR SET-CLOSE RATIO-STRAIGHT CUT	1		
5	AEG 3138	Shaft-1st Motion	1		
6	AEG 3139	Gear-2nd speed	1		
7	AEG 3140	Gear-3rd speed	1		
8	22G 306	Laygear	1		
9	22G 165	Gasket-front cover	1		
10	2A 3341	Gasket-cover-change speed lever	1		
11	2A 3286	Gasket-side cover	1		
12	22A 481	Gasket-extension to gearbox	1		
13	2A 3344	Gasket-casing to extension-front	1		
14	2A 3345	Gasket-casing to extension-rear	1		
15	2A 3035	Washer-lock-shaft	2		

NOTE (1).
Gear set AJJ 3319 can also be used on gearboxes fitted to 1098cc engines prior to change point(i.e.10CC prefix) provided 1st speed wheel and synchronizer 22G 326 and reverse wheel 22G 240 are fitted.
NOTE (2).
All parts listed with the remark C-MG are competition parts and must be ordered direct from British Leyland Special Tuning Dept., Abingdon-on-Thames,Berkshire.

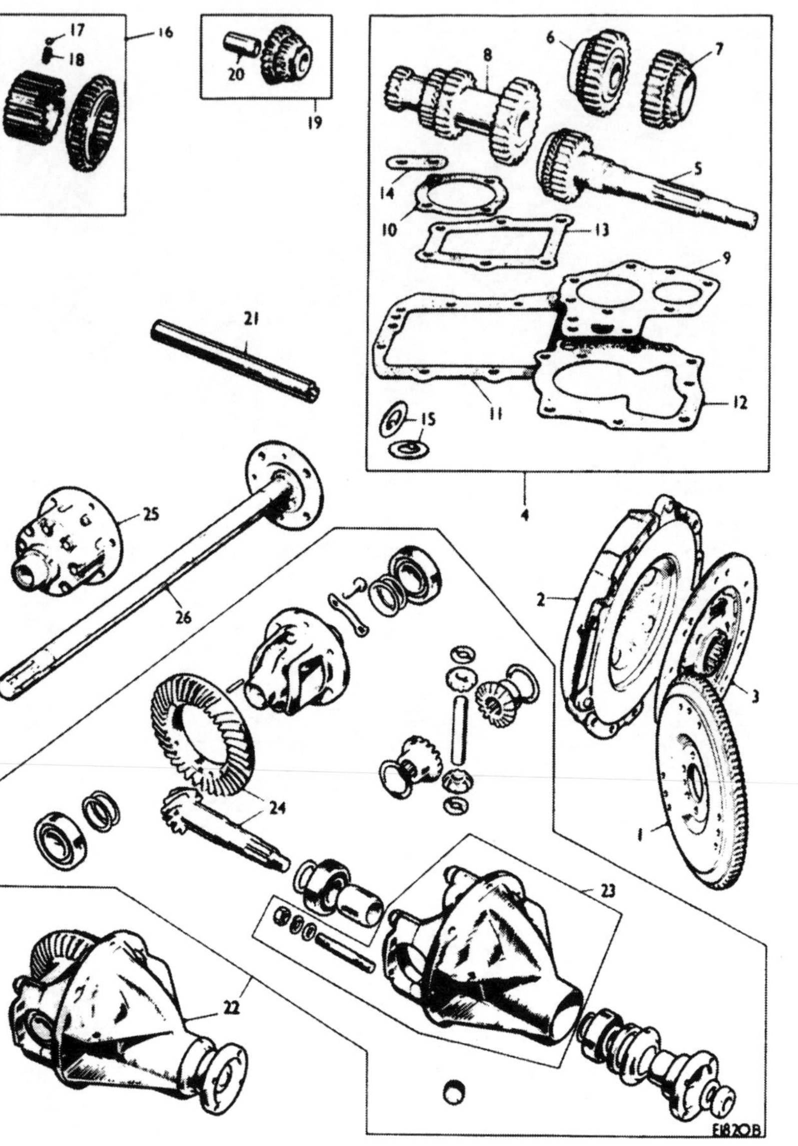

AUSTIN-HEALEY SPRITE MK. 3 AND MK. 4 & MG MIDGET MK. 2 AND MK. 3

NO.	PART NO.	DESCRIPTION	QTY	CHANGE POINT	REMARKS
		SPECIAL TUNING-FLYWHEEL,CLUTCH,GEARBOX,FINAL DRIVE AND AXLE SHAFT-continued.			
16	22G 1118	1ST SPEED WHEEL-2ND SPEED SYNCHRONIZER ASSEMBLY	1		
17	BLS 107	Ball	3		
18	22G 317	Spring	3		
19	22G 1114	WHEEL ASSEMBLY-REVERSE	1		
20	2A 3282	Bush	1		
21	22G 673	Layshaft	1		Use with close ratio gear set AJJ 3319 Standard for (E)12CC Da/H101.
23	BTA 549	Carrier	1		
		CROWN WHEEL AND PINION			
24	BTA 535	3.727:1 ratio	1		
24	BTA 816	4.555:1 ratio	1		C-MG.
24	BTA 1223	3.9:1 ratio-standard	1		
24	BTA 539	4.22:1 ratio	1		
25	BTA 1226	Differential-limited slip	1		C-MG.
26	BTA 940	Shaft-axle-heavy duty(disc wheels)	2		C-MG.
	BTA 939	Shaft-axle-heavy duty(wire wheels)	2		C-MG.

NOTE.
All parts listed with the remark C-MG are competition parts and must be ordered direct from British Leyland Special Tuning Dept., Abingdon-on-Thames,Berkshire.

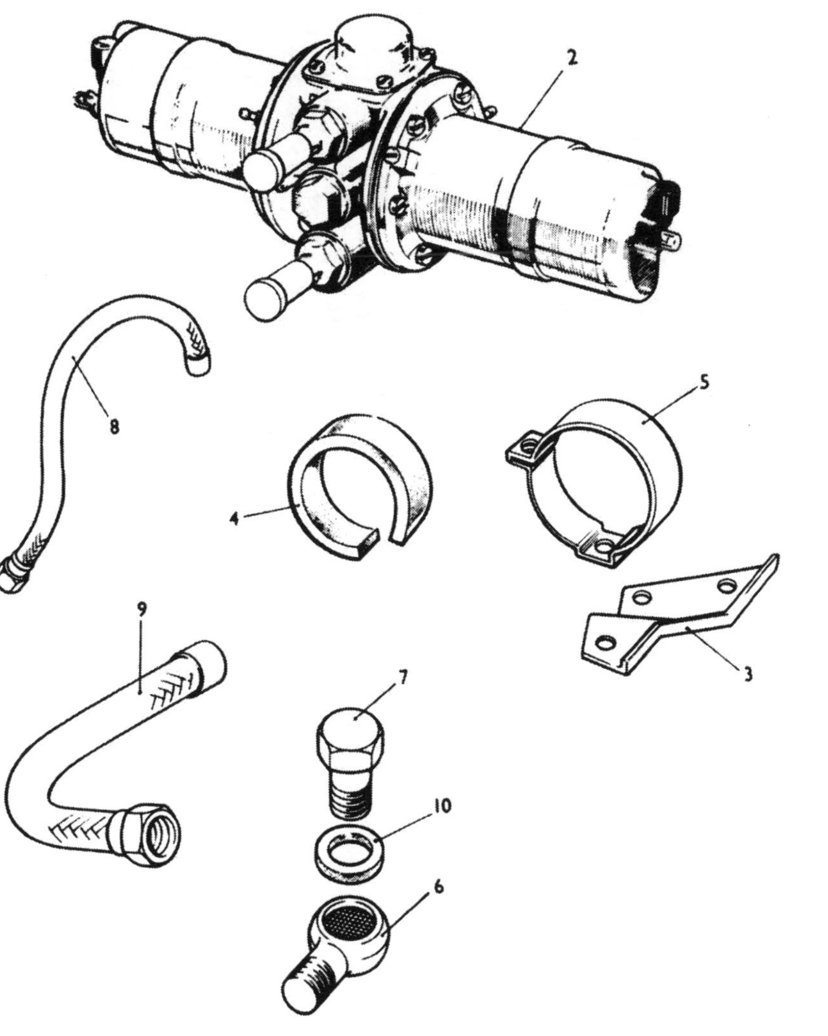

AUSTIN-HEALEY SPRITE MK. 3 AND MK. 4 & MG MIDGET MK. 2 AND MK. 3

NO.	PART NO.	DESCRIPTION	QTY	CHANGE POINT	REMARKS
		SPECIAL TUNING-FUEL SYSTEM.			
1	AJJ 4015	KIT-DUAL FUEL PUMP	1		C-MG.
2	AUF 400	Pump-petrol-dual	1		
3	21A 750	Bracket	2		
4	ACB 9252	Rubber	2		
5	21A 632	Clips	2		
6	AUC 1833	Banjo	2		
7	AUC 2698	Bolts	2		
8	AHB 6715	Hose-flexible	1		
9	AHH 6707	Hose-flexible	1		
10	AUC 2141	Washer-fibre	4		

NOTE.
All parts listed with the remark C-MG are competition parts and must be ordered direct from British Leyland Special Tuning Dept., Abingdon-on-Thames, Berkshire.

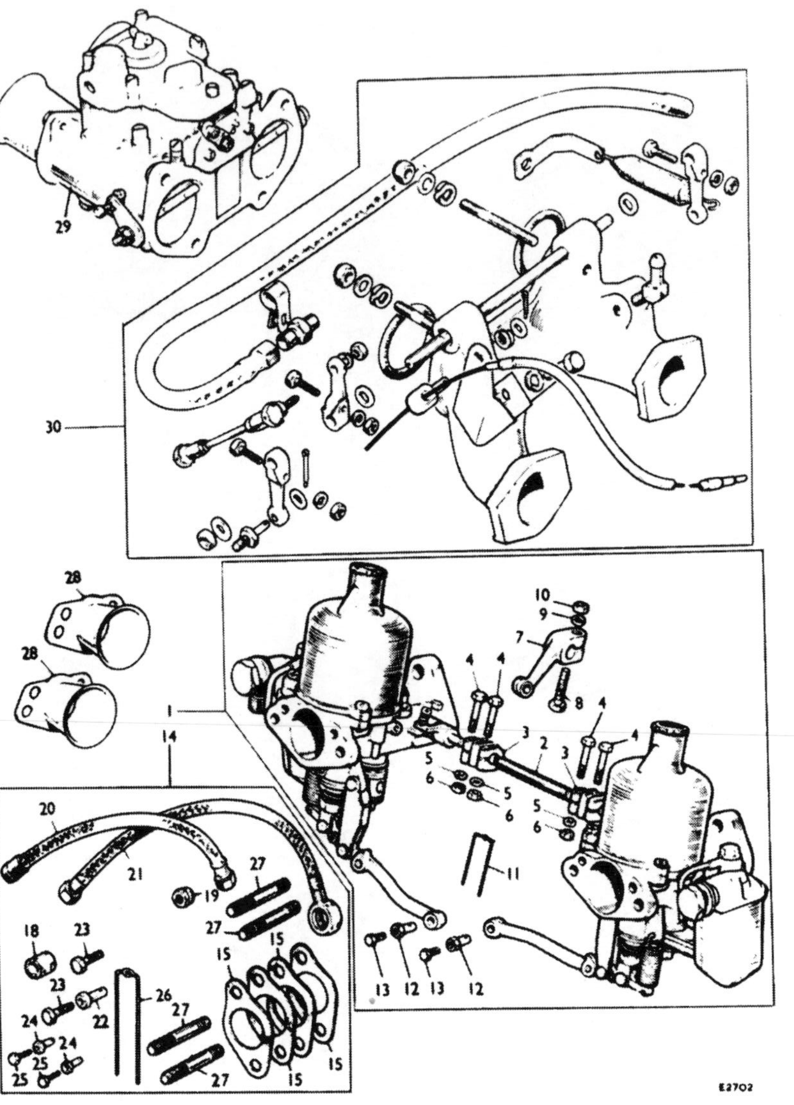

AUSTIN-HEALEY SPRITE MK. 3 AND MK. 4 & MG MIDGET MK. 2 AND MK. 3

SPECIAL TUNING-CARBURETTER.

NO.	PART NO.	DESCRIPTION	QTY	CHANGE POINT	REMARKS
1	AUD 194	CARBURETTER INSTALLATION	1PR		C-MG.
3	AUC 4334	Coupling-rod	2		
4	AUC 2669	Bolt-coupling	4		
5	AUC 4612	Washer-plain	4		
6	AJD 8014 Z	Nut-bolt	4		
7	AUC 4454	Lever-throttle	1		
8	AJD 1042	Bolt-lever	1		
9	LWZ 303	Washer-spring	1		
10	AJD 8012 Z	Nut-bolt	1		
13	AUC 5047	Screw-pin	2		
14	AJJ 3334	KIT-INSTALLATION-CARBURETTER	1		C-MG.
15	AEH 551	Gasket	4		
19	53K 1392	Nut-lock	1		
20	ACH 8977	Pipe-petrol-connecting	1		
21	AHB 9059	Pipe-petrol-feed	1		
22	1B 2697	Trunnion	1		
23	53K 1023	Bolt	2		
24	AUC 5058	Trunnion	2		
25	AUC 5047	Screw	2		
26	AUC 1025	Stirrup	1		
27	CHS 2614	Stud	4		
	AHT 247	Pipe-flare for carburetter	2		C-MG.

NOTE.
All parts listed with the remark C-MG are competition parts and must be ordered direct from British Leyland Special Tuning Dept.,
Abingdon-on-Thames, Berkshire.

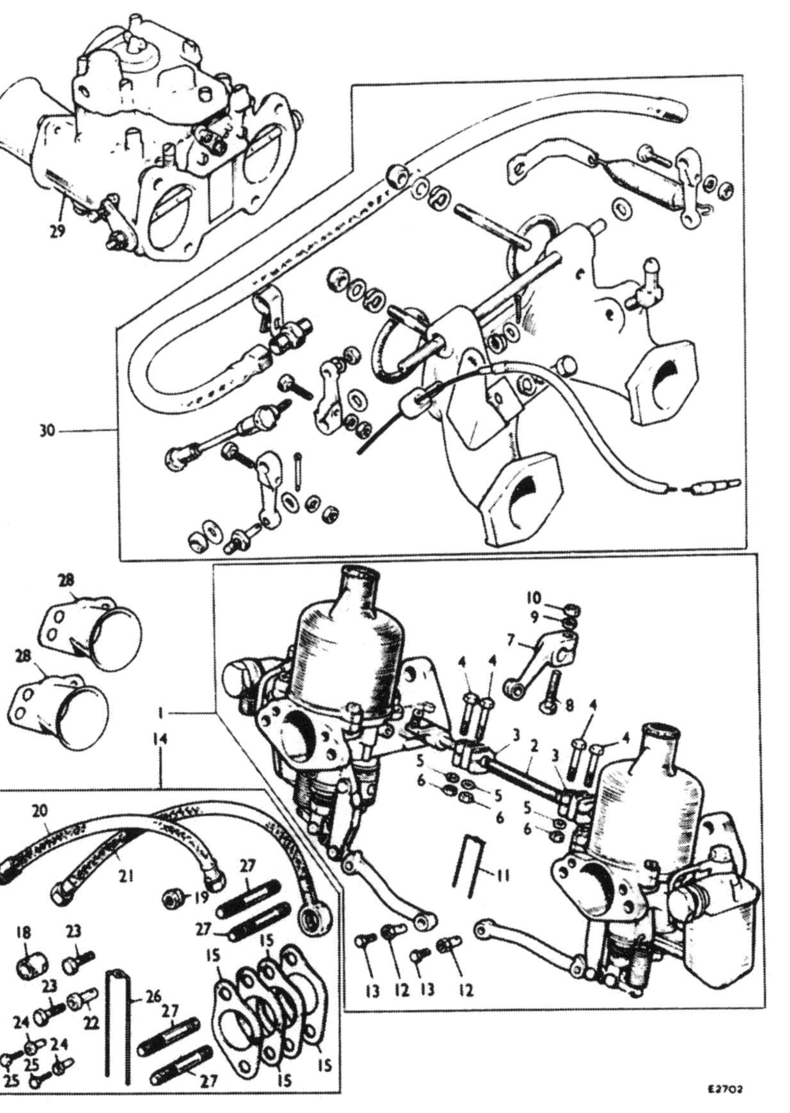

AUSTIN-HEALEY SPRITE MK. 3 AND MK. 4 & MG MIDGET MK. 2 AND MK. 3

NO.	PART NO.	DESCRIPTION	QTY	CHANGE POINT	REMARKS
		SPECIAL TUNING-CARBURETTER-WEBER TYPE.			
29	AHT 143	Carburetter-Weber(45 DCOE)	1		
30	AJJ 3360	KIT-INSTALLATION-WEBER-CARB.	1		C-MG.
31	AHT 113	Manifold	1		
32	AHT 199	Bracket-throttle	1		
33	SH 505061	Bolt	2		
34	LWZ 305	Washer	2		
35	ACA 5289	Bracket-abutment	1		
37	PWZ 203	Washer	2		
39	AHT 85	Cable-throttle	1		C-MG.
40	ACC 5062	Trunnion	1		
42	FNZ 204	Nut	1		
44	AUC 1501	Lever	1		
45	53K 128	Bolt	3		
46	LWZ 203	Washer	4		
47	FNZ 103	Nut	6		
48	PWZ 105	Washer	6		
49	AUC 4454	Lever	2		
50	ACB 5311	Ball-joint	2		
51	AHB 6114	Rod	1		
52	AHT 156	Petrolflex 26"	1		C-MG.
53	PCR 809	Clip	1		
54	AEH 786	Adaptor-union	1		C-MG.
55	12A 5	Bracket for spring	1		
56	AEC 2075	Spring	1		
57	AEH 776	Stud	4		C-MG.
59	LNZ 205	Nut	4		
60	AHT 155	Spindle	1		
61	AHT 157	Adaptor-servo	1		C-MG.
62	AEA 605	'O'ring	2		
	7H 2566	Plug-servo	1		
	3H 2287	Washer	1		

NOTE.
All parts listed with the remark C-MG are competition parts and must be ordered direct from British Leyland Special Tuning Dept., Abingdon-on-Thames, Berkshire.

AUSTIN-HEALEY SPRITE MK. 3 AND MK. 4 & MG MIDGET MK. 2 AND MK. 3

SPECIAL TUNING-TWIN CARBURETTER ASSEMBLY.

NO.	PART NO.	DESCRIPTION	QTY	CHANGE POINT	REMARKS
1	AUC 9353	CARBURETTER ASSEMBLY-FRONT	1		C-MG.
	AUC 9354	CARBURETTER ASSEMBLY-REAR	1		C-MG.
2	AUD 7047	BODY ASSEMBLY-FRONT	1		C-MG.
	AUD 9024	BODY ASSEMBLY-REAR	1		C-MG.
3	AUC 1249	Pin-piston lifting	2		
4	AUC 1151	Spring-pin	2		
5	AUC 1250	Circlip-pin	2		
7	AUD 2500	CHAMBER AND PISTON ASSEMBLY	2		
8	AUC 2057	Screw-needle locking	2		
10	AUC 4900	Washer(fibre)	2		
11	AUC 4587	Spring-piston-blue	2		
12	AUC 2175	Screw-chamber to body	6		
13	AUC 8182	Jet	2		
14	AUC 2121	Nut-adjusting	2		
15	AUC 2114	Spring-adjusting nut	2		
16	AUC 3232	Nut-gland sealing	2		
17	AUC 2117	Ring-sealing(aluminium)	2		
18	AUC 2118	Ring-sealing(cork)	2		
19	AUC 3233	Washer-bottom bearing	NLA		
20	AUC 3231	Bearing-bottom	2		
21	AUC 2120	Washer-gland(cork)	4		
22	AUC 2119	Washer-gland(brass)	4		
23	AUC 1158	Spring-gland	2		
24	AUC 3230	Bearing-top	2		
25	AUC 2122	Washer-top bearing	NLA		
26	AUD 1005	Needle-jet standard(No.6)	2		
27	AUC 4045	Lever-jet	NLA		
28	AUC 4667	Spring-jet-lever-return	2		
29	AUC 4719	Link-jet lever	2		
30	AUC 2381	Pin-link to body	2		
31	AUC 5009	Pin-link to lever	2		
32	AUC 2381	Pin-lever to jet	2		
33	CPS 204	Pin-split	NLA		
34	AUC 5004	Washer-starlock	2		
35	AUC 3212	Spindle-throttle(front)	NLA		
	AUC 3513	Spindle-throttle(rear)	1		
36	AUC 2199	Lever-throttle stop	NLA		
37	AUC 2521	Screw-adjusting	2		
	AUC 2106	Pin-taper	NLA		
40	AUC 8209	Lever-return spring	2		
41	AJD 1042	Bolt-lever	2		
42	AUC 8396	Washer-plain	2		
43	AJD 8012 Z	Nut-bolt	2		
44	AUC 3116	Disc-throttle	2		
45	AUC 1358	Screw-disc	4		
46	AUC 3496	Chamber-float(front)	2		

NOTE.
All parts listed with the remark C-MG are competition parts and must be ordered direct from British Leyland Special Tuning Dept., Abingdon-on-Thames, Berkshire.

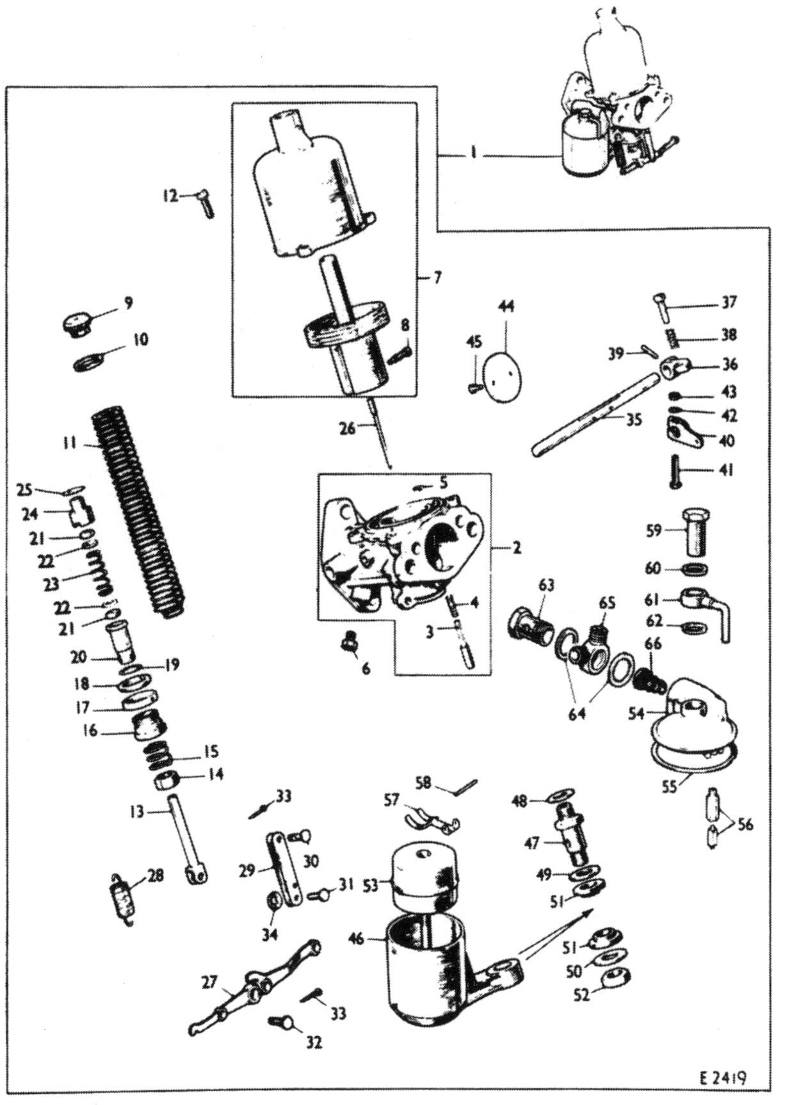

AUSTIN-HEALEY SPRITE MK. 3 AND MK. 4 & MG MIDGET MK. 2 AND MK. 3

SPECIAL TUNING-TWIN CARBURETTER ASSEMBLY-continued

NO.	PART NO.	DESCRIPTION	QTY	CHANGE POINT	REMARKS
48	AUC 1384	Washer-plain-pillar	2		
49	AUC 1389	Washer-inner(steel)	2		
50	AUC 1388	Washer-outer(steel)	2		
51	AUC 1534	Grommet(rubber)	4		
52	AJD 8206 Z	Locknut-pillar	2		
53	AUC 1123	Float	2		
54	AUD 2283	Lid-float chamber(front)	1		
	AUD 2284	Lid-float chamber(rear)	1		
55	AUC 1147	Gasket-lid	2		
56	AUD 9096	Needle and seat	2		
57	AUD 2285	Lever-hinged	2		
58	AUC 1152	Pin-hinge	2		
59	AUC 1867	Nut-cap	2		
60	AUC 1557	Washer(aluminium)	2		
61	AUC 3200	Pipe-air vent and overflow	2		
62	AUC 1928	Washer(fibre)	2		
63	AUC 2698	Bolt-banjo	2		
64	AUC 2141	Washer(fibre)	4		
66	AUC 2139	Filter	2		

NOTE.
All parts listed with the remark C-MG are competition parts and must be ordered direct from British Leyland Special Tuning Dept., Abingdon-on-Thames, Berkshire.

ILLUSTRATION NOT USED

AUSTIN-HEALEY SPRITE MK. 3 AND MK. 4 & MG MIDGET MK. 2 AND MK. 3

NO.	PART NO.	DESCRIPTION	QTY	CHANGE POINT	REMARKS
		SPECIAL TUNING-INSTALLATION KIT FOR HS6 CARBURETTERS			
	AJJ 4001	KIT-INSTALLATION FOR HS6 CARBURETTER	1		C-MG.Use with AUD 416 SU HS6 carburetters
	12G 297	Ferrule	2		
	PWZ 105	Washer-plain	8		
	LNZ 205	Nut	12		
	12G 2463	Manifold-inlet	1		
	ADP 210	Plug-screwed	1		
	37H 4760	Pipe-petrol(flexible)	A/R		Supplied in 10' (3.048m)lengths C-MG
	AHT 85	Cable-accelerator	1		
	12H 889	Piece-'T'	1		
	ACH 5854	Clip	6		
	12H 1001	Clip	2		
	27H 3073	Adaptor	1		
	51K 3811	Washer-copper	2		
	AHH 5791	Joint	2		C-MG
	HZS 510	Screw	4		
	AHT 239	Bracket-throttle return spring	1		C.MG
	AEC 2075	Spring	4		
	CHS 2513	Stud	8		
	ACC 5062	Trunnion	1		
	FNZ 204	Nut	1		
	AHA 6367	Trunnion	1		
	53K 3503	Screw	1		
	AEG 349	Bracket-abutment	1		
	AAA 649	Washer-tab	1		
	ZCS 405	Screw	1		
	LWZ 304	Washer-spring	1		
	PWZ 105	Washer-plain	4		
	ADP 210	Plug	1		
	AHH 7209	Pipe-flare	2		]Alternatives
	AHT 392	Pipe-flare-1.75" alloy	1		]C-MG

NOTE.
All parts listed with the remark C-MG are competition parts and must be ordered direct from British Leyland Special Tuning Dept.
Abingdon-on-Thames,Berkshire

MQ OO22A

AUSTIN-HEALEY SPRITE MK. 3 AND MK. 4 & MG MIDGET MK. 2 AND MK. 3

SPECIAL TUNING-TWIN HS6 CARBURETTERS

NO.	PART NO.	DESCRIPTION	QTY	CHANGE POINT	REMARKS
1	AUD 416	CARBURETTER INSTALLATION (HS6)	1		C-MG
	CUD 9093	CARBURETTER ASSEMBLY-FRONT	1		
	CUD 9094	CARBURETTER ASSEMBLY-REAR	1		
	AUD 9544	BODY ASSEMBLY-FRONT	1		
2	AUD 9550	BODY ASSEMBLY-REAR	1		
3	AUC 1249	Pin-lift piston	2		
4	AUC 1151	Spring-piston lift pin	2		
	AUC 1206	Washer-tab	1		
5	AUC 1250	Circlip-piston lift pin	2		
6	AUD 9187	SUCTION CHAMBER ASSEMBLY	2		
7	AUC 2057	Screw-needle locking	2		
8	AUC 8114	Cap and damper	2		
9	AUC 4900	Washer(fibre)	2		
10	AUC 4387	Spring-piston-Red	2		
11	AUC 2175	Screw-securing	6		
12	AUD 9148	JET-ASSEMBLY-FRONT	1		
12	AUD 9149	JET-ASSEMBLY-REAR	1		
13	AUD 2129	Nut	2		
14	AUD 2193	Washer	2		
15	AUD 2194	Gland	2		
16	AUD 2195	Ferrule	2		
17	AUC 8460	Bearing-jet	2		
18	AUC 8478	Washer-jet bearing	2		
19	AUC 2002	Screw-jet locking	2		
20	AUC 2114	Spring	2		
21	AUC 8461	Screw-jet adjusting	2		
23	AUC 1310	Chamber-float	2		
26	AUC 1329	Washer-support	2		
	AUD 2677	Grommet(rubber)-front	1		
33	AUD 2676	Grommet(rubber)-rear	1		
25	AUC 1318	Bolt-mounting	2		
24	AUD 3017	Bolt-float chamber fixing	2		
27	AUD 9904	Float	2		
29	AUD 9585	Needle and seat assembly	2		
	AUD 9258	Lid-float chamber-front	1		
30	AUD 9203	Lid-float chamber-rear	1		
31	AUC 8459	Gasket-lid	2		
32	AUC 2175	Screw-lid	6		
	LWZ 303	Washer-spring	6		
34	AUC 8494	Throttle-spindle	2		
35	AUC 3280	Throttle-disc	2		
36	AUC 1358	Screw-disc	4		
	AUD 2788	Lever-throttle-front	1		
37	AUD 2787	Lever-throttle-rear	1		
38	AUC 1400	Lever-lost motion	2		

NOTE.
All parts listed with the remark C-MG are competition parts and must be ordered direct from British Leyland Special Tuning Dept. Abingdon-on-Thames,Berkshire.

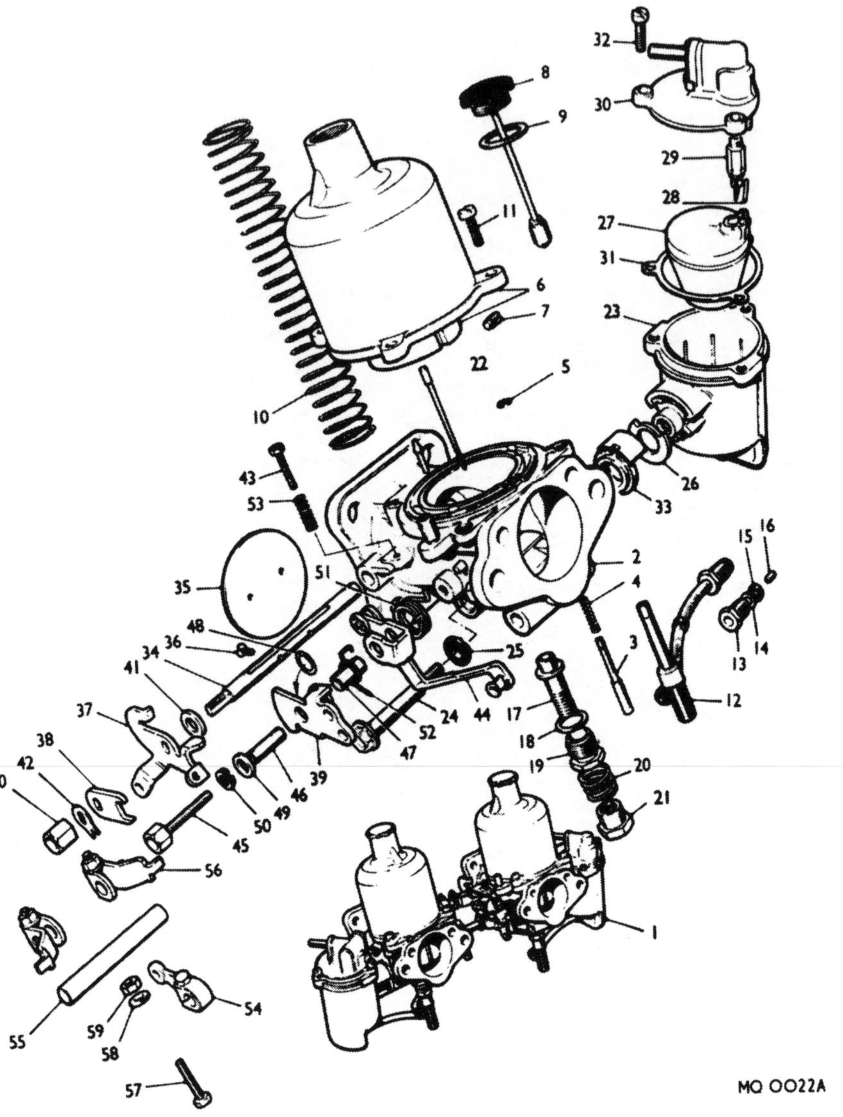

AUSTIN-HEALEY SPRITE MK. 3 AND MK. 4 & MG MIDGET MK. 2 AND MK. 3

SPECIAL TUNING-TWIN HS6 CARBURETTERS-continued

NO.	PART NO.	DESCRIPTION	QTY	CHANGE POINT	REMARKS
	AUD 2163	Lever-cam-front	1		
39	AUD 2164	Lever-cam-rear	1		
40	AUC 1424	Bearing-nut	2		
41	AUC 2625	Washer-spacing	1		
43	AUC 8483	Screw-stop	4		
53	AUC 2451	Spring-screw locking	4		
	AUD 9492	Lever-pick-up-front	1		
44	AUD 9493	Lever-pick-up-rear	1		
	PTZ 605	Screw-self-tapping	2		
45	AUC 1426	Bolt-pivot-cam lever	2		
46	AUC 8473	Tube-pivot bolt	2		
50	AUD 2076	Washer-spring	2		
49	AUC 5032	Washer-distance	4		
	AUC 8462	Spring-pick-up lever-front	1		
51	AUC 1375	Spring-pick-up lever-rear	1		
	AUD 2050	Spring-cam lever-front	1		
52	AUD 2049	Spring-cam lever-rear	1		
55	AUC 2439	Rod-connecting	1		
	AUE 586	LEVER ASSEMBLY-FRONT	2		
56	AUE 587	LEVER-ASSEMBLY-REAR	2		
57	AJD 1042	Bolt-lever	4		
58	AUC 8396	Washer-plain	4		
58	AJD 8012 Z	Nut-bolt	4		
54	AUE 180	Lever-throttle	1		
57	AJD 1042	Bolt-lever	1		
	LWZ 303	Washer-spring	1		
59	AJD 8012 Z	Nut-bolt	1		

NOTE.
All parts listed with the remark C-MG are competition parts and must be ordered direct from British Leyland Special Tuning Dept.
Abingdon-on-Thames,Berkshire

AUSTIN-HEALEY SPRITE MK. 3 AND MK. 4 & MG MIDGET MK. 2 AND MK. 3

SPECIAL TUNING-SHOCK ABSORBER AND ANTI-ROLL BAR

NO.	PART NO.	DESCRIPTION	QTY	CHANGE POINT	REMARKS
		ABSORBER-SHOCK			
1	AHA 6451	Front-RH	1		C-MG
2	AHA 6452	Front-LH	1		C-MG
5	AHA 7906	Rear-RH-adjustable	1		C-MG
6	AHA 7907	Rear-LH-adjustable	1		C-MG
7	AHA 8272	Spring-rear road-lowered-semi-elliptic	2		C-MG
8	AJJ 3322	KIT-FRONT SUSPENSION-LOWERING	1		C-MG
9	AHA 8277	Piece-distance	8		
10	AHA 8278	Plate-bump stop	2		
11	CMZ 210	Screw	4		
12	LWZ 203	Washer-spring	4		
14	53K 1369	Bolt	8		
15	LWZ 405	Washer	8		
16	LNZ 205	Nut	8		
18	AJJ 3314	KIT-ANTI-ROLL BAR-.5625" (14.3mm)DIA.BAR	1		C-MG
19	AHA 7013	Bar-anti-roll	1		
20	AHA 7011	Link-anti-roll bar-RH	1		
21	AHA 7012	Link-anti-roll bar-LH	1		
22	AHA 7028	Bracket-link	2		
23	HZS 506	Screw-bracket to lower link	6		
24	WL 600051	Washer-spring	6		
25	NH 605041	Nut	6		
26	AHH 6541	Bearing-anti-roll bar	2		
27	1B 7356	Strap-bearing	2		
28	HZS 505	Screw-strap to frame	4		
29	WL 600051	Washer-spring	4		
30	AHH 6546	Stop-end	4		
31	PMZ 307	Screw-clamping-end top	4		
32	LWZ 203	Washer-spring	4		
33	FNZ 103	Nut	4		
34	AHT 56	Bar-anti-roll-.625"(15.9mm)dia.	1		C-MG
34	AHT 57	Bar-anti-roll-.6875" (17.5mm)dia	1		C-MG
35	AJJ 3356	KIT-INSTALLATION-ANTI-ROLL BAR	1		C-MG
20	AHA 7011	Link-anti-roll bar-RH	1		
21	AHA 7012	Link-anti-roll bar-LH	1		
22	AHA 7028	Bracket-link	2		
23	HZS 506	Screw-bracket to lower link	6		
24	WL 600051	Washer-spring	6		
25	NH 605041	Nut-screw	6		
27	1B 7356	Strap-bearing	2		
28	HZS 506	Screw-strap to frame	4		
29	WL 600051	Washer-spring	4		

NOTE.
All parts listed with the remark C-MG are competition parts and must be ordered direct from British Leyland Special Tuning Dept. Abingdon-on-Thames,Berkshire

AUSTIN-HEALEY SPRITE MK. 3 AND MK. 4 & MG MIDGET MK. 2 AND MK. 3

SPECIAL TUNING-BRAKES-ROAD WHEELS-BODYWORK AND LITERATURE

NO.	PART NO.	DESCRIPTION	QTY	CHANGE POINT	REMARKS
	AJJ 404	KIT-DUAL BRAKING SYSTEM	1		C-MG
	BHA 4666	Box-pedal	1		
	AHH 8421	Master-cylinder	1		
	AHH 8522	Pedal-brake-RHD	1		
	BCA 4002	Connector	1		
	3H 2428	Screw-bleed	1		
	17H 7769	Pipe-brake-front-21.25"	1		
	21A 36	Pipe-brake-rear-17"	1		
	21K 8983	Clips-brake pipes	2		
36	AHT 16	Set-brake pad-DS11 linings	1		
37	AHA 7573	Wheel-wire-60 spoke-13" x 5"	5		
41	AJJ 3381	KIT-BONNET STRAP	1		C-MG
38	AHH 5518	Buckle-half	1		
39	AHH 5519	Tongue-half	1		
40	AHH 5517	Retainer	2		
	AJJ 3385	KIT-HEADLAMP COWL	1		
	AJJ 4016	KIT-RUBBER TOGGLE-RETAINER	1		
	4K 7717	Strap-rubber	1		
	4K 7715	Clip-retaining	NLA		
	AHT 287	Ferrule-rubber strap retainer	1		
	AKD 5007	Special tuning booklet-1098cc	1		
	AKD 5098	Special tuning booklet-1275cc	1		
	AJJ 3333	Special tuning data set	1		C-MG
	AKD 5061	Binder for special tuning sheets	1		
	AKD 5093	Divider set for binder	1		
	AKD 5125	British Leyland special tuning emblem	1PR		
	AHT 2000	British Leyland special tuning lapel badge	1		
	AKD 4021 A	Workshop manual	1		
	AHT 333	Badge-woven-special tuning	1		
		JACKET-RALLY-BRITISH LEYLAND			
	AHT 352	Small	1		
	AHT 353	Medium	1		C-MG
	AHT 354	Large	1		
	AHT 355	Extra large	1		

NOTE.
All parts listed with the remark C-MG are competition parts and must be ordered direct from British Leyland Special Tuning Dept.
Abingdon-on-Thames,Berkshire

PART NUMBER	GRP	PAGE	PART NUMBER	GRP	PAGE	PART NUMBER	GRP	PAGE	PART NUMBER	GRP	PAGE	PART NUMBER	GRP	PAGE	PART NUMBER	GRP	PAGE
3632	H	28	105121	B	86	121831	B	80	143943	B	86	154117	D	50.06	201350	B	84
3632	H	30	105123	B	88	122132	B	94	143992	E	10	154209	B	96	206175	C	14
3632	H	30	105124	B	90	122566	C	14	144070	B	90	154209	B	96.02	207887	C	14
9403	H	56	105125	B	90	122689	B	102	144195	B	80	154209	B	96.04	208375	E	10
9403	H	56	105131	B	82	125170	D	16.02	144297	B	92	154210	B	96	211126	B	84
9403	H	56.02	105143	B	80	125252	B	82	144580	C	18	154210	B	96.04	212935	B	94
9403	H	56.02	105321	B	78	126765	E	10	144595	C	18	154211	B	96	212935	B	94.02
9403	H	60	105322	B	90	127883	B	80	144648	B	88	154211	B	96	213863	B	86
9403	H	62	105745	B	94	127916	H	78	144686	B	78	154211	B	96.02	214814	B	90
9403	H	64	106262	C	16	127997	E	10	144686	B	88	154220	B	96	215350	B	86
9405	H	58	106270	C	18	128000	E	10	144687	B	78	154220	B	96	215372	B	86
11727	H	76	106365	C	16	128004	E	10	144688	B	78	154220	B	96	215997	D	16.02
11730	H	76	106388	C	16	128262	B	96.04	144938	D	16.02	154220	B	96.02	216924	B	96.02
32307	B	86	106477	C	18	128262	B	96.04	144961	F	2	154220	B	96.04	217789	B	84
33214	B	82	106663	B	88	128262	D	4.04	144962	B	90	154220	B	96.04	217790	B	84
35960	B	82	107246	B	86	128262	H	6.06	144965	B	88	154334	H	20.04	244700	H	64
36234	B	78	107401	B	80	129077	B	86	144973	B	90	154934	B	96	244700	H	66
36411	B	82	109023	B	90	129358	C	14	144974	B	90	154935	B	96	244700	H	76
37948	C	16	109024	B	90	129383	B	94	144975	B	90	155357	B	84	244700	H	76
37948	C	18	109495	B	90	129383	B	94.02	145197	D	50.04	155371	B	86	244700	H	78
42425	B	82	110748	B	88	129410	C	14	145275	B	82	155755	C	18	262342	H	58
43752	B	82	111422	C	16	129412	C	14	145276	B	82	155756	C	18	262342	H	58
57110	B	90	111870	B	88	129862	C	18	146176	C	14	155805	C	18	309141	B	92
58258	B	94	112394	C	18	130031	E	10	146454	B	80	155806	C	18	310221	D	16.02
58258	B	94.02	112509	C	14	130032	E	10	146485	B	80	155807	C	18	311702	B	92
58923	B	88	112516	C	14	131211	B	96.02	146914	B	90	155808	C	18	312151	C	14
100498	B	94	112654	C	16	131211	B	96.02	147354	C	16	155959	D	16.02	312188	B	82
100498	B	94.02	112654	C	18	131211	D	4.04	147483	H	20.04	156084	C	16	500464	C	14
100500	B	82	112907	B	86	131211	H	6.06	147737	B	90	156336	C	14	500469	B	78
100501	B	78	113071	C	18	131368	D	50.06	147738	B	90	156464	H	20.04	500469	B	78
101022	B	78	113229	C	18	131535	B	86	147899	H	20.04	156530	B	78	500469	B	88
101022	B	88	114774	B	86	131570	H	22.02	147990	H	20.04	156572	D	50.06	500974	B	82
101302	B	94	114774	B	88	131786	B	78	148006	D	50.02	156607	B	96.02	505158	H	34
101302	B	94.02	114774	C	20	131843	C	16	148090	B	90	156607	B	96.04	508978	B	80
101343	B	94	116516	B	78	132098	B	86	148353	B	78	156608	B	96.02	510451	B	86
101343	B	94.02	117400	B	96.02	132107	B	86	149011	H	36	156608	B	96.04	510618	C	18
101962	B	86	117400	D	4.04	132495	B	88	149380	B	96.02	156712	B	96.02	511269	H	28
101962	B	86	118632	B	78	132872	C	14	149380	B	96.02	156712	B	96.04	511269	H	30
101962	B	86	119389	B	82	133103	E	10	149380	B	96.04	156952	D	16.02	511269	H	36.02
101962	B	92	119390	B	82	134933	B	86	149699	B	94	157229	B	88	513123	G	16
102488	D	50.02	119758	B	86	137532	C	18	149699	B	94.02	157409	B	86	515218	H	56
102488	D	50.02	119758	B	86	137811	B	90	149963	C	16	157476	B	88	515218	H	56
104433	C	16	119758	B	86	137834	C	16	150022	B	78	157508	B	88	515218	H	56.02
104433	C	18	119813	B	80	137845	B	94	150328	C	16	157510	B	88	515218	H	56.02
104445	C	18	119891	C	18	137845	B	94.02	150328	C	18	157690	C	14	515218	H	58
104549	H	22.02	119893	C	18	138176	B	90	150844	H	82	157732	C	18	515218	H	60
104618	H	28	120331	B	96.02	138530	B	94	150844	H	86	158308	D	4.04	515218	H	62
104618	H	30	120331	B	96.02	138701	B	92	151103	H	6.06	158941	B	86	515218	H	64
104618	H	30	120331	D	16.02	138702	B	92	151134	B	78	159123	D	50.06	515399	H	28
104618	N	20	120946	E	10	138791	D	16.02	152184	B	96.02	159942	B	94	517644	H	82
104859	B	90	120948	E	10	138869	E	10	152184	B	96.04	159942	B	94.02	517644	H	86
104860	B	82	120949	E	10	139563	C	14	153300	D	16.02	159942	B	96	518528	D	50.06
104861	B	82	120957	E	10	142649	B	90	153408	C	20	159942	B	96.02	518529	D	50.06
104939	B	82	120959	E	10	143456	B	78	153417	D	50.06	159942	B	96.04	519364	H	76
105114	B	82	121217	B	86	143552	B	88	153886	B	88	159978	C	18	563417	H	34
105115	B	82	121217	B	86	143747	D	50.04	153957	D	50.04	160108	B	94	600226	H	56
105118	B	88	121217	B	86	143802	H	20.04	153959	D	50.04	160108	B	96.04	600226	H	56
105120	B	90	121530	B	82	143943	B	86	154053	B	94.02	201344	B	86	600226	H	60

PART NUMBER	GRP	PAGE
600226	H	60
600226	H	60
600226	H	62
600226	H	62
600226	H	64
601721	H	78
606078	H	78
608092	H	82
608224	H	76
623312	G	20
623312	G	28
630661	D	16.02
1A 1559	B	6
1A 1559	B	28
1A 1964	B	2
1A 1964	B	26
1A 2156	B	14
1A 2156	B	40
2A 11	B	10
2A 11	Q	2
2A 13	B	8
2A 13	B	32
2A 13 10	B	8
2A 13 10	B	32
2A 13 20	B	8
2A 14	B	8
2A 18	B	12
2A 21	B	12
2A 21	B	38
2A 21	Q	4
2A 54	B	26
2A 84	B	6
2A 84	B	30
2A 85	B	6
2A 113	B	44
2A 150	B	14
2A 150	B	40
2A 180	B	10
2A 180	B	36
2A 243	B	14
2A 243	B	22
2A 243	B	52
2A 258	B	12
2A 258	B	38
2A 259	B	12
2A 265	B	44
2A 269	B	18
2A 269	B	46
2A 299	B	6
2A 299	Q	2
2A 497	H	20.02
2A 515	B	12
2A 515	B	12
2A 515	B	38
2A 526	B	22
2A 533	B	12
2A 601	B	22
2A 601	B	54

PART NUMBER	GRP	PAGE
2A 640	B	10
2A 660	B	6
2A 664	B	22
2A 664	B	52
2A 668	B	18
2A 668	B	46
2A 715	B	50.02
2A 759	B	6
2A 759	B	30
2A 778	B	22
2A 778	B	52
2A 803	B	22
2A 879	B	10
2A 879	Q	2
2A 940	B	8
2A 964	B	12
2A 1768	B	20
2A 2069	D	6
2A 2077	G	2
2A 2183	G	18
2A 3006	B	74
2A 3024	C	4
2A 3024	C	4
2A 3025	C	4
2A 3026	C	4
2A 3027	C	4
2A 3028	C	2
2A 3035	C	4
2A 3035	C	6
2A 3035	Q	10
2A 3061	C	8
2A 3108	C	2
2A 3110	C	2
2A 3245	C	4
2A 3253	C	2
2A 3282	C	6
2A 3282	Q	10.02
2A 3284	C	2
2A 3286	C	2
2A 3286	Q	10
2A 3289	B	74
2A 3325	C	8
2A 3335	C	8
2A 3339	C	12
2A 3340	C	8
2A 3341	C	8
2A 3341	Q	10
2A 3344	C	8
2A 3344	Q	10
2A 3345	C	8
2A 3345	Q	10
2A 3371	C	6
2A 3375	C	8
2A 3375	C	8
2A 3378	C	8
2A 3385	C	8
2A 3388	C	8
2A 3390	C	10

PART NUMBER	GRP	PAGE
2A 3420	C	8
2A 3467	C	10
2A 3468	C	8
2A 3492	C	2
2A 4003	E	24
2A 4005	E	22
2A 4006	E	22
2A 4010	E	22
2A 4020	E	22
2A 4024	E	26
2A 4028	E	26
2A 4067	E	24
2A 4082	E	26
2A 4205	E	22
2A 4206	E	22
2A 4214	E	26
2A 4272	E	26
2A 5076	B	74
2A 5420	B	76
2A 5509	I	4
2A 5509	I	12
2A 5552	B	76
2A 5570	B	76
2A 5570	B	76
2A 5571	B	76
2A 5571	B	76
2A 5574	G	4
2A 5574	G	14
2A 5576	G	16
2A 5591	D	2
2A 5591	D	4
2A 5592	D	2
2A 5592	D	4
2A 5606	G	18
2A 5609	G	18
2A 5611	G	18
2A 5615	G	10
2A 5619	G	18
2A 5626	P	4
2A 5635	H	98
2A 6128	E	8
2A 6133	E	14
2A 7015	F	4
2A 7016	F	4
2A 7027	F	4
2A 7057	G	30
2A 7058	G	30
2A 7062	F	4
2A 7087	F	6
2A 7089	F	6
2A 7091	F	6
2A 7103	F	4
2A 7168	F	8
2A 7226	F	4
2A 7228	F	8
2A 7250	F	4
2A 7271	F	4
2A 7291	G	30

PART NUMBER	GRP	PAGE
2A 7291	G	30
2A 7308	G	30
2A 8055	P	2
2A 9119	H	78
2A 9156	H	68
12A 5	Q	16
12A 13 20	B	32
12A 186	B	10
12A 186	Q	2
12A 186 10	B	10
12A 250	B	8
12A 303	B	18
12A 314	B	22
12A 398	B	32
12A 402	B	40
12A 403	B	14
12A 403	B	40
12A 403	B	40
12A 451	B	18
12A 451	B	46
12A 526	B	56
12A 715	B	20
12A 747	B	8
12A 956	B	16
12A 956	B	44
12A 1002	B	26
12A 1052	B	24
12A 1052	B	64
12A 1093	B	14
12A 1136	B	8
12A 1136	B	32
12A 1139	B	16
12A 1148	B	16
12A 1148	B	44
12A 1175	B	16
12A 1176	B	16
12A 1177	B	16
12A 1205	B	14
12A 1205	B	40
12A 1211	B	24
12A 1211	B	62
12A 1211	D	52
12A 1211	D	52
12A 1212	B	16
12A 1212	B	16
12A 1215	B	12
12A 1215	B	38
12A 1344	B	22
12A 1344	B	54
12A 1358	B	14
12A 1358	B	40
12A 1381	B	26
12A 1382	B	16
12A 1530	B	14
12A 1530	B	40
12A 1591	B	20
12A 1591	B	20
12A 1591	B	20

PART NUMBER	GRP	PAGE
12A 1591	B	20
12A 1591	B	50
12A 1591	B	50
12A 1726	B	50
12A 1768	B	42
12A 1768	B	50.02
12A 1768	B	72
12A 1768	Q	6
12A 1802	B	22
12A 1802	B	52
12A 1851	B	18
12A 1950	B	12
12A 1950	B	38
12A 1968	B	14
12A 1968	B	40
12A 2032	B	50.02
12A 2035	B	50.02
12A 2075	B	42
12A 2178	B	42
14A 366	K	2
14A 764	O	6
14A 1162	N	12
14A 4497	O	30
14A 4684	K	2
14A 5519	O	34
14A 5520	O	34
14A 5542	K	2
14A 5772	N	24
14A 6536	K	10
14A 6537	K	10
14A 6745	O	6
14A 6797	J	4
14A 7074	K	2
14A 7552	L	14
21A 36	Q	30
21A 137	E	26
21A 168	D	6
21A 632	Q	12
21A 750	Q	12
22A 71	C	8
22A 75	C	10
22A 84	C	10
22A 85	C	10
22A 233	G	6
22A 367	C	4
22A 367	C	6
22A 453	C	6
22A 463	C	6
22A 465	C	6
22A 466	C	6
22A 468	C	2
22A 469	C	2
22A 470	C	2
22A 471	C	2
22A 472	C	2
22A 474	C	8
22A 475	C	8
22A 476	C	8

PART NUMBER	GRP	PAGE
22A 480	C	8
22A 481	C	10
22A 481	Q	10
22A 495	C	6
22A 495	C	6
24A 1032	P	2
AAA 81	G	6
AAA 629	F	10
AAA 629	F	10
AAA 649	Q	22
AAA 743	M O	36
AAA 836	N	8
AAA 1524	K	8
AAA 1628	G	4
AAA 1628	G	14
AAA 1628	G	22
AAA 1645	L	6.02
AAA 2398	K	4
AAA 4756	G	16
AAA 4757	G	16
AAA 4758	G	16
AAA 5981	H	10
AAA 5981	H	10
AAA 5981	H	10
AAA 5981	H	10
AAA 5981	H	10
AAA 5981	H	10
AAA 5981	H	12
AAA 5981	M H	12
AAA 5981	M H	12
AAA 5981	M H	12
AAA 5981	M H	12
AAA 5981	M H	12
AAA 5981	M H	12
AAA 5981	M H	14
AAA 5981	M H	14
AAA 5981	M H	14
AAA 5981	M H	14
AAA 5981	M H	14
AAA 5981	M H	14
AAK 769	G	10
AAK 806	G	10
AAM 222	H	44
AAU 1110	H	52
AAU 1110	O	34
AAU 1161	E	16
AAU 1161	E	18
AAU 1161	H	54
AAU 1949	F	14
AAU 2092	H	52
AAU 2143	H	78
AAU 2298	G	6
AAU 2346	D	4.04
AAU 2492	G	30
AAU 2499	L	14
AAU 2583	G	28
AAU 2641	D	4.04
AAU 2641	H	96

PART NUMBER	GRP	PAGE
AAU 2641	H	96
AAU 2748	M B	96.02
AAU 3247	O	34
AAU 3469	G	6
AAU 3469	G	16
AAU 3499	H	90
AAU 3815	G	24
AAU 4365	H	6.04
AAU 5101	H	52
AAU 5113	H	78
AAU 5944	H	52
AAU 6008	H	52
AAU 6311	H	6.04
AAU 6312	H	6.04
AAU 6313	H	6.04
AB 606031	N	12
AB 606033	O	6
AB 606043	O	18
AB 608041	L	4
AB 608061	O	34
AB 610041	K	4
AB 612061	O	2
AC 606041	O	18
AC 610061	M	8
AC 610061	M	8
ACA 5000	F	10
ACA 5000	F	10
ACA 5128	D	12
ACA 5128	D	12
ACA 5129	D	12
ACA 5129	D	12
ACA 5138	F	12
ACA 5139	F	12
ACA 5208	C	12
ACA 5244	E	2
ACA 5245	E	2
ACA 5246	E	8
ACA 5247	E	8
ACA 5248	E	2
ACA 5249	E	2
ACA 5257	E	6
ACA 5258	E	6
ACA 5259	E	6
ACA 5260	E	6
ACA 5261	E	6
ACA 5275	E	2
ACA 5284	E	2
ACA 5285	E	2
ACA 5286	E	2
ACA 5289	Q	16
ACA 5301	E	8
ACA 5302	E	8
ACA 5303	E	8
ACA 5304	E	8
ACA 5307	E	6
ACA 5320	E	6
ACA 5374	D	4.02
ACA 5375	G	18.02

PART NUMBER	GRP	PAGE
ACA 5375	G	28
ACA 5421	H	98
ACA 5422	H	98
ACA 5456	N	8
ACA 6015	E	8
ACA 6017	E	8
ACA 6018	E	8
ACA 6019	E	2
ACA 6026	E	2
ACA 6027	E	4
ACA 6028	E	4
ACA 6029	E	8
ACA 6031	E	8
ACA 8014	D	50
ACA 9673	H	24
ACA 9872	D	4
ACB 5311	Q	16
ACB 9162	G	18
ACB 9162	G	26
ACB 9252	Q	12
ACB 9641	G	6
ACC 5062	D	50
ACC 5062	G	2
ACC 5062	Q	16
ACC 5062	Q	22
ACC 5509	G	12
ACG 5179	H	78.02
ACG 6009	E	2
ACG 6010	E	2
ACH 5854	B	64
ACH 5854	D	10
ACH 5854	D	12
ACH 5854	Q	22
ACH 6001	E	14
ACH 6173	E	8
ACH 8529	H	90
ACH 8977	Q	14
ACH 9009	H	8
ACH 9041	H	8
ACH 9287	L	6
ACH 9287	L	8
ACH 9373	N	2
ADA 1874	O	4
ADA 1874	O	8
ADA 1874	O	10
ADA 2493	I	16
ADB 509	N	2
ADB 509	N	4
ADB 709	J	12
ADB 4811	K	10
ADB 4811	K	16
ADB 4811	K	16
ADB 4811	K	24
ADB 4811	K	24
ADB 4811	K	28
ADB 4811	M	4
ADB 4811	O	18
ADH 2475	K	6

PART NUMBER	GRP	PAGE
ADH 2476	K	6
ADH 4492	K	8
ADH 5481	J	12
ADP 210	B	12
ADP 210	B	24
ADP 210	B	42
ADP 210	B	62
ADP 210	B	62
ADP 210	B	62
ADP 210	B	62
ADP 210	Q	22
ADP 210	Q	22
ADP 212	B	94
ADP 212	B	94.02
AEA 301	B	22
AEA 311	B	10
AEA 311	Q	2
AEA 312	B	8
AEA 312	B	32
AEA 399	Q	4
AEA 400	B	10
AEA 400	Q	2
AEA 401	B	10
AEA 401	Q	2
AEA 402	B	10
AEA 402	Q	2
AEA 403	B	10
AEA 403	B	36
AEA 403	Q	2
AEA 411	Q	6
AEA 494	Q	4
AEA 494	Q	4
AEA 511	Q	6
AEA 524	Q	4
AEA 524	Q	4
AEA 535	Q	8
AEA 539	Q	4
AEA 579	H	8
AEA 586	D	50
AEA 597	D	50
AEA 597	G	2
AEA 602	D	50
AEA 602	G	2
AEA 605	Q	16
AEA 635	B	24
AEA 635	B	62
AEA 635	B	62
AEA 635	B	62
AEA 647	Q	6
AEA 648	Q	2
AEA 652	Q	4
AEA 653	Q	4
AEA 654	Q	4
AEA 657	B	20
AEA 657	B	50
AEA 658	B	20
AEA 678	B	20
AEA 679	B	22

PART NUMBER	GRP	PAGE
AEA 679	B	22
AEA 679	B	56
AEA 687	B	8
AEA 687	B	30
AEA 687	Q	4
AEA 692	Q	4
AEA 695	B	28
AEA 695	Q	4
AEA 696	B	30
AEA 731	Q	2
AEA 763	B	10
AEA 767	Q	4
AEA 771	B	34
AEC 671	B	48
AEC 699	B	94
AEC 699	B	94.02
AEC 876	B	26
AEC 2075	Q	16
AEC 2075	Q	22
AED 172	B	50.02
AED 172	B	92
AEG 147	B	28
AEG 148	B	6
AEG 159	B	6
AEG 159	B	28
AEG 159 3	B	6
AEG 159 3	B	28
AEG 159 3	B	28
AEG 159 30	B	6
AEG 160	B	6
AEG 160	B	28
AEG 160 3	B	6
AEG 160 3	B	28
AEG 160 30	B	6
AEG 160 30	B	28
AEG 167	B	38
AEG 168	B	38
AEG 189	Q	2
AEG 240	B	2
AEG 240	B	26
AEG 314	B	32
AEG 327	B	36
AEG 349	Q	22
AEG 351	B	24
AEG 392	Q	4
AEG 399	B	38
AEG 417	Q	2
AEG 428	B	26
AEG 477	B	36
AEG 519	B	28
AEG 520	B	28
AEG 522	B	30
AEG 523	B	30
AEG 529	Q	2
AEG 538	B	30
AEG 542	Q	2
AEG 544	Q	4
AEG 546	Q	10

PART NUMBER	GRP	PAGE
AEG 547	Q	10
AEG 552	B	44
AEG 553	B	44
AEG 554	B	16
AEG 554	B	44
AEG 558	D	50
AEG 560	B	54
AEG 565	B	28
AEG 567	Q	2
AEG 569	Q	4
AEG 578	Q	2
AEG 578	Q	4
AEG 584	B	32
AEG 584 10	B	32
AEG 584 20	B	32
AEG 624	B	28
AEG 3009	C	4
AEG 3122	C	10
AEG 3123	C	10
AEG 3138	Q	10
AEG 3139	Q	10
AEG 3140	Q	10
AEH 551	Q	14
AEH 592	B	2
AEH 776	Q	16
AEH 786	Q	16
AHA 3390	Q	6
AHA 5211	L	12
AHA 5211	L	14
AHA 5211	L	14
AHA 5217	K	10
AHA 5326	G	4
AHA 5326	G	14
AHA 5326	G	14
AHA 5326	G	22
AHA 5388	I	2
AHA 5391	E	8
AHA 5392	E	8
AHA 5435	E	14
AHA 5445	D	6
AHA 5465	I	4
AHA 5465	I	12
AHA 5466	I	4
AHA 5466	I	12
AHA 5484	B	76
AHA 5496	E	8
AHA 5506	P	4
AHA 5508	G	10
AHA 5512	L	2
AHA 5513	L	2
AHA 5514	K	2
AHA 5514	L	2
AHA 5515	L	2
AHA 5517	K	4
AHA 5518	K	2
AHA 5521	L	6.02
AHA 5522	L	6.02
AHA 5533	L	12

PART NUMBER	GRP	PAGE
AHA 5543	K	4
AHA 5546	I	18
AHA 5549	I	4
AHA 5549	I	12
AHA 5552	I	4
AHA 5552	I	12
AHA 5553	I	4
AHA 5553	I	12
AHA 5617	K	2
AHA 5620	I	4
AHA 5620	I	12
AHA 5622	I	4
AHA 5622	I	12
AHA 5624	I	4
AHA 5624	I	12
AHA 5626	I	4
AHA 5626	I	12
AHA 5642	I	4
AHA 5642	I	12
AHA 5653	K	4
AHA 5654	K	2
AHA 5660	P	2
AHA 5662	D	6
AHA 5663	D	6
AHA 5663	D	8
AHA 5673	L	8
AHA 5674	K	2
AHA 5675	L	8
AHA 5677	L	12
AHA 5678	L	12
AHA 5679	L	12
AHA 5683	K	6
AHA 5686	L	6
AHA 5686	L	8
AHA 5695	L	6
AHA 5696	L	6
AHA 5699	K	6
AHA 5699	N	4
AHA 5700	K	2
AHA 5701	K	2
AHA 5701	O	12
AHA 5702	K	2
AHA 5729	I	2
AHA 5730	I	2
AHA 5731	I	2
AHA 5732	I	2
AHA 5746	G	2
AHA 5755	I	2
AHA 5756	I	2
AHA 5757	I	2
AHA 5765	L	12
AHA 5791	L	12
AHA 5799	N	2
AHA 5804	L	12
AHA 5804	L	14
AHA 5807	K	8
AHA 5810	K	8
AHA 5811	K	8

PART NUMBER		GRP	PAGE
AHA	5811	K	8
AHA	5817	I	20
AHA	5817	J	2
AHA	5818	I	20
AHA	5822	I	20
AHA	5823	J	2
AHA	5824	J	2
AHA	5825	I	20
AHA	5837	I	2
AHA	5837	I	10
AHA	5838	I	10
AHA	5893	E	12
AHA	6206	I	4
AHA	6206	I	14
AHA	6207	K	8
AHA	6213	K	8
AHA	6223	I	4
AHA	6223	I	14
AHA	6252	K	8
AHA	6255	G	2
AHA	6256	G	2
AHA	6257	K	2
AHA	6296	I	16
AHA	6305	H	24
AHA	6314	K	8
AHA	6315	K	8
AHA	6331	H	98
AHA	6331	H	98.02
AHA	6331	H	98.02
AHA	6352	I	20
AHA	6357	K	8
AHA	6366	G	14
AHA	6366	G	14
AHA	6367	G	2
AHA	6367	Q	22
AHA	6368	H	78.02
AHA	6369	H	78.02
AHA	6377	P	2
AHA	6378	E	26
AHA	6392	H	98
AHA	6392	H	98.02
AHA	6392	H	98.02
AHA	6392	H	98.02
AHA	6399	K	8
AHA	6406	G	30
AHA	6423	B	72
AHA	6423	Q	6
AHA	6424	B	72
AHA	6424	Q	6
AHA	6451	Q	28
AHA	6452	Q	28
AHA	6455	P	2
AHA	6482	G	18
AHA	6482	G	26
AHA	6498	L	6.02
AHA	6498	L	10.02
AHA	6657	H	54
AHA	6658	H	54

PART NUMBER		GRP	PAGE
AHA	6664	P	2
AHA	6785	O	10
AHA	6881	O	6
AHA	6934	H	24
AHA	7011	E	30
AHA	7011	Q	28
AHA	7011	Q	28
AHA	7012	E	30
AHA	7012	Q	28
AHA	7012	Q	28
AHA	7013	E	30
AHA	7013	Q	28
AHA	7028	E	30
AHA	7028	Q	28
AHA	7028	Q	28
AHA	7029	E	22
AHA	7029	E	30
AHA	7033	J	6
AHA	7034	J	6
AHA	7035	J	8
AHA	7036	J	8
AHA	7037	J	6
AHA	7038	J	10
AHA	7039	J	10
AHA	7040	J	6
AHA	7041	J	6
AHA	7042	J	10
AHA	7056	J	10
AHA	7057	J	10
AHA	7060	M	6
AHA	7061	M	6
AHA	7063	M	4
AHA	7064	M	4
AHA	7065	M	4
AHA	7067	M	6
AHA	7070	M	6
AHA	7071	M	6
AHA	7074	M	2
AHA	7075	M	2
AHA	7080	M	6
AHA	7081	M	6
AHA	7085	J	8
AHA	7091	M	6
AHA	7092	M	6
AHA	7093	M	6
AHA	7094	M	6
AHA	7144	J	6
AHA	7145	J	6
AHA	7157	J	6
AHA	7172	F	12
AHA	7173	F	12
AHA	7174	F	12
AHA	7178	F	12
AHA	7179	F	12
AHA	7180	F	12
AHA	7182	F	12
AHA	7184	F	10
AHA	7188	J	6

PART NUMBER		GRP	PAGE
AHA	7190	I	2
AHA	7201	F	12
AHA	7212	I	2
AHA	7213	I	2
AHA	7229	I	2
AHA	7229	I	8
AHA	7230	I	2
AHA	7230	I	8
AHA	7238	I	4
AHA	7238	I	12
AHA	7239	I	4
AHA	7239	I	12
AHA	7240	I	2
AHA	7240	I	10
AHA	7241	I	2
AHA	7241	I	10
AHA	7248	I	2
AHA	7301	I	2
AHA	7304	I	2
AHA	7304	I	8
AHA	7305	I	2
AHA	7305	I	8
AHA	7350	K	10
AHA	7350	K	12
AHA	7350	K	18
AHA	7350	K	22
AHA	7359	F	10
AHA	7359	F	10
AHA	7360	F	10
AHA	7360	F	10
AHA	7361	F	10
AHA	7361	F	10
AHA	7368	K	10
AHA	7370	K	10
AHA	7371	K	10
AHA	7373	P	2
AHA	7374	P	2
AHA	7378	J	8
AHA	7379	J	8
AHA	7381	D	12
AHA	7383	D	10
AHA	7383	D	12
AHA	7384	D	12
AHA	7393	I	18
AHA	7402	J	14
AHA	7403	J	14
AHA	7404	J	8
AHA	7405	J	8
AHA	7408	J	8
AHA	7412	O	12
AHA	7413	O	12
AHA	7416	J	14
AHA	7417	J	14
AHA	7423	I	4
AHA	7423	I	12
AHA	7428	J	2
AHA	7431	J	10
AHA	7434	O	4

PART NUMBER		GRP	PAGE
AHA	7434	O	4
AHA	7435	O	4
AHA	7438	N	2
AHA	7439	N	2
AHA	7463	J	14
AHA	7464	J	14
AHA	7465	J	14
AHA	7466	J	14
AHA	7467	J	14
AHA	7468	J	14
AHA	7469	J	16
AHA	7470	J	16
AHA	7473	J	14
AHA	7474	J	16
AHA	7475	J	16
AHA	7476	J	16
AHA	7477	J	16
AHA	7478	J	16
AHA	7480	J	14
AHA	7481	J	14
AHA	7482	J	14
AHA	7483	J	14
AHA	7484	J	16
AHA	7485	J	16
AHA	7541	N	2
AHA	7543	J	16
AHA	7544	J	14
AHA	7549	B	72
AHA	7550	B	70
AHA	7551	M F	10
AHA	7551	M F	10
AHA	7554	J	14
AHA	7573	Q	30
AHA	7617	O	4
AHA	7618	O	4
AHA	7634	J	4
AHA	7635	J	4
AHA	7645	K	10
AHA	7646	K	10
AHA	7686	F	12
AHA	7687	F	12
AHA	7698	M	6
AHA	7703	J	12
AHA	7709	K	10
AHA	7709	K	12
AHA	7709	K	18
AHA	7709	K	20
AHA	7719	J	4
AHA	7720	J	4
AHA	7746	J	16
AHA	7747	J	16
AHA	7748	G	2
AHA	7750	O	2
AHA	7751	O	2
AHA	7769	H	24
AHA	7775	J	14
AHA	7776	H	32
AHA	7779	M	6

PART NUMBER		GRP	PAGE
AHA	7780	H	26
AHA	7785	K	24
AHA	7786	K	24
AHA	7787	K	24
AHA	7792	K	28
AHA	7807	F	10
AHA	7807	F	10
AHA	7813	F	10
AHA	7813	F	10
AHA	7814	K	18
AHA	7837	K	18
AHA	7838	J	4
AHA	7845	K	18
AHA	7845	K	20
AHA	7846	K	18
AHA	7846	K	20
AHA	7883	O	34
AHA	7884	O	34
AHA	7906	Q	28
AHA	7907	Q	28
AHA	7914	B	72
AHA	7955	I	4
AHA	7955	I	12
AHA	7956	I	4
AHA	7956	I	12
AHA	7959	M	2
AHA	7960	M	2
AHA	8007	M	2
AHA	8008	M	2
AHA	8014	I	8
AHA	8015	I	8
AHA	8017	I	10
AHA	8023	I	6
AHA	8024	I	6
AHA	8025	I	8
AHA	8025	I	8
AHA	8033	I	10
AHA	8034	I	10
AHA	8035	I	10
AHA	8036	I	10
AHA	8055	I	2
AHA	8055	I	10
AHA	8058	O	12
AHA	8064	K	20
AHA	8069	G	22
AHA	8071	G	4
AHA	8072	G	14
AHA	8072	G	22
AHA	8073	G	14
AHA	8073	G	22
AHA	8075	G	14
AHA	8075	G	22
AHA	8082	K	22
AHA	8083	K	20
AHA	8084	K	20
AHA	8085	K	20
AHA	8086	K	20
AHA	8087	K	20

PART NUMBER		GRP	PAGE
AHA	8090	N	8
AHA	8091	N	14
AHA	8092	N	14
AHA	8093	F	10
AHA	8097	F	12
AHA	8098	L	2
AHA	8140	O	12
AHA	8141	O	12
AHA	8145	G	14
AHA	8145	G	22
AHA	8146	G	14
AHA	8146	G	22
AHA	8161	D	10
AHA	8161	G	12
AHA	8162	O	6
AHA	8163	O	6
AHA	8185	K	16
AHA	8188	K	12
AHA	8272	Q	28
AHA	8275	N	2
AHA	8276	N	2
AHA	8277	Q	28
AHA	8278	Q	28
AHA	8284	I	12
AHA	8285	I	12
AHA	8295	K	14
AHA	8307	F	10
AHA	8308	F	10
AHA	8309	K	16
AHA	8309	O	12
AHA	8310	K	16
AHA	8310	O	12
AHA	8313	K	30
AHA	8314	K	30
AHA	8315	K	20
AHA	8317	N	16
AHA	8324	K	16
AHA	8331	N	8
AHA	8355	K	12
AHA	8355	K	20
AHA	8369	K	16
AHA	8386	B	70
AHA	8387	I	14
AHA	8390	B	72
AHA	8396	Q	6
AHA	8401	B	72
AHA	8401	I	16
AHA	8401	Q	6
AHA	8405	J	10
AHA	8406	J	10
AHA	8408	G	14
AHA	8408	G	22
AHA	8415	N	14
AHA	8416	N	14
AHA	8417	N	16
AHA	8419	D	50
AHA	8420	D	50
AHA	8421	H	30

PART NUMBER		GRP	PAGE
AHA	8421	H	30
AHA	8431	J	10
AHA	8432	J	1C
AHA	8433	J	6
AHA	8436	J	2
AHA	8437	J	2
AHA	8446	J	16
AHA	8447	J	16
AHA	8476	M	2
AHA	8479	M	4
AHA	8483	M	4
AHA	8483	M	4
AHA	8483	M	4
AHA	8484	M	6
AHA	8486	M	6
AHA	8486	M	6
AHA	8486	M	6
AHA	8491	K	12
AHA	8491	K	20
AHA	8496	E	18
AHA	8498	E	18
AHA	8501	N	16
AHA	8510	G	26
AHA	8514	G	2
AHA	8517	J	12
AHA	8518	J	2
AHA	8519	J	2
AHA	8525	H	54
AHA	8530	J	6
AHA	8531	J	8
AHA	8532	J	8
AHA	8533	J	10
AHA	8534	J	10
AHA	8551	G	26
AHA	8552	G	26
AHA	8557	M	4
AHA	8559	M	4
AHA	8560	M	4
AHA	8561	M	6
AHA	8565	N	12
AHA	8566	N	12
AHA	8570	N	4
AHA	8602	I	6
AHA	8606	N	4
AHA	8615	I	12
AHA	8674	H	24
AHA	8683	G	28
AHA	8683	H	98
AHA	8688	D	52
AHA	8692	H	26.02
AHA	8694	H	26
AHA	8696	H	82
AHA	8696	H	86
AHA	8697	H	32
AHA	8706	N	4
AHA	8713	G	2
AHA	8716	N	20
AHA	8718	E	8

PART NUMBER		GRP	PAGE
AHA	8720	E	20
AHA	8724	O	16
AHA	8726	D	2
AHA	8728	D	2
AHA	8729	M	10
AHA	8730	D	4
AHA	8731	D	4
AHA	8732	D	4
AHA	8739	D	4
AHA	8739	D	4.C6
AHA	8742	D	4
AHA	8746	K	4
AHA	8750	D	2
AHA	8752	H	40
AHA	8752	H	40
AHA	8755	H	90
AHA	8756	H	98
AHA	8758	K	26
AHA	8763	N	4
AHA	8768	N	24
AHA	8769	E	20
AHA	8777	B	72
AHA	8777	Q	6
AHA	8778	B	72
AHA	8778	Q	6
AHA	8779	B	72
AHA	8779	Q	6
AHA	8780	N	4
AHA	8782	N	8
AHA	8785	E	24
AHA	8785	F	6
AHA	8785	P	2
AHA	8860	I	12
AHA	8866	N	4
AHA	8892	P	2
AHA	8896	O	28
AHA	8897	O	28
AHA	8905	O	4
AHA	8906	O	4
AHA	8939	O	34
AHA	8950	P	2
AHA	8953	H	26.C2
AHA	8964	O	2
AHA	9028	O	10
AHA	9051	K	14
AHA	9053	F	2
AHA	9054	K	14
AHA	9061	K	14
AHA	9086	K	30
AHA	9087	K	30
AHA	9102	O	30
AHA	9153	K	26
AHA	9157	K	26
AHA	9158	K	28
AHA	9159	K	28
AHA	9160	K	30
AHA	9166	K	24
AHA	9166	K	30

PART NUMBER		GRP	PAGE
AHA	9167	O	12
AHA	9172	N	24
AHA	9173	J	6
AHA	9174	J	6
AHA	9190	K	16
AHA	9193	E	14
AHA	9194	E	18
AHA	9200	H	78
AHA	9202	H	78
AHA	9220	O	20
AHA	9221	O	20
AHA	9224	O	14
AHA	9225	O	14
AHA	9226	O	14
AHA	9228	O	16
AHA	9240	O	18
AHA	9307	B	76
AHA	9315	L	4
AHA	9316	L	4
AHA	9318	L	4
AHA	9319	L	4
AHA	9333	D	10
AHA	9338	H	76
AHA	9339	H	76
AHA	9440	I	14
AHA	9447	I	14
AHA	9447	I	20
AHA	9448	E	18
AHA	9449	L	4
AHA	9450	L	4
AHA	9451	L	4
AHA	9453	L	6
AHA	9455	L	6
AHA	9458	L	8
AHA	9459	L	8
AHA	9465	L	8
AHA	9468	L	8.02
AHA	9482	L	4
AHA	9484	H	76
AHA	9485	H	76
AHA	9486	C	12
AHA	9487	C	12
AHA	9487	C	22
AHA	9488	C	12
AHA	9524	P	2
AHA	9537	M	4
AHA	9538	M	4
AHA	9539	M	4
AHA	9541	M	6
AHA	9556	D	12
AHA	9606	D	10
AHA	9606	D	50
AHA	9607	D	10
AHA	9608	D	10
AHA	9611	H	26.02
AHA	9612	H	26
AHA	9613	H	30
AHA	9614	H	30

PART NUMBER		GRP	PAGE
AHA	9614	H	30
AHA	9633	L	6
AHA	9633	L	8
AHA	9652	D	8
AHA	9653	D	8
AHA	9658	I	14
AHA	9661	L	4
AHA	9665	K	6
AHA	9666	B	96
AHA	9666	B	96.02
AHA	9666	D	10
AHA	9668	D	8
AHA	9670	D	10
AHA	9681	M	2
AHA	9682	M	4
AHA	9684	M	2
AHA	9685	M	4
AHA	9687	M	6
AHA	9692	M	2
AHA	9694	O	12
AHA	9695	O	12
AHA	9716	K	8
AHA	9717	K	4
AHA	9718	K	4
AHA	9719	K	26
AHA	9720	N	20
AHA	9721	N	20
AHA	9722	C	12
AHA	9723	G	14
AHA	9723	G	22
AHA	9727	N	8
AHA	9728	O	18
AHA	9730	H	26.02
AHA	9763	H	26
AHA	9764	H	30
AHA	9765	H	30
AHA	9767	H	78.02
AHA	9769	H	78.02
AHA	9779	O	32
AHA	9782	N	8
AHA	9792	E	12
AHA	9793	O	6
AHA	9794	O	6
AHA	9800	K	4
AHA	9801	E	14
AHA	9802	N	6
AHA	9805	N	6
AHA	9807	N	6
AHA	9809	N	6
AHA	9812	N	6
AHA	9813	N	6
AHA	9881	P	2
AHA	9882	E	12
AHA	9915	L	4
AHA	9916	K	6
AHA	9919	K	28
AHA	9922	H	26.02
AHA	9923	H	26

PART NUMBER		GRP	PAGE
AHA	9925	L	4
AHA	9928	O	28
AHA	9931	O	6
AHA	9940	P	2
AHA	9941	D	8
AHA	9943	O	34
AHA	9944	O	34
AHA	9945	O	34
AHA	9946	O	34
AHA	9947	O	34
AHA	9952	H	30
AHA	9955	E	10
AHA	9956	E	10
AHA	9957	E	24
AHA	9958	E	24
AHA	9959	E	10
AHA	9960	E	10
AHA	9961	E	10
AHA	9962	H	26.02
AHA	9963	H	30
AHA	9965	N	6
AHA	9973	J	14
AHA	9974	J	14
AHA	9981	J	14
AHA	9982	J	14
AHA	9983	J	14
AHA	9984	J	14
AHA	9985	J	14
AHA	9986	J	16
AHA	9987	J	16
AHA	9988	J	16
AHA	9989	J	14
AHA	9990	J	14
AHA	9991	J	14
AHA	9992	J	14
AHA	9993	J	16
AHA	9994	J	16
AHB	6114	Q	16
AHB	6707	F	10
AHB	6707	F	10
AHB	6707	F	10
AHB	6707	F	10
AHB	6715	Q	12
AHB	9059	Q	14
AHB	9656	O	6
AHC	190	D	10
AHC	234	D	10
AHC	579	B	56
AHC	752	N	20
AHC	805	H	98.02
AHH	5081	F	12
AHH	5255	N	4
AHH	5258	N	2
AHH	5258	N	4
AHH	5261	K	6
AHH	5452	H	32
AHH	5514	I	16
AHH	5517	Q	30

PART NUMBER		GRP	PAGE
AHH	5518	Q	30
AHH	5519	Q	30
AHH	5593	N	24
AHH	5791	Q	22
AHH	5839	P	4
AHH	6162	Q	6
AHH	6247	G	20
AHH	6247	G	28
AHH	6267	M	4
AHH	6267	M	4
AHH	6334	H	42
AHH	6343	J	16
AHH	6417	O	12
AHH	6438	K	10
AHH	6438	K	18
AHH	6439	K	10
AHH	6439	K	12
AHH	6541	E	30
AHH	6541	Q	28
AHH	6546	E	30
AHH	6546	Q	28
AHH	6678	H	98.02
AHH	6707	Q	12
AHH	6708	D	12
AHH	6848	M	10
AHH	6848	M	10
AHH	6848	M	10
AHH	6865	B	72
AHH	6865	Q	6
AHH	6866	B	72
AHH	6866	Q	6
AHH	6939	D	10
AHH	6940	M	8
AHH	6940	M	8
AHH	6951	M	8
AHH	7010	H	36.02
AHH	7074	F	12
AHH	7108	H	32
AHH	7138	M	4
AHH	7138	M	4
AHH	7138	M	4
AHH	7138	M	4
AHH	7138	M	4
AHH	7138	M	4
AHH	7138	M	6
AHH	7138	M	6
AHH	7138	M	6
AHH	7138	M	6
AHH	7138	M	6
AHH	7209	Q	22
AHH	7355	D	10
AHH	7448	J	16
AHH	8177	L	12
AHH	8382	D	52
AHH	8382	D	56
AHH	8394	N	8
AHH	8421	Q	30
AHH	8522	Q	30

PART NUMBER	GRP	PAGE	PART NUMBER	GRP	PAGE	PART NUMBER	GRP	PAGE	PART NUMBER	GRP	PAGE	PART NUMBER	GRP	PAGE	PART NUMBER	GRP	PAGE
AHH 8522	Q	30	AHT 352	Q	30	AJJ 3323	Q	6	ARA 1215	L	2	AUA 878	D	16	AUC 1145	D	38
AHH 8561	E	18	AHT 353	Q	30	AJJ 3324	Q	6	ARA 1216	L	2	AUA 1433	D	14	AUC 1145	D	40
AHH 8589	J	8	AHT 354	Q	30	AJJ 3325	Q	4	ARA 1218	L	2	AUA 1435	D	14	AUC 1145	D	42.02
AHH 8682	H	54	AHT 355	Q	30	AJJ 3333	Q	30	ARA 1501	D	6	AUA 1435	D	16	AUC 1147	Q	20
AHH 8715	J	8	AHT 383	Q	10	AJJ 3334	Q	14	ARA 1501	D	8	AUA 1453	D	14	AUC 1151	D	20
AHH 8749	M	6	AHT 392	Q	22	AJJ 3356	Q	28	ARA 1502	D	6	AUA 1459	D	14	AUC 1151	D	22
AHH 8758	M	4	AHT 409	Q	10	AJJ 3360	Q	16	ARA 1502	D	8	AUA 1459	D	16	AUC 1151	D	26
AHH 8766	H	82	AHT 2000	Q	30	AJJ 3377	3 Q	2	ARA 1618	D	4	AUA 1468	D	14	AUC 1151	D	28
AHH 8766	H	86	AHT 4013	Q	2	AJJ 3377	23 Q	2	ARA 2069	L	2	AUA 1468	D	16	AUC 1151	D	28.02
AHH 8783	H	76	AID 4150	D	38	AJJ 3377	43 Q	2	ARA 2070	L	2	AUA 1661	D	14	AUC 1151	D	28.04
AHH 8790	D	12	AJA 5117	K	2	AJJ 3381	Q	30	ARA 2148	L	2	AUA 1661	D	16	AUC 1151	D	32
AHH 8799	O	12	AJA 5118	I	4	AJJ 3385	Q	30	ARA 2175	L	2	AUA 1662	D	14	AUC 1151	D	34
AHH 8846	M	4	AJA 5118	I	12	AJJ 4001	Q	22	ARA 2404	D	4	AUA 1662	D	16	AUC 1151	D	38
AHH 8889	H	52	AJC 8459	D	32	AJJ 4010	Q	8	ARA 2634	B	92	AUA 1863	D	14	AUC 1151	D	40
AHH 8895	H	48	AJD 1042	D	16	AJJ 4012	Q	8	ARC 90	D	52	AUA 1863	D	14	AUC 1151	D	42
AHH 8899	D	10	AJD 1042	D	18	AJJ 4015	Q	12	ARG 923	D	6	AUA 1863	D	16	AUC 1151	D	44
AHH 8920	H	48	AJD 1042	D	24	AJJ 4016	Q	30	ARG 923	D	8	AUA 1863	D	16	AUC 1151	D	46
AHH 8921	H	48	AJD 1042	D	30	AKD 4021	A Q	30	ARH 59	N	4	AUA 5059	D	16	AUC 1151	D	48
AHH 8935	J	16	AJD 1042	D	36	AKD 5007	Q	30	ARH 186	B	70	AUA 6036	D	14	AUC 1151	D	48.04
AHH 8971	N	20	AJD 1042	D	50.C4	AKD 5061	Q	30	ARH 186	Q	6	AUA 6036	D	16	AUC 1151	D	48.08
AHH 9158	F	12	AJD 1042	Q	14	AKD 5093	Q	30	ARH 250	D	4	AUB 106	D	16	AUC 1151	Q	18
AHH 9239	J	8	AJD 1042	Q	18	AKD 5098	Q	30	ARH 302	D	8	AUB 597	D	16	AUC 1151	Q	24
AHH 9295	O	32	AJD 1042	Q	26	AKD 5125	Q	30	ARH 596	L	2	AUB 613	D	14	AUC 1152	D	20
AHH 9441	O	32	AJD 1042	Q	26	AKE 5620	M O	36	ARH 672	D	6	AUB 617	D	14	AUC 1152	D	22
AHH 9658	B	96	AJD 2193	D	38	AKE 5621	M O	36	ARH 672	D	6	AUB 617	D	16	AUC 1152	D	26
AHH 9658	D	10	AJD 2193	D	40	AKE 5643	M O	36	ARH 672	D	8	AUB 651	D	16	AUC 1152	D	28
AHH 9662	D	10	AJD 2193	D	42	AKF 1446	P	2	ARO 9809	Q	6	AUB 652	D	16	AUC 1152	D	28.02
AHH 9711	O	32	AJD 3803	Z D	16	AKF 1447	P	2	ATA 4132	E	24	AUB 653	D	16	AUC 1152	D	28.04
AHH 9838	M	4	AJD 6155	Z E	6	AKF 1448	P	2	ATA 7036	F	4	AUB 656	D	16	AUC 1152	D	32
AHH 9950	D	50	AJD 7721	O	12	AKF 1449	P	2	ATA 7037	F	4	AUB 657	D	16	AUC 1152	D	34
AHT 11	Q	6	AJD 7742	K	4	AKF 1450	P	2	ATA 7039	F	4	AUB 660	D	16	AUC 1152	D	38
AHT 12	Q	6	AJD 8012	Z D	18	AKF 1451	P	2	ATA 7044	F	6	AUB 662	D	16	AUC 1152	D	40
AHT 14	Q	6	AJD 8012	Z D	24	ALA 3647	I	14	ATA 7056	F	6	AUB 663	D	14	AUC 1152	D	42.02
AHT 16	Q	30	AJD 8012	Z D	30	ALA 3647	I	20	ATA 7123	F	6	AUB 676	D	14	AUC 1152	D	44
AHT 32	Q	8	AJD 8012	Z D	36	ALA 3647	I	20	ATA 7124	F	6	AUB 676	D	16	AUC 1152	D	46
AHT 56	Q	28	AJD 8012	Z D	50.04	ALA 3647	J	2	ATA 7125	F	6	AUB 707	D	16	AUC 1152	D	48.02
AHT 57	Q	28	AJD 8012	Z J	6	ALH 1527	J	12	ATA 7126	F	6	AUB 716	D	14	AUC 1152	D	48.04
AHT 70	Q	10	AJD 8012	Z K	24	ALK 3268	L	12	ATA 7127	F	6	AUB 716	D	16	AUC 1152	D	48.08
AHT 85	Q	16	AJD 8012	Z K	30	ANZ 102	L	4	ATA 7128	F	6	AUB 758	D	14	AUC 1152	Q	20
AHT 85	Q	22	AJD 8012	Z Q	14	ARA 205	B	70	ATA 7129	F	6	AUB 759	D	16	AUC 1158	Q	18
AHT 113	Q	16	AJD 8012	Z Q	18	ARA 241	D	2	ATA 7130	F	6	AUB 794	D	16	AUC 1206	D	20
AHT 141	Q	2	AJD 8012	Z Q	26	ARA 249	L	2	ATA 7166	F	6	AUB 795	D	16	AUC 1206	D	22
AHT 143	Q	16	AJD 8012	Z Q	26	ARA 281	D	54	ATA 7225	F	6	AUB 809	D	14	AUC 1206	D	32
AHT 155	Q	16	AJD 8014	Z D	48.06	ARA 318	D	4	ATA 7232	F	6	AUB 849	D	16	AUC 1206	D	34
AHT 156	Q	16	AJD 8014	Z D	48.10	ARA 326	D	4.02	ATA 7269	F	4	AUB 6062	D	14	AUC 1206	Q	24
AHT 157	Q	16	AJD 8014	Z N	4	ARA 333	D	52	ATA 7320	G	30	AUB 6062	D	16	AUC 1215	D	20
AHT 181	Q	6	AJD 8014	Z Q	14	ARA 373	D	8	ATJ 8880	H	42	AUB 6079	D	16	AUC 1215	D	22
AHT 199	Q	16	AJD 8019	Z H	36	ARA 384	D	52	ATJ 8880	H	52	AUB 6080	D	14	AUC 1215	D	26
AHT 239	Q	22	AJD 8052	H	78	ARA 967	D	6	AU 614081	B	94.02	AUB 6080	D	16	AUC 1215	D	28
AHT 247	Q	14	AJD 8206	Z Q	20	ARA 967	D	6	AUA 573	D	16	AUB 6097	D	14	AUC 1215	D	32
AHT 265	Q	8	AJD 9012	Z M	10	ARA 969	D	8	AUA 585	D	14	AUB 6097	D	16	AUC 1215	D	34
AHT 266	Q	8	AJH 5057	H	78.02	ARA 1205	L	2	AUA 585	D	16	AUB 6106	D	14	AUC 1215	D	38
AHT 269	Q	8	AJH 5057	H	78.02	ARA 1206	L	2	AUA 692	D	14	AUC 1025	Q	14	AUC 1215	D	40
AHT 287	Q	30	AJH 5079	H	80	ARA 1207	L	2	AUA 692	D	16	AUC 1123	Q	20	AUC 1215	D	44
AHT 288	Q	2	AJJ 404	Q	30	ARA 1208	L	2	AUA 692	D	16	AUC 1145	D	20	AUC 1215	D	46
AHT 326	Q	2	AJJ 3314	Q	28	ARA 1209	L	2	AUA 699	D	14	AUC 1145	D	26	AUC 1249	D	48.04
AHT 332	Q	8	AJJ 3319	Q	10	ARA 1210	L	2	AUA 699	D	16	AUC 1145	D	28.02	AUC 1249	D	48.08
AHT 333	Q	30	AJJ 3322	Q	28	ARA 1215	L	2	AUA 878	D	14	AUC 1145	D	32	AUC 1249	Q	18

PART NUMBER		GRP	PAGE
AUC	1249	Q	18
AUC	1249	Q	24
AUC	1250	D	20
AUC	1250	D	22
AUC	1250	D	26
AUC	1250	D	28
AUC	1250	D	28.02
AUC	1250	D	28.04
AUC	1250	D	32
AUC	1250	D	34
AUC	1250	D	38
AUC	1250	D	40
AUC	1250	D	42
AUC	1250	D	44
AUC	1250	D	46
AUC	1250	D	48
AUC	1250	D	48.04
AUC	1250	D	48.08
AUC	1250	Q	18
AUC	1250	Q	24
AUC	1302	D	48.06
AUC	1302	D	48.10
AUC	1310	D	20
AUC	1310	D	22
AUC	1310	D	26
AUC	1310	D	28
AUC	1310	D	28.02
AUC	1310	D	28.04
AUC	1310	D	32
AUC	1310	D	34
AUC	1310	D	38
AUC	1310	D	40
AUC	1310	D	42.02
AUC	1310	D	44
AUC	1310	D	46
AUC	1310	D	48.02
AUC	1310	Q	24
AUC	1316	D	48.04
AUC	1317	D	20
AUC	1317	D	22
AUC	1318	D	20
AUC	1318	D	22
AUC	1318	D	26
AUC	1318	D	28
AUC	1318	D	28.02
AUC	1318	D	28.04
AUC	1318	D	32
AUC	1318	D	34
AUC	1318	D	38
AUC	1318	D	40
AUC	1318	D	42.02
AUC	1318	D	44
AUC	1318	D	46
AUC	1318	D	48.02
AUC	1318	D	48.04
AUC	1318	D	48.08
AUC	1318	Q	24
AUC	1329	D	20

PART NUMBER		GRP	PAGE
AUC	1329	D	22
AUC	1329	D	26
AUC	1329	D	28
AUC	1329	D	28.02
AUC	1329	D	28.04
AUC	1329	D	32
AUC	1329	D	34
AUC	1329	D	38
AUC	1329	D	40
AUC	1329	D	42.02
AUC	1329	D	44
AUC	1329	D	46
AUC	1329	D	48.02
AUC	1329	D	48.04
AUC	1329	D	48.08
AUC	1329	Q	24
AUC	1358	D	20
AUC	1358	D	22
AUC	1358	D	26
AUC	1358	D	28
AUC	1358	D	28.02
AUC	1358	D	28.04
AUC	1358	D	32
AUC	1358	D	34
AUC	1358	D	38
AUC	1358	D	40
AUC	1358	D	42.02
AUC	1358	D	44
AUC	1358	D	46
AUC	1358	D	48.02
AUC	1358	D	48.06
AUC	1358	D	48.10
AUC	1358	Q	18
AUC	1358	Q	24
AUC	1366	D	48.08
AUC	1371	D	22
AUC	1371	D	28
AUC	1371	D	32
AUC	1371	D	38
AUC	1375	D	22
AUC	1375	D	28
AUC	1375	D	28.04
AUC	1375	D	34
AUC	1375	D	44
AUC	1375	D	46
AUC	1375	D	48.02
AUC	1375	D	48.06
AUC	1375	Q	26
AUC	1384	Q	20
AUC	1388	Q	20
AUC	1389	Q	20
AUC	1400	D	20
AUC	1400	D	22
AUC	1400	D	26
AUC	1400	D	28
AUC	1400	D	28.02
AUC	1400	D	28.04
AUC	1400	D	32

PART NUMBER		GRP	PAGE
AUC	1400	D	34
AUC	1400	D	38
AUC	1400	D	40
AUC	1400	D	42.02
AUC	1400	D	44
AUC	1400	D	46
AUC	1400	D	48.02
AUC	1400	Q	24
AUC	1424	D	20
AUC	1424	D	22
AUC	1424	D	26
AUC	1424	D	28
AUC	1424	D	28.02
AUC	1424	D	28.04
AUC	1424	D	32
AUC	1424	D	34
AUC	1424	D	38
AUC	1424	D	40
AUC	1424	D	42.02
AUC	1424	D	44
AUC	1424	D	46
AUC	1424	D	48.02
AUC	1424	D	48.06
AUC	1424	D	48.10
AUC	1424	Q	26
AUC	1426	D	20
AUC	1426	D	22
AUC	1426	D	26
AUC	1426	D	28
AUC	1426	D	28.02
AUC	1426	D	28.04
AUC	1426	D	32
AUC	1426	D	34
AUC	1426	D	38
AUC	1426	D	40
AUC	1426	D	42.02
AUC	1426	D	44
AUC	1426	D	46
AUC	1426	D	48.02
AUC	1426	D	48.06
AUC	1426	D	48.10
AUC	1426	Q	26
AUC	1457	D	18
AUC	1457	D	24
AUC	1457	D	30
AUC	1457	D	36
AUC	1501	Q	16
AUC	1520	D	22
AUC	1520	D	28
AUC	1520	D	32
AUC	1520	D	38
AUC	1534	Q	20
AUC	1557	Q	20
AUC	1833	Q	12
AUC	1867	Q	20
AUC	1928	Q	20
AUC	2002	D	20
AUC	2002	D	22

PART NUMBER		GRP	PAGE
AUC	2002	D	22
AUC	2002	D	26
AUC	2002	D	28
AUC	2002	D	28.02
AUC	2002	D	28.04
AUC	2002	D	32
AUC	2002	D	34
AUC	2002	D	38
AUC	2002	D	40
AUC	2002	D	42
AUC	2002	D	44
AUC	2002	D	46
AUC	2002	D	48
AUC	2002	D	48.04
AUC	2002	D	48.08
AUC	2002	Q	24
AUC	2057	D	20
AUC	2057	D	22
AUC	2057	D	26
AUC	2057	D	28
AUC	2057	D	32
AUC	2057	D	34
AUC	2057	Q	18
AUC	2057	Q	24
AUC	2106	Q	18
AUC	2114	D	20
AUC	2114	D	22
AUC	2114	D	26
AUC	2114	D	28
AUC	2114	D	28.02
AUC	2114	D	28.04
AUC	2114	D	32
AUC	2114	D	34
AUC	2114	D	38
AUC	2114	D	40
AUC	2114	D	42
AUC	2114	D	44
AUC	2114	D	46
AUC	2114	D	48
AUC	2114	D	48.04
AUC	2114	D	48.08
AUC	2114	Q	18
AUC	2114	Q	24
AUC	2117	Q	18
AUC	2118	Q	18
AUC	2119	Q	18
AUC	2120	Q	18
AUC	2121	Q	18
AUC	2122	Q	18
AUC	2139	Q	20
AUC	2141	Q	12
AUC	2141	Q	20
AUC	2169	D	20
AUC	2169	D	22
AUC	2169	D	26
AUC	2169	D	28
AUC	2169	D	28.02
AUC	2169	D	28.04

PART NUMBER		GRP	PAGE
AUC	2175	D	20
AUC	2175	D	22
AUC	2175	D	26
AUC	2175	D	28
AUC	2175	D	28.02
AUC	2175	D	28.04
AUC	2175	D	32
AUC	2175	D	34
AUC	2175	D	38
AUC	2175	D	40
AUC	2175	D	42.02
AUC	2175	D	44
AUC	2175	D	46
AUC	2175	D	48.02
AUC	2175	D	48.04
AUC	2175	D	48.04
AUC	2175	D	48.08
AUC	2175	D	48.08
AUC	2175	Q	18
AUC	2175	Q	24
AUC	2175	Q	24
AUC	2199	Q	18
AUC	2381	Q	18
AUC	2381	Q	18
AUC	2432	D	48.06
AUC	2439	Q	26
AUC	2451	D	20
AUC	2451	D	22
AUC	2451	D	26
AUC	2451	D	28
AUC	2451	D	28.02
AUC	2451	D	28.04
AUC	2451	D	32
AUC	2451	D	34
AUC	2451	D	38
AUC	2451	D	40
AUC	2451	D	42.02
AUC	2451	D	44
AUC	2451	D	46
AUC	2451	D	48.02
AUC	2451	D	48.06
AUC	2451	D	48.10
AUC	2451	Q	26
AUC	2521	Q	18
AUC	2625	D	48.06
AUC	2625	D	48.10
AUC	2625	Q	26
AUC	2669	Q	14
AUC	2676	D	48.02
AUC	2698	Q	12
AUC	2698	Q	20
AUC	3116	Q	18
AUC	3200	Q	20
AUC	3212	Q	18
AUC	3230	Q	18
AUC	3231	Q	18
AUC	3232	Q	18
AUC	3233	Q	18

PART NUMBER		GRP	PAGE
AUC	3280	Q	24
AUC	3288	D	46
AUC	3288	D	48.02
AUC	3496	Q	18
AUC	3513	Q	18
AUC	4045	Q	18
AUC	4334	Q	14
AUC	4387	D	48.04
AUC	4387	D	48.08
AUC	4387	Q	24
AUC	4454	Q	14
AUC	4454	Q	16
AUC	4587	D	20
AUC	4587	D	22
AUC	4587	D	26
AUC	4587	D	28
AUC	4587	D	28.02
AUC	4587	D	28.04
AUC	4587	D	32
AUC	4587	D	34
AUC	4587	D	38
AUC	4587	D	40
AUC	4587	D	42
AUC	4587	D	44
AUC	4587	D	46
AUC	4587	D	48
AUC	4587	Q	18
AUC	4612	Q	14
AUC	4667	Q	18
AUC	4719	Q	18
AUC	4900	D	20
AUC	4900	D	22
AUC	4900	D	26
AUC	4900	D	28
AUC	4900	D	32
AUC	4900	D	34
AUC	4900	D	38
AUC	4900	D	40
AUC	4900	D	42
AUC	4900	D	44
AUC	4900	D	46
AUC	4900	D	48
AUC	4900	D	48.04
AUC	4900	D	48.08
AUC	4900	Q	18
AUC	4900	Q	24
AUC	5004	Q	18
AUC	5009	Q	18
AUC	5032	D	20
AUC	5032	D	22
AUC	5032	D	26
AUC	5032	D	28
AUC	5032	D	32
AUC	5032	D	34
AUC	5032	D	38
AUC	5032	D	44
AUC	5032	Q	26
AUC	5047	D	14

PART NUMBER	GRP	PAGE
AUC 5047	D	14
AUC 5047	D	16
AUC 5047	Q	14
AUC 5047	Q	14
AUC 5058	Q	14
AUC 5156	D	20
AUC 5156	D	22
AUC 5156	D	26
AUC 5156	D	28
AUC 5156	D	28.02
AUC 5156	D	28.04
AUC 5156	D	32
AUC 5156	D	34
AUC 5156	D	38
AUC 5156	D	40
AUC 5156	D	42
AUC 5156	D	44
AUC 5156	D	46
AUC 5156	D	48
AUC 8103	D	28.02
AUC 8103	D	28.04
AUC 8114	D	20
AUC 8114	D	22
AUC 8114	D	26
AUC 8114	D	28
AUC 8114	D	32
AUC 8114	D	34
AUC 8114	D	38
AUC 8114	D	40
AUC 8114	D	42
AUC 8114	D	44
AUC 8114	D	46
AUC 8114	D	48
AUC 8114	D	48.04
AUC 8114	D	48.08
AUC 8114	Q	24
AUC 8182	Q	18
AUC 8209	Q	18
AUC 8396	D	18
AUC 8396	D	24
AUC 8396	D	30
AUC 8396	D	36
AUC 8396	D	50.04
AUC 8396	Q	18
AUC 8396	Q	26
AUC 8456	D	20
AUC 8456	D	26
AUC 8456	D	34
AUC 8456	D	44
AUC 8459	D	20
AUC 8459	D	22
AUC 8459	D	26
AUC 8459	D	28
AUC 8459	D	28.02
AUC 8459	D	28.04
AUC 8459	D	34
AUC 8459	D	38
AUC 8459	D	40
AUC 8459	D	42.02
AUC 8459	D	44
AUC 8459	D	46
AUC 8459	D	48.02
AUC 8459	D	48.04
AUC 8459	D	48.08
AUC 8459	Q	24
AUC 8460	D	20
AUC 8460	D	22
AUC 8460	D	26
AUC 8460	D	28
AUC 8460	Q	24
AUC 8461	D	20
AUC 8461	D	22
AUC 8461	D	26
AUC 8461	D	28
AUC 8461	D	28.02
AUC 8461	D	28.04
AUC 8461	D	42
AUC 8461	D	48
AUC 8461	D	48.04
AUC 8461	D	48.08
AUC 8461	Q	24
AUC 8462	D	20
AUC 8462	D	26
AUC 8462	D	28.02
AUC 8462	D	32
AUC 8462	D	38
AUC 8462	D	42.02
AUC 8462	D	48.10
AUC 8462	Q	26
AUC 8463	D	20
AUC 8463	D	26
AUC 8463	D	34
AUC 8463	D	44
AUC 8464	D	20
AUC 8464	D	22
AUC 8464	D	26
AUC 8464	D	28
AUC 8464	D	28.02
AUC 8464	D	28.04
AUC 8464	D	32
AUC 8464	D	34
AUC 8464	D	38
AUC 8464	D	40
AUC 8464	D	42
AUC 8464	D	44
AUC 8464	D	46
AUC 8464	D	48
AUC 8467	D	40
AUC 8469	D	20
AUC 8469	D	22
AUC 8469	D	26
AUC 8469	D	28
AUC 8469	D	28.02
AUC 8469	D	28.04
AUC 8469	D	32
AUC 8469	D	34
AUC 8469	D	38
AUC 8469	D	40
AUC 8469	D	42.02
AUC 8469	D	44
AUC 8469	D	46
AUC 8469	D	48.02
AUC 8473	D	20
AUC 8473	D	22
AUC 8473	D	26
AUC 8473	D	28
AUC 8473	D	28.02
AUC 8473	D	28.04
AUC 8473	D	32
AUC 8473	D	34
AUC 8473	D	38
AUC 8473	D	40
AUC 8473	D	42.02
AUC 8473	D	44
AUC 8473	D	46
AUC 8473	D	48.02
AUC 8473	D	48.06
AUC 8473	D	48.10
AUC 8473	Q	26
AUC 8474	D	20
AUC 8474	D	22
AUC 8474	D	26
AUC 8474	D	28
AUC 8474	D	32
AUC 8474	D	34
AUC 8474	D	38
AUC 8474	D	44
AUC 8478	D	20
AUC 8478	D	22
AUC 8478	D	26
AUC 8478	D	28
AUC 8478	D	48.04
AUC 8478	D	48.08
AUC 8478	Q	24
AUC 8483	D	20
AUC 8483	D	22
AUC 8483	D	26
AUC 8483	D	28.02
AUC 8483	D	32
AUC 8483	D	34
AUC 8483	D	38
AUC 8483	D	40
AUC 8483	D	42.02
AUC 8483	D	44
AUC 8483	D	46
AUC 8483	D	48.02
AUC 8483	D	48.06
AUC 8483	D	48.10
AUC 8483	Q	26
AUC 8484	D	28
AUC 8484	D	28.04
AUC 8494	Q	24
AUC 8700	D	20
AUC 8713	D	22
AUC 8713	D	22
AUC 9268	D	20
AUC 9269	D	22
AUC 9353	Q	18
AUC 9354	Q	18
AUC 9460	D	32
AUC 9461	D	34
AUD 136	D	18
AUD 194	Q	14
AUD 266	D	30
AUD 289	D	46
AUD 289	D	48.02
AUD 327	D	24
AUD 328	D	36
AUD 404	D	36
AUD 416	Q	24
AUD 502	D	36
AUD 1005	Q	18
AUD 1149	D	32
AUD 1211	D	20
AUD 1211	D	22
AUD 1211	D	26
AUD 1211	D	28
AUD 1242	D	20
AUD 1242	D	22
AUD 1242	D	26
AUD 1242	D	28
AUD 1242	D	32
AUD 1478	D	20
AUD 1478	D	22
AUD 1478	D	26
AUD 1478	D	28
AUD 1478	D	32
AUD 1478	D	34
AUD 2049	Q	26
AUD 2050	Q	26
AUD 2076	Q	26
AUD 2101	D	22
AUD 2101	D	28
AUD 2101	D	28.04
AUD 2101	D	34
AUD 2101	D	44
AUD 2101	D	46
AUD 2101	D	48.02
AUD 2120	D	22
AUD 2129	D	20
AUD 2129	D	26
AUD 2129	D	28
AUD 2129	D	28.02
AUD 2129	D	28.04
AUD 2129	D	32
AUD 2129	D	34
AUD 2129	D	38
AUD 2129	D	40
AUD 2129	D	42
AUD 2129	D	44
AUD 2129	D	46
AUD 2129	D	48
AUD 2129	D	48.04
AUD 2129	D	48.08
AUD 2129	Q	24
AUD 2140	D	48.04
AUD 2140	D	48.08
AUD 2163	Q	26
AUD 2164	Q	26
AUD 2193	D	20
AUD 2193	D	22
AUD 2193	D	26
AUD 2193	D	28
AUD 2193	D	28.02
AUD 2193	D	28.04
AUD 2193	D	32
AUD 2193	D	34
AUD 2193	D	44
AUD 2193	D	46
AUD 2193	D	48
AUD 2193	D	48.04
AUD 2193	D	48.08
AUD 2193	Q	24
AUD 2194	D	20
AUD 2194	D	22
AUD 2194	D	26
AUD 2194	D	28
AUD 2194	D	28.02
AUD 2194	D	28.04
AUD 2194	D	32
AUD 2194	D	34
AUD 2194	D	38
AUD 2194	D	40
AUD 2194	D	42
AUD 2194	D	44
AUD 2194	D	46
AUD 2194	D	48
AUD 2194	D	48.04
AUD 2194	D	48.08
AUD 2194	Q	24
AUD 2195	D	20
AUD 2195	D	22
AUD 2195	D	26
AUD 2195	D	28
AUD 2195	D	28.02
AUD 2195	D	28.04
AUD 2195	D	32
AUD 2195	D	34
AUD 2195	D	38
AUD 2195	D	40
AUD 2195	D	42
AUD 2195	D	44
AUD 2195	D	46
AUD 2195	D	48
AUD 2195	D	48.04
AUD 2195	D	48.08
AUD 2195	Q	24
AUD 2283	Q	20
AUD 2284	Q	20
AUD 2285	Q	20
AUD 2429	D	28.02
AUD 2429	D	28.04
AUD 2429	D	40
AUD 2429	D	42.02
AUD 2429	D	46
AUD 2429	D	48.02
AUD 2429	D	48.06
AUD 2429	D	48.10
AUD 2430	D	28.02
AUD 2430	D	28.04
AUD 2430	D	40
AUD 2430	D	42.02
AUD 2430	D	46
AUD 2430	D	48.02
AUD 2430	D	48.06
AUD 2430	D	48.10
AUD 2431	D	28.02
AUD 2431	D	40
AUD 2431	D	42.02
AUD 2431	D	48.10
AUD 2432	D	28.04
AUD 2432	D	46
AUD 2432	D	48.02
AUD 2433	D	28.02
AUD 2433	D	28.04
AUD 2433	D	40
AUD 2433	D	42.02
AUD 2433	D	46
AUD 2433	D	48.02
AUD 2433	D	48.06
AUD 2433	D	48.10
AUD 2500	Q	18
AUD 2676	D	22
AUD 2676	D	28
AUD 2676	D	28.04
AUD 2676	D	34
AUD 2676	D	44
AUD 2676	D	46
AUD 2676	Q	24
AUD 2677	D	20
AUD 2677	D	26
AUD 2677	D	28.02
AUD 2677	D	32
AUD 2677	D	38
AUD 2677	D	40
AUD 2677	D	42.02
AUD 2677	Q	24
AUD 2787	Q	24
AUD 2788	Q	24
AUD 2891	D	20
AUD 2891	D	22
AUD 2891	D	26
AUD 2891	D	28
AUD 2891	D	28.02
AUD 2891	D	28.04
AUD 2891	D	32
AUD 2891	D	34
AUD 2891	D	38

PART NUMBER	GRP	PAGE
AUD 2891	D	38
AUD 2891	D	40
AUD 2891	D	42.02
AUD 2891	D	44
AUD 2987	D	32
AUD 2987	D	34
AUD 2987	D	38
AUD 2987	D	44
AUD 3011	D	32
AUD 3011	D	34
AUD 3011	D	38
AUD 3011	D	40
AUD 3011	D	42.02
AUD 3011	D	44
AUD 3011	D	46
AUD 3011	D	48.02
AUD 3017	D	48.04
AUD 3017	D	48.08
AUD 3017	Q	24
AUD 3101	D	32
AUD 3101	D	34
AUD 3193	D	32
AUD 3193	D	34
AUD 3193	D	38
AUD 3193	D	40
AUD 3193	D	44
AUD 3193	D	46
AUD 3235	D	32
AUD 3235	D	34
AUD 3235	D	38
AUD 3235	D	40
AUD 3235	D	42
AUD 3235	D	44
AUD 3235	D	46
AUD 3235	D	48
AUD 3287	D	40
AUD 3287	D	42.02
AUD 3306	D	28.02
AUD 3306	D	28.04
AUD 3306	D	38
AUD 3306	D	40
AUD 3306	D	42.02
AUD 3306	D	44
AUD 3306	D	46
AUD 3306	D	48.02
AUD 3306	D	48.04
AUD 3306	D	48.08
AUD 3308	D	42
AUD 3308	D	48
AUD 3323	D	26
AUD 3323	D	28
AUD 3323	D	28.02
AUD 3323	D	28.04
AUD 3323	D	38
AUD 3323	D	40
AUD 3323	D	42.02
AUD 3323	D	44
AUD 3323	D	46
AUD 3323	D	48.02
AUD 3323	D	48.06
AUD 3323	D	48.10
AUD 3410	D	28.02
AUD 3410	D	28.04
AUD 3410	D	38
AUD 3410	D	40
AUD 3410	D	42
AUD 3410	D	44
AUD 3410	D	46
AUD 3410	D	48
AUD 3414	D	48.04
AUD 3414	D	48.08
AUD 3836	D	38
AUD 3836	D	40
AUD 3836	D	42.02
AUD 3836	D	44
AUD 3836	D	46
AUD 3836	D	48.02
AUD 4007	D	38
AUD 4007	D	40
AUD 4007	D	44
AUD 4007	D	46
AUD 4150	D	20
AUD 4150	D	22
AUD 4150	D	26
AUD 4150	D	28
AUD 4150	D	28.02
AUD 4150	D	28.04
AUD 4150	D	32
AUD 4150	D	34
AUD 4150	D	40
AUD 4150	D	42
AUD 4150	D	44
AUD 4150	D	46
AUD 4150	D	48
AUD 4150	D	48.04
AUD 4150	D	48.08
AUD 4250	D	28.02
AUD 4250	D	28.04
AUD 4252	D	48.04
AUD 4252	D	48.08
AUD 4288	D	28.02
AUD 4288	D	28.04
AUD 4288	D	48.04
AUD 4288	D	48.08
AUD 4410	D	28.02
AUD 4411	D	28.04
AUD 4860	D	48.10
AUD 4861	D	48.06
AUD 4862	D	48.06
AUD 4863	D	48.10
AUD 4886	D	48.06
AUD 4886	D	48.10
AUD 4939	D	48.06
AUD 4939	D	48.10
AUD 7047	Q	18
AUD 9004	D	20
AUD 9004	D	26
AUD 9004	D	32
AUD 9004	D	38
AUD 9005	D	22
AUD 9005	D	28
AUD 9005	D	34
AUD 9005	D	44
AUD 9024	Q	18
AUD 9095	D	28.02
AUD 9095	D	28.04
AUD 9095	D	42.02
AUD 9095	D	46.02
AUD 9095	D	48.04
AUD 9095	D	48.08
AUD 9096	D	20
AUD 9096	D	22
AUD 9096	D	26
AUD 9096	D	28
AUD 9096	D	32
AUD 9096	D	34
AUD 9096	D	38
AUD 9096	D	40
AUD 9096	D	44
AUD 9096	D	46
AUD 9096	Q	20
AUD 9141	D	20
AUD 9141	D	26
AUD 9141	D	28.02
AUD 9141	D	32
AUD 9141	D	38
AUD 9141	D	42
AUD 9142	D	22
AUD 9142	D	28
AUD 9142	D	28.04
AUD 9142	D	44
AUD 9142	D	46
AUD 9142	D	48
AUD 9148	Q	24
AUD 9149	Q	24
AUD 9181	D	20
AUD 9181	D	22
AUD 9181	D	26
AUD 9181	D	28
AUD 9181	D	32
AUD 9181	D	34
AUD 9187	Q	24
AUD 9203	D	22
AUD 9203	D	28
AUD 9203	D	28.04
AUD 9203	D	34
AUD 9203	D	44
AUD 9203	Q	24
AUD 9207	D	40
AUD 9207	D	42.02
AUD 9254	D	48.08
AUD 9255	D	20
AUD 9255	D	26
AUD 9255	D	28.02
AUD 9255	D	28.02
AUD 9255	D	32
AUD 9255	D	38
AUD 9257	D	48.04
AUD 9258	Q	24
AUD 9450	D	48.08
AUD 9451	D	48.04
AUD 9492	Q	26
AUD 9493	Q	26
AUD 9544	Q	24
AUD 9550	Q	24
AUD 9585	Q	24
AUD 9651	D	46
AUD 9651	D	48.02
AUD 9860	D	40
AUD 9861	D	34
AUD 9870	D	32
AUD 9871	D	34
AUD 9876	D	32
AUD 9876	D	34
AUD 9876	D	38
AUD 9876	D	40
AUD 9876	D	44
AUD 9876	D	46
AUD 9904	D	20
AUD 9904	D	22
AUD 9904	D	26
AUD 9904	D	28
AUD 9904	D	28.02
AUD 9904	D	28.04
AUD 9904	D	32
AUD 9904	D	34
AUD 9904	D	38
AUD 9904	D	40
AUD 9904	D	42.02
AUD 9904	D	44
AUD 9904	D	46
AUD 9904	D	48.02
AUD 9904	D	48.04
AUD 9904	D	48.08
AUD 9904	Q	24
AUD 9988	D	48.04
AUD 9988	D	48.08
AUD 9990	D	42
AUD 9995	D	28
AUD 9995	D	28.04
AUD 9998	D	28.02
AUD 9998	D	28.04
AUD 9998	D	38
AUD 9998	D	40
AUD 9998	D	42
AUD 9998	D	44
AUD 9998	D	46
AUD 9998	D	48
AUE 34	D	50.04
AUE 180	Q	26
AUE 399	D	14
AUE 496	D	36
AUE 586	D	18
AUE 586	D	24
AUE 586	D	30
AUE 586	D	36
AUE 586	D	50.04
AUE 586	Q	26
AUE 587	D	18
AUE 587	D	24
AUE 587	D	30
AUE 587	D	36
AUE 587	D	50.04
AUE 587	Q	26
AUE 685	D	36
AUF 214	D	14
AUF 305	D	10
AUF 305	D	16
AUF 400	Q	12
AWZ 104	G	30
1B 2697	Q	14
1B 2802	H	32
1B 2925	B	14
1B 2925	B	40
1B 3498	G	16
1B 3664	B	24
1B 3664	B	24
1B 3664	B	42
1B 3664	B	62
1B 3664	B	64
1B 7356	E	30
1B 7356	Q	28
1B 7356	Q	28
1B 8806	B	22
1B 8806	B	56
1B 8806	H	20.02
1B 8995	P	4
4B 3479	J	2
4B 8644	K	2
4B 8646	K	2
4B 8646	K	2
4B 8768	K	2
4B 8769	K	2
4B 9713	N	8
4B 9713	N	24
11B 2037	H	98
11B 5721	L	6
11B 5721	L	8
12B 2062	H	8
12B 2062	H	8
12B 2095	B	96.04
12B 2095	D	4.04
12B 2492	D	50.06
14B 1730	K	10
14B 2685	I	16
14B 2685	L	12
14B 7889	K	16
14B 7889	M	8
14B 7889	M	8
22B 65	C	14
22B 612	C	10
22B 614	C	10
24B 4057	O	30
BCA 4002	Q	30
BCA 4294	H	36
BCA 4308	H	34
BCA 4370	G	12
BCA 4501	H	36
BCA 4568	H	76
BCA 4590	I	20
BCA 4780	H	92
BCA 4780	H	92
BCA 4964	G	16
BDA 500	I	14
BFS 323	H	78.02
BFS 355	H	58
BFS 415	H	58
BH 505041	D	50.06
BH 505131	B	94
BH 505131	B	94.02
BH 604121	B	92
BH 604131	B	46
BH 604201	D	4.02
BH 605101	B	102
BH 605101	C	14
BH 605111	B	52
BH 605111	C	14
BH 605141	B	22
BH 605141	B	56
BH 605151	D	56
BH 605151	D	56
BH 605151	H	20.02
BH 605161	B	52
BH 606071	H	22.02
BH 606121	D	56
BH 606141	H	22
BH 606161	L	6
BH 606161	L	8.02
BH 606261	L	6
BH 606281	B	102
BHA 4082	I	20
BHA 4082	K	6
BHA 4082	N	2
BHA 4151	H	80
BHA 4153	H	78
BHA 4163	P	2
BHA 4175	H	70
BHA 4176	H	70
BHA 4204	H	68
BHA 4205	N	16
BHA 4253	P	2
BHA 4254	P	2
BHA 4257	H	32
BHA 4259	P	2
BHA 4339	O	30
BHA 4361	D	12
BHA 4361	M	10
BHA 4380	H	92

PART NUMBER		GRP	PAGE
BHA	4380	H	92
BHA	4381	H	94
BHA	4436	H	88
BHA	4437	H	88
BHA	4441	H	54
BHA	4442	H	54
BHA	4448	Q	10
BHA	4460	H	28
BHA	4461	K	10
BHA	4473	H	32
BHA	4473	H	32
BHA	4487	H	66
BHA	4488	H	70
BHA	4494	H	78
BHA	4510	M	10
BHA	4514	H	54
BHA	4515	H	54
BHA	4519	Q	10
BHA	4536	I	16
BHA	4552	H	28
BHA	4558	K	6
BHA	4558	K	6
BHA	4586	H	96
BHA	4587	H	96
BHA	4602	H	88
BHA	4615	G	6
BHA	4621	H	74
BHA	4627	H	38
BHA	4628	H	38
BHA	4631	K	16
BHA	4634	H	88
BHA	4635	H	88
BHA	4639	H	92
BHA	4645	K	28
BHA	4645	K	30
BHA	4645	M	4
BHA	4652	H	88
BHA	4653	H	88
BHA	4660	G	16
BHA	4661	G	16
BHA	4666	Q	30
BHA	4675	G	20
BHA	4675	G	28
BHA	4685	H	94
BHA	4689	H	88
BHA	4690	H	92
BHA	4696	H	44
BHA	4706	G	26
BHA	4706	G	26.02
BHA	4710	H	92
BHA	4711	D	6
BHA	4711	D	8
BHA	4715	E	20
BHA	4732	H	46
BHA	4735	M	8
BHA	4736	H	94
BHA	4736	H	94
BHA	4742	H	46

PART NUMBER		GRP	PAGE
BHA	4744	N	8
BHA	4745	N	14
BHA	4748	H	68
BHA	4752	D	12
BHA	4765	H	52
BHA	4771	H	88
BHA	4774	H	82
BHA	4774	H	86
BHA	4776	H	84
BHA	4778	H	84
BHA	4780	H	42
BHA	4780	H	42
BHA	4780	H	50
BHA	4780	H	52
BHA	4783	M	8
BHA	4790	B	76
BHA	4790	H	82
BHA	4790	H	86
BHA	4792	N	20
BHA	4792	N	20
BHA	4794	H	88
BHA	4801	M	8
BHA	4802	H	50
BHA	4803	H	50
BHA	4804	H	52
BHA	4805	H	46
BHA	4823	N	4
BHA	4824	H	96
BHA	4831	H	46
BHA	4831	H	46
BHA	4832	H	48
BHA	4832	H	48
BHA	4832	H	48
BHA	4843	H	76
BHA	4844	H	88
BHA	4845	H	88
BHA	4846	H	88
BHA	4863	H	88
BHA	4893	H	84
BHA	4893	H	86
BHA	4894	H	84
BHA	4895	H	38
BHA	4896	H	38
BHA	4900	H	96
BHA	4900	H	96
BHA	4902	H	72
BHA	4905	H	68
BHA	4919	M	10
BHA	4920	M	10
BHA	4929	H	88
BHA	4931	H	96
BHA	4933	H	46
BHA	4948	H	40
BHA	4960	M	8
BHA	4963	M	4
BHA	4964	P	4
BHA	4968	H	76
BHA	4969	H	76

PART NUMBER		GRP	PAGE
BHA	4972	H	76
BHA	4973	H	72
BHA	4974	H	50
BHA	4979	E	16
BHA	4979	H	54
BHA	4985	O	32
BHA	4990	H	46
BHA	4991	L	10
BHA	4992	H	50
BHA	4992	H	50
BHA	4993	H	48
BHA	4993	H	48
BHA	4993	H	48
BHA	4993	H	48
BHA	5008	L	4
BHA	5009	K	30
BHA	5010	E	16
BHA	5010	H	54
BHA	5040	H	78.02
BHA	5041	E	16
BHA	5041	E	18
BHA	5041	H	54
BHA	5042	E	16
BHA	5042	E	18
BHA	5042	H	54
BHA	5043	E	16
BHA	5043	E	18
BHA	5043	H	54
BHA	5050	E	20
BHA	5053	E	16
BHA	5053	H	54
BHA	5056	E	20
BHA	5058	H	40
BHA	5058	H	50
BHA	5062	H	32
BHA	5063	H	50
BHA	5070	E	20
BHA	5094	H	88
BHA	5095	H	92
BHA	5097	O	28
BHA	5102	N	4
BHA	5103	N	6
BHA	5109	H	36
BHA	5111	H	36
BHA	5112	H	36
BHA	5122	H	92
BHA	5123	H	92
BHA	5124	H	50
BHA	5125	H	50
BHA	5125	H	92
BHA	5132	G	24
BHA	5135	E	16
BHA	5135	E	18
BHA	5135	H	54
BHA	5137	H	52
BHA	5138	H	78.02
BHA	5140	O	28
BHA	5141	E	10

PART NUMBER		GRP	PAGE
BHA	5141	E	10
BHA	5146	M	10
BHA	5149	H	46
BHA	5150	H	46
BHA	5153	H	48
BHA	5153	H	48
BHA	5166	H	88
BHA	5167	H	74
BHA	5167	H	74
BHA	5183	H	46
BHA	5184	H	46
BHA	5185	H	46
BHA	5191	H	46
BHA	5192	H	46
BHA	5193	H	46
BHA	5197	H	98.02
BHA	5207	H	84
BHA	5207	H	86
BHA	5208	H	84
BHA	5221	H	92
BHA	5222	H	92
BHA	5232	M	10
BHA	5239	D	4.04
BHA	5260	H	72
BHA	5262	H	74
BHA	5267	H	36
BHA	5274	O	28
BHA	5277	H	88
BHA	5292	E	20
BHA	5294	E	20
BHA	5303	H	78
BHA	5310	H	50
BHA	5315	H	56.02
BHA	5318	H	66
BHA	5320	H	68
BHA	5329	P	4
BHA	5339	H	88
BHA	5341	H	88
BHA	5342	H	94
BHA	5357	G	2
BHA	5358	G	2
BHA	5367	H	54
BHA	5368	H	54
BHA	5370	H	90
BHA	5371	H	90
BHA	5372	H	90
BHA	5373	H	90
BHA	5375	G	10
BHA	5376	G	10
BHA	5414	P	4
BHH	102	B	96.02
BHH	102	D	10
BHH	119	E	14
BHH	119	E	18
BHH	178	D	8
BHH	178	D	8
BHH	185	B	96
BHH	185	D	10

PART NUMBER		GRP	PAGE
BHH	185	D	10
BHH	185	D	10
BHH	196	D	8
BHH	197	D	8
BHH	254	H	40
BHH	291	E	14
BHH	291	E	18
BHH	342	J	8
BHH	364	N	4
BHH	402	H	50
BHH	649	H	98.02
BHH	786	E	14
BHH	786	E	18
BHH	879	B	76
BHH	989	F	12
BHH	1012	N	20
BHH	1085	H	48
BHH	1085	H	48
BHH	1139	K	22
BHH	1163	D	50.02
BHH	1281	H	98.02
BHH	1301	H	40
BHH	1307	E	14
BHH	1307	E	18
BHH	1395	M	8
BHH	1396	M	8
BHH	1540	B	76
BHH	1625	D	8
BHH	1626	D	8
BHH	1642	L	14
BHH	1663	D	8
BHH	1883	D	8
BHM	538	L	10.02
BHM	539	L	10.02
BHM	558	O	34
BHM	1056	B	80
BHM	1056 10	B	80
BHM	1056 20	B	80
BHM	1056 30	B	80
BHM	1057	B	80
BHM	1057 10	B	80
BHM	1057 20	B	80
BHM	1057 30	B	80
BHM	1058	B	80
BHM	1058	B	80
BHM	1058 20	B	80
BHM	1058 20	B	80
BHM	1059	B	80
BHM	1059 20	B	80
BHM	1060	B	80
BHM	1060 20	B	80
BHM	1066	B	80
BHM	1066	B	80
BHM	1066 20	B	80
BHM	1066 20	B	80
BHM	1075	D	48.12
BHM	1076	D	48.12
BHM	1077	D	48.12

PART NUMBER		GRP	PAGE
BHM	1078	D	48.12
BHM	1080	D	48.12
BHM	1081	D	48.12
BHM	5003	N C	16
BHM	7054	F	8
BHM	7055	C	14
BHM	7058	H	56
BHM	7058	H	56.02
BHM	7058	H	60
BHM	7058	H	62
BHM	7058	H	64
BHM	7061	G	8
BHM	7090	H	44
BHM	7125	G	16
BHN	102	B	96.04
BLA	768	C	12
BLS	107	C	4
BLS	107	C	6
BLS	107	Q	10.02
BLS	108	C	16
BLS	108	C	18
BLS	110	C	2
BLS	110	C	10
BMK	385	H	32
BMK	385	H	98
BMK	449	H	28
BMK	924	E	8
BMK	924	N	12
BMK	1241	H	18
BMK	1398	H	28
BMK	1398	H	30
BMK	1409	H	28
BMK	1727	H	36.02
BMK	1727	H	48
BMK	1989	H	6
BMK	1989	H	10
BMK	2259	E	12
BMK	2259	E	12
BMK	2435	H	56
BMK	2435	H	56
BMK	2435	H	56.02
BMK	2435	H	56.02
BMK	2435	H	60
BMK	2435	H	62
BMK	2435	H	64
BNN	105	B	24
BNN	105	B	62
BNN	105	D	52
BRA	960	D	6
BRA	960	D	8
BRT	2805	D	12
BTA	339	E	24
BTA	370	E	28
BTA	383	E	28
BTA	444	E	28.02
BTA	469	E	28
BTA	472	E	28
BTA	473	E	28

PART NUMBER		GRP	PAGE
BTA	473	E	28
BTA	490	F	6
BTA	492	F	6
BTA	493	F	8
BTA	494	G	30
BTA	495	G	30
BTA	497	G	30
BTA	498	G	30
BTA	532	F	6
BTA	535	Q	10.02
BTA	539	F	6
BTA	539	Q	10.02
BTA	549	F	4
BTA	549	Q	10.02
BTA	550	F	4
BTA	566	F	8
BTA	567	F	8
BTA	606	E	22
BTA	648	E	24
BTA	649	E	24
BTA	652	E	28
BTA	653	E	28
BTA	686	E	24
BTA	687	E	24
BTA	688	F	6
BTA	689	F	6
BTA	694	F	4
BTA	695	F	4
BTA	744	E	22
BTA	745	E	22
BTA	789	E	28.02
BTA	792	E	22
BTA	793	E	22
BTA	806	F	6
BTA	807	F	6
BTA	816	Q	10.02
BTA	939	Q	10.02
BTA	940	Q	10.02
BTA	941	E	4
BTA	942	E	4
BTA	1096	E	2
BTA	1097	E	2
BTA	1222	F	4
BTA	1223	F	6
BTA	1223	Q	10.02
BTA	1226	Q	10.02
BTA	1254	E	24
BTA	9008	E	6
BTB	440	F	6
BTC	114	E	28.02
BTC	392	E	24
5C	2436	B	12
5C	2436	B	38
5C	2436	Q	4
C	5574	H	80
C	5574	H	82
C	5574	H	86
C	16062	G	20

PART NUMBER		GRP	PAGE
C	37430	D	4.04
CA	600254	D	4.04
CAM	151	B	2
CAM	151	B	26
CCN	116	C	16
CCN	116	C	18
CCN	210	B	4
CCN	216	G	8
CFP	625	I	16
CHA	1	N	20
CHA	4	O	28
CHA	5	O	28
CHA	23	O	28
CHA	24	O	28
CHA	28	O	34
CHA	38	O	34
CHA	42	L	6.02
CHA	43	L	6.02
CHA	46	H	26
CHA	54	N	6
CHA	55	N	6
CHA	59	N	4
CHA	64	O	12
CHA	65	O	12
CHA	69	C	12
CHA	70	K	26
CHA	86	K	12
CHA	93	K	16
CHA	96	O	28
CHA	97	O	28
CHA	98	O	28
CHA	111	N	20
CHA	119	K	26
CHA	121	K	26
CHA	123	K	28
CHA	125	K	28
CHA	127	K	30
CHA	128	K	16
CHA	129	E	26
CHA	130	O	6
CHA	131	O	6
CHA	142	H	26.02
CHA	149	K	8
CHA	172	L	8.02
CHA	176	M	8
CHA	176	M	8
CHA	182	L	6.02
CHA	183	L	6.02
CHA	184	L	8
CHA	185	L	8.02
CHA	187	L	6
CHA	187	L	8
CHA	188	L	6
CHA	188	L	8
CHA	190	L	6.02
CHA	191	L	6.02
CHA	192	L	6.02
CHA	201	L	6

PART NUMBER		GRP	PAGE
CHA	203	L	8
CHA	204	L	8
CHA	207	L	6
CHA	207	L	8
CHA	208	L	6
CHA	208	L	8
CHA	209	L	8
CHA	212	L	6.02
CHA	213	H	26.02
CHA	214	H	26
CHA	215	H	30
CHA	217	L	8
CHA	218	B	76
CHA	219	B	76
CHA	223	O	34
CHA	223	O	34
CHA	224	I	4
CHA	224	I	14
CHA	225	I	14
CHA	238	L	10.02
CHA	244	L	10.02
CHA	250	L	10.02
CHA	252	L	10.02
CHA	253	L	10.02
CHA	254	L	10.02
CHA	256	B	94
CHA	257	B	102
CHA	258	B	102
CHA	260	B	76
CHA	263	B	76
CHA	266	B	102
CHA	276	B	76
CHA	279	B	76
CHA	280	B	102
CHA	281	D	4.02
CHA	281	D	4.06
CHA	287	D	56
CHA	288	G	2
CHA	289	B	86
CHA	290	N	16
CHA	295	D	50.02
CHA	298	L	10.02
CHA	299	L	10.02
CHA	301	B	98
CHA	301	B	98.02
CHA	304	H	20.04
CHA	307	L	10.02
CHA	307	L	10.02
CHA	321	L	10.02
CHA	323	B	94
CHA	327	D	48.12
CHA	328	B	92
CHA	328	H	20.04
CHA	330	B	86
CHA	333	G	22
CHA	336	F	2
CHA	341	E	18
CHA	343	B	92

PART NUMBER		GRP	PAGE
CHA	343	B	92
CHA	344	L	10.02
CHA	345	N	8
CHA	347	I	20
CHA	348	I	20
CHA	349	N	8
CHA	351	N	8
CHA	352	N	8
CHA	359	N	8
CHA	360	B	94
CHA	360	B	94.02
CHA	363	L	14
CHA	365	L	10.02
CHA	375	G	22
CHA	378	D	8
CHA	379	D	50.02
CHA	380	B	96
CHA	384	B	96
CHA	384	B	96.02
CHA	390	H	32
CHA	397	D	12
CHA	398	E	26
CHA	401	B	96
CHA	401	B	96.02
CHA	401	B	96.04
CHA	404	B	96
CHA	404	B	96.02
CHA	405	G	2
CHA	407	H	30
CHA	420	D	4.02
CHA	420	D	4.06
CHA	429	H	30
CHA	430	N	12
CHA	431	C	22
CHA	432	H	30
CHA	434	D	4.06
CHA	434	M	10
CHA	440	B	92
CHA	441	B	92
CHA	444	D	6
CHA	446	G	2
CHA	447	N	20
CHA	448	N	8
CHA	449	N	8
CHA	450	N	8
CHA	452	D	6
CHA	452	D	8
CHA	453	D	8
CHA	454	H	26.02
CHA	455	H	26
CHA	457	E	14
CHA	458	D	4.06
CHA	458	M	10
CHA	466	C	22
CHA	471	D	56
CHA	475	G	2
CHA	478	L	4
CHA	483	B	102

PART NUMBER		GRP	PAGE
CHA	485	G	2
CHA	487	B	102
CHA	488	B	102
CHA	491	D	50.02
CHA	493	F	10
CHA	494	G	2
CHA	496	G	2
CHA	501	D	50.04
CHA	503	B	94
CHA	503	B	94.02
CHA	507	L	10.02
CHA	508	K	6
CHA	511	D	48.12
CHA	521	N	8
CHA	523	O	34
CHA	524	H	26.02
CHA	525	H	30
CHA	534	L	10.02
CHA	536	L	10.02
CHA	544	L	10.02
CHA	545	K	6
CHA	554	D	50.02
CHA	555	B	96.04
CHA	556	B	96.02
CHA	556	B	96.04
CHA	557	B	96.02
CHA	557	B	96.04
CHA	558	E	12
CHA	559	E	14
CHA	565	B	102
CHA	567	G	30
CHA	569	H	26.02
CHA	570	E	26
CHA	582	D	4.04
CHA	582	D	4.06
CHA	585	D	4.04
CHA	590	D	4.04
CHA	591	D	4.04
CHA	594	L	14
CHA	595	B	92
CHA	595	D	4.04
CHA	600	H	98.02
CHA	600	H	98.02
CHA	603	D	4.06
CHA	609	D	4.06
CHA	615	B	102
CHA	616	D	4.06
CHA	634	G	30
CHA	638	G	30
CHA	641	B	92
CHA	644	B	96.C4
CHA	645	G	96.04
CHA	659	N	4
CHA	660	N	2
CHM	1	C	22
CHM	63	C	20
CHR	307	G	20
CHR	405	H	32

PART NUMBER		GRP	PAGE
CHS	522	B	34
CHS	613	B	50
CHS	2408	B	62
CHS	2513	Q	22
CHS	2515	B	10
CHS	2614	Q	14
CHS	2620	B	24
CHS	2620	B	62
CHS	2620	B	62
CJ	3020	B	98
CJ	3020	B	98
CLS	2620	B	62
CLZ	314	G	30
CLZ	411	G	30
CLZ	414	G	30
CLZ	513	G	6
CLZ	513	G	16
CLZ	513	G	24
CLZ	514	G	30
CLZ	515	G	30
CLZ	517	G	6
CLZ	517	G	8
CMP	305	M	6
CMP	308	M	4
CMP	310	M	4
CMZ	210	Q	28
CMZ	402	J	8
CMZ	410	F	8
CMZ	410	J	8
CMZ	410	K	14
CMZ	416	J	6
CNZ	102	H	52
CNZ	102	H	76
CNZ	102	K	2
CNZ	102	K	8
CPS	204	Q	18
CTP	404	K	20
CTZ	604	K	10
CTZ	604	K	10
CTZ	604	K	12
CTZ	604	K	12
CUD	1002	D	28.02
CUD	1002	D	28.04
CUD	1002	D	38
CUD	1002	D	40
CUD	1002	D	44
CUD	1002	D	46
CUD	1017	D	42
CUD	1017	D	48
CUD	1026	D	42
CUD	1026	D	48
CUD	1041	D	48.04
CUD	1041	D	48.08
CUD	2316	D	26
CUD	2316	D	38
CUD	2316	D	40
CUD	2318	D	44
CUD	2318	D	46

PART NUMBER		GRP	PAGE
CUD	2318	D	46
CUD	2318	D	48
CUD	2686	D	28.02
CUD	2686	D	40
CUD	2686	D	42.02
CUD	2687	D	28.04
CUD	2687	D	46
CUD	2687	D	48.02
CUD	2799	D	42.02
CUD	2799	D	48.02
CUD	3070	D	48.06
CUD	3070	D	48.10
CUD	3072	D	48.10
CUD	3073	D	48.06
CUD	9029	D	26
CUD	9030	D	28
CUD	9031	D	38
CUD	9032	D	44
CUD	9081	D	40
CUD	9082	D	46
CUD	9093	Q	24
CUD	9094	Q	24
CUD	9180	D	42
CUD	9181	D	48
CUD	9236	D	42
CUD	9237	D	48
CUD	9296	D	28.02
CUD	9297	D	28.04
CUD	9334	D	48.04
CUD	9335	D	48.08
CZA	2364	J	2
CZA	2365	J	2
CZA	2366	J	2
CZA	3310	J	8
CZA	3311	J	8
CZA	4263	O	32
CZA	4500	O	32
CZA	4713	O	28
CZA	7109	J	12
CZA	7194	J	12
CZD	1593	M	10
CZG	782	O	2
CZG	1668	K	2
CZG	1864	L	2
CZH	657	I	20
CZH	2717	I	20
CZH	2889	O	28
CZH	3521	M	8
CZJ	34	I	10
CZJ	70	I	2
CZJ	70	I	6
CZJ	70	I	6
CZJ	104	K	2
CZJ	105	K	2
CZJ	140	I	6
CZJ	150	I	10
CZJ	151	I	10
CZJ	176	I	4
CZJ	176	I	12
CZJ	177	I	4
CZJ	177	I	12
CZJ	220	I	8
CZJ	221	I	8
CZJ	258	I	10
CZJ	258	I	14
CZJ	267	I	10
CZJ	279	I	18
CZJ	334	L	10
CZJ	334	L	10
CZJ	335	L	10
CZJ	335	L	10
CZJ	336	L	10
CZJ	336	L	10
CZJ	337	L	10
CZJ	337	L	10
CZJ	347	I	6
CZJ	351	K	6
CZJ	361	I	18
CZJ	365	I	6
CZJ	380	K	2
CZJ	391	I	6
CZJ	400	I	10
CZJ	401	I	10
CZJ	408	I	8
CZJ	409	I	8
CZJ	422	N	2
CZJ	423	N	2
CZJ	432	I	4
CZJ	432	I	12
CZJ	433	I	4
CZJ	433	I	12
CZJ	452	J	2
CZJ	453	J	2
CZJ	458	I	8
CZJ	459	I	8
CZJ	464	I	8
CZJ	465	I	8
CZJ	475	I	6
CZJ	478	J	2
CZJ	479	J	2
CZJ	480	J	2
CZJ	481	J	2
CZJ	482	L	10
CZJ	483	L	10
CZJ	488	N	2
CZJ	494	I	6
CZJ	565	I	12
CZJ	569	I	10
CZJ	586	I	12
CZJ	587	I	12
CZJ	590	I	8
CZJ	591	I	8
CZJ	592	I	8
CZJ	593	I	8
CZJ	594	I	18
CZJ	595	I	18
CZJ	598	I	6
CZJ	599	I	6
CZJ	614	I	10
CZJ	615	I	10
CZJ	616	I	10
CZJ	617	I	10
CZJ	638	I	12
CZJ	639	I	12
CZJ	642	I	6
CZJ	644	I	10
CZJ	645	I	10
CZJ	662	N	2
CZJ	663	I	6
CZJ	676	I	12
CZJ	682	I	12
CZJ	683	I	12
CZJ	694	I	12
CZJ	695	I	12
CZJ	704	K	2
CZK	3693	L	14
CZK	3721	L	14
CZK	6342	M	8
CZM	3521	M	8
CZP	404	J	16
11D	5050	G	18
11D	5050	G	26
11D	5050	G	26.02
11D	5264	G	18.02
11D	5264	G	28
17D	11	B	22
17D	11	B	56
DAM	73	C	14
DAM	518	C	22
DAM	671	C	22
DAM	738	C	16
DAM	739	C	16
DAM	1005	C	16
DAM	1650	C	20
DAM	1714	C	20
DAM	1723	C	22
DAM	2483	F	4
DAM	2484	F	4
DAP	829	K	10
DAP	829	K	12
DMP	721	I	14
DMP	721	I	20
DMP	721	I	20
DMP	721	J	2
DMP	819	L	2
DMP	829	K	10
DMP	829	K	24
DMP	829	L	2
DMP	829	L	4
DMP	835	K	16
DMP	2840	K	30
DP	205	C	14
DP	514	B	78
DP	610	B	86
DP	610	B	86
DP	616	B	86
DS	914	C	14
DS	1908	C	18
DS	2512	B	94
DS	2512	B	94.02
DZB	5208	M	8
FHS	2518	B	34
FNN	104	B	10
FNN	105	B	12
FNN	107	F	4
FNN	207	H	16
FNN	207	H	18
FNN	604	C	2
FNN	605	B	38
FNN	612	F	6
FNP	103	M	6
FNZ	103	E	22
FNZ	103	E	30
FNZ	103	G	20
FNZ	103	G	28
FNZ	103	H	32
FNZ	103	H	36.02
FNZ	103	H	42
FNZ	103	H	58
FNZ	103	H	82
FNZ	103	H	86
FNZ	103	I	4
FNZ	103	I	14
FNZ	103	I	14
FNZ	103	I	20
FNZ	103	I	20
FNZ	103	J	2
FNZ	103	J	6
FNZ	103	K	2
FNZ	103	K	2
FNZ	103	K	4
FNZ	103	K	4
FNZ	103	K	10
FNZ	103	L	2
FNZ	103	M	10
FNZ	103	M	10
FNZ	103	N	4
FNZ	103	N	14
FNZ	103	N	14
FNZ	103	N	16
FNZ	103	N	24
FNZ	103	O	12
FNZ	103	Q	16
FNZ	103	Q	28
FNZ	104	B	72
FNZ	104	B	72
FNZ	104	C	2
FNZ	104	Q	6
FNZ	105	D	54
FNZ	105	D	54
FNZ	105	D	54
FNZ	105	D	58
FNZ	105	D	58
FNZ	105	D	58
FNZ	105	E	18
FNZ	105	E	18
FNZ	106	B	76
FNZ	106	B	76
FNZ	106	B	76
FNZ	106	D	50
FNZ	106	E	20
FNZ	106	F	12
FNZ	106	F	12
FNZ	106	G	16
FNZ	106	G	18.02
FNZ	106	G	28
FNZ	106	G	30
FNZ	106	L	6
FNZ	106	L	8
FNZ	106	L	10
FNZ	106	L	12
FNZ	106	M	6
FNZ	204	G	2
FNZ	204	G	4
FNZ	204	Q	16
FNZ	204	Q	22
FNZ	205	G	16
FNZ	205	K	2
FNZ	206	G	20
FNZ	206	G	28
FNZ	206	K	4
FNZ	207	G	30
FNZ	207	H	16
FNZ	306	E	26
FNZ	307	E	22
FNZ	407	E	8
FNZ	505	G	6
FNZ	505	G	16
FNZ	505	G	24
FNZ	506	F	8
FNZ	506	G	14
FNZ	506	G	22
FNZ	507	F	14
FNZ	508	F	14
FWP	106	K	18
FWP	106	K	22
FWP	206	K	10
FWP	206	K	18
FWP	206	K	22
FWP	706	N	4
FWP	710	N	2
FWP	710	N	4
FWP	906	O	2
FWP	906	O	2
FWP	906	O	4
FWP	906	O	10
FWZ	206	K	12
FWZ	210	N	2
16	752	B	16
16	752	B	44
16	752	C	2
16	1167	B	28
16	1319	B	8
16	2062	B	8
16	2062	B	32
16	2624	D	50
16	2673	H	12
16	2984	B	8
16	2984	B	30
16	3530	C	6
16	3584	F	4
16	3707	C	8
16	3863	C	8
16	7439	F	6
16	8781	B	76
16	9198	G	18.02
16	9198	G	28
16	9529	H	98
16	9529	N	12
46	877	O	34
46	1588	K	4
46	1851	I	16
46	2494	K	4
46	3035	K	4
46	3676	K	4
46	4920	I	16
46	9763	I	16
86	149	B	2
86	150	B	2
86	179	N B	26
86	180	N B	26
86	189	N B	26
86	190	B	26
86	548	H	36.02
86	549	B	6
86	576	H	10
86	589	E	22
86	621	E	26
86	725	B	6
86	726	H	2
86	726	H	4
86	727	H	8
86	727	Q	8
86	728	H	12
86	733	B	22
86	733	B	52
86	745	B	4
86	745	20 B	4
86	2198	B	6
86	2198	10 B	6
86	2198	20 B	6
86	2198	30 B	6
86	2198	40 B	6
86	2391	B	6
86	2391	B	28
86	2391	10 B	6
86	2391	10 B	28
86	2391	20 B	6

PART NUMBER	GRP	PAGE
22G 1975	C	16
22G 1976	C	18
22G 2015	C	22
22G 2028	C	14
22G 2045	C	8
22G 2046	C	8
22G 2047	C	22
22G 2052	C	22
22G 2053	C	20
22G 2198	C	20
22G 2202	C	22
22G 2210	C	16
22G 2276	C	20
22G 2277	C	20
22G 2285	C	22
22G 2286	C	22
22G 2291	C	20
22G 2353	C	18
22G 2797	C	22
24G 1052	K	4
24G 1345	H	36.02
24G 1345	H	50
24G 1345	H	50
24G 1482	N	20
28G 118	I	4
28G 118	I	12
28G 121	I	4
28G 122	I	4
28G 133	B	2
28G 222	B	10
31G 957	P	4
34G 252	K	6
34G 1289	M	10
34G 1290	M	10
34G 1295	M	10
34G 2065	H	24
38G 313	C	2
38G 369	B	2
38G 370	B	2
38G 371	B	2
38G 372	N B	2
38G 395	N B	26
38G 396	N B	26
38G 397	B	26
38G 398	B	26
38G 399	B	34
38G 430	N C	2
38G 430	N C	2
38G 431	B	34
38G 506	N B	26
38G 514	N C	2
88G 214	C	2
88G 215	B	22
88G 215	B	52
88G 216	C	6
88G 219	B	14
88G 219	B	42
88G 219	Q	4

PART NUMBER	GRP	PAGE
88G 221	B	10
88G 221	B	36
88G 221	N	8
88G 229	Q	2
88G 257	B	18
88G 257	B	48
88G 274	E	26
88G 291	D	2
88G 295	G	30
88G 305	B	32
88G 308	B	96
88G 308	B	96.02
88G 308	D	10
88G 308	D	10
88G 308	D	50
88G 308	D	50
88G 308	H	98
88G 308	H	98.02
88G 308	H	98.02
88G 320	F	6
88G 321	E	24
88G 329	P	4
88G 396	C	4
88G 402	B	20
88G 402	B	20
88G 402	B	50
88G 402	B	50
88G 402	B	50.02
88G 409	C	4
88G 414	E	8
88G 446	B	22
88G 446	B	52
88G 455	M	2
88G 459	B	36
88G 534	D	14
88G 534	D	16
88G 538	B	50.02
88G 561	B	16
88G 561	B	44
88G 570	P	4
88G 577	E	24
88G 577	F	6
88G 582	C	20
88G 588	N	8
88G 606	P	2
88G 607	P	2
88G 618	B	42
GAM 101	M	8
GAM 102	M	8
GAM 113	M	8
GBH 109	G	18.02
GBH 109	G	28
GBH 111	G	18.02
GBH 111	G	28
GBH 139	G	18.02
GBH 139	G	28
GBH 157	G	18.02
GBH 157	G	28

PART NUMBER	GRP	PAGE
GBH 158	G	18.02
GBH 158	G	28
GBP 108	E	28
GBP 108	E	28.02
GBS 512	F	8
GBS 625	F	8
GCC 114	B	74
GCC 115	B	74
GCC 196	C	14
GCL 110	H	8
GCL 111	H	6.06
GCL 111	H	8
GCP 103	B	74
GCP 181	B	74
GCP 230	C	14
GCS 101	H	2
GCS 101	H	4
GCS 101	H	6
GCS 101	H	6
GCS 101	Q	8
GCS 111	H	4
GCS 118	H	6.02
GDC 102	H	2
GDC 102	H	4
GDC 102	H	4
GDC 102	H	6
GDC 102	H	6
GDC 102	Q	8
GDC 132	H	6.02
GDC 132	H	6.04
GDC 136	H	6.04
GEG 102	B	58
GEG 126	B	60
GEG 201	B	58
GEG 225	B	60
GEG 239	B	58
GEG 279	B	94
GEG 301	B	38
GEG 302	B	12
GEG 373	B	88
GEG 401	B	14
GEG 401	B	40
GEG 414	B	90
GEG 501	B	18
GEG 501	Q	6
GEG 517	B	86
GEG 528	B	48
GEG 601	B	24
GEG 601	B	62
GEG 648	B	94
GEG 648	B	94.02
GEG 742	D	56
GEG 1140	B	60
GEG 1212	B	94
GEU 708	H	86
GEX 142	D	52
GEX 142	D	52
GEX 161	D	56

PART NUMBER	GRP	PAGE
GEX 161	D	56
GEX 164	D	56
GEX 1306	D	52
GEX 1618	D	56
GEX 3365	D	54
GEX 3369	D	54
GEX 7072	D	52
GEX 7073	D	52
GEX 7073	D	56
GEX 7074	D	52
GEX 7151	D	54
GEX 7151	D	54
GEX 7151	D	58
GEX 7152	D	54
GEX 7153	D	52
GEX 7154	D	52
GEX 7155	D	52
GEX 7155	D	54
GEX 7155	D	56
GEX 7155	D	58
GEX 7166	D	54
GEX 7166	D	58
GEX 7168	D	54
GEX 7169	D	54
GEX 7170	D	54
GEX 7170	D	58
GEX 7193	D	52
GEX 7203	D	56
GEX 7250	D	52
GEX 7250	D	54
GEX 7250	D	56
GEX 7250	D	58
GEX 7250	D	58
GEX 7251	D	58
GEX 7252	D	56
GEX 7364	D	54
GEX 7364	D	58
GEX 7365	D	54
GEX 7365	D	58
GEX 7468	D	58
GEX 7470	D	56
GFB 105	H	20.04
GFB 120	B	22
GFB 120	B	56
GFB 121	B	56
GFB 186	B	56
GFB 190	B	22
GFB 193	B	56
GFB 197	B	56
GFB 248	B	92
GFB 253	B	56
GFE 103	B	20
GFE 103	B	20
GFE 103	B	20
GFE 103	B	20
GFE 103	B	50
GFE 103	B	50
GFE 119	B	86

PART NUMBER	GRP	PAGE
GFE 139	B	50.02
GFE 148	B	50.02
GFE 1004	D	50
GFE 1060	D	50.02
GFE 1063	D	50.02
GFS 35	H	34
GFS 35	H	34
GFS 410	H	30
GFU 103	H	42
GFU 107	H	42
GFU 107	H	50
GGB 102	H	16
GGB 102	H	16
GGB 102	H	18
GGB 102	H	18
GHB 128	E	24
GHB 129	E	24
GHB 130	F	6
GHC 406	B	40
GHC 507	B	24
GHC 507	B	24
GHC 507	B	64
GHC 507	B	94
GHC 507	B	94.02
GHC 507	E	10
GHC 507	N	8
GHC 709	B	66
GHC 709	B	68
GHC 709	B	98
GHC 709	B	98.02
GHC 709	B	98.02
GHC 709	D	4
GHC 709	D	4.06
GHC 709	N	8
GHC 709	N	12
GHC 709	N	12
GHC 811	E	10
GHC 913	B	96
GHC 913	B	96.02
GHC 913	B	96.04
GHC 913	D	2
GHC 1217	D	2
GHC 1217	D	4
GHC 1217	D	4.02
GHC 1217	D	4.06
GHC 1622	D	6
GHC 3036	N	16
GHF 103	H	20.04
GHF 223	E	10
GHF 223	E	26
GHF 223	F	12
GHF 223	F	14
GHF 301	B	56
GHF 301	H	20.02
GHF 321	B	32
GHS 142	E	24
GHS 147	F	6
GHT 152	H	6.06

PART NUMBER	GRP	PAGE
GLB 254	H	78
GLB 254	H	78
GLB 254	H	78.02
GLB 254	H	78.02
GLB 270	H	74
GLB 270	H	74
GLB 273	H	74
GLB 281	H	28
GLB 380	H	68
GLB 380	H	68
GLB 380	H	68
GLB 380	H	68
GLB 380	H	70
GLB 380	H	72
GLB 380	H	72
GLB 380	H	72
GLB 382	H	66
GLB 382	H	66
GLB 382	H	70
GLB 382	H	72
GLB 382	H	72
GLB 382	H	72
GLB 410	H	58
GLB 410	H	60
GLB 410	H	60
GLB 410	H	64
GLB 411	H	62
GLB 411	H	62
GLB 501	H	56.02
GLB 987	H	28
GLB 989	H	66
GLB 989	H	76
GLB 989	H	76
GLB 989	H	78
GLB 989	H	78
GLU 101	H	56
GLU 104	H	56.02
GLU 112	H	56
GLU 513	H	60
GLU 513	H	60
GLU 513	H	62
GLU 513	H	62
GLU 515	H	64
GLZ 127	O	32
GLZ 131	O	32
GLZ 133	O	32
GLZ 135	O	32
GMC 112	G	16
GMC 113	G	16
GMC 151	G	16
GRA 101	H	2
GRA 101	H	4
GRA 101	H	4
GRA 101	H	6
GRA 101	H	6
GRA 101	Q	8
GRA 114	H	6.02
GRA 114	H	6.04

PART NUMBER	GRP	PAGE
GRA 114	H	6.04
GRA 114	H	6.04
GRB 102	B	74
GRB 107	B	74
GRB 207	C	14
GRC 101	D	2
GRC 110	D	4
GRC 110	D	4.02
GRH 313	D	2
GRH 315	D	2
GRH 508	D	2
GRH 509	D	4
GRH 510	D	4
GRH 525	D	4.02
GRH 525	D	4.06
GRH 534	D	4.02
GRH 1001	M D	4.04
GRH 1001	M D	4.06
GRH 1002	M D	4
GRH 1002	M D	4.02
GRH 1002	M D	4.04
GRH 1002	M D	4.04
GRH 1002	M D	4.06
GRH 1003	M N	12
GSA 102	E	26
GSA 103	E	26
GSA 149	F	14
GSA 150	F	14
GSB 105	H	22
GSB 105	H	22.02
GSC 101	H	2
GSC 101	H	4
GSC 101	H	4
GSC 101	H	6
GSC 101	H	6
GSC 101	Q	8
GSC 110	H	6.02
GSD 104	H	90
GSD 114	H	90
GSD 118	H	90
GSD 145	H	90
GSD 288	H	90
GSS 127	D	6
GSS 156	K	20
GTG 101	B	14
GTG 101	B	42
GTG 101	Q	8
GTG 103	B	92
GTS 102	B	14
GTS 102	B	42
GTS 104	B	14
GTS 104	B	42
GTS 104	B	92
GTS 106	B	14
GTS 106	B	42
GTS 106	B	92
GUJ 101	F	2
GUJ 101	F	2

PART NUMBER	GRP	PAGE
GWB 145	H	84
GWB 145	H	86
GWB 159	H	80
GWB 159	H	84
GWB 164	H	84
GWB 164	H	86
GWC 1102	F	8
GWC 1129	F	8
GWP 101	B	22
GWP 101	B	52
GWP 102	B	52
GWP 128	B	92
GWP 132	B	22
GWP 132	B	52
GWS 121	J	4
1H 3101	C	8
1H 3101	C	10
1H 3364	F	4
1H 5452	B	66
2H 400	G	20
2H 1082	D	6
2H 2065	H	28
2H 4245	H	10
2H 4245	H	12
2H 4245	H	14
2H 4528	H	28
2H 4905	B	30
2H 4905	Q	4
2H 8198	I	16
2H 8445	O	18
3H 550	G	12
3H 550	G	18.02
3H 550	G	28
3H 554	C	14
3H 576	B	2
3H 576	B	26
3H 693	C	12
3H 693	C	12
3H 1422	H	10
3H 2127	B	6
3H 2138	H	2
3H 2138	H	4
3H 2138	H	4
3H 2138	H	6
3H 2138	H	6
3H 2138	Q	8
3H 2249	G	12
3H 2249	G	18
3H 2249	G	26
3H 2249	G	26.02
3H 2287	G	6
3H 2287	G	18.02
3H 2287	G	28
3H 2287	Q	16
3H 2424	G	18.02
3H 2424	G	18.02
3H 2424	G	28
3H 2428	E	28

PART NUMBER	GRP	PAGE
3H 2428	G	6
3H 2428	G	8
3H 2428	Q	30
3H 2615	K	4
3H 2963	B	14
3H 2963	B	42
3H 2963	E	8
7H 25	B	20
7H 25	B	20
7H 25	B	20
7H 25	B	20
7H 25	B	50
7H 25	B	50
7H 28	B	20
7H 28	B	20
7H 28	B	20
7H 28	B	20
7H 28	B	50
7H 28	B	50
7H 1709	P	2
7H 2566	Q	16
7H 3008	B	74
7H 3009	B	74
7H 3043	B	74
7H 3057	B	74
7H 3060	B	74
7H 3207	B	74
7H 3209	B	74
7H 3565	E	8
7H 3762	E	8
7H 3763	E	8
7H 5038	H	22
7H 5040	H	22
7H 5045	H	22
7H 5045	H	22
7H 5045	H	22.02
7H 5051	H	22
7H 5066	H	34
7H 5123	H	78
7H 5130	H	80
7H 5156	H	22
7H 5390	H	16
7H 5390	H	16
7H 5390	H	18
7H 5390	H	18
7H 5522	H	34
7H 5947	G	30
7H 5951	G	30
7H 5991	H	80
7H 6887	H	22
7H 6887	H	22
7H 6887	H	22.02
7H 6894	H	10
7H 6894	H	12
7H 6902	H	54
7H 6950	H	4
7H 6978	H	30
7H 7520	G	24

PART NUMBER	GRP	PAGE
7H 7520	G	24
7H 7851	G	18.02
7H 7913	G	8
7H 7991	G	10
7H 9568	K	24
7H 9864	K	10
7H 9864	K	12
7H 9864	K	16
7H 9864	K	24
7H 9864	K	28
7H 9866	K	10
7H 9866	K	12
7H 9866	K	16
7H 9866	K	24
7H 9866	K	28
7H 9868	K	30
12H 241	B	68
12H 865	B	18
12H 865	B	46
12H 889	Q	22
12H 941	B	16
12H 1001	Q	22
12H 1060	B	54
12H 1060	B	56
12H 1062	B	54
12H 1062	B	56
12H 1293	N	8
12H 1388	B	54
12H 1388	B	56
12H 1405	B	24
12H 1405	B	64
12H 1407	B	24
12H 1407	B	64
12H 1581	B	54
12H 1734	B	2
12H 1734	B	26
12H 1734	B	34
12H 1734	B	34
12H 1734	B	34
12H 1734	B	62
12H 2178	B	38
12H 2178	B	38
12H 2178	Q	4
12H 2457	B	64
12H 2457	B	68
12H 2461	H	8
12H 2479	B	66
12H 2479	B	98
12H 2479	B	98.02
12H 2515	H	20.02
12H 2729	B	68
12H 2958	B	64
12H 2958	B	68
12H 3348	H	14
12H 3868	N	8
12H 4295	B	96
12H 4295	B	96.02
12H 4295	B	96.04

PART NUMBER	GRP	PAGE
13H 21	G	6
13H 51	N	14
13H 56	N	24
13H 57	N	24
13H 58	N	16
13H 59	N	12
13H 66	H	80
13H 68	H	80
13H 217	I	20
13H 219	H	16
13H 227	M	10
13H 231	M	10
13H 232	M	10
13H 320	D	12
13H 337	H	36
13H 391	H	40
13H 412	P	2
13H 428	H	66
13H 429	H	66
13H 559	H	22
13H 568	E	12
13H 569	E	12
13H 783	B	74
13H 783	B	74
13H 784	H	92
13H 826	H	16
13H 926	H	36
13H 989	B	74
13H 1265	G	26
13H 1923	H	28
13H 1925	H	28
13H 1926	H	28
13H 2050	H	28
13H 2055	H	28
13H 2296	B	14
13H 2296	B	40
13H 2296	B	40
13H 2567	H	90
13H 2792	B	8
13H 2792	B	32
13H 2792	C	22
13H 3276	B	68
13H 3654	G	8
13H 3655	G	8
13H 4014	O	6
13H 4044	H	22
13H 4216	C	12
13H 4322	B	66
13H 4358	B	66
13H 4485	H	36
13H 4485	H	36.02
13H 4485	H	48
13H 4653	B	28
13H 4665	H	52
13H 4666	H	52
13H 4689	H	76
13H 4705	B	66
13H 4813	H	18

PART NUMBER	GRP	PAGE
13H 5191	B	24
13H 5191	B	64
13H 5412	H	80
13H 5412	H	82
13H 5412	H	86
13H 5798	H	22
13H 5798	H	22.02
13H 5905	G	26
13H 5905	G	28
13H 5952	H	36.02
13H 5952	H	48
13H 5991	H	78
13H 5994	D	10
13H 6084	C	22
13H 6107	B	96
13H 6107	G	2
13H 6107	H	30
13H 6189	B	68
13H 6199	D	10
13H 6322	H	46
13H 6322	H	46
13H 6322	H	46
13H 6472	M	10
13H 6473	M	10
13H 6473	M	10
13H 6473	M	10
13H 6473	M	10
13H 6692	P	4
13H 6952	H	46
13H 7061	H	20.02
13H 7553	M	10
13H 7846	M	10
13H 7986	H	52
13H 7986	N	4
13H 8328	P	2
13H 8329	P	2
13H 8330	P	2
13H 8331	P	2
13H 8332	P	2
13H 8333	P	2
13H 8335	P	2
13H 8336	P	2
13H 8337	P	2
13H 8433	H	6
13H 8511	B	96
13H 8511	B	96.02
13H 8511	D	10
13H 8600	H	50
13H 9016	H	78
13H 9334	P	2
13H 9407	H	90
13H 9408	H	52
13H 9440	H	8
13H 9475	H	34
13H 9513	C	16
13H 9551	H	20.02
13H 9571	H	52
13H 9801	H	52

PART NUMBER	GRP	PAGE
13H 9801	H	52
13H 9801	O	34
17H 756	H	90
17H 819	N	14
17H 819	N	14
17H 843	H	90
17H 844	H	90
17H 1148	B	20
17H 1148	B	20
17H 1148	B	20
17H 1148	B	20
17H 1148	B	50
17H 1148	B	50
17H 1169	B	20
17H 1169	B	20
17H 1169	B	20
17H 1169	B	50
17H 1172	B	20
17H 1172	B	20
17H 1172	B	20
17H 1172	B	50
17H 1173	B	20
17H 1173	B	20
17H 1173	B	50
17H 1455	N	14
17H 1574	N	14
17H 1590	N	8
17H 1601	N	16
17H 1601	N	20
17H 1601	N	24
17H 1602	N	16
17H 1603	N	16
17H 1603	N	20
17H 1603	N	24
17H 2091	G	30
17H 2093	G	30
17H 2281	B	20
17H 2281	B	50
17H 2458	H	80
17H 2460	E	28
17H 2460	E	28.02
17H 2669	M	10
17H 2721	B	74
17H 2824	F	8
17H 2825	F	8
17H 3613	P	2
17H 3828	F	2
17H 3828	F	2
17H 3984	P	2
17H 5065	H	2
17H 5065	H	4
17H 5065	H	4
17H 5065	H	6
17H 5065	H	6
17H 5065	Q	8
17H 5106	H	2
17H 5106	H	4

PART NUMBER	GRP	PAGE
17H 5106	H	6
17H 5106	G	8
17H 5143	H	62
17H 5205	H	58
17H 5205	H	60
17H 5205	H	62
17H 5216	H	66
17H 5217	H	16
17H 5217	H	16
17H 5217	H	18
17H 5217	H	18
17H 5231	H	58
17H 5231	H	60
17H 5231	H	62
17H 5287	H	28
17H 5302	H	78
17H 5306	H	58
17H 5306	H	58
17H 5394	H	58
17H 5394	H	60
17H 5394	H	62
17H 5396	H	80
17H 5400	H	66
17H 5400	H	66
17H 5400	H	68
17H 5400	H	78.02
17H 5431	H	80
17H 5444	H	22
17H 5449	H	80
17H 6657	H	2
17H 6821	H	16
17H 6821	H	18
17H 6822	H	16
17H 6836	N	14
17H 6861	G	6
17H 6861	G	16
17H 6861	G	16
17H 7108	G	18.02
17H 7268	G	6
17H 7417	G	8
17H 7540	G	6
17H 7554	G	6
17H 7554	G	16
17H 7554	G	16
17H 7554	G	16
17H 7560	G	6
17H 7560	G	16
17H 7560	G	16
17H 7580	G	6
17H 7580	G	8
17H 7612	F	8
17H 7613	F	8
17H 7618	F	8
17H 7619	F	8
17H 7621	F	8
17H 7622	F	8
17H 7623	F	8
17H 7623	F	8

PART NUMBER	GRP	PAGE
17H 7679	E	28
17H 7679	E	28.02
17H 7769	Q	30
17H 7819	G	8
17H 7841	G	6
17H 7868	G	6
17H 7890	G	30
17H 7917	E	28
17H 7947	F	8
17H 7948	F	8
17H 7963	E	28
17H 7963	E	28.02
17H 8148	M	8
17H 8250	E	28
17H 8250	E	28.02
17H 8399	F	8
17H 8579	M	10
17H 8579	M D	12
17H 8622	H	2
17H 9184	E	12
17H 9185	E	12
17H 9275	F	14
17H 9438	E	28.02
17H 9439	E	28.02
17H 9463	B	20
17H 9603	D	12
22H 1337	B	74
27H 602	N	14
27H 1193	N	14
27H 1193	N	20
27H 1232	N	14
27H 1253	N	8
27H 1253	N	8
27H 1258	N	14
27H 2330	H	82
27H 2330	H	86
27H 2358	E	12
27H 2359	E	12
27H 2361	E	12
27H 2573	B	50
27H 2573	B	50
27H 3073	Q	22
27H 3351	J	14
27H 3387	H	54
27H 3542	H	80
27H 3548	H	16
27H 3548	H	18
27H 3573	D	6
27H 3590	H	78.02
27H 3755	H	22
27H 3755	H	22
27H 3755	H	22.02
27H 3798	H	16
27H 3798	H	18
27H 3831	H	16
27H 3831	H	18
27H 3832	H	16
27H 3832	H	18

PART NUMBER	GRP	PAGE
27H 3832	H	18
27H 4146	H	58
27H 4146	H	60
27H 4146	H	60
27H 4146	H	62
27H 4146	H	62
27H 4146	H	64
27H 4463	H	80
27H 4464	H	80
27H 4798	K	18
27H 5253	H	58
27H 5253	H	60
27H 5253	H	62
27H 5309	H	80
27H 5309	H	80
27H 5354	H	56
27H 5354	H	56
27H 5354	H	56.02
27H 5354	H	58
27H 5354	H	58
27H 5354	H	60
27H 5354	H	60
27H 5354	H	62
27H 5354	H	62
27H 5354	H	64
27H 5374	H	80
27H 5386	H	38
27H 5401	H	54
27H 5576	H	36
27H 5713	H	62
27H 5903	H	30
27H 5977	H	64
27H 5978	H	64
27H 5982	Q	4
27H 6237	E	12
27H 6243	H	66
27H 6243	H	68
27H 6547	H	2
27H 6547	H	4
27H 6547	H	4
27H 6547	H	6
27H 6547	H	6
27H 6547	H	6.02
27H 6547	H	6.04
27H 6547	H	6.04
27H 6679	H	68
27H 6713	H	56
27H 6713	H	56
27H 6713	H	56.02
27H 6713	H	58
27H 6713	H	58
27H 6713	H	60
27H 6713	H	60
27H 6713	H	62
27H 6713	H	64
27H 6713	H	66
27H 6713	H	68
27H 6713	H	76

PART NUMBER	GRP	PAGE
27H 6713	H	76
27H 6713	H	78
27H 6767	H	78.02
27H 6768	H	22
27H 6787	H	38
27H 6841	O	36
27H 7645	H	4
27H 7647	H	16
27H 7647	H	18
27H 7751	G	6
27H 7751	G	16
27H 7751	G	16
27H 7751	G	16
27H 7756	B	24
27H 7756	B	64
27H 7757	B	24
27H 7757	B	64
27H 7758	B	24
27H 7758	B	64
27H 7759	B	24
27H 7759	B	64
27H 7760	B	24
27H 7760	B	64
27H 7766	Q	8
27H 7824	H	56
27H 7824	H	56
27H 7824	H	58
27H 7824	H	60
27H 7824	H	62
27H 7824	H	64
27H 7877	H	96
27H 7877	H	96
27H 8022	Q	8
27H 8052	H	92
27H 8204	H	58
27H 8204	H	60
27H 8204	H	64
27H 8206	H	58
27H 8207	H	56
27H 8210	H	64
27H 8215	H	92
27H 8266	H	56.02
27H 8442	G	24
27H 8443	G	24
27H 8445	G	24
27H 8445	G	24
27H 8446	G	24
27H 8449	G	24
27H 8450	G	24
27H 8453	G	24
27H 8454	G	24
27H 8456	G	24
27H 8459	G	6
27H 8459	G	16
27H 8499	H	56
27H 8705	M J	14
27H 8807	B	46
27H 8807	B	46

PART NUMBER	GRP	PAGE
27H 8808	B	46
27H 8811	H	74
27H 8811	H	74
27H 8849	H	28
27H 9070	H	80
27H 9394	E	12
27H 9623	M	10
27H 9735	H	36.02
27H 9735	H	52
32H 352	H	14
37H 689	B	20
37H 689	B	20
37H 689	B	20
37H 689	B	20
37H 689	B	50
37H 689	B	50
37H 861	B	18
37H 863	B	18
37H 864	B	18
37H 1368	H	62
37H 1547	H	74
37H 1759	H	74
37H 1759	H	74
37H 1759	H	74
37H 1759	H	74
37H 1760	H	74
37H 1811	J	4
37H 1878	H	16
37H 1878	H	18
37H 1894	H	66
37H 2148	Q	4
37H 2149	Q	4
37H 2171	G	24
37H 2257	H	20
37H 2257	H	20.04
37H 2258	H	20
37H 2258	H	20.04
37H 2260	H	4
37H 2496	G	16
37H 2498	B	66
37H 2498	B	98.02
37H 2499	B	66
37H 2502	M	8
37H 2503	H	52
37H 2505	H	52
37H 2508	K	18
37H 2508	K	22
37H 2533	B	66
37H 2678	H	44
37H 2678	H	44
37H 2679	H	46
37H 2679	H	46
37H 2687	H	72
37H 2687	H	72
37H 2687	H	72
37H 2688	H	72
37H 2688	H	72
37H 2688	H	72

PART NUMBER	GRP	PAGE
57H 5465	H	70
57H 5496	H	70
57H 5559	H	80
57H 5589	H	80
67H 5010	H	22
67H 5010	H	22
67H 5010	H	22.02
67H 5012	H	22
67H 5013	H	22
67H 5013	H	22
67H 5013	H	22.02
67H 5014	H	22
67H 5021	H	38
67H 5025	H	56
67H 5025	H	56
67H 5025	H	56.02
67H 5025	H	56.02
67H 5025	H	58
67H 5025	H	60
67H 5025	H	62
67H 5025	H	64
67H 5026	H	56
67H 5026	H	56
67H 5026	H	56.02
67H 5026	H	56.02
67H 5026	H	58
67H 5026	H	60
67H 5026	H	62
67H 5026	H	64
97H 222	F	14
97H 626	H	16
97H 626	H	16
97H 626	H	18
97H 626	H	18
97H 717	K	24
97H 717	K	30
97H 2679	M M	10
HB 722	B	86
HB 816	B	82
HB 818	B	92
HB 818	B	98
HB 818	B	98.02
HB 819	B	92
HB 821	B	98
HB 821	B	98.02
HB 822	B	92
HB 836	B	98
HB 836	B	98.02
HB 839	H	20.04
HB 841	B	98
HB 841	B	98.02
HB 841	H	20.04
HB 867	D	50.02
HB 1024	B	78
HBN 408	C	8
HBN 414	B	18
HBZ 406	D	4
HBZ 408	E	14
HBZ 408	G	18.02
HBZ 408	G	28
HBZ 410	G	18.02
HBZ 410	G	28
HBZ 411	H	84
HBZ 411	H	86
HBZ 414	Q	6
HBZ 510	D	52
HBZ 510	F	2
HBZ 511	C	12
HBZ 512	C	12
HBZ 512	D	54
HBZ 512	D	58
HBZ 515	B	16
HBZ 518	C	14
HBZ 524	K	2
HBZ 526	K	18
HBZ 528	B	66
HBZ 611	L	8
HBZ 624	G	16
HBZ 630	B	76
HBZ 630	F	12
HCS 116	B	66
HCS 116	B	68
HCS 122	D	4
HCS 407	B	64
HCS 507	B	64
HCS 608	B	20
HCZ 536	D	50
HCZ 630	B	20
HCZ 630	B	50
HN 2005	D	50.06
HN 2005	D	50.06
HN 2007	B	98
HN 2008	B	82
HN 2008	B	82
HN 2008	B	84
HN 2008	B	92
HN 2008	B	94
HN 2009	B	90
HNS 507	C	14
HPS 408	M	6
HU 504	D	50.06
HU 708	B	98
HU 755	B	98
HU 755	B	98.02
HU 805	B	86
HU 806	B	86
HU 806	B	86
HU 807	B	82
HU 807	B	84
HU 809	B	78
HU 858	H	20.04
HU 909	C	14
HZA 5025	N	4
HZA 5074	M	8
HZA 5075	M	8
HZS 403	B	16
HZS 403	B	44
HZS 404	B	18
HZS 404	B	18
HZS 404	B	18
HZS 404	B	46
HZS 404	B	46
HZS 404	B	48
HZS 404	B	70
HZS 404	B	72
HZS 404	C	8
HZS 404	G	2
HZS 404	H	2
HZS 404	H	4
HZS 404	J	10
HZS 404	J	12
HZS 404	J	16
HZS 404	N	14
HZS 404	N	24
HZS 404	Q	6
HZS 405	C	10
HZS 405	D	2
HZS 405	D	4
HZS 405	D	8
HZS 405	D	12
HZS 405	D	50
HZS 405	G	14
HZS 405	G	14
HZS 405	G	14
HZS 405	G	14
HZS 405	G	22
HZS 405	G	22
HZS 405	H	8
HZS 405	I	14
HZS 405	I	20
HZS 405	K	2
HZS 405	K	4
HZS 405	K	8
HZS 405	K	8
HZS 405	K	18
HZS 405	K	18
HZS 405	K	20
HZS 405	N	2
HZS 407	B	44
HZS 407	B	72
HZS 407	C	10
HZS 407	D	50
HZS 407	D	52
HZS 407	D	56
HZS 407	G	2
HZS 407	G	2
HZS 407	K	4
HZS 407	Q	6
HZS 408	G	4
HZS 408	G	14
HZS 411	B	54
HZS 411	B	54
HZS 503	E	28
HZS 504	D	4
HZS 504	D	4
HZS 504	H	32
HZS 505	B	8
HZS 505	B	16
HZS 505	B	16
HZS 505	B	76
HZS 505	D	52
HZS 505	D	54
HZS 505	D	56
HZS 505	D	58
HZS 505	E	30
HZS 505	F	12
HZS 505	G	30
HZS 505	J	2
HZS 505	Q	28
HZS 506	B	44
HZS 506	B	74
HZS 506	B	74
HZS 506	B	76
HZS 506	B	76
HZS 506	D	52
HZS 506	D	54
HZS 506	D	54
HZS 506	D	58
HZS 506	D	58
HZS 506	E	10
HZS 506	E	18
HZS 506	E	18
HZS 506	E	30
HZS 506	G	30
HZS 506	L	6.02
HZS 506	L	12
HZS 506	Q	28
HZS 506	Q	28
HZS 506	Q	28
HZS 507	B	44
HZS 507	D	52
HZS 507	E	20
HZS 507	F	8
HZS 507	F	12
HZS 507	G	6
HZS 507	G	16
HZS 507	J	16
HZS 507	K	18
HZS 507	L	6.02
HZS 508	B	76
HZS 509	B	16
HZS 509	B	68
HZS 509	D	52
HZS 509	K	22
HZS 510	B	52
HZS 510	B	52
HZS 510	D	52
HZS 510	Q	22
HZS 515	B	22
HZS 515	B	52
HZS 515	B	52
HZS 515	D	50
HZS 518	D	52
HZS 607	F	12
HZS 608	L	12
HZS 612	E	20
HZS 612	F	14
HZS 614	F	12
HZS 616	E	20
J2A 9475	O	4
J2A 9476	O	4
J2A 9529	O	28
J2A 9531	O	30
J2A 9532	O	30
J2A 9533	O	30
J2A 9573	O	2
J2A 9575	O	2
J2A 9579	O	8
J2A 9581	O	8
J2A 9590	O	10
J2A 9599	N	4
J2A 9966	N	4
J2K 9475	O	4
J2K 9476	O	4
J2K 9529	O	28
J2K 9530	O	28
J2K 9531	O	30
J2K 9532	O	30
J2K 9533	O	30
J2K 9564	O	6
J2K 9579	O	8
J2K 9581	O	8
J2K 9590	O	10
J2K 9628	O	32
J2N 9532	O	30
J2N 9533	O	30
J2N 9564	O	6
J2N 9628	O	32
JGK 9216	O	18
JGK 9220	O	20
JGK 9221	O	20
JGK 9224	O	14
JGK 9225	O	14
JGK 9226	O	14
JGK 9228	O	16
JN 2158	H	20.04
1K 2158	B	40
2K 1345	B	2
2K 1345	B	10
2K 1345	B	26
2K 1345	B	34
2K 4608	B	12
2K 4608	B	38
2K 4608	B	38
2K 4608	Q	4
2K 4936	K	10
2K 4936	K	24
2K 4936	K	30
2K 4954	B	2
2K 4954	B	26
2K 4954	B	62
2K 4956	B	18
2K 4956	C	2
2K 4956	C	2
2K 4958	B	16
2K 4974	B	22
2K 4974	B	52
2K 4975	B	2
2K 4994	B	18
2K 4994	B	46
2K 5197	B	18
2K 5197	B	48
2K 5291	G	30
2K 5377	E	24
2K 5806	D	52
2K 5813	B	74
2K 5820	G	30
2K 5830	C	2
2K 5943	F	4
2K 6167	H	32
2K 6677	C	4
2K 6677	C	6
2K 6930	G	30
2K 7778	F	4
2K 7779	F	4
2K 8158	C	8
2K 8160	F	6
2K 8169	B	2
2K 8645	H	24
2K 8686	G	12
2K 8737	C	4
2K 8737	C	6
2K 8738	C	4
2K 8738	C	6
2K 8739	C	4
2K 8739	C	6
4K 7715	Q	30
4K 7717	Q	30
6K 35	D	10
6K 35	D	12
6K 35	G	20
6K 35	G	28
6K 431	B	18
6K 431	B	46
6K 433	B	86
6K 464	B	18
6K 464	B	46
6K 464	B	46
6K 499	F	4
6K 499	F	4
6K 555	B	12
6K 555	B	38
6K 556	B	12
6K 556	B	38
6K 558	C	4
6K 558	C	6
6K 628	B	6
6K 628	B	28

PART NUMBER		GRP	PAGE
6K	628	B	28
6K	629	B	6
6K	629	B	30
6K	630	B	8
6K	631	F	4
6K	638	B	2
6K	638	B	18
6K	638	B	26
6K	638	B	48
6K	643	C	2
6K	649	H	8
6K	650	H	8
6K	650	H	8
6K	653	E	22
6K	654	B	12
6K	654	B	38
6K	690	G	30
6K	808	B	10
6K	808	B	34
6K	831	B	8
6K	836	B	6
6K	836	B	28
6K	853	B	18
6K	853	B	46
6K	871	Q	6
6K	878	B	12
6K	878	B	38
6K	878	B	38
6K	878	Q	4
11K	2846	B	42
11K	2846	B	92
11K	5564	K	10
21K	8341	D	4
21K	8341	D	4.02
21K	8341	D	4.04
21K	8341	D	4.06
21K	8564	G	6
21K	8983	Q	30
21K	9068	H	36
51K	276	B	2
51K	277	B	2
51K	279	B	2
51K	279	B	26
51K	280	B	2
51K	280	B	26
51K	328	E	24
51K	371	B	12
51K	371	B	38
51K	371	B	50
51K	885	B	10
51K	885	B	34
51K	886	F	4
51K	1029	B	30
51K	1473	B	10
51K	1769	E	22
51K	2751	E	22
51K	2824	H	98
51K	3424	E	22

PART NUMBER		GRP	PAGE
51K	3575	B	28
51K	3575	B	28
51K	3811	Q	22
51K	4001	E	12
51K	4001	E	20
53K	126	J	6
53K	126	K	10
53K	126	K	14
53K	126	N	6
53K	126	N	14
53K	126	N	14
53K	126	N	14
53K	126	N	20
53K	128	Q	16
53K	152	G	6
53K	152	G	8
53K	402	B	10
53K	402	B	34
53K	487	B	10
53K	487	B	34
53K	507	B	62
53K	528	C	8
53K	535	C	8
53K	615	B	2
53K	1013	E	14
53K	1013	E	20
53K	1016	K	4
53K	1016	N	20
53K	1023	Q	14
53K	1364	E	26
53K	1368	E	26
53K	1369	Q	28
53K	1370	E	24
53K	1389	B	76
53K	1389	E	26
53K	1392	Q	14
53K	1420	K	8
53K	1420	O	12
53K	1433	B	22
53K	1433	B	52
53K	1435	C	2
53K	1663	B	102
53K	1663	F	2
53K	2853	B	2
53K	2853	B	26
53K	3159	E	20
53K	3503	G	2
53K	3503	Q	22
54K	205	O	30
KXR	416	J	16
5L	287	H	28
1AL	706	M O	36
1BL	116	M O	36
1KL	1113	M O	36
1KL	1115	M O	36
1KL	3636	M O	36
1KL	5329	M O	36
LBS	810	G	4

PART NUMBER		GRP	PAGE
LBS	810	G	14
LBS	810	G	22
LFP	6	K	24
LFP	116	K	30
LFP	116	O	34
LFS	100	K	24
LFS	100	K	28
LFS	107	K	24
LFS	107	K	28
LNZ	102	G	20
LNZ	102	H	52
LNZ	103	D	10
LNZ	104	E	14
LNZ	104	E	20
LNZ	104	O	34
LNZ	105	B	76
LNZ	105	D	52
LNZ	105	D	54
LNZ	105	D	56
LNZ	105	D	58
LNZ	105	E	26
LNZ	105	F	2
LNZ	105	F	10
LNZ	105	F	12
LNZ	106	E	26
LNZ	203	B	96
LNZ	203	G	20
LNZ	203	G	28
LNZ	203	H	2
LNZ	203	H	76
LNZ	203	H	78
LNZ	203	O	12
LNZ	204	H	78
LNZ	204	K	8
LNZ	204	L	14
LNZ	205	B	22
LNZ	205	B	22
LNZ	205	B	38
LNZ	205	B	56
LNZ	205	B	56
LNZ	205	C	14
LNZ	205	D	50
LNZ	205	D	50
LNZ	205	D	54
LNZ	205	E	26
LNZ	205	F	2
LNZ	205	F	8
LNZ	205	H	20.02
LNZ	205	H	20.02
LNZ	205	L	10
LNZ	205	O	34
LNZ	205	Q	16
LNZ	205	Q	22
LNZ	205	Q	28
LNZ	206	B	22
LNZ	206	B	56
LNZ	206	H	20.02
LNZ	405	F	10

PART NUMBER		GRP	PAGE
LNZ	405	F	10
LNZ	405	K	2
LNZ	607	B	2
LWN	204	B	44
LWN	204	C	2
LWN	204	C	2
LWN	204	D	50
LWN	205	B	12
LWN	207	H	16
LWN	207	H	18
LWN	304	B	10
LWN	304	C	2
LWN	304	C	10
LWN	305	B	56
LWN	305	B	74
LWN	305	C	12
LWN	305	C	14
LWN	305	H	20.02
LWN	307	F	4
LWN	403	J	6
LWN	404	B	18
LWN	404	B	18
LWN	404	B	46
LWN	404	B	46
LWN	404	C	2
LWN	404	G	24
LWN	405	E	26
LWN	405	E	26
LWN	406	G	18.02
LWN	406	G	28
LWZ	202	H	52
LWZ	202	H	76
LWZ	202	H	78.02
LWZ	202	H	78.02
LWZ	202	K	2
LWZ	202	K	8
LWZ	202	K	14
LWZ	203	D	4
LWZ	203	D	10
LWZ	203	D	10
LWZ	203	D	50
LWZ	203	E	22
LWZ	203	E	30
LWZ	203	G	20
LWZ	203	G	20
LWZ	203	G	28
LWZ	203	H	32
LWZ	203	H	32
LWZ	203	M	34
LWZ	203	H	34
LWZ	203	H	34
LWZ	203	H	34
LWZ	203	H	36
LWZ	203	H	36
LWZ	203	H	36.02
LWZ	203	H	36.02
LWZ	203	H	42
LWZ	203	H	58

PART NUMBER		GRP	PAGE
LWZ	203	I	4
LWZ	203	I	14
LWZ	203	I	14
LWZ	203	I	20
LWZ	203	J	2
LWZ	203	J	6
LWZ	203	J	6
LWZ	203	J	6
LWZ	203	J	6
LWZ	203	J	12
LWZ	203	K	2
LWZ	203	K	2
LWZ	203	K	2
LWZ	203	K	4
LWZ	203	K	4
LWZ	203	K	4
LWZ	203	K	8
LWZ	203	K	10
LWZ	203	K	10
LWZ	203	K	10
LWZ	203	K	14
LWZ	203	K	16
LWZ	203	K	18
LWZ	203	K	18
LWZ	203	K	20
LWZ	203	K	20
LWZ	203	K	24
LWZ	203	K	30
LWZ	203	L	2
LWZ	203	M	6
LWZ	203	P	8
LWZ	203	M	8
LWZ	203	M	10
LWZ	203	M	10
LWZ	203	N	4
LWZ	203	N	6
LWZ	203	Q	6
LWZ	203	Q	16
LWZ	203	Q	28
LWZ	203	Q	28
LWZ	204	B	16
LWZ	204	B	24
LWZ	204	B	26
LWZ	204	B	36
LWZ	204	B	44
LWZ	204	B	62
LWZ	204	B	62
LWZ	204	B	70
LWZ	204	B	72
LWZ	204	B	72
LWZ	204	B	72
LWZ	204	C	8
LWZ	204	C	8
LWZ	204	D	2
LWZ	204	D	4
LWZ	204	D	4
LWZ	204	D	8
LWZ	204	D	12

PART NUMBER		GRP	PAGE
LWZ	204	D	12
LWZ	204	D	52
LWZ	204	E	6
LWZ	204	E	14
LWZ	204	E	14
LWZ	204	G	2
LWZ	204	G	2
LWZ	204	G	18.02
LWZ	204	G	18.02
LWZ	204	G	20
LWZ	204	G	28
LWZ	204	G	28
LWZ	204	G	28
LWZ	204	H	8
LWZ	204	H	24
LWZ	204	H	30
LWZ	204	H	32
LWZ	204	H	36.02
LWZ	204	H	42
LWZ	204	H	50
LWZ	204	H	54
LWZ	204	H	84
LWZ	204	H	86
LWZ	204	H	90
LWZ	204	I	4
LWZ	204	I	12
LWZ	204	I	20
LWZ	204	J	10
LWZ	204	J	12
LWZ	204	J	14
LWZ	204	J	16
LWZ	204	J	16
LWZ	204	K	2
LWZ	204	K	4
LWZ	204	K	4
LWZ	204	K	8
LWZ	204	K	18
LWZ	204	K	18
LWZ	204	K	20
LWZ	204	L	2
LWZ	204	L	4
LWZ	204	M	6
LWZ	204	N	2
LWZ	204	N	4
LWZ	204	Q	6
LWZ	204	Q	6
LWZ	205	B	76
LWZ	205	D	4
LWZ	205	D	4.02
LWZ	205	D	4.06
LWZ	205	D	52
LWZ	205	D	56
LWZ	205	E	18
LWZ	205	E	18
LWZ	205	E	20
LWZ	205	K	8
LWZ	206	B	2
LWZ	206	B	20

PART NUMBER	GRP	PAGE	PART NUMBER	GRP	PAGE	PART NUMBER	GRP	PAGE	PART NUMBER	GRP	PAGE	PART NUMBER	GRP	PAGE	PART NUMBER	GRP	PAGE
LWZ 206	B	20	LWZ 305	B	8	LWZ 405	D	6	NH 604041	L	14	NT 610041	E	8	PJZ 604	D	28.04
LWZ 206	B	50	LWZ 305	B	16	LWZ 405	Q	28	NH 604041	L	14	PC 7	B	82	PJZ 604	D	32
LWZ 206	B	50	LWZ 305	B	16	LWZ 406	G	30	NH 604041	N	4	PC 10	B	90	PJZ 604	D	34
LWZ 206	B	76	LWZ 305	B	22	LWZ 505	E	28	NH 604041	N	8	PCR 209	H	8	PJZ 604	D	38
LWZ 206	B	76	LWZ 305	B	22	LWZ 505	J	2	NH 604041	N	14	PCR 211	H	8	PJZ 604	D	40
LWZ 206	B	76	LWZ 305	B	22	LWZ 505	J	12	NH 604041	Q	6	PCR 307	G	20	PJZ 604	D	42.02
LWZ 206	E	20	LWZ 305	B	22	LWZ 510	G	12	NH 604041	Q	6	PCR 307	G	20	PJZ 604	D	44
LWZ 206	F	12	LWZ 305	B	22	LWZ 607	D	8	NH 604061	B	24	PCR 307	G	28	PJZ 604	D	46
LWZ 206	F	12	LWZ 305	B	30	MA 805	B	86	NH 605041	B	14	PCR 307	H	98	PJZ 604	D	48.02
LWZ 206	F	12	LWZ 305	B	44	MCZ 605	B	66	NH 605041	B	42	PCR 307	K	4	PJZ 804	L	2
LWZ 206	F	14	LWZ 305	B	44	MNZ 206	B	98	NH 605041	B	44	PCR 309	G	20	PJZ 1004	L	2
LWZ 206	G	14	LWZ 305	B	54	MNZ 206	B	98.02	NH 605041	B	66	PCR 407	D	10	PJZ 1004	L	4
LWZ 206	G	16	LWZ 305	B	56	MTP 402	J	6	NH 605041	B	74	PCR 407	D	10	PJZ 1005	H	36.02
LWZ 206	G	22	LWZ 305	B	56	N 5	B	14	NH 605041	B	76	PCR 407	D	50	PJZ 1005	H	48
LWZ 206	K	4	LWZ 305	B	56	N 9	Y B	42	NH 605041	B	102	PCR 409	C	12	PJZ 1005	N	8
LWZ 206	L	6	LWZ 305	B	66	N 12	Y B	90	NH 605041	B	102	PCR 409	D	10	PMP 308	K	18
LWZ 206	L	8	LWZ 305	B	68	NH 105041	H	78	NH 605041	B	102	PCR 409	D	12	PMP 308	K	20
LWZ 206	L	12	LWZ 305	B	68	NH 506041	C	14	NH 605041	C	10	PCR 409	G	12	PMP 516	K	8
LWZ 206	M	6	LWZ 305	B	74	NH 604041	B	36	NH 605041	C	12	PCR 409	G	12	PMZ 103	G	28
LWZ 207	F	12	LWZ 305	B	74	NH 604041	B	44	NH 605041	C	14	PCR 507	H	32	PMZ 105	G	30
LWZ 207	H	16	LWZ 305	B	76	NH 604041	B	62	NH 605041	D	4	PCR 607	D	10	PMZ 207	H	78.02
LWZ 212	F	6	LWZ 305	B	76	NH 604041	B	64	NH 605041	D	4.06	PCR 607	H	32	PMZ 207	H	78.02
LWZ 303	D	14	LWZ 305	C	10	NH 604041	B	68	NH 605041	D	6	PCR 607	H	32	PMZ 305	G	20
LWZ 303	D	16	LWZ 305	D	50	NH 604041	B	70	NH 605041	D	16.02	PCR 709	H	30	PMZ 305	G	20
LWZ 303	D	20	LWZ 305	D	52	NH 604041	B	92	NH 605041	D	50.06	PCR 709	H	90	PMZ 305	K	10
LWZ 303	D	22	LWZ 305	D	52	NH 604041	C	2	NH 605041	D	52	PCR 807	H	32	PMZ 306	H	36
LWZ 303	D	26	LWZ 305	F	2	NH 604041	D	8	NH 605041	D	52	PCR 809	H	98.02	PMZ 306	H	90
LWZ 303	D	28	LWZ 305	F	4	NH 604041	D	12	NH 605041	D	56	PCR 809	H	98.02	PMZ 306	H	98
LWZ 303	D	28.02	LWZ 305	G	6	NH 604041	D	12	NH 605041	E	30	PCR 809	N	8	PMZ 306	I	4
LWZ 303	D	28.04	LWZ 305	G	8	NH 604041	D	48.06	NH 605041	F	4	PCR 809	Q	16	PMZ 306	I	14
LWZ 303	D	32	LWZ 305	G	30	NH 604041	D	48.10	NH 605041	F	10	PFR 106	L	10.02	PMZ 306	K	2
LWZ 303	D	34	LWZ 305	H	8	NH 604041	D	50	NH 605041	G	30	PFS 103	K	6	PMZ 306	K	4
LWZ 303	D	38	LWZ 305	H	20.02	NH 604041	D	50	NH 605041	H	8	PFS 104	N	4	PMZ 306	K	4
LWZ 303	D	40	LWZ 305	H	20.02	NH 604041	D	50	NH 605041	J	12	PFS 106	K	6	PMZ 306	M	10
LWZ 303	D	42.02	LWZ 305	H	20.02	NH 604041	D	52	NH 605041	K	8	PFS 106	K	6	PMZ 306	N	14
LWZ 303	D	44	LWZ 305	H	32	NH 604041	D	56	NH 605041	K	22	PFS 308	L	2	PMZ 306	O	32
LWZ 303	D	46	LWZ 305	Q	16	NH 604041	G	2	NH 605041	L	6.02	PFS 310	L	2	PMZ 307	E	30
LWZ 303	D	48.02	LWZ 306	B	20	NH 604041	G	18.02	NH 605041	L	8	PFS 310	L	4	PMZ 307	G	20
LWZ 303	D	48.04	LWZ 306	B	76	NH 604041	G	20	NH 605041	L	10	PFS 410	J	10	PMZ 307	G	28
LWZ 303	D	48.08	LWZ 306	E	26	NH 604041	G	28	NH 605041	Q	28	PFS 512	N	2	PMZ 307	H	90
LWZ 303	Q	14	LWZ 306	H	32	NH 604041	G	28	NH 605041	Q	28	PJ 8504	D	50.06	PMZ 307	H	98
LWZ 303	Q	24	LWZ 307	F	14	NH 604041	G	30	NH 606041	H	22	PJ 8514	D	50.06	PMZ 307	Q	28
LWZ 303	Q	26	LWZ 308	F	14	NH 604041	H	8	NH 606041	H	22.02	PJZ 602	H	56	PMZ 308	D	4
LWZ 304	B	24	LWZ 402	L	4	NH 604041	H	24	NH 606041	L	10.02	PJZ 602	H	56	PMZ 308	D	4.02
LWZ 304	B	24	LWZ 403	D	14	NH 604041	H	30	NH 606041	L	10.02	PJZ 602	H	56.02	PMZ 308	D	4.06
LWZ 304	B	64	LWZ 403	D	16	NH 604041	H	54	NH 608041	L	6.02	PJZ 602	H	56.02	PMZ 308	D	50
LWZ 304	B	64	LWZ 403	N	14	NH 604041	H	84	NRP 6	D	8	PJZ 602	H	58	PMZ 308	H	32
LWZ 304	B	68	LWZ 403	N	14	NH 604041	H	90	NRP 8	D	6	PJZ 602	H	58	PMZ 308	H	36.02
LWZ 304	C	2	LWZ 403	N	14	NH 604041	I	20	NRP 9	D	6	PJZ 602	H	60	PMZ 308	H	36.02
LWZ 304	C	8	LWZ 403	N	20	NH 604041	J	10	NRP 1028	D	4.02	PJZ 602	H	60	PMZ 308	H	48
LWZ 304	C	10	LWZ 404	B	6	NH 604041	J	14	NRP 1141	D	4.06	PJZ 602	H	62	PMZ 308	H	98
LWZ 304	C	10	LWZ 404	B	8	NH 604041	J	16	NRP 1199	D	6	PJZ 602	H	62	PMZ 308	J	6
LWZ 304	D	2	LWZ 404	B	18	NH 604041	K	4	NRP 1201	D	8	PJZ 602	H	64	PMZ 308	J	6
LWZ 304	D	4	LWZ 404	G	16	NH 604041	L	2	NT 605041	H	6.06	PJZ 604	D	20	PMZ 308	J	12
LWZ 304	G	14	LWZ 404	G	16	NH 604041	L	4	NT 606041	B	22	PJZ 604	D	22	PMZ 308	K	4
LWZ 304	G	14	LWZ 404	H	2	NH 604041	L	12	NT 606041	B	56	PJZ 604	D	26	PMZ 308	K	8
LWZ 304	J	16	LWZ 404	H	4	NH 604041	L	14	NT 606041	H	20.02	PJZ 604	D	28	PMZ 308	M	10
LWZ 304	Q	22	LWZ 404	J	2	NH 604041	L	14	NT 607041	D	8	PJZ 604	D	28.02	PMZ 310	D	10

PART NUMBER		GRP	PAGE	PART NUMBER		GRP	PAGE	PART NUMBER		GRP	PAGE	PART NUMBER		GRP	PAGE	PART NUMBER		GRP	PAGE	PART NUMBER		GRP	PAGE
PMZ	310	D	10	PTZ	1003	N	2	PWZ	104	I	20	PWZ	108	G	14	RFR	305	H	90	SE	106501	L	14
PMZ	310	H	34	PTZ	1003	N	4	PWZ	104	J	10	PWZ	108	G	22	RFR	503	H	90	SE	604051	G	14
PMZ	310	H	36.02	PTZ	1004	H	42	PWZ	104	J	14	PWZ	108	K	18	RGK	6476	O	2	SE	604051	G	22
PMZ	310	H	58	PTZ	1004	H	50	PWZ	104	J	16	PWZ	202	H	78.02	RGN	6476	O	2	SE	604051	L	2
PMZ	310	H	98	PTZ	1004	J	10	PWZ	104	J	16	PWZ	202	M	6	RKC	92	B	92	SE	604051	L	4
PMZ	310	N	16	PTZ	1004	M	10	PWZ	104	K	2	PWZ	203	D	4	RKC	638	H	6.02	SE	604051	L	14
PMZ	310	N	24	PTZ	1004	M	10	PWZ	104	K	4	PWZ	203	D	4.02	RKC	698	B	98	SE	604061	L	14
PMZ	314	Q	6	PTZ	6034	H	50	PWZ	104	K	4	PWZ	203	D	4.06	RKC	723	B	94	SE	604081	N	8
PMZ	316	G	96	PWN	105	B	38	PWZ	104	K	8	PWZ	203	D	50	RKC	918	B	80	SF	604101	O	34
PMZ	316	D	10	PWN	106	B	12	PWZ	104	K	8	PWZ	203	G	2	RKC	1624	D	16.02	SH	504051	D	50.04
PMZ	316	H	34	PWN	106	B	12	PWZ	104	K	18	PWZ	203	G	2	RKC	3056	B	94.02	SH	505051	B	22
PMZ	316	H	44	PWN	106	B	20	PWZ	104	L	2	PWZ	203	H	2	RKC	3137	B	98.02	SH	505051	B	56
PMZ	316	N	24	PWN	106	B	38	PWZ	104	L	4	PWZ	203	H	76	RKC	3169	D	48.12	SH	505051	H	20.02
PMZ	318	H	34	PWN	106	B	50	PWZ	104	N	2	PWZ	203	K	10	RKC	3170	D	48.12	SH	505061	B	76
PMZ	320	H	34	PWN	106	B	50	PWZ	104	N	4	PWZ	203	M	10	RMP	212	K	14	SH	505061	B	76
PMZ	406	H	48	PWN	106	B	50	PWZ	104	O	34	PWZ	203	N	6	RMP	308	H	70	SH	505061	Q	16
PMZ	408	B	72	PWZ	102	H	52	PWZ	105	B	14	PWZ	203	O	12	RMP	308	H	70	SH	505071	D	50.02
PMZ	408	H	36.02	PWZ	102	K	14	PWZ	105	B	24	PWZ	203	Q	16	RMP	310	J	2	SH	505091	D	50.04
PMZ	408	H	42	PWZ	102	M	4	PWZ	105	B	42	PWZ	204	D	2	RMP	2307	M	8	SH	506091	B	50.02
PMZ	408	J	2	PWZ	103	D	10	PWZ	105	B	62	PWZ	204	D	4	RMZ	204	H	48	SH	604041	C	20
PMZ	408	L	2	PWZ	103	G	20	PWZ	105	B	66	PWZ	204	D	8	RP	504	B	82	SH	604041	C	22
PMZ	408	L	4	PWZ	103	H	36.02	PWZ	105	B	68	PWZ	204	H	8	RPS	1012	C	20	SH	604041	D	50.02
PMZ	408	N	2	PWZ	103	H	36.02	PWZ	105	B	76	PWZ	204	H	84	RTC	198	H	82	SH	604041	G	30
PMZ	408	Q	6	PWZ	103	H	48	PWZ	105	B	76	PWZ	204	H	86	RTC	198	H	86	SH	604041	H	98.02
PMZ	410	B	70	PWZ	103	H	48	PWZ	105	B	76	PWZ	204	I	4	RTC	220	H	28	SH	604041	H	98.02
PMZ	410	G	14	PWZ	103	H	90	PWZ	105	D	4	PWZ	204	I	12	RTC	432	H	36	SH	604051	L	6.02
PMZ	410	G	22	PWZ	103	H	98	PWZ	105	D	6	PWZ	204	J	12	RTC	465	H	56	SH	604061	B	2
PMZ	410	H	54	PWZ	103	I	14	PWZ	105	D	50	PWZ	204	J	16	RTC	465	H	56	SH	604061	B	6
PMZ	410	L	2	PWZ	103	J	6	PWZ	105	D	50	PWZ	204	N	14	RTC	465	H	58	SH	604061	B	8
PMZ	410	L	4	PWZ	103	J	6	PWZ	105	D	52	PWZ	204	N	14	RTC	465	H	58	SH	604061	B	22
PMZ	410	N	8	PWZ	103	K	2	PWZ	105	D	54	PWZ	205	B	76	RTC	465	H	60	SH	604061	B	24
PMZ	410	Q	6	PWZ	103	K	8	PWZ	105	D	58	PWZ	205	D	50	RTC	465	H	60	SH	604061	B	26
PMZ	412	D	10	PWZ	103	M	10	PWZ	105	F	12	PWZ	205	D	54	RTC	465	H	62	SH	604061	B	30
PMZ	412	H	32	PWZ	103	N	4	PWZ	105	G	6	PWZ	205	E	18	RTC	465	H	62	SH	604061	B	32
PMZ	416	H	36.02	PWZ	103	N	8	PWZ	105	G	6	PWZ	205	E	20	RTC	465	H	64	SH	604061	B	64
PMZ	416	L	12	PWZ	103	N	24	PWZ	105	G	6	PWZ	205	K	18	RTC	603	H	28	SH	604061	B	92
PMZ	416	L	14	PWZ	104	B	16	PWZ	105	G	8	PWZ	205	L	10	RTC	603	H	30	SH	604061	C	20
PT	803	B	84	PWZ	104	B	24	PWZ	105	G	16	PWZ	205	L	10	RTC	702	H	86	SH	604061	D	2
PT	805	B	78	PWZ	104	B	44	PWZ	105	G	16	PWZ	205	L	10	RTC	1733	H	6.04	SH	604061	D	4
PTP	603	N	12	PWZ	104	B	44	PWZ	105	G	24	PWZ	205	L	10	RTC	1738	H	6.04	SH	604061	D	4.02
PTZ	603	H	32	PWZ	104	B	62	PWZ	105	G	30	PWZ	205	O	34	RTC	1738	H	6.04	SH	604061	D	4.06
PTZ	603	H	52	PWZ	104	B	70	PWZ	105	H	8	PWZ	206	D	50	RTC	1739	H	6.04	SH	604061	G	30
PTZ	603	K	8	PWZ	104	D	2	PWZ	105	I	16	PWZ	206	F	12	RTC	1739	H	6.04	SH	604061	I	4
PTZ	604	H	40	PWZ	104	D	4	PWZ	105	J	12	PWZ	206	F	14	RTC	1760	B	94	SH	604061	I	12
PTZ	604	H	50	PWZ	104	D	4	PWZ	105	K	4	PWZ	305	E	18	RTC	1773	H	6.02	SH	604061	N	8
PTZ	605	D	48.06	PWZ	104	D	12	PWZ	105	K	8	PWZ	305	E	18	RTC	1773	H	6.04	SH	604061	O	34
PTZ	605	D	48.10	PWZ	104	D	50	PWZ	105	K	14	PWZ	306	E	20	RTC	1773	H	6.04	SH	604101	B	54
PTZ	605	Q	26	PWZ	104	D	50	PWZ	105	K	18	PWZ	306	M	6	RTC	1775	H	6.02	SH	605041	D	4.02
PTZ	606	H	78.02	PWZ	104	E	14	PWZ	105	L	6.02	PZZ	606	L	2	RTC	1776	H	6.02	SH	605041	D	4.06
PTZ	803	C	12	PWZ	104	E	14	PWZ	105	L	12	PZZ	1006	L	2	RTC	1780	H	6.04	SH	605051	K	8
PTZ	803	H	88	PWZ	104	G	2	PWZ	105	Q	16	RFR	102	H	98.02	RTC	1781	H	6.04	SH	605061	B	22
PTZ	804	N	6	PWZ	104	G	2	PWZ	105	Q	22	RFR	110	H	32	RTC	1782	H	6.04	SH	605061	B	30
PTZ	804	N	6	PWZ	104	G	20	PWZ	105	Q	22	RFR	207	I	16	RTP	403	K	18	SH	605061	B	56
PTZ	804	N	6	PWZ	104	G	28	PWZ	106	E	10	RFR	208	D	8	RTP	403	K	22	SH	605061	B	102
PTZ	805	C	12	PWZ	104	G	30	PWZ	106	K	4	RFR	210	I	16	RTP	604	K	14	SH	605061	E	8
PTZ	805	C	22	PWZ	104	H	78	PWZ	107	E	8	RFR	210	I	16	RTP	604	K	24	SH	605061	G	30
PTZ	806	C	22	PWZ	104	I	4	PWZ	107	F	4	RFR	305	H	32	RTP	604	K	30	SH	605061	L	8
PTZ	806	N	6	PWZ	104	I	12	PWZ	108	G	14	RFR	305	H	32	RZS	1216	C	20	SH	605061	L	10

PART NUMBER	GRP	PAGE
SH 605061	L	10
SH 605061	L	10
SH 605071	B	102
SH 605071	H	20.02
SH 605081	C	20
SH 605081	D	56
SH 605081	E	8
SH 605081	E	10
SH 605081	K	14
SH 605081	L	8.02
SH 605081	L	10
SH 605091	B	94.02
SH 605101	B	22
SH 605101	B	22
SH 605101	B	56
SH 605111	B	56
SH 605131	H	20.02
SH 606061	B	102
SH 606061	L	6.02
SH 606071	L	8.02
SH 606081	B	102
SH 606081	L	6.02
SH 606101	B	102
SH 606101	F	12
SK 604031	B	94.02
SM 105161	M	8
SM 105161	M	8
TCZ 106	B	50.02
TD 861	B	94
TFP 1006	K	10
TFP 1006	K	16
TFP 1010	K	16
TFS 106	K	10
TFS 106	K	12
TFS 106	K	16
TFS 106	K	24
TFS 106	K	28
TKC 285	B	94
TKC 1155	B	88
TKC 1224	H	6.04
TKC 1409	B	88
TKC 1409	B	88
TKC 1423	B	98
TKC 1424	B	98
TKC 1425	B	84
TKC 1466	B	90
TKC 1470	B	94
TKC 1570	D	50.02
TKC 1615	B	98
TKC 1615	B	98.02
TKC 1830	B	86
TKC 1832	D	50.06
TKC 1840	B	84
TKC 1974	B	86
TKC 1990	D	50.06
TKC 2006	B	86
TKC 2748	B	88
TKC 2755	H	6.04

PART NUMBER	GRP	PAGE
TKC 3215	B	98.02
TKC 3222	D	16.02
TKC 3238	B	90
TKC 3239	B	88
TKC 3287	H	6.04
TKC 3289	H	6.04
TKC 3305	B	96.04
TKC 3306	B	96.04
TKC 3320	B	96.04
TL 5	B	96.04
TL 11	B	94
TL 11	B	94
TL 11	B	94.02
TL 11	B	96.04
TL 11	B	98.02
TN 3208	B	90
TRS 710	C	12
TRS 912	C	20
TRS 1114	B	86
TRS 1418	B	92
UHN 105	G	30
UHN 305	E	8
UHN 305	E	8
UHN 400	E	22
UHN 445	E	22
UHN 490	E	22
UHN 490	G	30
UKC 490	D	50.06
UKC 673	D	50.06
UKC 759	B	92
UKC 769	C	16
UKC 774	B	92
UKC 1110	B	84
UKC 1413	B	94
UKC 1413	B	96.04
UKC 1413	B	98.02
UKC 1813	B	94
UKC 1846	B	94
UKC 1905	B	96.02
UKC 1905	B	96.02
UKC 1925	B	96.02
UKC 1925	B	96.02
UKC 1938	B	84
UKC 2130	B	96.02
UKC 2284	B	94
UKC 2334	B	88
UKC 2335	B	88
UKC 2460	B	88
UKC 2598	B	80
UKC 2643	B	98
UKC 2643	B	98.02
UKC 2683	B	98
UKC 2992	D	50.04
UKC 3009	D	50.04
UKC 3120	B	98
UKC 3123	B	98
UKC 3124	B	98
UKC 3126	B	98

PART NUMBER	GRP	PAGE
UKC 3126	B	98.02
UKC 3127	B	98
UKC 3127	B	98.02
UKC 3128	B	98
UKC 3128	B	98.02
UKC 3128	H	20.04
UKC 3131	B	98
UKC 3131	B	98.02
UKC 3272	D	50.04
UKC 3281	D	50.04
UKC 3532	B	92
UKC 3649	B	96.02
UKC 3652	B	90
UKC 3653	B	90
UKC 3793	D	16.02
UKC 4073	B	98
UKC 4073	B	98.02
UKC 4090	B	94
UKC 4131	D	50.06
UKC 4209	B	94.02
UKC 4222	D	50.06
UKC 4223	D	50.06
UKC 4254	B	84
UKC 4260	H	90
UKC 4294	B	96.04
UKC 4309	B	96.04
UKC 4415	D	50.06
UKC 4620	D	50.06
UKC 4902	B	88
UKC 4960	D	56
UKC 4962	D	16.02
UKC 5254	B	102
UKC 5374	D	50.04
UKC 5955	B	78
UKC 5956	B	78
UKC 5957	B	78
UKC 5958	B	78
UKC 7375	B	94.02
UKC 7722	B	96.04
UKC 7764	B	96.04
UKC 7765	B	96.04
UKC 7851	B	88
UKC 7916	B	94.02
UKC 8119	B	94.02
UKC 8307	B	96.04
UKC 8544	B	96.04
URP 1145	D	4.04
URP 1145	D	4.06
URP 1148	D	4.04
URP 1159	D	4.06
WA 106041	B	54
WA 106041	B	54
WA 106041	B	92
WA 106041	D	4.02
WA 106041	D	4.02
WA 106041	D	4.06
WA 106041	D	50.02
WA 106041	G	30

PART NUMBER	GRP	PAGE
WA 106041	G	30
WA 106041	G	30
WA 106041	L	14
WA 106041	L	14
WA 106041	L	14
WA 106041	N	8
WA 106041	N	24
WA 108051	B	30
WA 108051	B	76
WA 108051	B	94.02
WA 108051	B	94.02
WA 108051	B	98
WA 108051	B	98
WA 108051	B	98.02
WA 108051	B	98.02
WA 108051	B	102
WA 108051	B	102
WA 108051	B	102
WA 108051	B	102
WA 108051	D	50.06
WA 108051	E	8
WA 108051	G	30
WA 108051	L	6.02
WA 108051	L	8
WA 108051	L	8
WA 108051	L	8.02
WA 108051	L	10
WA 108051	O	34
WA 110061	B	20
WA 110061	B	20
WA 110061	B	20
WA 110061	B	20
WA 110061	B	50.02
WA 110061	B	76
WA 110061	B	76
WA 110061	B	76
WA 110061	B	102
WA 110061	B	102
WA 110061	C	22
WA 110061	E	26
WA 110061	F	12
WA 110061	F	12
WA 110061	F	14
WA 110061	G	2
WA 110061	L	6
WA 110061	L	6
WA 110061	L	6.02
WA 110061	L	8
WA 110061	L	8.02
WA 110061	L	12
WA 116101	C	18
WA 702101	H	78
WA 702101	I	20
WA 702101	N	16
WA 702101	O	12
WA 704061	N	20
WC 200	H	12
WC 108051	B	98

PART NUMBER	GRP	PAGE
WC 108051	B	98.02
WC 108051	D	56
WC 108051	H	20.02
WC 110061	B	102
WC 110061	L	10.02
WE 600061	H	22.02
WE 702101	O	12
WF 8	B	94
WF 508	B	90
WF 511	B	86
WF 513	B	94
WF 513	B	94.02
WF 524	B	94
WF 524	B	94
WF 524	B	96
WF 524	B	96.02
WF 524	B	96.04
WF 600041	B	30
WF 600071	D	8
WKN 404	C	8
WKN 404	H	16
WKN 404	H	16
WKN 404	H	18
WKN 505	B	6
WKN 505	B	30
WL 205	D	50.06
WL 207	B	98
WL 208	B	78
WL 208	B	78
WL 208	B	82
WL 208	B	82
WL 208	B	82
WL 208	B	84
WL 208	B	84
WL 208	B	86
WL 208	B	86
WL 208	B	86
WL 208	B	92
WL 208	B	92
WL 208	B	94
WL 210	B	78
WL 221	B	86
WL 105001	H	78
WL 106001	L	14
WL 600040	D	4.06
WL 600040	D	56
WL 600041	B	22
WL 600041	B	54
WL 600041	B	54
WL 600041	B	92
WL 600041	B	98
WL 600041	B	98.02
WL 600041	C	20
WL 600041	C	20
WL 600041	C	22
WL 600041	D	4.02
WL 600041	D	50.02
WL 600041	D	50.04

PART NUMBER	GRP	PAGE
WL 600041	G	30
WL 600041	G	30
WL 600041	H	98.02
WL 600041	H	98.02
WL 600041	L	6.02
WL 600041	L	12
WL 600041	L	14
WL 600041	L	14
WL 600041	L	14
WL 600041	L	14
WL 600041	N	8
WL 600041	N	8
WL 600041	N	14
WL 600041	N	14
WL 600041	N	24
WL 600041	O	34
WL 600051	B	44
WL 600051	B	76
WL 600051	B	76
WL 600051	B	76
WL 600051	B	94.02
WL 600051	B	102
WL 600051	B	102
WL 600051	B	102
WL 600051	B	102
WL 600051	B	102
WL 600051	C	8
WL 600051	C	14
WL 600051	C	14
WL 600051	C	18
WL 600051	C	20
WL 600051	D	4
WL 600051	D	4.06
WL 600051	D	50
WL 600051	D	50
WL 600051	D	50.02
WL 600051	D	50.02
WL 600051	D	50.04
WL 600051	D	50.06
WL 600051	D	52
WL 600051	D	52
WL 600051	D	54
WL 600051	D	54
WL 600051	D	54
WL 600051	D	54
WL 600051	D	56
WL 600051	D	56
WL 600051	D	58
WL 600051	D	58
WL 600051	D	58
WL 600051	D	58
WL 600051	E	8
WL 600051	E	10
WL 600051	E	30
WL 600051	E	30
WL 600051	F	12
WL 600051	F	12
WL 600051	G	6

PART NUMBER	GRP	PAGE
WL 600051	G	6
WL 600051	G	14
WL 600051	G	14
WL 600051	G	16
WL 600051	G	22
WL 600051	G	22
WL 600051	G	24
WL 600051	G	30
WL 600051	G	30
WL 600051	H	6.06
WL 600051	H	20.04
WL 600051	H	36
WL 600051	I	16
WL 600051	J	16
WL 600051	K	8
WL 600051	K	14
WL 600051	K	18
WL 600051	K	22
WL 600051	L	6.02
WL 600051	L	6.02
WL 600051	L	8
WL 600051	L	8
WL 600051	L	8.02
WL 600051	L	10
WL 600051	L	10
WL 600051	L	10
WL 600051	L	10
WL 600051	L	12
WL 600051	Q	28
WL 600051	Q	28
WL 600051	Q	28
WL 600051	Q	28
WL 600061	B	22
WL 600061	B	50.02
WL 600061	B	56
WL 600061	B	76
WL 600061	B	102
WL 600061	B	102
WL 600061	C	14
WL 600061	C	14
WL 600061	D	56
WL 600061	D	56
WL 600061	H	20.02
WL 600061	H	22
WL 600061	H	22.02
WL 600061	L	6
WL 600061	L	6
WL 600061	L	6.02
WL 600061	L	8.02
WL 600061	L	10.02
WL 600061	L	10.02
WL 600081	L	6.02
WL 600401	D	4.02
WL 605091	D	16.02
WL 700100	D	4.02
WL 700100	D	4.06
WL 700101	H	90
WL 700101	H	90

PART NUMBER	GRP	PAGE
WL 700101	I	20
WL 700101	N	14
WL 700101	N	16
WL 700101	N	24
WL 700101	N	24
WL 700101	O	12
WM 95	B	98
WNZ 103	H	6
WP 5	D	50.06
WP 5	D	50.06
WP 7	B	98
WP 7	B	98.02
WP 8	B	90
WP 9	B	88
WP 17	H	20.04
WP 18	B	82
WP 36	B	94
WP 36	B	94.02
WP 139	H	20.04
WP 184	B	90
X2A 2750	O	8
X2A 2751	O	8
X2A 2755	O	10
X2A 2768	O	4
X2A 2769	O	4
X2A 2794	O	30
X2A 2795	O	30
X2A 2796	O	30
X2A 3220	O	6
X2K 2095	O	8
X2K 2096	O	8
X2K 2116	O	10
X2K 2119	O	4
X2K 2120	O	4
X2K 2750	O	8
X2K 2751	O	8
X2K 2755	O	10
X2K 2768	O	4
X2K 2769	O	4
X2K 2794	O	30
X2K 2795	O	30
X2K 2796	O	30
X2K 3220	O	6
X2N 2095	O	8
X2N 2096	O	8
X2N 2116	O	10
X2N 2119	O	4
X2N 2120	O	4
X2N 2122	O	28
X2N 2750	O	8
X2N 2751	O	8
X2N 2755	O	10
X2N 2768	O	4
X2N 2769	O	4
X2N 2794	O	30
X2N 2795	O	30
X2N 2796	O	30
X2N 3220	O	6

PART NUMBER	GRP	PAGE
X2T 2750	O	8
X2T 2751	O	8
X2T 2755	O	10
X2T 2768	O	4
X2T 2769	O	4
X2T 2794	O	30
X2T 2795	O	30
X2T 2796	O	30
X2T 3220	O	6
XGA 2456	O	2
XGA 2772	O	18
XGA 2777	O	14
XGA 2778	O	14
XGA 2781	O	18
XGA 2786	O	14
XGA 2787	O	16
XGA 3223	O	6
XGK 2021	O	18
XGK 2022	O	14
XGK 2023	O	14
XGK 2024	O	14
XGK 2025	O	16
XGK 2027	O	18
XGK 2028	O	20
XGK 2029	O	20
XGK 2456	O	2
XGK 2772	O	18
XGK 2777	O	14
XGK 2778	O	14
XGK 2781	O	18
XGK 2786	O	14
XGK 2787	O	16
XGK 3223	O	6
XGN 1953	O	32
XGN 2021	O	18
XGN 2022	O	14
XGN 2023	O	14
XGN 2024	O	14
XGN 2025	O	16
XGN 2028	O	20
XGN 2029	O	20
XGN 2772	O	18
XGN 2777	O	14
XGN 2778	O	14
XGN 2781	O	18
XGN 2786	O	14
XGN 2787	O	16
XGN 3223	O	6
XGT 1953	O	32
XGT 2028	O	20
XGT 2029	O	20
XGT 2456	O	2
XGT 2772	O	18
XGT 2777	O	14
XGT 2778	O	14
XGT 2781	O	18
XGT 2786	O	14
XGT 2787	O	16

PART NUMBER	GRP	PAGE
XGT 2787	O	16
XGT 3223	O	6
YN 2908	B	98
YN 2908	B	98
YN 2908	B	98
YN 2908	B	98.02
YN 2908	B	98.02
YN 2908	B	98.02
ZCS 404	B	62
ZCS 405	B	24
ZCS 405	B	64
ZCS 405	Q	22
ZCS 406	B	24
ZCS 507	B	68
ZCS 609	M	6
ZCS 804	C	12
ZCT 605	K	16
ZPS 524	E	28
ZPS 524	E	28.02
ZPT 1003	H	44

PART NUMBER	GRP	PAGE

PART NUMBER	GRP	PAGE

Published by Brooklands Books Ltd., PO Box 146, Cobham, Surrey KT11 1LG, England Phone: 01932 865051 Fax: 01932 868803
E-mail: sales@brooklands-books.com www.brooklands-books.com

Part Number: AKM 0036

ISBN: 9780948207419 Ref: MG51PH 2332/11T4

OFFICIAL TECHNICAL BOOKS

Brooklands Technical Books has been formed to supply owners, restorers and professional repairers with official factory literature.

Model	Original Part No.	ISBN
Workshop Manuals		
Austin-Healey 100 BN1 & BN2	97H997D	9780907073925
Austin-Healey 100/6 & 3000 (100/6 - BN4, BN6, 3000 MK. 1, 2, 3 - BN7, BT7, BJ7 & BJ8)	AKD1179	9780948207471
Austin-Healey Sprite Mk. 1 Frogeye	AKD4884	9781855201262
Austin-Healey Sprite Mk. 2, Mk. 3 & Mk. 4 and MG Midget Mk. 1, Mk. 2 & Mk. 3	AKD4021	9781855202818
Parts Catalogues / Service Parts Lists		
Austin-Healey 100 BN1 & BN2	050 Edition 3	9781783180363
Austin-Healey 100/6 BN4	AKD1423	9781783180493
Austin-Healey 100/6 BN6	AKD855 Ed.2	9781783180486
Austin-Healey 3000 Mk. 1 and Mk. 2 (BN7 & BT7) Mk. 1 BN7 & BT7 Car no. 101 to 13750, Mk. 2 BN7 Car no. 13751 to 18888, Mk. 2 BT7 Car no. 13751 to 19853	AKD1151 Ed.5	9781783180370
Austin-Healey 3000 Mk. 2 and Mk. 3 (BJ7 & BJ8) BJ7 Mk. 2 Car no. 17551 to 25314 and BJ8 Mk. 3 Car no. 25315 to 43026	AKD 3523 & AKD 3524	9781783180387
Austin-Healey Sprite Mk. 1 & Mk. 2 and MG Midget Mk. 1	AKD 3566 & AKD 3567	9781783180509
Austin-Healey Sprite Mk. 3 & Mk. 4 and MG Midget Mk. 2 & Mk. 3 (Mechanical & Body Edition 1969)	AKD 3513 & AKD 3514	9781783180554
Austin-Healey Sprite Mk. 3 & Mk. 4 and MG Midget Mk. 2 & Mk. 3 (Feb 1977 Edition)	AKM 0036	9780948207419
Handbooks		
Austin-Healey 100	97H996E	9781869826352
Austin-Healey 100/6	97H996H	9781870642903
Austin-Healey 3000 Mk 1 & 2	AKD3915A	9781869826369
Austin-Healey 3000 Mk 3	AKD4094B	9781869826376
Austin-Healey Sprite Mk 1 'Frogeye'	97H1583A	9780948207945
Also Available		
Austin-Healey 100/6 & 3000 Mk. 1, 2 & 3 Owners Workshop Manual		9781783180455
Austin-Healey Sprite Mk. 1, 2, 3 & 4 MG Midget 1, 2, 3 & 1500 1958-1980 Owners Workshop Manual Glovebox Edition		9781855201255
Austin-Healey Sprite Mk. 1, 2, 3 & 4 MG Midget 1, 2, 3 & 1500 1958-1980 Owners Workshop Manual		9781783180332
Carburetters		
SU Carburetters Tuning Tips & Techniques		9781855202559
Restoration Guide		
Restoring Sprite & Midgets		9781855205987
Road Test Series		
Austin-Healey 100 & 100/6 Gold Portfolio 1952-1959		9781855200487
Austin-Healey 3000 Road Test Portfolio		9791783180394
Austin-Healey Frogeye Sprite Road Test Portfolio 1958-1961		9781783180530
Austin-Healey Sprite Gold Portfolio 1958-1971		9781855203716

From Austin-Healey specialists, Amazon and all good motoring bookshops.

Brooklands Books Ltd., P.O. Box 146, Cobham, Surrey, KT11 1LG, England, UK

OFFICIAL TECHNICAL BOOKS

Brooklands Technical Books has been formed to supply owners, restorers and professional repairers with official factory literature.

Workshop Manuals

Title	Part No.	ISBN
Midget Instruction Manual		9781855200739
Midget TD & TF	AKD580A	9781870642552
MGA 1500 1600 & 1600 Mk. 2	AKD600D	9781869826307
MGA Twin Cam	AKD926B	9781855208179
Austin-Healey Sprite Mk. 2, Mk. 3 & Mk. 4 and MG Midget Mk. 1, Mk. 2 & Mk. 3	AKD4021	9781855202818
Midget 1500	AKM4071B	9781855201699
MGB & MGB GT	AKD3259 & AKD4957	9781855201743
MGB GT V8 Supplement		9781855201859
MGB, MGB GT and MGB GT V8		9781783180578
MGC	AKD 7133	9781855201828
Rover 25 & MG ZR 1999-2005	RCL0534ENGBB	9781855208834
Rover 75 & MG ZT 1999-2005	RCL0536ENGBB	9781855208841
MGF - 1.6 MPi, 1.8 MPi, 1.8VVC	RCL 0051ENG, RCL0057ENG & RCL0124	9781855207165
MGF Electrical Manual 1996-2000 MY	RCL0341	9781855209077
MG TF	RCL0493	9781855207493
MGB Tourer & GT (Pub 1969)	AKD3900J	9781855200609
MGB Tourer & GT (Pub 1974)	AKD7598	9781869826727
MGB Tourer & GT (Pub 1976)	AKM3661	9781869826703
MGB GT V8	AKD8423	9781869826710
MGB Tourer & GT (US 1968)	AKD7059B	9781870642514
MGB Tourer & GT (US 1971)	AKD7881	9781870642521
MGB Tourer & GT (US 1973)	AKD8155	9781870642538
MGB Tourer (US 1975)	AKD3286	9781870642545
MGB (US 1979)	AKM8098	9781855200722
MGB Tourer & GT Tuning	CAKD4034L	9780948207051
MGB Special Tuning 1800cc	AKD4034	9780948207006
MGC	AKD4887B	9781869826734
MGF (Modern shape)	RCL0332ENG	9781855208339

Parts Catalogues

Title	Part No.	ISBN
MGA 1500	AKD1055	9781870642569
MGA 1600 Mk. 1 & Mk. 2	AKD1215	9781870642613
Austin-Healey Sprite Mk. 1 & Mk. 2 and MG Midget Mk. 1 (Mechanical & Body Edition)	AKD3566 & AKD3567	9781783180509
Austin-Healey Sprite Mk. 3 & Mk. 4 and MG Midget Mk. 2 & Mk. 3 (Mechanical & Body Edition 1969)	AKD3513 & AKD35149781783180554	
Austin-Healey Sprite Mk. 3 & Mk. 4 and MG Midget Mk. 2 & Mk. 3 (Feb 1977 Edition)	AKM0036	9780948207419
MGB up to Sept 1976	AKM0039	9780948207068
MGB Sept 1976 on	AKM0037	9780948207440

Owners Handbooks

Title	Part No.	ISBN
Midget Series TD		9781870642910
Midget TF and TF 1500 Operation Manual	AKD658A	9781870642934
MGA 1500	AKD598G	9781855202924
MGA 1600	AKD1172C	9781855201668
MGA 1600 Mk. 2	AKD1958A	9781855201675
MGA Twin Cam (Operation)	AKD879	9781855207929
MGA Twin Cam (Operation)	AKD879B	9781855207936
MGA 1500 Special Tuning	AKD819A	9781783181728
MGA 1500 and 1600 Mk. 1 Special Tuning	AKD819B	9781783181735
Midget TF and TF 1500	AKD210A	9781855202979
Midget Mk. 3 (GB 1967-74)	AKD7596	9781855201477
Midget (Pub 1978)	AKM3229	9781855200906
Midget Mk. 3 (US 1967-74)	AKD7883	9781855206311
Midget Mk. 3 (US 1976)	AKM3436	9781855201767
Midget Mk. 3 (US 1979)	AKM4386	9781855201774
MGB Tourer (Pub 1965)	AKD3900C	9781869826741

Owners Workshop Manuals - Autobooks

Title	ISBN
MGA & MGB & GT 1955-1968 (Glove Box Autobooks Manual)	9781855200937
MGA & MGB & GT 1955-1968 (Autobooks Manual)	9781783180356
Austin-Healey Sprite Mk. 1, 2, 3 & 4 and MG Midget Mk. 1, 2, 3 & 1500 1958-1980 (Glove Box Autobooks Manual)	9781855201255
Austin-Healey Sprite Mk. 1, 2, 3 & 4 and MG Midget Mk. 1, 2, 3 & 1500 1958-1980 (Autobooks Manual)	9781783180332
MGB & MGB GT 1968-1981 (Glove Box Autobooks Manual)	9781855200944
MGB & MGB GT 1968-1981 (Autobooks Manual)	9781783180325

Carburetters

Title	ISBN
SU Carburetters Tuning Tips & Techniques	9781855202559
Solex Carburetters Tuning Tips & Techniques	9781855209770
Weber Carburettors Tuning Tips and Techniques	9781855207592

Restoration Guide

Title	ISBN
MG T Series Restoration Guide	9781855202115
MGA Restoration Guide	9781855203020
Restoring Sprites & Midgets	9781855205987
Practical Classics On MGB Restoration	9780946489428

MG - Road Test Books

Title	ISBN
MG Gold Portfolio 1929-1939	9781855201941
MG TA & TC GOLD PORT 1936-1949	9781855203150
MG TD & TF Gold Portfolio 1949-1955	9781855203167
MG Y-Type & Magnette Road Test Portfolio	9781855208629
MGB & MGC GT V8 GP 1962-1980	9781855200715
MGA & Twin Cam Gold Portfolio 1955-1962	9781855200784
MGB Roadsters 1962-1980	9781869826109
MGC & MGB GT V8 LEX	9781855203631
MG Midget Road Test Portfolio 1961-1979	9781855208957
MGF & TF Performance Portfolio 1995-2005	9781855207073
Road & Track On MG Cars 1949-1961	9780946489398
Road & Track On MG Cars 1962-1980	9780946489817

From MG specialists, Amazon and all good motoring bookshops.

Brooklands Books Ltd., P.O. Box 146, Cobham, Surrey, KT11 1LG, England, UK

www.brooklandsbooks.com

Printed in Great Britain
by Amazon